# General Theory
# of
# Functions and Integration

A BLAISDELL BOOK IN THE PURE AND APPLIED MATHEMATICS

# General Theory of Functions and Integration

ANGUS E. TAYLOR

*University of California, Los Angeles*

BLAISDELL PUBLISHING COMPANY

*A Division of Ginn and Company*

NEW YORK · TORONTO · LONDON

FIRST EDITION, 1965


Library of Congress Catalog Card Number: 65-14566
Printed in the United States of America

*à*

*La Girelle*

*notre balcon sur le Léman*

# Preface

THIS BOOK had its beginning in a course of lectures which I first gave in the Fall of 1951. It is intended as a basic text in certain fundamental parts of higher analysis. The scope of the book will be indicated in subsequent parts of this preface. The book can be used as a text in a variety of ways, at various levels of study. It is also well adapted to use in certain kinds of honors courses and in "reading courses," for it is planned to be read and used as a guide for further reading by students who are, by independent study, seeking to acquire a mastery of these parts of analysis. Moreover, the book is arranged so as to provide a natural transition from the classical theory of point sets in Euclidean space, and the theory of functions of one or more real variables, to the more abstract settings in which the ideas of topology, continuous functions, and integration find their most natural development and reveal their essential structures in the simplest and most transparent fashion.

Chapter 1, dealing with the real number system and point sets on the real line, provides a basis for the development, in Chapter 2, of general point-set theory in the Euclidean space $R^k$. Chapter 2 provides motivation and sets the stage for Chapter 3. The introductory sections in Chapters 2 and 3 explain the carefully planned structural relationship between Chapters 2 and 3. Rather than to repeat or summarize these introductions here, I suggest that the reader examine these introductions as if they were part of this preface. Well-prepared students will not need to study Chapter 1 intensely as new material. Such students can begin directly with Chapter 2.

As a teacher and counselor of students I have observed during the past twenty five years that the available expositions of the theory of integration have fallen short in various ways when measured against the desires of students to learn reasonably quickly and effectively what they need in order to qualify for more advanced graduate study and for research work. The character of this book is to a large extent the outcome of my attempt to bring together in one volume a judicious blend of the particular and the general, of the concrete and the abstract, as an aid to graduate students and as a guide to the further expansion of their mathematical horizons.

There has been a proliferation of ways to approach the theory of integration. When students do not carry their study of integration far enough, the existence of the various approaches can lead to various difficulties later on when students schooled in the various approaches enter a common course of study in which extensive use is made of modern theories of integration. There are students who have studied integration without measure theory (*à la* Riesz or Daniell), who know only the rudiments of general measure theory, and who know little or nothing about the detailed theory of Lebesgue measure in Euclidean spaces. If they know only the bare outlines of how to found measure theory on what they know about integrals, it is for them more than a short exercise to work out what they may find it necessary to know about Lebesgue measure in its classical setting.

Or, it may be that a student is attracted to functional analysis, but has learned his integration by the classical route: measure theory and then integration of functions of one real variable. Perhaps he has even spent most of his time on bounded point sets and functions defined on a compact interval. He then finds it necessary in functional analysis to cope with what at first looks like a vast and formidable extension of this theory: integration of functions defined on general measure spaces. Moreover, he encounters the idea that certain types of linear functionals induce measures (in some instances, even, the functionals themselves are called measures), and he sees reference to the fact that the linear functionals are representable as integrals of a Lebesgue type. Such a student may feel overwhelmed in trying to decide where to begin in filling in his knowledge.

This book aims to help students round out their knowledge of integration and measure theory and to understand the approach via linear functionals as well as the older, more standard approach via measure. The subjects are done fairly completely from two points of view: once with measure theory first and then integration based on measure, and once by the Daniell method of integration first, with subsequent theory of the measure induced by the integral. Then the two approaches are linked, and the ultimate complete theories are shown to be equivalent under rather general conditions. Chapter 5 is devoted to the theory of integration, as based on the prior development of the theory of measure in Chapter 4. The theory in Chapter 4 includes both the abstract theory of measures and outer measures, and the concrete theory of Lebesgue measure in Euclidean space of $k$-dimensions, as well as the theory of Lebesgue-Stieltjes measures on the real line. Chapter 6 begins with the general abstract theory of integration and the induced measure, by the Daniell method. A comparison is then made with the result of using this induced measure to develop a theory of integration, as in Chapter 5. The last part of Chapter 6 is concerned with the particular case of measures (among them classical Lebesgue measure) induced in Euclidean space by certain linear functionals.

The general theory of integrals and measures is continued in Chapters 7 and 8, with the theorems of Fubini and Radon-Nikodym among the main objectives. The general Riesz representation theory for continuous linear functionals on $C_\infty(R^k)$ occurs in Section 8–7 (as Theorem 8–7 IV).

Much of Chapter 9 could be studied before Chapters 4–8. The introduction to Chapter 9 explains this in more detail.

In concluding this preface, I wish to comment on the names used to describe the parts of analysis dealt with in this book. Earlier generations of graduate students studied "the theory of functions" in two distinct parts: the theory of functions of a complex variable, and the theory of functions of one or more real variables. In fact, of course, the theory of functions of a complex variable is not a theory of arbitrary functions of a complex variable, but a theory of analytic functions. Because of this stringent limitation, the theory is relatively free of pathology, and the subject matter in its main lines is remarkably neat and elegant. The theory of functions of real variables, on the other hand, came under the influence of the general investigations of point-set theory, the study of discontinuous functions, and the abstractionist tendencies of Fréchet, Hausdorff, Hahn, and others. In the outcome, a good part of the traditional "theory of functions of real variables" was displaced by a theory of more or less arbitrary real-valued functions defined on an abstract space of some sort—a metric space, a Hausdorff space, or a measure space. More recently, abstraction has gone still further, and the function values need no longer be real. Instead, they may be in a real or complex linear space of some kind, with some sort of topological structure. For some years now it has been a rather common thing to refer to this evolved form of the old theory of functions of a real variable as "real analysis" or "the theory of real functions." Now, it is true that the real number system plays a vital role in this part of analysis. But its role is no less vital in the theory of analytic functions, for the topology of the complex plane derives from the real number system. The theory of analytic functions of a complex variable does, of course, lean heavily on a special fact about complex numbers—the fact that they form a field. In this respect the complex plane must be distinguished from the two-dimensional real Euclidean space. Likewise, some forms of the theory of integration lean heavily on the special fact that the real numbers form a totally ordered system. But the true distinction between the theory of analytic functions and the kind of analysis considered in this book is not well drawn by the use of the adjectives "complex" and "real," respectively. Rather the kind of analysis here considered is characterized by its generality and by the absence of highly restrictive assumptions about the properties of the functions which are considered. It is on this account that I have named the book *General Theory of Functions and Integration*, rather than give it some title which invokes the word "real."

ANGUS E. TAYLOR

*Los Angeles*

# Acknowledgments

THE GREAT BULK of the writing of this book was done during my 1961–62 sabbatical leave from the University of California, Los Angeles. I offer sincere thanks to the UCLA Administration for allowing me to interrupt my duties as Chairman of the Department of Mathematics to take this leave. Without it quite possibly the book would never have been written.

During this period of leave I lived in the charming village of Lutry, on Lake Geneva close to the city of Lausanne, Switzerland. I was accorded the use of the Mathematics Library at the École Polytechnique of the University of Lausanne, and I enjoyed the courtesies and kind help of various members of the Mathematics Faculty there. I am especially grateful to Professors Blanc, Methée, de Rham, and Vincent.

The book has been in my thoughts since 1952, and has been much influenced by my teaching and my contacts with graduate students. For the appreciation and responsiveness of many students I am deeply grateful.

I wish also to acknowledge my appreciation and thanks to Elaine Barth, who prepared the typed manuscript with skill and patience. Finally, I have been helped in many ways by my late and lamented secretary, Mrs. Mildred Webb, and by her successor, Mrs. Helene Gale.

A. E. T.

# Contents

# General Theory
# of
# Functions and Integration

CHAPTER ONE

# The Real Numbers. Point Sets and Sequences

## 1–0 Introduction

The foundation stone of analysis is the real number system. Generalizations in point of view and in actual subject matter sometimes take us far from the real numbers, or even far from real-valued functions of a real variable. But most of the structures which are built up in analysis are in some way related to the real numbers. The system of all real numbers can be looked upon geometrically by thinking of the numbers as the points on a line. This line is then called *the real line*. It is a one-dimensional Euclidean space.

The real line, or some part of it, occupies our attention when we study a function of one real variable. When we pass to functions of two or more real variables we need to study higher dimensional spaces. These spaces are compound structures formed by using the real line or parts of it several times over. Hence it is fundamental to begin by gaining a firm understanding of the properties of the real number system. In this chapter we describe the system of real numbers axiomatically as a complete ordered field (Section 1–1). Since the rational numbers play a very important role in the real number system, it is essential for a student to be aware of the fundamental facts about rational and irrational numbers. These are considered in Section 1–4.

It is a matter of judgment and taste to decide how far a student should go, in the early stages of his work, toward the actual construction of a model complete ordered field. In Section 1–3 we describe the construction of such a model, using Dedekind's method of sections in the ordered field of rational numbers. This section requires the use of the most elementary notions of general set theory. These notions, and the common notations for set operations (union, intersection, difference, complement) are explained in Section 1–2. The ideas of point-set topology are not taken up in this chapter, however. Such ideas come in Chapter 2, where they are developed in a manner as free as possible of entanglement with dimensionality. Our main concern with point sets on the real line, in Chapter 1, is in the discussion of least upper bounds and greatest lower bounds, in Section 1–5.

Chapter 1 concludes with several sections on sequences. The aim is to present the basic ideas and theorems in a logical order without unnecessary ramification. Much or all of this may not be new to the student at this stage—depending on his schooling in advanced calculus. However, the discussion of inferior and superior limits and of the extended real number system (by adjunction of the symbols $+\infty$, $-\infty$) may be new to many students. It is in Section 1–7.

## DISCUSSION OF THE CONCEPT OF COMPLETENESS

In this book we choose to define the concept of completeness of an ordered field by the requirement that to each section $(L, R)$ in the field corresponds an element which is either the largest element of $L$ or the smallest element in $R$ (see Section 1–1). As is well known, an equivalent alternative requirement is this: The field shall have the property that each nonempty set in the field which has an upper bound shall have a least upper bound (see Section 1–5). There are still other ways of characterizing the property of completeness. Let us consider the following properties which may be possessed by an ordered field $F$:

1. $F$ is complete, as defined in Section 1–1.
2. Every nonempty set $S$ in $F$ with an upper bound in $F$ has a least upper bound in $F$.
3. (a) $F$ is archimedean (see Section 1–4).
   (b) Every Cauchy sequence in $F$ has a limit in $F$ (see Section 1–8).
4. (a) $F$ is archimedean.
   (b) If $\{I_n\}$ is a nest in $F$, there is an element of $F$ which is in every $I_n$ (see Section 1–9).

The Properties 1, 2, 3, 4 are equivalent. This is shown by the following list of implications.

$1 \rightarrow 2$ (see Theorem 1–5 I)
$2 \rightarrow 1$ (see Problem 1 in Section 1–5)
$1 \rightarrow 3$(a) (see Theorem 1–4 I)
$2 \rightarrow 3$(b) (see Theorem 1–8 I)
$2 \rightarrow 4$(b) (see Theorem 1–9 I)
3(b) $\rightarrow 4$(b) (see Problem 1(a) in Section 1–9)
$4 \rightarrow 2$ (see Problem 1(b) in Section 1–9).

Because 3(a) is the same as 4(a), the foregoing implications are sufficient to show the equivalence which is claimed for the Properties 1, 2, 3, 4.

Property 1 is not as convenient in practice as Property 2, for the purposes of analysis, but it is in some ways more intuitively natural at the outset.

## 1–1 The real line

It is presumed that a person studying this book already has some knowledge of the rudiments of analysis, and that this knowledge extends beyond what is ordinarily encompassed in a course based on a beginning text in calculus. In particular, it is presumed that readers of this book have studied continuous functions of one real variable, using the "$\epsilon$-$\delta$ definition," and that they have become acquainted to some extent with such things as least upper bounds, greatest lower bounds, points of accumulation, and Cauchy's necessary and sufficient condition for convergence of a sequence of real numbers. A reasonable prerequisite ought to include at least the equivalent of Chapters 2, 3, and 14 in the author's *Advanced Calculus* (A. E. Taylor [1]†). Accordingly, the discussion here of the real number system and its geometrical representation as the real line, is briefer and less detailed than

† Numbers in square brackets after an author's name refer to the bibliography.

such a presentation would be for complete novices. However, in a logical sense, all the essentials are here.

The collection of all real numbers can be characterized by the statement: *The real numbers form a complete ordered field.* To elaborate the meaning of this we must explain what a *field* is, what it means for a field to be *ordered*, and what it means for an ordered field to be *complete*.

## FIELDS

In modern algebra we say that a collection $F$ of elements $a, b, \ldots$ is a field if each pair of elements (distinct or not) can be combined in two ways, called addition and multiplication, each combination yielding an element of $F$, these rules of combination being subjected to certain laws, as follows:

(I) The additive combination of $a$, $b$, denoted by $a + b$ and called the sum, and the multiplicative combination of $a$, $b$, denoted by $ab$ and called the product, satisfy the commutative, associative, and distributive laws:

$$a + b = b + a, \qquad ab = ba,$$
$$a + (b + c) = (a + b) + c, \qquad a(bc) = (ab)c,$$
$$a(b + c) = ab + ac.$$

(II) $F$ contains distinct special elements, denoted by 0, 1, such that

$$a + 0 = a \quad \text{and} \quad a \cdot 1 = a$$

for each $a$ in $F$.

(III) Corresponding to each $a$ in $F$ there is an element in $F$ denoted by $-a$, such that

$$a + (-a) = 0.$$

(IV) Corresponding to each $a$ in $F$, with the exception of 0, there is an element in $F$, denoted by $a^{-1}$, such that

$$a(a^{-1}) = 1.$$

In terms of the notations introduced in (III) and (IV) two further rules of combination (subtraction and division) are defined as follows:

$$a - b \quad \text{is} \quad a + (-b),$$
$$\frac{a}{b} \quad \text{is} \quad ab^{-1} \text{ (assuming } b \neq 0\text{).}$$

We shall not dwell on the details of deducing from the definition of a field all of the familiar algebraic facts and the rules governing manipulations. The facts and rules are common knowledge, and the complete story of what can be proved about fields, as well as the development of technique of proof, are part of the study of modern abstract algebra.

## ORDERED FIELDS

A field $F$ is said to be *ordered* if there is a special class $P$ of elements in $F$ such that

(1) If $a$ is an element of $F$, then either $a$ is in $P$, or $a = 0$, or $-a$ is in $P$, and exactly one of these three situations actually occurs;
(2) if $a$ and $b$ are in $P$, then so is $a + b$;
(3) if $a$ and $b$ are in $P$, then so is $ab$.

It follows from (1) and (3) that $a^2$ is in $P$ if $a \neq 0$. For, either $a$ or $-a$ is in $P$, and $a^2$ can be expressed either as $aa$ or $(-a)(-a)$. Since $0 \neq 1$ and $1 = 1^2$, it follows in particular that 1 is in $P$.

The elements of $P$ are called *the positive elements* of the field. When $-a$ is a positive element, we say that $a$ is *negative*. Each nonzero element is either positive or negative, but not both.

Given two elements $a, b$ in $F$, we write $a < b$ and say "$a$ is less than $b$" if $b - a$ is in the class $P$. Then $0 < b$ means the same as "$b$ is in $P$." The following assertions about the relation $<$ are valid.

(i) If $a, b$ are in $F$, then either $a < b$, or $a = b$, or $b < a$, and no more than one of these things is true (law of trichotomy).
(ii) If $a < b$ and $b < c$, then $a < c$ (law of transitivity).
(iii) If $a < b$, then $a + c < b + c$ for each $c$.
(iv) If $a < b$ and $0 < c$, then $ac < bc$.

We express the two properties of the relation $<$ given in (i) and (ii) by saying that $F$ is *totally ordered* by $<$. The properties (iii) and (iv) connect the order relation with the two basic operations of addition and multiplication.

The statement $a < b$ is sometimes called an *inequality*. There are rules for working with inequalities, just as there are rules for working with equalities, or equations. The basic rules are those in (i)–(iv); other working rules are derived from these. The rule of transposition is often used:

$$a < b + c \text{ is equivalent to } a - c < b,$$

and

$$a + b < c \text{ is equivalent to } a < c - b.$$

Justification is left to the student.

It is convenient to define $a > b$ to mean $b < a$. We also use $a \leq b$ to mean "either $a < b$ or $a = b$." And $b \geq a$ means the same as $a \leq b$.

## COMPLETENESS OF AN ORDERED FIELD

The collection of all *rational* numbers forms an ordered field. So does the collection of all *real* numbers. But there is a very important difference between these two ordered fields. The field of rationals lacks a property called *completeness*, while the field of reals does have this property. Since the completeness property is crucial in analysis, we must discuss it fully and carefully.

First we define what is meant by a *section* in an ordered field $F$. Let all the members of $F$ be separated into two collections $L$, $R$ in such a way that neither collection is void, and so that, if $x$ is in $L$ and $y$ is in $R$, then $x < y$. Then the pair $(L, R)$ is called a *section* in $F$. We refer to $L$ and $R$ respectively as the left and right parts of the section. Clearly $L$ and $R$ have no elements in common.

*Example 1.* In $L$ put 0 and all negative real numbers. In $R$ put all positive real numbers. Then $(L, R)$ is a section in the field of real numbers.

*Example 2.* In $L$ put 0 and all negative rational numbers, and all positive rational numbers $x$ such that $x^2 < 2$. In $R$ put all positive rational numbers $y$ such that $2 < y^2$. Then $(L, R)$ is a section in the field of rational numbers.

*Example 3.* In $L$ put all rational numbers $x$ such that there is some positive integer $n$ for which

$$x < \frac{6}{10} + \frac{6}{10^2} + \cdots + \frac{6}{10^n},$$

and in $R$ put all rational numbers $x$ for which there is no such $n$. That is, "$x$ is in $R$" means that

$$\frac{6}{10} + \frac{6}{10^2} + \cdots + \frac{6}{10^n} \leq x$$

for each positive integer $n$. Then $(L, R)$ is a section in the field of rational numbers.

*Example 4.* Define $L$ and $R$ as in Example 2, except that every reference to "rational numbers" is replaced by "real numbers," and the number $\sqrt{2}$ is also placed in $R$. Then $(L, R)$ is a section in the field of real numbers.

*Example 5.* Define $L$ and $R$ as in Example 3, with "real" in place of "rational" at every occurrence. Then $(L, R)$ is a section in the field of real numbers.

The student reader should, for each of these examples, check that $(L, R)$ is in fact a section as claimed. For instance, in Example 2, every rational number goes into either $L$ or $R$, because no rational number has 2 as its square. Clearly, 0 is in $L$ and 3 is in $R$, so that neither $L$ nor $R$ is void. Finally, if $x$ is in $L$ and $y$ is in $R$, then $x < y$. This is evident if $x \leq 0$, so we have only to make the verification when $0 < x$. In that case $0 < x$, $0 < y$, $x^2 < 2$, and $2 < y^2$. Then $0 < y^2 - x^2 = (y - x)(y + x)$. But certainly $0 < y + x$. Hence $0 < y - x$ also, for $y - x \leq 0$ would imply $(y - x)(y + x) \leq 0$. Since $0 < y - x$ is equivalent to $x < y$, we are through with the verification.

Now, we come to the definition of completeness. An ordered field $F$ is called *complete* if for every section $(L, R)$ in $F$ it is true that either $L$ has a largest member or $R$ has a smallest member. (A largest member of $L$ is a member $u$ of $L$ such that $x < u$ for all other members of $L$. Clearly, there cannot be more than one such largest member of $L$. However, there may not be any largest member. Similar remarks apply with reference to a smallest member of $R$.)

If $(L, R)$ is a section in $F$ and if $c$ is either the largest member of $L$ or the smallest member of $R$, it is easily proved that if $x$ is in $F$ then $x$ is in $L$ if $x < c$ and $x$ is in $R$ if $c < x$. Suppose, for instance, that $c$ is the largest member of $L$, and that $x < c$. Then $x$ cannot be in $R$, by one of the properties of the section. Hence $x$ is in $L$. If $c < x$, $x$ must be in $R$, not in $L$, because $c$ is the largest member of $L$. The arguments for the case in which $c$ is the smallest member of $R$ are similar.

When an ordered field is *not* complete, there is at least one section $(L, R)$ such that $L$ has no largest member and $R$ has no smallest member. This is the case in Example 2, and this shows that the field of rationals is not complete. When we go to Example 4, however, we find that $\sqrt{2}$ is the smallest member of $R$.

It never happens, with a section $(L, R)$ in an ordered field $F$, that there is both a largest member of $L$ *and* a smallest member of $R$. For, suppose this could occur, with $u$ the largest member of $L$ and $v$ the smallest member of $R$. Then necessarily $u < v$. But this inequality leads to a contradiction. The number $(u + v)/2$ is certainly in $F$, therefore either in $L$

or in $R$. But $u/2 < v/2$, so that

$$\tfrac{1}{2}(u + v) < \tfrac{1}{2}(v + v) = v.$$

Consequently $(u + v)/2$ cannot be in $R$. Also,

$$u = \tfrac{1}{2}(u + u) < \tfrac{1}{2}(u + v),$$

and so $(u + v)/2$ cannot be in $L$.

When $(L, R)$ is a section in a complete ordered field $F$, the unique element $c$ of $F$ which is either the largest member of $L$ or the smallest member of $R$ is called the *section number* corresponding to the section. Sometimes the word "cut" is used instead of "section."

*The fundamental fact about the real number system is that it is a complete ordered field.* We do not prove this fact in this book; we take it for granted. In order to prove it, it would be necessary to describe in some way how the real number system is constructed, and to show that the construction does lead to a complete ordered field. There are various ways to do this. But, to carry out the program in full detail would require more space than we wish to give to the subject in this book. In Section 1–3, where we discuss some aspects of the relation of the field of rationals to the field of reals, there is a brief indication of how one may construct the system of real numbers from the system of rational numbers, the latter system being taken as known.

## THE REAL LINE

The "real line" is just another name for the real number system. When we use the words "real line" instead of the words "real number system" it is because we have in mind a more geometrical point of view. We refer to an element of the real line as a *point*. If $x$ and $y$ are real numbers, and if $x < y$, then in the geometric terminology we say that $x$ is to the left of $y$.

An alternative point of view is possible. One may develop the concept of a line by other axiomatic methods. But if the line is to deserve the name of a Euclidean space of one dimension, it will turn out to be an assemblage of elements (points) which is totally ordered, and which may be put into one-to-one correspondence with the collection of all real numbers in such a way that the total ordering of the points corresponds to the total ordering of the real numbers. That is, if $a$ and $b$ are points corresponding to numbers $x$ and $y$, respectively, then the ordering "$a$ is to the left of $b$" will correspond to the inequality $x < y$.

## ISOMORPHISM

The idea of a one-to-one correspondence which preserves structural features, such as order relations, is very important in mathematics. Various kinds of mathematical systems are defined by sets of axioms. A field is an example of such a system. An ordered field is another example, and a complete ordered field is still another example. When two specimens of the same kind of mathematical system can be put into one-to-one correspondence in such a way as to preserve all structural features, we say the two specimens are *isomorphic*. Two particular fields may or may not be isomorphic. For instance, the field of real numbers and the field of complex numbers are not isomorphic. Two ordered fields need not be isomorphic; the rational field and the real field provide an illustration. *But any two complete ordered fields are isomorphic*. This is a theorem. Proofs may be found in several of the books listed for suggested reading at the end of this chapter. (See McShane and Botts [1], p. 22 or Graves [1] p. 35.) It is this fact that all complete ordered fields are isomorphic, and hence abstractly indistinguishable, that makes it immaterial how the real number system is constructed. All that is necessary for us is the knowledge that a complete ordered field can be constructed.

## 1–2 Notation and terminology concerning sets

For convenience in the exposition of ideas it is desirable to consider some notions about sets. In mathematical discourse we are frequently speaking about collections of things. For example: the collection of all real numbers; the collection of all points $(x, y)$ in the plane such that $x^2 + y^2 < 1$ and $y > 0$; the collection of all continuous real-valued functions $f$ defined on the closed interval $0 \leq x \leq 1$ of the real $x$ axis, such that the derivative $f'(x)$ exists when $0 < x < 1$. In this book the words *collection*, *class*, and *set* are used essentially synonymously. The things which compose a set are called the *elements* of the set. If $S$ is a set and $x$ is an element of $S$, the fact that $x$ belongs to $S$ is indicated by writing $x \in S$. If $y$ is not an element of $S$, we can indicate this by writing $y \notin S$.

*Example 1.* Let $S$ be the set of prime positive integers: 2, 3, 5, 7, 11, .... Then $17 \in S$ and $12 \notin S$.

If $S$ is a set, a *subset* of $S$ is a set $A$ such that if $x \in A$, then also $x \in S$. In particular, $S$ is a subset of itself. The fact that $A$ is a subset of $S$ is indicated by writing $A \subset S$, or $S \supset A$. Two sets $A$, $B$ are the same if and only if $A \subset B$ and $B \subset A$. If $A \subset B$ but $A \neq B$, we call $A$ a *proper* subset of $B$.

*Example 2.* The set of prime positive integers is a proper subset of all positive integers.

### SETS DEFINED BY CONDITIONS

We often define sets by a convenient notation in which a condition of definition is displayed in curly brackets. For instance, if $A$ denotes the set of all real numbers $x$ not less than 2 and not more than 4, we write

$$A = \{x : 2 \leq x \leq 4\}.$$

In this notation $x$ is a symbol or variable to which real number values can be assigned. After the colon stands the condition of membership in $A$, which is expressed by the two inequalities $2 \leq x$ and $x \leq 4$. This sort of notation may also be used for sets whose elements are functions, and for many other kinds of sets.

*Example 3.* If $S$ denotes the set of all continuous real-valued functions $f$ defined for all real $x$ and such that $f(0) = 1$, we can write

$$S = \{f : f(0) = 1\}.$$

In this case the full specification of conditions on $f$ is not included in the parenthesis. Among all the continuous functions $f$ we pick out that subset $S$ characterized by the condition $f(0) = 1$. The rest of the specifications are to be gathered from the context, or from an explicit accompanying statement.

### THE EMPTY SET

It may happen that a condition is given which is not satisfied by any of the prospective elements. In that case we say that the condition defines *the empty set*. The empty set is denoted by the symbol $\varnothing$. The concept of the set with no elements may at first seem peculiar, but it is a technical necessity in the theory of sets.

### SETS WITH ONE ELEMENT

If $x$ is a member of the set $S$, the subset of $S$ whose sole member is $x$ is denoted by $\{x\}$. We sometimes use an analogous notation for sets with a specific finite number of elements, for example, $\{x, y, z\}$ or $\{x_1, \ldots, x_n\}$.

### THE UNION OF SETS

Suppose we have under consideration various subsets $A, B, \ldots$ of a specified set $S$. If $A_1, \ldots, A_n$ are subsets of $S$, the union of $A_1, \ldots, A_n$ is defined as the set of all elements of $S$ which belong to *at least* one of the sets $A_1, \ldots, A_n$. This union is denoted by

$$A_1 \cup A_2 \cup \cdots \cup A_n \qquad \text{or} \qquad \bigcup_{i=1}^{n} A_i.$$

*Example 4.* Let $S$ be the $xy$ plane. Let

$$\begin{aligned} A &= \{(x, y) : 0 < x \text{ and } 1 \le y\}, \\ B &= \{(x, y) : 1 \le x \text{ and } 0 < y\}, \\ C &= \{(x, y) : 1 \le x \text{ and } 1 \le y\}, \\ D &= \{(x, y) : 0 < x < 1 \text{ and } 1 \le y\}, \\ E &= \{(x, y) : 1 \le x \text{ and } 0 < y < 1\}. \end{aligned}$$

Then $A = D \cup C$, $B = C \cup E$, and $A \cup B = C \cup D \cup E$. Observe that while $A$ and $B$ have points in common, no two of the sets $C, D, E$ have points in common. The student reader may find it helpful to draw a diagram showing the sets $A, B, C, D, E$ by various kinds of characteristic shading. Care must be taken to show where edges are included and where not.

We may also define the union of arbitrarily many sets (even infinitely many). The union of the infinite collection $A_1, A_2, \ldots$ is denoted by $\bigcup_{n=1}^{\infty} A_i$. If $\mathscr{A}$ is a family of sets $A$, the union of all the members of $\mathscr{A}$ is denoted by $\bigcup_{A\in\mathscr{A}} A$.

### THE INTERSECTION OF SETS

If $A_1, \ldots, A_n$ are subsets of $S$, the intersection of these sets, denoted by

$$A_1 \cap A_2 \cap \cdots \cap A_n \qquad \text{or} \qquad \bigcap_{i=1}^{n} A_i,$$

is defined as the set of all elements of $S$ which belong simultaneously to all the $A_i$'s. We may also consider intersections of infinitely many $A_i$'s, or of all the $A$'s in a family.

*Example 5.* In the situation of Example 4, $A \cap B = C$, $A \cap D = D$, $D \cap C = \varnothing$, $D \cap E = \varnothing$, $C \cap E = \varnothing$, and $B \cap C = C$.

## COMPLEMENTS

When a given set $S$ is fixed for consideration, and subsets of $S$ are under discussion, the notion of *complement* is often used. If $A \subset S$, the complement of $A$ (relative to $S$) is the part of $S$ not in $A$. Various notations have been used for complements; we use a now fairly standard notation and represent the complement of $A$ by $A^\sim$. Hence $x \in A^\sim$ means $x \in S$ but $x \notin A$. Observe that $(A^\sim)^\sim = A$. Also, if $A$ and $B$ are subsets of $S$, and $A \subset B$, then $B^\sim \subset A^\sim$.

## THE DIFFERENCE OF TWO SETS

If $A$ and $B$ are subsets of $S$, the difference $A - B$ is defined as the set $A \cap B^\sim$. That is, $x \in A - B$ means that $x$ is in $A$ but not in $B$. In particular, $A^\sim = S - A$.

## RULES OF COMPLEMENTATION

The validity of the rule

$$\left(\bigcup_{i=1}^{n} A_i\right)^\sim = \bigcap_{i=1}^{n} A_i^\sim \tag{1}$$

is evident from the definitions of unions, intersections, and complements. This rule is also valid for any infinite number of sets. An equivalent form of the rule (1) is

$$\left(\bigcap_{i=1}^{n} A_i\right)^\sim = \bigcup_{i=1}^{n} A_i^\sim. \tag{2}$$

## THE DISTRIBUTIVE LAW

We can regard union and intersection as binary operations in an *algebra* of sets. That is, $A$ can be combined with $B$ in two ways, yielding $A \cap B$ and $A \cup B$, respectively. This kind of algebra is called Boolean algebra, after George Boole (1815–1864). See Birkhoff [1], Chapter 10. We shall not need to make an extensive formal development of this algebra. If and when a student wants such a development, he can readily consult some of the references listed at the end of this chapter. We shall often have occasion to use the distributive law:

$$A \cap (B \cup C) = (A \cap B) \cup (A \cap C). \tag{3}$$

The truth of this law, as a proposition about sets, is immediately evident from the definitions of $\cap$ and $\cup$. Algebraically, it is analogous to the distributive law

$$a(b + c) = ab + ac$$

of ordinary elementary algebra.

The distributive law is also valid in a more general form, with the union of any number of sets instead of just the two sets $B$, $C$.

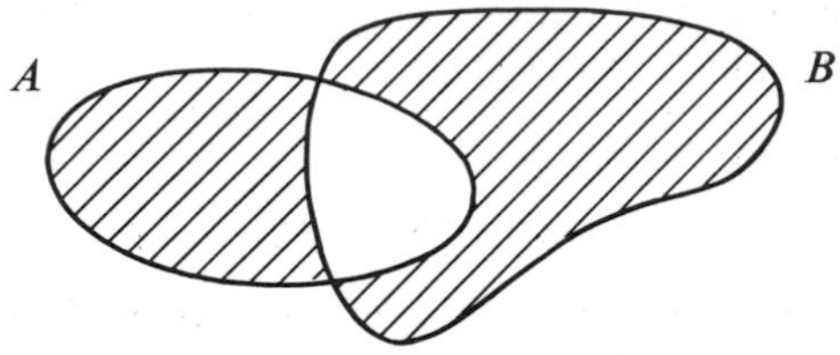


Shaded portion is $A \,\Delta\, B$

FIGURE 1

## DISJOINTNESS

Two sets $A, B$ are said to be *disjoint* if $A \cap B = \varnothing$. The members of a collection or family of sets are said to be *mutually disjoint* if each two sets from the family are disjoint. For convenience and brevity we often refer to a family whose members are mutually disjoint as a *disjoint family*.

## THE SYMMETRIC DIFFERENCE

The symmetric difference of two sets $A$, $B$, denoted by $A \,\Delta\, B$, is defined as

$$A \,\Delta\, B = (A - B) \cup (B - A). \tag{4}$$

Evidently $A \,\Delta\, B = \varnothing$ if and only if $A = B$. A schematic representation of $A \,\Delta\, B$ is shown in Figure 1.

We shall find an important use of the symmetric difference in Chapter 4 (see Theorem 4–8 VI and the ensuing discussion).

## LIMITS SUPERIOR AND INFERIOR

Let $E_1, E_2, \ldots$ be a sequence of subsets of $S$. The set of all points $x \in S$ such that $x \in E_n$ for infinitely many values of $n$ is called the *limit superior* of $\{E_n\}$ and denoted by $\limsup_{n\to\infty} E_n$. It may be verified that

$$\limsup_{n\to\infty} E_n = \bigcap_{n=1}^{\infty}\left[\bigcup_{k=n}^{\infty} E_k\right]. \tag{5}$$

The set of all points $x \in S$ such that $x \in E_n$ for all sufficiently large values of $n$ (how large may depend on $x$) is called the *limit inferior* of $\{E_n\}$ and denoted by $\liminf_{n\to\infty} E_n$. It may be verified that

$$\liminf_{n\to\infty} E_n = \bigcup_{n=1}^{\infty}\left[\bigcap_{k=n}^{\infty} E_k\right]. \tag{6}$$

In case $\liminf_{n\to\infty} E_n$ and $\limsup_{n\to\infty} E_n$ are the same set, this set is called the limit of $\{E_n\}$ and written $\lim_n E_n$.

*Example 6.* Let $S$ be the $xy$ plane. Define

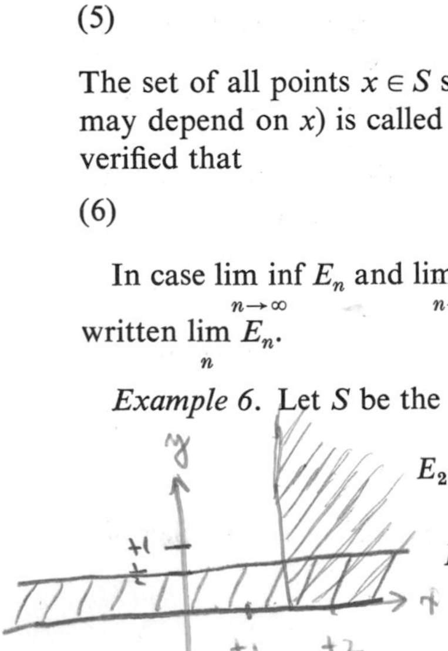

$$E_{2n-1} = \left\{(x, y) : y \geq 0 \text{ and } x \geq 1 + \frac{1}{n}\right\},$$

$$E_{2n} = \left\{(x, y) : x \geq 0 \text{ and } 0 \leq y \leq \frac{1}{n}\right\},$$

where $n = 1, 2, \ldots$. Here it turns out that

$$\limsup_{n\to\infty} E_n = \{(x, y) : y \geq 0 \text{ and } x > 1 \text{ or } 0 \leq x \text{ and } y = 0\},$$

and

$$\liminf_{n\to\infty} E_n = \{(x, y) : y = 0 \text{ and } x > 1\}.$$

The reader should make the verifications himself.

## PROBLEMS

1. Two sets $S_1$, $S_2$ which are defined in apparently different ways may nevertheless be identical. Evidently, $S_1 = S_2$ if and only if $S_1 \subset S_2$ and $S_2 \subset S_1$. Here we have one way of proving that $S_1 = S_2$. By this or any other convenient method prove the following set equalities:
   (a) The distributive law, $A \cap (B \cup C) = (A \cap B) \cup (A \cap C)$.
   (b) $(A \cup B) \cap (A \cup C) = A \cup (B \cap C)$.
   (c) $A - (A - B) = A \cap B$.
   (d) $(A - B) - C = A - (B \cup C)$.
   (e) $A - (B - C) = (A - B) \cup (A \cap C)$.
   (f) $A \cap (B - C) = (A \cap B) - (A \cap C)$.
   (g) $(A - B) \cap (C - D) = (A \cap C) - (B \cup D)$.
2. Show that $A - B = A - (A \cap B) = (A \cup B) - B$.
3. Show that
   (a) $B \subset A$ is equivalent to $A \cup B = A$;
   (b) $A \subset B$ is equivalent to $A \cap B = A$;
   (c) $A \cap B = \varnothing$ is equivalent to the two conditions $A - B = A$ and $B - A = B$.
4. Show that $(A \cap B) \cup C = A \cap (B \cup C)$ if and only if $C \subset A$.
5. If $E_n = \{x : x \text{ is real and } x \leq -n\}$, what is $\bigcap_{n=1}^{\infty} E_n$?
6. Suppose that $A_n \subset A_{n+1}$, $n = 1, 2, \ldots$. Show that

$$\bigcup_{n=1}^{\infty} A_n = A_1 \cup \bigcup_{n\geq 2} (A_n - A_{n-1}).$$

7. Verify the following assertions about the symmetric difference:
   (a) $A^{\sim} \,\Delta\, B^{\sim} = A \,\Delta\, B$;
   (b) $A \,\Delta\, B = B \,\Delta\, A$;
   (c) $A \,\Delta\, B = (A \cup B) - (A \cap B)$;
   (d) $A \,\Delta\, C \subset (A \,\Delta\, B) \cup (B \,\Delta\, C)$;
   (e) $(A \,\Delta\, B) \,\Delta\, C = (A \cap B^{\sim} \cap C^{\sim}) \cup (A^{\sim} \cap B \cap C^{\sim}) \cup (A^{\sim} \cap B^{\sim} \cap C) \cup (A \cap B \cap C)$.
   (f) $A \,\Delta\, (B \,\Delta\, C) = (A \,\Delta\, B) \,\Delta\, C$.
8. Verify (5) and (6). Explain why $\liminf_{n\to\infty} E_n \subset \limsup_{n\to\infty} E_n$.
9. Show that

$$(\limsup_{n\to\infty} E_n)^{\sim} = \liminf_{n\to\infty} E_n^{\sim}.$$

What is the complement of $\liminf_{n\to\infty} E_n$?

10. Suppose that $E_1 = E_3 = E_5 = \cdots = E$ and $E_2 = E_4 = \cdots = F$. What are the limits inferior and superior of $\{E_n\}$ in this case?
11. What are the limits superior and inferior of $\{E_n\}$ (a) if $E_n \subset E_{n+1}$ for every $n$? (b) if $E_{n+1} \subset E_n$ for every $n$?

12. Given $A_n \subset A_{n+1}$, $A = \bigcup_{n=1}^{\infty} A_n$ and $B_{n+1} \subset B_n$, $B = \bigcap_{n=1}^{\infty} B_n$, let $E_{2n-1} = A_n$ and $E_{2n} = B_n$, $n = 1, 2, \ldots$. Show that $\liminf_{n\to\infty} E_n = A \cap B$ and $\limsup_{n\to\infty} E_n = A \cup B$.

13. Construct a sequence $\{E_n\}$ where each $E_n$ is a set of points on the real line and $\liminf_{n\to\infty} E_n$ is the open interval $(0, 1)$ (that is, $\{x : 0 < x < 1\}$) while $\limsup_{n\to\infty} E_n$ is the closed interval $[0, 2]$ (that is, $\{x : 0 \le x \le 2\}$).

14. Let $\{a_n\}$ and $\{b_n\}$ be sequences of real numbers such that $0 < a_n < 1 < b_n$, $a_{n+1} < a_n$, $b_{n+1} < b_n$, $a_n \to 0$, $b_n \to 1$. Let $E_n = \{x : a_n \le x \le b_n\}$. Determine the limits inferior and superior of $\{E_n\}$.

## 1–3 Construction of a complete ordered field

In this section we shall describe briefly how one may construct a system of objects forming a complete ordered field. The construction starts by assuming the ordered field of rational numbers as a known system.

The study of this section is not essential as a prerequisite to further study of the book. The fundamental facts about complete ordered fields are set forth elsewhere in Chapter 1: the axiomatic presentation and the definitions in Section 1–1, the most essential consequences of the axioms, from the point of view of the analyst, in Section 1–4 to Section 1–8 inclusive.

The purpose of this section is to give the student a clear point of departure in case he wishes to investigate in some detail the problem of creating a complete ordered field. He may do this by himself, or he may be stimulated to read other literature on the subject. A highly readable account of a method of constructing the real number system, starting from the positive integers, is given by Landau in his book *Grundlagen der Analysis* [1] (English translation [2]). The basic ideas in this section are very close to those employed by Landau.

Before going further the reader should review the definitions of completeness and of sections in an ordered field, in Section 1–1. We shall denote the field of rational numbers by $F$.

We now consider sections $(L, R)$ in $F$ such that $L$ has no greatest member. Let $\mathscr{S}$ be the collection of all such sections in $F$, and let $\mathscr{F}$ be the collection of all the left parts $L$ coming from sections belonging to $\mathscr{S}$. Then each $L$ is a certain set of rational numbers. If $(L, R) \in \mathscr{S}$, observe that $R = F - L$.

The set of *all* sections in $F$ can be divided into three parts: (1) those sections $(L, R)$ in which $L$ has no greatest member but $R$ *does* have a least member, (2) those in which $L$ has no greatest member and $R$ has no smallest member, and (3) those in which $L$ has a greatest member but $R$ has no smallest member. We reject the sections forming the third part; the other two parts form the collection $\mathscr{S}$ as already defined.

*Example 1.* If $r$ is any rational number, let $L = \{x : x < r\}$ and $R = \{x : r \le x\}$, where in each case all the $x$'s considered are rational. Then $(L, R) \in \mathscr{S}$, $L$ has no largest member, and $r$ is the smallest member of $R$.

In Example 2 of Section 1–1 we defined a section $(L, R)$ such that $L$ has no greatest member and $R$ has no smallest member.

The collection $\mathscr{F}$ is going to be our real number system. That is, even though the elements of $\mathscr{F}$ are certain sets of rational numbers, we shall regard each $L$ in $\mathscr{F}$ as an entity, and call it a real number. The justification for doing this is that it is possible to give appropriate definitions of addition and multiplication of elements of $\mathscr{F}$, and to define an order relation in $\mathscr{F}$, and then prove that these definitions make $\mathscr{F}$ into a complete ordered field. We shall not carry this program out in all detail, but we shall discuss some aspects of the program.

When an $L \in \mathscr{F}$ is such that $R$ has a smallest member $r$ (where $R = F - L$), this rational number $r$ completely determines and is determined by $L$. Hence the set of all $L$'s of this particular kind is in one-to-one correspondence with the set of all elements of the rational field $F$. These elements $L$ will be called *the rational elements* of $\mathscr{F}$. Observe that, if $L$ is the rational element of $\mathscr{F}$ corresponding to the rational number $r$ in $F$, then $L = \{x : x \in F$ and $x < r\}$, while $R = F - L = \{y : y \in F$ and $r \leq y\}$.

An element $L$ of $\mathscr{F}$ such that $R(= F - L)$ has no smallest member will be called *an irrational element of* $\mathscr{F}$.

### DEFINITION OF ORDER IN $\mathscr{F}$

Suppose that $L_1$ and $L_2$ are two members of $\mathscr{F}$. We define $L_1 < L_2$ to be $L_1 \subset L_2$ (set inclusion) and $L_1 \neq L_2$. This provides a total ordering of $\mathscr{F}$. The concept of total ordering was defined in Section 1–1. To prove that we have a total ordering of $\mathscr{F}$, we first observe that the transitive law obviously holds. That is, $L_1 < L_2$ and $L_2 < L_3$ imply $L_1 < L_3$. Verification is left to the reader. To show that the law of trichotomy holds, suppose $L_1$ and $L_2$ are given, and that neither $L_1 < L_2$ nor $L_1 = L_2$ is true. Then $L_1 - L_2$ is not empty. Suppose $x \in L_1 - L_2$. Let $R_1 = F - L_1$, $R_2 = F - L_2$. Since $(L_2, R_2)$ is a section and $x \notin L_2$, it must be that $x \in R_2$. Now we shall prove that $L_2 \subset L_1$, whence $L_2 < L_1$. Suppose $y \in L_2$. Since $x \in R_2$, the definition of a section implies that $y < x$. (Here we have the order relation in the rational field $F$.) But $x \in L_1$ and $y < x$ together imply $y \in L_1$. Otherwise we should have $y \in R_1$, and this, with $x \in L_1$, would imply $x < y$. We have thus shown that every member of $L_2$ is in $L_1$, and the argument is finished.

### DEFINITION OF ADDITION IN $\mathscr{F}$

Suppose that $L_1$, $L_2$ are in $\mathscr{F}$. Let $L$ be the set of rational numbers formed by taking all possible sums of the form $x_1 + x_2$, where $x_1$ is chosen from $L_1$ and $x_2$ is chosen from $L_2$. Let $R = F - L$. It can be shown that $(L, R)$ is a section in $F$. Indications of how to do this are given in the problems. The fact that neither $L_1$ nor $L_2$ has a greatest member guarantees that $L$ has the same property. Hence $L \in \mathscr{F}$. We define $L$ as the sum of $L_1$ and $L_2$:

$$L = L_1 + L_2.$$

This addition is clearly commutative. The zero of $\mathscr{F}$ is defined as the rational element of $\mathscr{F}$ corresponding to the rational number $0 \in F$. That is, the zero of $\mathscr{F}$ is the set of all negative rational numbers. If (for present purposes) we denote this zero of $\mathscr{F}$ by $Z$, then it is easy to prove that $L + Z = L$ for every $L$ in $\mathscr{F}$. This justifies calling $Z$ zero; in standard usage later on we shall of course denote $Z$ by 0.

Given $L$, it is necessary to know of an element of $\mathscr{F}$, denoted by $-L$, such that $L + (-L) = Z$. Here is how $-L$ can be obtained: There are two cases. Let $R = F - L$. If $R$ has a smallest member $r$, let $-L$ consist of all rationals $x$ such that $x < -r$. If $R$ does not have a smallest member, let $-L$ consist of all the numbers $-y$, where $y$ varies over all of $R$. It can be proved in each case that $-L \in \mathscr{F}$, and that $L + (-L) = Z$.

### DEFINITION OF MULTIPLICATION IN $\mathscr{F}$

We shall now indicate how to define multiplication of two elements of $\mathscr{F}$. To begin with, consider elements $L_1$, $L_2$ such that $Z < L_1$ and $Z < L_2$. Now, $Z < L_1$ means that $Z$ is a proper subset of $L_1$. Since $Z$ consists of all negative rationals and $L_1$ has no largest member, $L_1$ must contain some positive rationals. Let $L_1^+$ denote the set of positive rationals in $L_1$. The set $L_2^+$ is defined in a corresponding way. Now let $L$ be the set consisting of all the negative rationals, the number 0, and all possible products of the form $x_1x_2$, where $x_1$ is chosen from $L_1^+$ and $x_2$ is chosen from $L_2^+$. Let $R = F - L$. It can be shown that $(L, R)$ is a section in $F$; this is left as a problem. It is easy to see that $L$ has no largest member. Hence, $L \in \mathscr{F}$. We define $L$ as the product of $L_1$ and $L_2$:

$$L = L_1L_2.$$

It is still necessary to define multiplication when $L_1 \leq Z$ or $L_2 \leq Z$. We define

$$LZ = ZL = Z \qquad \text{for every } L.$$

If $L_1 < Z$ and $Z < L_2$, we define

$$L_1L_2 = -(-L_1)L_2.$$

This is meaningful, because $Z < -L_1$, so that $(-L_1)L_2$ is well defined. Likewise, we define

$$L_1L_2 = -[L_1(-L_2)] \qquad \text{if} \quad Z < L_1 \quad \text{and} \quad L_2 < Z,$$

and

$$L_1L_2 = (-L_1)(-L_2) \qquad \text{if} \quad L_1 < Z \quad \text{and} \quad L_2 < Z.$$

One sees easily that multiplication is commutative.

### THE MULTIPLICATIVE UNIT

If we let $U = \{z : x \in F, x < 1\}$, then $(U, F - U)$ is a section in $F$ and $U \in \mathscr{F}$. It is not difficult to prove that $UL = L$ for each $L$ in $\mathscr{F}$. Thus $U$ plays the role of 1 in multiplication. We observe that $U$ is the rational element of $\mathscr{F}$ corresponding to the rational number 1 in $F$.

### MULTIPLICATIVE INVERSES

For each $L$ in $\mathscr{F}$ such that $L \neq Z$ there is an element of $\mathscr{F}$, denoted by $L^{-1}$, such that $LL^{-1} = U$. It suffices to define $L^{-1}$ at first on the supposition that $Z < L$; then, if $L < Z$, we can define $L^{-1} = -(-L)^{-1}$.

Suppose then that $Z < L$. If $R = F - L$ and $R$ has a smallest member $r$, it may be seen that $r > 0$. In this case let $L^{-1} = \{x : x \in F, x < r^{-1}\}$. If $R$ has no smallest member, let $L^{-1}$ consist of 0, all negative rational numbers, and all rational numbers of the form $1/y$, where $y \in R$. (We observe that $y > 0$ when $y \in R$.) It can be verified that $LL^{-1} = U$ in each case.

We purposely omit the details of the full discussion which is necessary to show that the foregoing definitions really do make $\mathscr{F}$ into an ordered field. One must verify associativity of addition and multiplication, the distributive law of multiplication with respect to addition, and the laws relating addition and multiplication to order.

## COMPLETENESS OF $\mathscr{F}$

It is a comparatively simple matter to demonstrate that $\mathscr{F}$ is complete. To follow this demonstration it is not necessary to be familiar with all of the details of showing that $\mathscr{F}$ is a field. The concept of a section depends essentially on the notion of a totally ordered set, without reference to this set's being also a field.

Suppose, then, that $(\mathscr{L}, \mathscr{R})$ is a section in $\mathscr{F}$. That is, $\mathscr{L}$ and $\mathscr{R}$ are nonempty subsets of $\mathscr{F}$ such that $\mathscr{F} = \mathscr{L} \cup \mathscr{R}$ and such that $L_1 < L_2$ if $L_1 \in \mathscr{L}$ and $L_2 \in \mathscr{R}$. To prove that $\mathscr{F}$ is complete we have to show that there exists either a largest element of $\mathscr{L}$ or a smallest element of $\mathscr{R}$. The words "largest" and "smallest" in this context refer, of course, to the order relation introduced in $\mathscr{F}$ by our definition previously given.

Now, among the elements of $\mathscr{L}$ and $\mathscr{R}$, some are rational elements, as the reader may easily convince himself. (Recall that an element $L$ of $\mathscr{F}$ is called a rational element if $F - L$ has a smallest member; this smallest member is then a rational number, which we call *the rational number corresponding to L*.) Let $A$ be the class of all rational numbers in $F$ corresponding to rational elements of $\mathscr{L}$, and let $B$ be the class of all rational numbers in $F$ corresponding to rational elements of $\mathscr{R}$. *We shall show that $(A, B)$ is a section in $F$.* First of all, neither $A$ nor $B$ is empty. Since every rational number determines a rational element of $\mathscr{F}$, it is clear that $A \cup B = F$. Finally, if $r_1 \in A$ and $r_2 \in B$, we can show that $r_1 < r_2$. For, let $L_i$ be the rational element of $\mathscr{F}$ corresponding to $r_i$ $(i = 1, 2)$. Then $L_i = \{x : x < r_i\}$, where $x$ is a symbol for rational numbers. Then $L_1 \in \mathscr{L}$ and $L_2 \in \mathscr{R}$, and so $L_1 < L_2$. That is, $L_1$ is a proper subset of $L_2$. Now suppose that $r_2 \leq r_1$ (the contrary of $r_1 < r_2$). Then $x < r_2$ would imply $x < r_1$, and hence $L_2$ would be a subset of $L_1$, which is a contradiction. Hence $r_1 < r_2$.

With $(A, B)$ now known to be a section in $F$, there are three cases to consider.

*CASE 1.* $A$ has a largest member, say $r$. Let $L = \{x : x < r\}$. Then $L \in \mathscr{L}$. In this case $L$ is the largest member of $\mathscr{L}$. For, suppose that there could be an element $L_1$ of $\mathscr{L}$ larger than $L$. This would imply the existence of a rational number $r_0$ in $L_1 - L$ such that $r < r_0$. Let $L_0 = \{x : x < r_0\}$. Since $r_0 \in L_1$, we see that $L_0 < L_1$. This, with $L_1 \in \mathscr{L}$, implies $L_0 \in \mathscr{L}$. But then $L_0$ is a rational element of $\mathscr{L}$ and its corresponding rational number is $r_0$, so that $r_0 \in A$. This contradicts the fact that $r$ is the largest element of $A$. Hence, $L$ must be the largest element of $\mathscr{L}$.

In the two remaining cases $A$ has no largest member, so that $A$, as the left part of a section in $F$ of the class $\mathscr{S}$, is itself a member of $\mathscr{F}$. Accordingly either $A \in \mathscr{L}$ or $A \in \mathscr{R}$.

*CASE 2.* $A \in \mathscr{L}$. In this case $A$ is the largest member of $\mathscr{L}$. The proof is similar to that of Case 1. If we suppose $\mathscr{L}$ contains an element $L_1$ such that $A < L_1$, we can select a rational number $r_0$ from $L_1 - A$ and define $L_0 = \{x : x < r_0\}$. Then $L_0 < L_1$, whence $L_0 \in \mathscr{L}$ and $r_0 \in A$, a contradiction.

*CASE 3.* $A \in \mathscr{R}$. In this case we can prove that $A$ is the smallest member of $\mathscr{R}$. For, if it were not, there would be some $L_1 \in \mathscr{R}$ such that $L_1 < A$. We could then choose a rational number $r$ from $A - L_1$. Then, since $A$ has no largest element, we could choose $r_0 \in A$ so that $r < r_0$. Then $r_0 \notin L_1$ (as a consequence of the fact that $(L_1, F - L_1)$ is a section in $F$ and $r \in F - L_1$). Let $L_0 = \{x : x < r_0\}$. Then $L_1 < L_0$. Since $L_1 \in \mathscr{R}$, it follows that $L_0 \in \mathscr{R}$. This implies that $r_0 \in B$, for $r_0$ is the rational number corresponding to $L_0$. But

$r_0 \in A$, and so we have a contradiction. This finishes Case 3. We have thus proved that $\mathscr{F}$ is complete.

### CONCLUDING REMARKS

The construction of a set of objects which form a complete ordered field gives us at least this satisfaction: it shows us that discussion of complete ordered fields is not vacuous. Such things do exist. Quite different sorts of sets of objects may form complete ordered fields. The construction we have sketched is one of many possibilities. The basic idea of this construction originated with the nineteenth century German mathematician J. W. R. Dedekind (1831–1916). We emphasize, however, that, in order to build further mathematical structures on the real number system, it is not necessary to know explicitly what kind of objects real numbers are. It is merely necessary to know the axiomatic definition of a complete ordered field, and to be assured that such a field really exists. For this reason, a detailed knowledge of the present section is not essential to understanding of the rest of this book.

### PROBLEMS

1. Verify carefully the validity of the transitive law for the order which is defined in $\mathscr{F}$.
2. This probem deals with the definition of $L = L_1 + L_2$ in the text, where $L_1$ and $L_2$ are in $\mathscr{F}$. Let $R = F - L$ and $R_i = F - L_i$, $i = 1, 2$.
   (a) Prove that $R \neq \varnothing$ by showing that $y_1 + y_2 \in R$ when $y_i \in R_i$. (The assumption $y_1 + y_2 \in L$ leads to a contradiction.) Why is $L \neq \varnothing$ ?
   (b) Prove that $y < x$ and $x \in L$ imply $y \in L$. [*Hint.* Write $x = x_1 + x_2$, $x_i \in L_i$, and note that $y - x_2 = x_1 - (x_1 + x_2 - y)$. Deduce that $y - x_2 \in L_1$ and hence $y \in L$.]
   (c) Prove that $(L, R)$ is a section in $F$ and that $L \in \mathscr{F}$.
3. Prove that $L + Z = Z$ for each $L$ in $\mathscr{F}$, as asserted in the text.
4. Suppose that $(L, R)$ is any section in the rational field $F$, and that $r \in F$, $r > 0$. Show that there exist elements $x \in L$ and $y \in R$ such that $y - x < r$. $\Big[$*Hint.* Choose $x_0 \in L$ and $y_0 \in R$ arbitrarily, and show that one can get what is wanted by choosing positive integers $k$, $n$ suitably and taking $x = x_{k-1}$, $y = x_k$, where $x_j = x_0 + j\dfrac{y_0 - x_0}{n}$, $j = 1, \ldots, n.\Big]$
5. Prove that, if $L \in \mathscr{F}$ and if $-L$ is defined as in the text, then $L + (-L) = Z$. In case $F - L$ has no smallest member, it is convenient to use Problem 4 in showing that $Z \subset L + (-L)$.
6. This problem deals with the definition of $L = L_1L_2$ in the text, assuming that $Z < L_i$, $i = 1, 2$.
   (a) Suppose $0 < y < x_1x_2$, where $x_i \in L_i^+$. Show that $y \in L$. $\Big[$*Hint.* Since $y = x_1\left(\dfrac{y}{x_1}\right)$, it suffices to show that $\dfrac{y}{x_1} \in L_2^+$.$\Big]$
   (b) Show that $R \neq \varnothing$ and that $(L, R)$ is a section in $F$.
   (c) Show that $L$ has no largest member, and hence that $L \in \mathscr{F}$.
7. In the situation of Problem 6, let $R_i = F - L_i$, and let $Y$ be the set of all products $y_1y_2$ such that $y_i \in R_i$, $i = 1, 2$. Show that $Y \subset R$ and that $R - Y$ contains at most one element.

## 1–4 Archimedean order. Countability of the rationals

In Section 1–3 we gave definitions of rational and irrational real numbers in terms of the particular model of the real number system which was there constructed. However, we can give definitions of these concepts entirely in the context of an abstractly given complete ordered field. Let $\mathscr{F}$ denote such a field.

## RATIONALS AND IRRATIONALS

The field $\mathscr{F}$ contains a subset $F$ which is an ordered field (with the same operations and order relation as in $\mathscr{F}$) and which is isomorphic, with an order-preserving isomorphism, to the field of rational numbers. That is, for all practical purposes, we can regard $\mathscr{F}$ as *containing* the field of rational numbers. This gives us a meaning of "rational element of $\mathscr{F}$." We shall sketch the idea but omit the details of showing that $\mathscr{F}$ actually does contain this particular sort of subfield $F$. The first essential step of the demonstration is to define "the positive integer elements of $\mathscr{F}$." This involves the notion of mathematical induction and the elements $1$, $1 + 1$, $(1 + 1) + 1$, and so on. From the fact that the field is ordered it can be proved that these elements are all different and that none of them is 0. Next we pass to the "negative integer elements" in $\mathscr{F}$, then to the "integer elements" (positive, negative, and zero), and thence to the "rational elements" of $\mathscr{F}$: those expressible in the form $x = \frac{p}{q}$, where $p$ and $q$ are integer elements and $q \neq 0$.

The irrational elements of $\mathscr{F}$ are those elements in $\mathscr{F} - F$, where $F$ is the class of rational elements.

Hereafter we shall refer to an integer or rational element, respectively, of $\mathscr{F}$ simply as an integer or a rational number.

It may be proved by induction that in any nonempty set of integers, all of which are greater than or equal to some fixed number, there is a smallest integer. This principle will be used in our proof of Theorem 1–4 II.

## ARCHIMEDEAN ORDER

An ordered field is called *archimedean* (after Archimedes 287–212 B.C.) if, corresponding to each pair of positive elements $a$, $b$ in the field, there is some positive integer $n$ such that $b < na$. There do exist fields which are nonarchimedean, but we shall not have to be concerned with such fields. It is easy to see that the field of rational numbers is archimedean. For, if $a > 0$ and $b > 0$, where $a$ and $b$ are rational, then $b/a$ is rational and $b < na$ is equivalent to $\frac{b}{a} < n$. Hence it suffices to show that if $p$ and $q$ are positive integers, there is a positive integer $n$ such that $\frac{p}{q} < n$. It suffices to choose $n = p + 1$, because

$$\frac{p}{q} \leq p < p + 1.$$

The proof that the field of real numbers is archimedean utilizes the fact that this field is complete. The following theorem implies that the real field is archimedean. (After reading Theorem 1–4 I the reader should make sure of this implication.)

THEOREM 1–4 I. *Corresponding to each real number $a$ there exists an integer $n$ such that $a < n$.*

*Proof.* Suppose, contrary to what is asserted, that for some $a$ we have $n \leq a$ for each integer $n$. Let $L$ be the set of those real numbers $x$ such that $x < n$ for *some* integer $n$, and let $R$ be the set of those real numbers $x$ such that $n \leq x$ for *each* integer $n$. Then $a \in R$, by our initial supposition. Certainly $0 \in L$, because $0 < 1$. If $x \in L$ and $y \in R$, then there is an integer $m$ such that $x < m$; moreover, certainly $m \leq y$. Therefore, by the transitive law of order, we see that $x < y$. It follows that $(L, R)$ is a section in the field of real numbers. Accordingly, there is a uniquely determined real number $c$ which is either the largest element of $L$ or the smallest element of $R$. In either of these cases it is easily verified that $x < c$ implies $x \in L$ and that $c < x$ implies $x \in R$.

But now we shall be able to reach a contradiction. Let $n$ be any selected integer. Then $n + 1$ is also an integer, and $n < n + 1$. By the definition of $L$ this implies $n \in L$. Consequently $n \leq c$, for otherwise it would be true that $c < n$, and this would imply $n \in R$. Thus we have reached the conclusion that $n \leq c$ for each integer $n$. But, if $n$ is an integer, so is $n + 1$, and hence $n + 1 \leq c$. This implies $n \leq c - 1$ for each integer $n$. This by the definition of $R$, implies $c - 1 \in R$. But $c - 1 < c$, and this implies $c - 1 \in L$. Since no number can belong to both $L$ and $R$, we have reached a contradiction. The initial assumption must therefore be abandoned, and the proof is finished.

The foregoing theorem enables us to prove that between any two distinct real numbers there is a rational number.

THEOREM 1–4 II. *If $a$, $b$ are real numbers and $a < b$, there exists a rational number $r$ such that $a < r < b$.*

*Proof.* First we prove a preliminary lemma: *If $x$ is a real number, there exists an integer $m$ such that $m \leq x$ and $x < m + 1$.* In fact, the class of integers larger than $x$ is not empty, by Theorem 1–4 I. This class must contain a smallest integer $p$. Hence $p - 1 \leq x < p$. We can take $m = p - 1$.

Returning to the proof of Theorem 1–4 II, we apply the fact that the real field is archimedean to assert the existence of a positive integer $n$ such that $1 < n(b - a)$. This is possible, since 1 and $b - a$ are positive. Then, by the lemma, with $x = na$, we can assert the existence of an integer $m$ such that $m - 1 \leq na < m$. Then, since $1 < n(b - a) = nb - na$, we see that

$$na < m \leq na + 1 < nb,$$

whence

$$a < \frac{m}{n} < b.$$

This proves the theorem, with $r = \frac{m}{n}$.

It is also true that, if $a$ and $b$ are real numbers and $a < b$, there exists an irrational number between $a$ and $b$. We leave the proof as a problem.

## COUNTABLE AND UNCOUNTABLE SETS

To begin with we consider sets whose elements are unspecified objects of any kind. Later we shall apply our considerations to certain sets of real numbers.

A set $S$ is called *finite* if it is empty or if there is a positive integer $n$ such that a one-to-one correspondence can be established between the elements of $S$ and the elements of the set consisting of the integers $1, 2, \ldots, n$. This means that we can designate the elements of $S$ by $n$ symbols $x_1, \ldots, x_n$, where $x_i \neq x_j$ if $i \neq j$. A set is called *denumerable*, or *countably infinite* (also *enumerable*) if a one-to-one correspondence can be established between the elements of $S$ and the elements of the set of *all* positive integers. This means that we can designate the elements of $S$ by symbols $x_1, x_2, x_3, \ldots$, where $x_i \neq x_j$ if $i \neq j$. A set is called *countable* if it is either finite or countably infinite.

A set is called *infinite* if it is not finite. If $S$ is an infinite set, we can assert the existence of a countably infinite subset of $S$. See Problem 3.

In the general theory of sets there is developed the concept of the *cardinal number* of a set. To each set $S$ is attached such a number, called the *cardinality* of $S$ (or simply the cardinal number of $S$). Two sets have the same cardinality if and only if the elements of one set can be put into one-to-one correspondence with the elements of the other. Finite sets are those with cardinality a nonnegative integer. There is a total ordering of cardinal numbers. The cardinals of infinite sets are called *transfinite* cardinals. For the present we shall not need more than this passing reference to such things. Our present outlook on the theory of sets is informal. In a strictly logical and formal treatment of the theory of sets we should have to be much more detailed and precise.

Any subset of a countable set is countable.

The union of two countable sets is countable. For example, if the elements of two countably infinite classes $S$, $T$ are respectively $x_1, x_2, \ldots$ and $y_1, y_2, \ldots$, the elements of $S \cup T$ can be listed as $x_1, y_1, x_2, y_2, \ldots$, and this makes the result clear.

The union of a countably infinite class of countably infinite sets is a countably infinite set. For the case in which there are no elements common to any two of the sets we can make the result clear as follows: Let the sets be $A_1, A_2, \ldots$, and let the elements of $A_i$ be $a_{i1}, a_{i2}, \ldots$. Then the elements of the union $\bigcup_{i=1}^{\infty} A_i$ can be enumerated in the order indicated in the accompanying display. That is, first we take $a_{11}$,

$$\begin{array}{cccccccccc}
A_1 & a_{11} & & a_{12} & & a_{13} & & a_{14} & & \cdots \\
 & & \nearrow & & \nearrow & & \nearrow & & \nearrow & \\
A_2 & a_{21} & & a_{22} & & a_{23} & & a_{24} & & \cdots \\
 & & \nearrow & & \nearrow & & \nearrow & & & \\
A_3 & a_{31} & & a_{32} & & a_{33} & & a_{34} & & \cdots \\
 & & \nearrow & & \nearrow & & & & & \\
A_4 & a_{41} & & a_{42} & & \cdots & & & & \\
\cdots & & \nearrow & & & & & & &
\end{array}$$

then those $a_{ij}$'s such that $i + j = 3$, then those for which $i + j = 4$, and so on.

## ENUMERABILITY OF THE RATIONALS

The set of all positive rational numbers is enumerable. For, let $A_p$ be the set of positive rationals (expressed in fractional form in lowest terms) with numerator the positive integer $p$. Obviously $A_p$ is enumerable:

$$A_1 : \frac{1}{1}\,\frac{1}{2}\,\frac{1}{3}\,\frac{1}{4}\,\frac{1}{5}\cdots$$

$$A_2 : \frac{2}{1}\,\frac{2}{3}\,\frac{2}{5}\,\frac{2}{7}\cdots$$

$$A_3 : \frac{3}{1}\,\frac{3}{2}\,\frac{3}{4}\,\frac{3}{5}\cdots$$

$$\cdots$$

Hence the union of all the $A_p$'s is enumerable, and this is equivalent to our initial assertion.

The set of *all* rational numbers is likewise enumerable. Proof is left to the reader.

It will be apparent that if $S$ is a countably infinite set, one can establish a one-to-one correspondence between the elements of $S$ and the elements of any specified denumerable proper subset of $S$. For instance, if $S$ consists of $x_1, x_2, x_3, \ldots$ and $T$ consists of $x_2, x_4, x_6, \ldots$, then by pairing $x_n$ with $x_{2n}$ $(n = 1, 2, \ldots)$ we obtain a one-to-one correspondence between the elements of $S$ and $T$. The possibility of this sort of thing, which could not occur with a finite set, may cause surprise. There are many such surprises possible in dealings with infinite sets.

## NONDENUMERABILITY OF THE IRRATIONALS

The set of all real numbers is not a denumerable set (or, as we sometimes say, the real numbers form an *uncountable* set). The following theorem implies this.

THEOREM 1–4 III. *Suppose $a_0$ and $b_0$ are real numbers such that $a_0 < b_0$, and let $S = \{x : a_0 < x < b_0\}$ ($x$ varying over all admissible real numbers). Then $S$ is an uncountable set.*

*Proof.* Suppose, to the contrary, that $S$ is countable, say with elements $x_1, x_2, \ldots$. We shall use the fact that the real field is complete to prove the existence of a number $c$ in $S$ such that $c \neq x_n$ for each $n$. This contradiction will complete the proof of the theorem.

For any numbers $\alpha, \beta$ with $\alpha < \beta$ we shall use $(\alpha, \beta)$ to denote the "interval" consisting of all real $x$ such that $\alpha < x < \beta$. We now let $a_1, b_1$ be the numbers (with $a_1 < b_1$) such that $a_1, b_1$ divide $(x_1, b_0)$ into three equal parts (see Figure 2). That is,

$$a_1 = \tfrac{2}{3}x_1 + \tfrac{1}{3}b_0, \qquad b_1 = \tfrac{1}{3}x_1 + \tfrac{2}{3}b_0.$$

Now consider $x_2$. If $a_1 < x_2 < b_1$, choose $a_2, b_2$ (with $a_2 < b_2$) so that $a_2, b_2$ divide $(x_2, b_1)$ into three equal parts. But, if $x_2 \leq a_1$ or $b_1 \leq x_2$, let $a_2, b_2$ be points dividing $(a_1, b_1)$ into

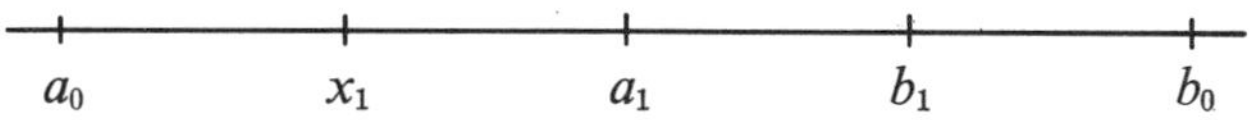


FIGURE 2

three equal parts. In either case, $a_1 < a_2 < b_2 < b_1$ and $x_2$ is not in $(a_2, b_2)$. We then proceed by induction to define $a_3, b_3$, then $a_4, b_4$, and so on, so that $a_n < a_{n+1} < b_{n+1} < b_n$ and $x_{n+1}$ is not in $(a_{n+1}, b_{n+1})$. Now let $R$ consist of all real numbers $y$ such that $a_n \leq y$ for each $n$, and let $L$ consist of all other real numbers. Evidently $a_n \in L$ and $b_n \in R$, for each $n$. It is easy to verify that $(L,R)$ is a section in the real field. Hence, since $L$ clearly cannot have a largest member (a number $y$ is in $L$ if $y < a_n$ for *some* $n$, and then also $\frac{1}{2}(y + a_n)$ is in $L$), $R$ must have a smallest member, which we shall denote by $c$. It is clear that $a_n < c$ for each $n$, because $a_n \in L$. Also, $c < b_n$ for each $n$, because $b_{n+1} < b_n$, the $b_n$'s are in $R$, and $c$ is the smallest member of $R$. Thus $a_n < c < b_n$; this guarantees that $x_n \neq c$, because we arranged things so that $x_n$ is not in $(a_n, b_n)$. Thus we have a point of $S$ different from all the points $x_1, x_2, \ldots$, and $S$ must be uncountable.

Since every real number is either rational or irrational, and since the set of rationals between $a_0$ and $b_0$ is denumerable, the set of irrationals between $a_0$ and $b_0$ must be uncountable.

For an instructive discussion of the notion of an infinite set, the reader is referred to Wilder [1], pp. 62–73. It will be seen that the assertion that an infinite set contains an enumerable subset involves a procedure whose legitimacy depends on a general principle in the theory of sets. One form of this general principle is called *the axiom of choice*, or *Zermelo's principle of choice*. For the present we need say no more about this matter. In Sections 3–10, 3–11 we shall again encounter a need for invoking this principle or something equivalent to it.

**PROBLEMS**

1. If $a$, $b$ are real and $a < b$, there exists an irrational $x$ such that $a < x < b$. More specifically, if $y$ is any positive irrational number, there exists an irrational number $x$ of the form $x = (m/n)y$ such that $a < x < b$, where $m$ and $n$ are integers and $n > 0$. Prove both assertions, giving a proof of the first which is independent of the second.

2. If the elements $a_{ij}(i, j = 1, 2, \ldots)$ are listed in order as described in connection with the diagram in Section 1–4:

$$a_{11}, a_{21}, a_{12}, a_{31}, a_{22}, a_{13}, a_{41}, a_{32}, \ldots,$$

show that the element $a_{ij}$ occupies the nth position in the list, where

$$n = j + \sum_{k=1}^{i+j-2} k \qquad \text{if} \quad i + j > 2.$$

3. If $S$ is an infinite set, $S \neq \varnothing$, and hence there exists an element $x_1$ such that $x_1 \in S$. Give an argument for the existence of distinct elements $x_1, x_2, \ldots$ such that $x_n \in S$ for each $n$.

4. Prove that the set of all rational numbers is enumerable.

## 1–5 Point sets. Upper and lower bounds

Let $S$ be a set of points on the real line. If $M$ is a point on the line such that $x \leq M$ whenever $x \in S$, we call $M$ an *upper bound* of the set $S$. Note that $M$ need not belong to $S$. If $M$ is an upper bound of $S$ and if $M < N$, then $N$ is also an upper bound of $S$. There may also be upper bounds of $S$ smaller than $M$. If $M$ is an upper bound of $S$ and if $N$ fails to be an upper bound of $S$ whenever $N < M$, then $M$ is called *the least upper bound* of $S$. Thus, in order to be the least upper bound of $S$, $M$ must satisfy two conditions:

(1) $x \leq M$ whenever $x \in S$

(2) corresponding to each $\epsilon > 0$ there must be at least one $x$ in $S$ such that $M - \epsilon < x$.

It is evident that two different points cannot both be least upper bounds of $S$.

*Example 1.* Let $S$ be the set of all numbers of the form $\dfrac{1}{x}$, where $x$ can be assigned all possible positive real values. There are no upper bounds for this set. For, if we consider a positive number $M$ to see if it might be an upper bound, we can choose a positive number $x$ such that $0 < x < \dfrac{1}{M}$. Then $M < \dfrac{1}{x}$. Since $\dfrac{1}{x} \in S$, this shows that $M$ is not an upper bound of $S$.

*Example 2.* Let $S$ be the set of all fractions of the form $\dfrac{n+1}{n}$, $n = 1, 2, \ldots$. That is, the elements of $S$ are

$$\frac{2}{1}, \frac{3}{2}, \frac{4}{3}, \ldots.$$

This set has 2 as its least upper bound. For since $2 \in S$, it is clear that nothing smaller than 2 can be an upper bound; and 2 itself is certainly an upper bound. This can be visualized directly by displaying the set $S$ on a number scale. Or, we can verify the fact that $\frac{n+1}{n} \leq 2$ when $n = 1, 2, \ldots$. This is equivalent to $n + 1 \leq 2n$, which is equivalent to $1 \leq n$, which is clearly true.

*Example 3.* Let $S$ be the set of all real numbers of the form $\frac{x}{x+1}$, $x$ being assignable any positive real value. This set has 1 as its least upper bound. Note, however, that 1 is not a member of $S$. Details are left to the student.

The empty set $\varnothing$ has the curious property that every real number is an upper bound of $\varnothing$. It is certainly true that if $M$ is any real number, then $x \leq M$ *whenever* $x$ *is a real number such that* $x \in \varnothing$. We say that the condition $x \leq M$ is satisfied *vacuously*, because there are no $x$'s of the required sort (that is, such that $x \in \varnothing$).

The following theorem is fundamental.

THEOREM 1–5 I. *Let $S$ be a nonempty set of points on the real line, and suppose there exists an upper bound of $S$. Then there is a unique least upper bound of $S$.*

*Proof.* This theorem depends on the fact that the field of real numbers is complete. Starting from what is given, we shall define a section in the real field. The student should remember that we use "point on the real line" and "real number" interchangeably, with the same meaning. Let $R$ be the collection of all upper bounds of $S$. Then $R$ is not empty, because of our explicit assumption to this effect. Let $L$ be the class of all real numbers not in $R$. To show that $L$ is not empty, observe that $S$ is not empty. Choose some $x \in S$. Then $x - 1 < x$. Hence $x - 1$ is *not* an upper bound of $S$, and therefore $x - 1 \in L$. Now suppose $u \in L$, $v \in R$. We want to prove that $u < v$. The fact that $u \in L$ implies the existence of an element $y$ of $S$ such that $u < y$. But $y \leq v$, for $v$ is an upper bound of $S$. Therefore $u < v$, by the transitive law for inequalities.

We now know that $(L, R)$ is a section in the real field. Hence there is a unique number $c$ which is either the largest member of $L$ or the smallest member of $R$. We shall show that $c$ cannot be the largest member of $L$, and hence must be the least upper bound of $S$. Suppose $c$ were the largest member of $L$. Then, from $c \in L$ we infer the existence of $x$ in $S$ such that $c < x$. Form the number $y = \frac{c+x}{2}$. Then $c < y < x$. Now, $c < y$ implies $y \in R$, but $y < x$ implies that $y \in L$. Because of this contradiction we must abandon the assumption that $c$ is the largest member of $L$.

The uniqueness of a least upper bound has already been pointed out.

The importance of completeness can readily be appreciated. The student should be able to think of a nonempty set of rational numbers for which there exists a rational upper bound but for which there is no least rational upper bound.

When a set of real numbers has an upper bound, we say that it is *bounded above*.

Entirely analogous to upper bounds are *lower bounds*. A set $S$ of real numbers is said to be *bounded below* if there is some number $m$ such that $m \leq x$ whenever $x \in S$. We call $m$

a lower bound of $S$. The largest lower bound of $S$ (if there is one) is called the *greatest lower bound* of $S$. It is a theorem that if $S$ is nonempty and has a lower bound, then it has a greatest lower bound. This can be proved by imitating the proof of Theorem 1–5 I, with suitable changes. But it can also be proved by a device which *applies* Theorem 1–5 I. Starting from the given set $S$, let $T$ be the set of all the negatives of the members of $S$; that is, $x \in T$ means $-x \in S$. Then, if $m$ is a lower bound of $S$, $-m$ is easily shown to be an upper bound of $T$. Hence, by Theorem 1–5 I, $T$ has a least upper bound. If we denote this least upper bound of $T$ by $M$, it is then easy to see that $-M$ is the greatest lower bound of $S$.

## NOTATIONS

The least upper bound of a set $S$ is also called the *supremum* of $S$. It is denoted by lub $S$ or sup $S$. If $S$ happens to be a set of values of a function, sup $S$ may be denoted in another way. Suppose, for instance, that $S$ is the set of all values $f(x)$ corresponding to $x > 0$, where $f(x) = \dfrac{x-1}{x}$. Then sup $S = 1$, and we may write this as

$$\sup S = \sup_{x>0} f(x) = 1.$$

Since $S = \{f(x) : x > 0\}$ in this case, we may also write

$$\sup \left\{\frac{x-1}{x} : x > 0\right\} = 1.$$

The greatest lower bound of a set $S$ is also called the *infimum* of $S$; we denote it by glb $S$ or inf $S$.

## MAXIMA AND MINIMA

The largest one of a finite set $x_1, \ldots, x_n$ of real numbers is denoted by max $\{x_1, \ldots, x_n\}$, and called the maximum of the set. For any set $S$ having a least upper bound, we call sup $S$ the maximum of $S$ if it belongs to $S$. Similar remarks apply to the minimum of a set. We denote the minimum of $S$ by min $S$ if it exists. For the set $S = \{e^{-x^2} : x \text{ real}\}$, max $S = 1$, but min $S$ does not exist, although inf $S = 0$.

## PROBLEMS

1. Suppose that $F$ is an ordered field with the property that, if $S$ is a nonempty set in $F$ which has an upper bound, then there exists in $F$ an element which is the least upper bound of $S$. Prove that $F$ is complete. [*Suggestion.* Let $(L, R)$ be a section in $F$, and let $c = \sup L$.]

2. Let $S$ be a nonempty set of real numbers having a positive infimum $c$. Let $T = \left\{x : \dfrac{1}{x} \in S\right\}$. Prove that $\sup T = \dfrac{1}{c}$.

3. Let $S$ be the set of all real numbers of the form $xe^{-x} \sin \dfrac{1}{x}$, $x$ real and positive. Show that the set $S$ is bounded both above and below. It is not required to find sup $S$ and inf $S$ exactly. Do you know any theorems which enable you to decide whether sup $S$ and inf $S$ are actually in $S$?

4. In the class of all real numbers let $S$ be the set $\{x : x > 0 \text{ and } x^2 < 3\}$. Show that $S$ is nonempty and bounded above. Let $c = \sup S$ and show that $c^2 = 3$.

5. Let $A$ be a positive real number and let $n$ be a positive integer. Show that there exists a unique positive number $c$ such that $c^n = A$. Use a method suggested by Problem 4.

## 1–6 Real sequences

Let us consider objects which are *pairs* $(n, x)$, where $n$ is a positive integer and $x$ is a real number. Suppose we have a collection of such objects which is such that for each value of $n$ there is exactly one object in the collection whose first member is $n$. Then the collection is called *a real sequence*. Clearly the collection is a denumerable set of objects. If the number which is paired with $n$ is denoted by $x_n$, the elements of the sequence are

$$(1, x_1), (2, x_2), (3, x_3), \ldots .$$

To specify a sequence we need to know what $x_n$ is when $n$ is given. In other words, we need to know $x_n$ as a function of $n$. In fact, a sequence is a particular kind of function—a function defined on the set of positive integers and having real numbers as values.

It is customary and convenient to use some short cuts of language in talking about sequences. Thus, the sequence with elements $(n, x_n)$ is often referred to as the sequence $\{x_n\}$. In particular examples we display in braces a symbol which exhibits the dependence of $x_n$ on $n$.

*Example 1.* We denote by $\{1 - (-1)^n\}$ the sequence for which

$$x_1 = 1 - (-1),\ x_2 = 1 - (-1)^2,\ x_3 = 1 - (-1)^3,$$

and so on.

It is also customary to call $x_1, x_2, x_3, \ldots$ the *terms* of the sequence.

A sequence must not be confused with a point set. The set $S$ consisting of the squares of all the positive integers is not the same thing as the sequence $\{n^2\}$. In fact, $S$ is a certain set whose elements are integers, whereas the sequence $\{n^2\}$ is a set whose elements are the pairs

$$(1, 1), (2, 4), (3, 9), (4, 16), \ldots .$$

Therefore $S$ and the sequence are quite different things. It is true that $S$ is the same as the set of all the terms of the sequence $\{x_n\}$. However, $S$ may also be the same as the set of all the terms of a quite different sequence. For instance, suppose we define

$$y_n = (n + 1)^2 \quad \text{if } n \text{ is odd},$$

$$y_n = (n - 1)^2 \quad \text{if } n \text{ is even}.$$

Then the elements of the sequence $\{y_n\}$ are

$$(1, 4), (2, 1), (3, 16), (4, 9), \ldots .$$

This is quite different from the first sequence $\{n^2\}$, but the set of all the terms of $\{n^2\}$ is the same as the set of all the terms of $\{y_n\}$.

### ABSOLUTE VALUE

In order to study real sequences it is convenient to make use of absolute values of numbers. Although the notion of absolute value is not assumed to be a new one at this stage, we review the elementary things about absolute values at this time.

If $c$ is a real number, its absolute value, denoted by $|c|$, is defined as

$$|c| = c \qquad \text{if} \quad c \geq 0,$$
$$|c| = -c \qquad \text{if} \quad c < 0.$$

Thus $|c| \geq 0$, and $|c| = 0$ if and only if $c = 0$.

One of the important rules for using absolute values is

(1) $$|ab| = |a|\,|b|.$$

One way of proving that (1) is correct is to consider separately the four cases: (i) either $a = 0$ or $b = 0$; (ii) $a > 0$ and $b > 0$; (iii) $a < 0$ and $b < 0$; (iv) $a > 0$ and $b < 0$, or $a < 0$ and $b > 0$. For example, in case (iv), if $a > 0$ and $b < 0$, $|ab| = -ab$ because $ab < 0$. But $-ab = a(-b) = |a|\,|b|$, and hence (1) is correct in this case. The other cases are left to the reader.

Note that (1) implies the fact that $|-a| = |a|$.

In work with inequalities, it is convenient to notice that if we assert $|x| \leq r$, where $r \geq 0$, this is equivalent to asserting the double inequality

$$-r \leq x \leq r;$$

that is, $x \leq r$ and $-r \leq x$. Also,

$$|a - b| < \epsilon$$

is equivalent to

$$-\epsilon < a - b < \epsilon,$$

which in turn is equivalent to

$$b - \epsilon < a < b + \epsilon.$$

The rule

(2) $$|a + b| \leq |a| + |b|$$

is of major importance. We call it the triangular inequality. Here is one way to prove it: Note that we always have

$$0 \leq a + |a| \quad \text{and} \quad 0 \leq -a + |a|,$$

and therefore

$$-|a| \leq a \leq |a|.$$

Hence also

$$-|b| \leq b \leq |b|.$$

But we can add inequalities. (That is, $A \leq B$ and $C \leq D$ imply $A + C \leq B + D$.) Therefore,

$$-(|a| + |b|) \leq a + b \leq |a| + |b|.$$

This double inequality is equivalent to (2).

The rule (2) implies another rule which is often useful, namely

(3) $$\big|\,|a| - |b|\,\big| \leq |a - b|.$$

To prove this, write

$$a = b + (a - b).$$

Then

$$|a| = |b + (a - b)| \leq |b| + |a - b|,$$

and so

(4) $$|a| - |b| \leq |a - b|.$$

This result must be valid for all pairs $a$, $b$, and hence

$$|b| - |a| \leq |b - a| = |a - b|. \tag{5}$$

Since $\big| |a| - |b| \big|$ is either $|a| - |b|$ or $|b| - |a|$, (4) and (5) together certainly imply (3).

## DISTANCE ON THE LINE

If $a$ and $b$ are points on the real line, the *distance* between them is *defined* to be the absolute value $|a - b|$. As a formal symbolism let us use $D(a, b)$ to denote the distance between $a$ and $b$. Then

$$D(a, b) = |a - b|. \tag{6}$$

Note the properties

$$D(a, b) = 0 \quad \text{is equivalent to} \quad a = b; \tag{7}$$

$$D(a, b) = D(b, a); \tag{8}$$

$$D(a, c) \leq D(a, b) + D(b, c). \tag{9}$$

To verify (9), note that it asserts

$$|a - c| \leq |a - b| + |b - c|.$$

This is true by application of (2), for

$$a - c = (a - b) + (b - c),$$

and we can use (2) with $a - b$ in place of $a$, $b - c$ in place of $b$.

The properties (7), (8), (9) are preserved when the concept of distance is applied in geometric contexts of many other sorts besides that of the real line.

Equalities and inequalities involving absolute values are often encountered in the study of analysis. One may gain facility in dealing with such matters by thorough familiarity with (1), (2), and (3), and by exploiting the meaning of $|a - b|$ as a distance.

*Example 2.* Let $S$ be the set $\{x : |x - 2| < 3\}$, it being understood that $x$ can be any admissible real number. Then $S$ is the set of all points $x$ on the real line such that the distance from $x$ to 2 is smaller than 3. Evidently the restriction on $x$ can be equally well expressed by $-1 < x < 5$.

## CONVERGENT SEQUENCES

Let $\{x_n\}$ be a real sequence. The sequence is called *convergent* if there exists a real number $A$ such that for each $\epsilon > 0$ the set of indices $n$ for which $|x_n - A| < \epsilon$ includes all but a finite (perhaps empty) set of the positive integers. That is, the requirement is that to each positive $\epsilon$ there correspond some positive integer $N$ such that $|x_n - A| < \epsilon$ if $N < n$. We write

$$x_n \to A \quad \text{or} \quad \lim_{n\to\infty} x_n = A \quad \text{or} \quad \lim x_n = A$$

to express this state of affairs, and call $A$ the *limit* of the sequence. We also say that $\{x_n\}$ converges to $A$.

We leave it for the reader to prove that there cannot be two different numbers $A_1$, $A_2$

meeting the requirement. However, there may be no $A$ at all; that is, there certainly do exist sequences which are not convergent.

It is presumed that readers of this book are to some extent familiar with the notion of convergence of a sequence, and that they have learned some of the facts and techniques which are needed in calculations which involve convergent sequences. Our concern is more with the place of the concept of convergence in the basic development of analysis than with the elementary facts and techniques. For review of these matters which we take for granted the student may find it useful to refer to Section 1.62 in the author's *Advanced Calculus.*

A real sequence $\{x_n\}$ is called *bounded above* if there is a number $A$ such that $x_n \leq A$ for all values of $n$. The sequence is called *bounded below* if there is a number $B$ such that $B \leq x_n$ for all $n$. If $\{x_n\}$ is bounded both above and below it is called *bounded.* A necessary and sufficient condition for $\{x_n\}$ to be bounded is that there exist a number $M$ such that $|x_n| \leq M$ for all $n$. For, if $B \leq x_n \leq A$ for every $n$, we can let $M$ be the maximum of the two numbers $|A|$, $|B|$, and then $-M \leq x_n \leq M$, which is equivalent to $|x_n| \leq M$.

It is an important fact that a convergent sequence is bounded. Proof is left as a problem. On the other hand, there are bounded sequences which do not converge.

## MONOTONIC SEQUENCES

A real sequence $\{x_n\}$ is called *monotonic* (or *monotone*) if either $x_n \leq x_{n+1}$ for each $n$, that is,

$$x_1 \leq x_2 \leq x_3 \leq \cdots,$$

or $x_{n+1} \leq x_n$ for each $n$, that is,

$$x_1 \geq x_2 \geq x_3 \geq \cdots.$$

In the first case the sequence is called *nondecreasing*, in the second case *nonincreasing*. By a *strictly monotonic* sequence we mean one which is either *increasing*,

$$x_1 < x_2 < x_3 < \cdots,$$

or *decreasing*,

$$x_1 > x_2 > x_3 > \cdots.$$

THEOREM 1–6 I. *A monotonic sequence is convergent if it is bounded. For a nondecreasing sequence the limit is the least upper bound of the terms; for a nonincreasing sequence the limit is the greatest lower bound of the terms.*

*Proof (for the nondecreasing case).* Supposing that $\{x_n\}$ is bounded, let $A$ be the least upper bound of the $x_n$'s (we write $A = \sup_n x_n$). Then $x_n \leq A$ for all values of $n$, and, if $\epsilon > 0$, $A - \epsilon$ is not an upper bound of the $x_n$'s, so that $A - \epsilon < x_N$ for some index $N$. Then, since the sequence is monotonic, we have $x_N \leq x_n$ when $N \leq n$, and so certainly $A - \epsilon < x_n \leq A$ if $N \leq n$. These last inequalities certainly imply $|x_n - A| < \epsilon$. Therefore $x_n \to A$.

The proof for the other case is left to the student.

## SUBSEQUENCES

A sequence $\{k_n\}$ is called a subsequence of the sequence of positive integers if each term $k_n$ is a positive integer and if the sequence $\{k_n\}$ is strictly increasing, that is,

$$k_1 < k_2 < k_3 < \cdots.$$

If $\{x_n\}$ is any sequence, by a *subsequence* of $\{x_n\}$ we mean a sequence $\{y_n\}$ such that $y_n = x_{k_n}$ for each $n$, where $\{k_n\}$ is some subsequence of the positive integers. In particular, $\{x_n\}$ is a subsequence of itself. Apart from this, however, a subsequence is formed by dropping out some (perhaps infinitely many) of the $x_n$'s, yet keeping infinitely many, and then relabeling the retained terms with indices 1, 2, 3, . . . in the order of their original occurrence.

*Example 3.* As instances of the subsequence $\{k_n\}$ of the indices we might have

$$1, 3, 5, 7, \ldots \qquad (k_n = 2n - 1),$$

or

$$1, 3, 7, 13, 21, \ldots \qquad (k_n = n^2 - n + 1).$$

It is apparent that if $\{x_n\}$ is convergent, with limit $A$, then every subsequence of $\{x_n\}$ is also convergent and has this same limit $A$. On the other hand, a sequence may fail to have any convergent subsequence.

*Example 4.* The sequence $\{n(-1)^n\}$ has no convergent subsequence, because it has no bounded subsequence.

We shall see later on (Theorem 2–4 IV) that if a sequence is bounded, there certainly are convergent subsequences of it. See also Problem 2 in Section 1–7.

In calculations with sequences we often use the elementary rules about limits of sums, products, and quotients. If $\{x_n\}$ and $\{y_n\}$ are convergent sequences, with $x_n \to x$, $y_n \to y$, then $x_n + y_n \to x + y$ and $x_n y_n \to xy$. If $y \neq 0$, we necessarily have $y_n \neq 0$ for all sufficiently large $n$, and if we deal only with $n$'s for which $y_n \neq 0$, we have $\dfrac{x_n}{y_n} \to \dfrac{x}{y}$.

**PROBLEMS**

1. (a) Prove that a convergent sequence is bounded. (b) Prove that $x_n \to A$ and $x_n \to B$ is impossible if $A \neq B$.
2. Prove Theorem 1–6 I for the nonincreasing case.
3. If $x_n \to x$, show that $|x_n| \to |x|$.
4. Suppose that $x_n \to x$. Let $N = f(\epsilon)$ be a function with positive integer values defined for $\epsilon > 0$, such that $|x_n - x| < \epsilon$ if $n \geq f(\epsilon)$. Suppose that $x \neq 0$. Show that $\dfrac{1}{x_n} \to \dfrac{1}{x}$ by showing that $\left|\dfrac{1}{x_n} - \dfrac{1}{x}\right| < \epsilon$ if $n \geq N_1$, where $N_1$ is the maximum of $f\left(\dfrac{|x|}{2}\right)$ and $f\left(\dfrac{\epsilon\,|x|^2}{2}\right)$.
5. Each positive integer $n$ is such that exactly one of the integers $n + 2, n + 1, n$ is evenly divisible by 3. Define $x_n$ to be $\dfrac{3}{n+2}, \dfrac{2n-1}{3} \cdot 2^{-[(n+1)/3]}, (-1)^{n/3}$ in the respective cases. (a) Is the sequence $\{x_n\}$ bounded? (b) Is it convergent? (c) Find all numbers $A$ such that $A$ is the limit of some subsequence of $\{x_n\}$. Try to describe conditions on a subsequence $\{k_n\}$ of the positive integers which are both necessary and sufficient for the convergence of $\{y_n\}$, where $y_n = x_{k_n}$.
6. Let $\{x_n\}$ be defined as follows: Suppose $0 < a < b$, $x_1 = a$, $x_2 = b$, $x_3 = \dfrac{a+b}{2}, \ldots, x_{n+2} = \dfrac{1}{2}(x_n + x_{n+1})$ if $n \geq 1$. Show that $\{x_n\}$ is bounded. It is not entirely simple to find an explicit formula for $x_n$ as a function of $n$. See if you can do this. Observe that one can write $x_n = \alpha_n a + \beta_n b$. Calculate $\alpha_n$ and $\beta_n$ for several values of $n$, and try to determine general formulas for $\alpha_n$ and $\beta_n$ by guesswork and induction. Then show that $\{x_n\}$ is convergent, and find the limit.

## 1–7 The extended real number system

From now on we shall regularly use the letter $R$ to denote the real number system. There are many situations in analysis where we find it desirable to introduce the symbols $+\infty$, $-\infty$. For a systematic explanation of the use of these symbols we have recourse to what is called *the extended real number system.* This is a collection of objects consisting of all the real numbers and two more objects, denoted by $+\infty$ and $-\infty$. We denote the extended real number system by $R^*$. At the present time our concern will be with the order relation $<$ in $R^*$. We make $R^*$ into a totally ordered system by extending the order relation which we already have in $R$. This is done by specifying that $-\infty < +\infty$, that $-\infty < b$ and $b < +\infty$ if $b \in R$, and that $a < b$ means the same in $R^*$ as it does in $R$ if $a$ and $b$ are in $R$.

Although $R$ is a field, we do not claim to make a field out of $R^*$. For certain purposes it is useful to define addition and multiplication in $R^*$, and also subtraction and division, at least in some cases. But even so, $R^*$ never becomes a field. We consider such matters in Section 4–1; for the present we shall have no concern with them.

If $S$ is a set in $R^*$, we define the concept of least upper bound of $S$ just as we did in Section 1–5 for sets in $R$, except that now all elements are in $R^*$. Likewise for greatest lower bounds. We use the notations lub, glb, sup, and inf for sets in $R^*$, just as we did for sets in $R$. The great convenience of $R^*$, as compared with $R$, is that every nonempty set in $R^*$ has both a least upper bound and a greatest lower bound (both unique). That this is true follows from Theorem 1–5 I and the fact that $+\infty$ is an upper bound for every set, while $-\infty$ is a lower bound for every set.

### SEQUENCES IN $R^*$

Suppose that $\{x_n\}$ is a sequence in $R^*$ (that is, each $x_n$ is an element of $R^*$). If $A \in R^*$, we say that $x_n \to A$ or $\lim x_n = A$ (the sequence $\{x_n\}$ has the limit $A$), provided that the following conditions are satisfied:

(i) if $a \in R^*$ and $a < A$, there is some $N_1$ such that $a < x_n$ when $N_1 < n$,
(ii) if $b \in R^*$ and $A < b$, there is some $N_2$ such that $x_n < b$ when $N_2 < n$.

Thus, if $A \neq \pm\infty$ and $a < A < b$, $n > \max\{N_1, N_2\}$ implies $a < x_n < b$. If $A = +\infty$, there is no $b$ such that $A < b$, and therefore condition (ii) is inapplicable. Likewise, (i) is inapplicable if $A = -\infty$.

The foregoing definition means that $\{x_n\}$ converges to $A$ in the sense of Section 1–6 if the $x_n$'s and $A$ are all real numbers. For, if $a < A < b$ and $a < x_n < b$, with $a$ and $b$ in $R$, we have

$$|x_n - A| < \max\{b - A, A - a\}.$$

The foregoing definition includes the usual definitions of $x_n \to +\infty$ and $x_n \to -\infty$, as given in calculus.

*Example 1.* Let $x_{2n-1} = n$, $x_{2n} = (n + 1)^2$, $n = 1, 2, \ldots$. Then $x_n \to +\infty$. In fact, if $a < +\infty$, take $N = 2k - 1$, where $k$ is a positive integer such that $k \geq a$. Then $n > N$ implies $x_n > a$.

It is easy to see that a sequence $\{x_n\}$ for which $x_1 \leq x_2 \leq \cdots$ has as its limit the supremum of the set consisting of $x_1, x_2, \ldots$. Likewise, if $x_1 \geq x_2 \geq \cdots$, the sequence $\{x_n\}$ has as its limit the infimum of the set just mentioned.

## LIMITS SUPERIOR AND INFERIOR

With every sequence $\{x_n\}$ in $R^*$, regardless of whether the sequence has a limit in $R^*$ or not, we can associate two elements of $R^*$, called the limits superior and inferior of the sequence. To define the limit superior of $\{x_n\}$, denoted by $\limsup_{n\to\infty} x_n$ or $\overline{\lim_{n\to\infty}}\, x_n$, let $S_k$ be the set with elements $x_k, x_{k+1}, \ldots$, and let $M_k = \sup S_k$. Since $S_{k+1} \subset S_k$, it is evident that $M_{k+1} \leq M_k$. Hence the sequence $\{M_k\}$ has a limit in $R^*$, namely the infimum of the $M_k$'s. This infimum is defined to be the *limit superior* of $\{x_n\}$:

(1) $$\limsup_{n\to\infty} x_n = \inf_{k\geq 1} \sup \{x_k, x_{k+1}, \ldots\}.$$

*Special cases:*

(a) $\limsup_{n\to\infty} x_n = -\infty$ if and only if $x_n \to -\infty$. This is evident on inspection.

(b) $\limsup_{n\to\infty} x_n = +\infty$ if and only if $M_k = +\infty$ for every $k$. This occurs if and only if there is some subsequence of $\{x_n\}$ having $+\infty$ as limit.

The *limit inferior* of a sequence $\{x_n\}$ is defined in a similar way. Define $S_k$ as before, and let $m_k = \inf S_k$. Then $m_k \leq m_{k+1}$, so that the sequence $\{m_k\}$ has as its limit the supremum of the $m_k$'s; this is defined to be the limit inferior of $\{x_n\}$. We denote it by $\liminf_{n\to\infty} x_n$ or $\underline{\lim}_{n\to\infty}\, x_n$:

(2) $$\liminf_{n\to\infty} x_n = \sup_{k\geq 1} \inf \{x_k, x_{k+1}, \ldots\}.$$

We can see from the definitions of $m_k$ and $M_k$ that $j < k$ implies

$$m_j \leq m_k \leq M_k \leq M_j.$$

Hence $\sup_j m_j \leq \inf_k M_k$. In other words,

(3) $$\liminf_{n\to\infty} x_n \leq \limsup_{n\to\infty} x_n.$$

For convenience in printing we shall often omit the symbols $n \to \infty$ in writing $\lim x_n$, $\limsup x_n$, and $\liminf x_n$.

*Example 2.* Let $x_n = 1 + \dfrac{1}{n}$ if $n$ is odd, $x_n = -\dfrac{n}{2}$ if $n$ is even. Then

$$\liminf x_n = -\infty, \qquad \limsup x_n = 1.$$

*Example 3.* Let $\{x_n\}$ be defined as follows:

$$x_n = 2 + \frac{(-1)^n}{n} \quad \text{if} \quad n = 1, 4, 7, 10, 13, \ldots$$

$$x_n = 1 + \frac{1-(-1)^n}{n} \quad \text{if} \quad n = 2, 5, 8, 11, 14, \ldots$$

$$x_n = 0 \quad \text{if} \quad n = 3, 6, 9, 12, \ldots.$$

Then

$$\liminf x_n = 0, \qquad \limsup x_n = 2.$$

The limit superior of $\{x_n\}$ may be characterized in another way, as described in the following theorem.

THEOREM 1–7 I. *Let $\{x_n\}$ be a sequence in $R^*$. Then $\limsup_{n\to\infty} x_n = A$ if and only if the following two conditions are satisfied:*

(i) *if $a < A$, then $a < x_n$ for infinitely many values of $n$;*

(ii) *if $A < b$, then $x_n < b$ for all sufficiently large values of $n$.*

*Proof.* Suppose conditions (i) and (ii) are satisfied. From condition (i) we see that if $a < A$, then $a < \sup\{x_k, x_{k+1}, \ldots\}$ for every $k$, and therefore $a \leq \limsup x_n$. This implies $A \leq \limsup x_n$, because of the arbitrariness of $a$. From condition (ii) we see that $A < b$ implies $\sup\{x_k, x_{k+1}, \ldots\} \leq b$ if $k$ is sufficiently large. Therefore $\limsup x_n \leq b$; because of the arbitrariness of $b$ this implies $\limsup x_n \leq A$. Thus $\limsup x_n = A$.

Suppose, conversely, that $A = \limsup x_n$. If $a < A$, this implies that

$$a < \sup\{x_k, x_{k+1}, \ldots\}$$

for every $k$, so that to each $k$ corresponds some $n$ with $k \leq n$ and $a < x_n$. Thus condition (i) is satisfied. If $A < b$, this means that

$$\sup\{x_k, x_{k+1}, \ldots\} < b$$

for some $k$. But then $x_n < b$ if $n \geq k$; this means that condition (ii) is satisfied. This finishes the proof of Theorem 1–7 I.

There is a theorem analogous to Theorem 1–7 I, relative to the limit inferior. See Problem 3.

There are still other useful ways of thinking about the limits superior and inferior. If $\limsup x_n = A$, no subsequence of $\{x_n\}$ can have a limit $B$ with $A < B$ (because of condition (ii) in Theorem 1–7 I); there will, however, be some subsequence of $\{x_n\}$ which has the limit $A$. We leave it to the reader to show this.

There is a simple relationship between the notions of limit superior and limit inferior. Let $P$ be a set of elements $p$ in $R^*$, and let $Q$ be the set of all the elements $-p$. (We understand that $-(+\infty) = -\infty$ and $-(-\infty) = +\infty$.) Then

$$\sup Q = -\inf P, \qquad \inf Q = -\sup P. \tag{4}$$

If we apply (4), we see that

$$\inf\{x_k, x_{k+1}, \ldots\} = -\sup\{-x_k, -x_{k+1}, \ldots\},$$

and hence

$$\sup_{k\geq 1} \inf\{x_k, x_{k+1}, \ldots\} = -\inf_{k\geq 1} \sup\{-x_k, -x_{k+1}, \ldots\},$$

or

$$\liminf_{n\to\infty} x_n = -\limsup_{n\to\infty} (-x_n). \tag{5}$$

It follows, of course, that

$$\limsup_{n\to\infty} x_n = -\liminf_{n\to\infty} (-x_n). \tag{6}$$

Sequences which have a limit are characterized in the next theorem.

THEOREM 1–7 II. *A sequence* $\{x_n\}$ *in* $R^*$ *has the limit A if and only if*

$$\liminf_{n\to\infty} x_n = A = \limsup_{n\to\infty} x_n. \tag{7}$$

*Proof.* If we suppose that (7) holds, it is clear from condition (ii) in Theorem 1–7 I and condition (i) in the corresponding proposition about the limit inferior (see Problem 3) that $x_n \to A$. On the other hand, if $x_n \to A$, it is clear, by the criteria of Theorem 1–7 I, that $\limsup x_n = A$; the situation is similar for the limit inferior.

If $\{x_n\}$ is a sequence of real numbers, there is some possibility of confusion in terminology unless we make clear whether we are speaking about limits in $R$ or in $R^*$. When we are speaking about sequences in $R$, the assertion "$\{x_n\}$ is convergent" means that there is an $A$ in $R$ such that $x_n \to A$. When a real sequence $\{x_n\}$ is such that $x_n \to +\infty$ or $x_n \to -\infty$, we do not call it convergent. Nevertheless, if we are thinking in terms of $R^*$, it is natural to say $x_n$ converges to $+\infty$ when $x_n \to +\infty$, even if the $x_n$'s are all in $R$. To clarify the situation and avoid the possibility of confusion we sometimes say "$\{x_n\}$ has a finite limit," or "$x_n$ converges to the finite limit $A$," to emphasize that the limit is not $\pm\infty$.

### PROBLEMS

1. If $\limsup x_n = A$, show that there exists a subsequence of $\{x_n\}$ with $A$ as limit.
2. Let $\{x_n\}$ be a bounded sequence of real numbers. Show that $\{x_n\}$ contains a convergent subsequence. [*Suggestion.* See the preceding problem.]
3. Show that $\liminf x_n = A$ is characterized by the two conditions:
   (i) if $a < A$, then $a < x_n$ for all sufficiently large values of $n$;
   (ii) if $A < b$, then $x_n < b$ for infinitely many values of $n$.

Give a proof directly from the definition (2); then give a proof using Theorem 1–7 I and formula (5).

4. If $\{x_n\}$ is a sequence in $R^*$, let $S$ be the set of all elements $A$ of $R^*$ such that $A$ is the limit of some subsequence of $\{x_n\}$. Show that $\max S = \limsup x_n$ and $\min S = \liminf x_n$.
5. Let $S$ be an arbitrary countable set in $R$. Construct a sequence $\{x_n\}$ in $R$ such that each member of $S$ is the limit of some subsequence of $\{x_n\}$. [*Suggestion.* Begin by constructing a countable collection of subsequences of the sequence 1, 2, 3, . . . such that each positive integer occurs as a term of exactly one subsequence.]
6. Show that, if $\{x_n\}$ and $\{y_n\}$ are bounded sequences in $R$, then

$$\limsup (x_n + y_n) \le \limsup x_n + \limsup y_n$$

and

$$\liminf x_n + \liminf y_n \le \liminf (x_n + y_n).$$

## 1–8 Cauchy's convergence condition

In this section we continue the discussion of real sequences with special attention to convergent sequences. It is of major importance to be able to decide that certain sequences are convergent without knowing precisely, in each particular case, to what limit the sequence converges. There is an important criterion which is useful for this purpose.

THEOREM 1–8 I. *Let* $\{x_n\}$ *be a real sequence. In order that* $\{x_n\}$ *be convergent it is necessary and sufficient that to each* $\epsilon > 0$ *correspond some positive integer N such that* $|x_n - x_m| < \epsilon$ *whenever* $N \le m$ *and* $N \le n$.

*Proof of necessity.* Suppose that $x_n \to A$ and $\epsilon > 0$. Then $|x_n - A| < \frac{\epsilon}{2}$ for all except a finite set of values of $n$. Choose $N$ so that $N \leq n$ implies $|x_n - A| < \frac{\epsilon}{2}$. Now suppose $N \leq m$ and $N \leq n$. Then, applying the triangular inequality, we have

$$x_n - x_m = (x_n - A) + (A - x_m),$$

$$|x_n - x_m| \leq |x_n - A| + |x_m - A| < \frac{\epsilon}{2} + \frac{\epsilon}{2} = \epsilon.$$

*Proof of sufficiency.* Suppose that to each $\epsilon > 0$ there corresponds an $N$ so that the condition stated in the theorem is fulfilled. (When this is so we say that the sequence satisfies *Cauchy's condition.*) We begin by proving that the sequence is bounded. To do this, let $M$ be a value of $N$ corresponding to $\epsilon = 1$ in Cauchy's condition, so that $|x_n - x_M| < 1$ if $M \leq n$. Let $A$ and $B$ be the smallest and largest numbers, respectively, in the finite set $x_1, \ldots, x_{M-1}$. Thus we have $A \leq x_n \leq B$ if $1 \leq n < M$, and $x_M - 1 < x_n < x_M + 1$ if $M \leq n$. Let

$$C = \min\{A, x_M - 1\}, \qquad D = \max\{x_M + 1, B\}.$$

Then $C \leq x_n \leq D$ for all values of $n$, and $\{x_n\}$ is bounded.

The general idea of what we are doing here is conveyed by the diagram in Figure 3, where it is supposed that $M = 5$. In this special case

$$x_2 = A = \min\{x_1, x_2, x_3, x_4\}, \qquad x_1 = B = \max\{x_1, x_2, x_3, x_4\},$$

and $C = x_2$, $D = x_5 + 1$.

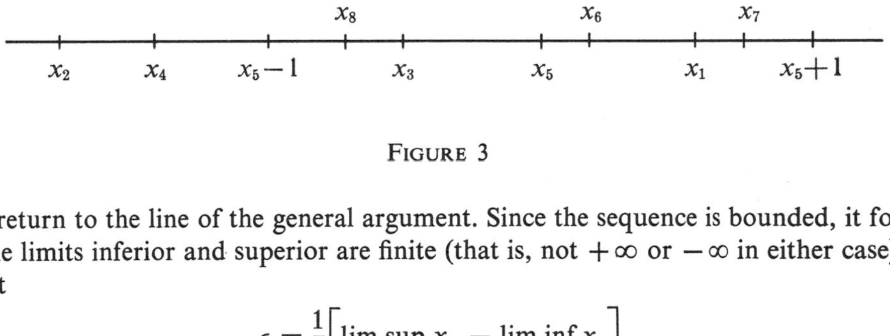


FIGURE 3

We return to the line of the general argument. Since the sequence is bounded, it follows that the limits inferior and superior are finite (that is, not $+\infty$ or $-\infty$ in either case). We now let

$$\epsilon = \frac{1}{2}\left[\limsup_{n\to\infty} x_n - \liminf_{n\to\infty} x_n\right].$$

If $\epsilon = 0$, the sequence is convergent, by Theorem 1–7 II. We shall show that the assumption $\epsilon > 0$ leads to a contradiction, and thus complete the proof. We do assume $\epsilon > 0$. Then, with

$$\alpha = \liminf_{n\to\infty} x_n, \qquad \beta = \limsup_{n\to\infty} x_n,$$

we know that there exist infinitely many values of $n$ such that $\beta - \frac{\epsilon}{2} < x_n$ and also infinitely many values of $n$ (but perhaps different values) such that $x_n < \alpha + \frac{\epsilon}{2}$. We can then assert the existence of subsequences $m_1, m_2, m_3, \ldots$ and $n_1, n_2, n_3, \ldots$ such that

$$x_{m_i} < \alpha + \frac{\epsilon}{2} \quad \text{and} \quad \beta - \frac{\epsilon}{2} < x_{n_i}$$

for $i = 1, 2, \ldots$. We can rewrite the first of these inequalities as $-\alpha - \frac{\epsilon}{2} < -x_{m_i}$. Then, on adding inequalities, we obtain

$$\beta - \alpha - \epsilon < x_{n_i} - x_{m_i}.$$

But $\beta - \alpha = 2\epsilon$, and so we have

$$\epsilon < x_{n_i} - x_{m_i} = |x_{n_i} - x_{m_i}|.$$

Now, no matter how large $N$ is chosen, we can arrange to make $N < m_i$ and $N < n_i$ by choosing $i$ large enough. Thus it is not true that $|x_m - x_n| < \epsilon$ whenever $N \leq m$ and $N \leq n$. Consequently, since no suitable $N$ can be found for this $\epsilon$, Cauchy's condition is not satisfied. This contradicts our initial hypothesis, so our proof is finished.

Theorem 1–8 I could be proved in a variety of other ways. A generalization of the theorem will be found in Section 2–4; the generalization applies to sequences whose terms are points in a Euclidean space of dimension $k$. Our present theorem is the case $k = 1$.

For convenience we call $\{x_n\}$ a Cauchy sequence if it satisfies Cauchy's condition.

Although the condition on the sequence in Theorem 1–8 I is now generally known as Cauchy's convergence condition, there is reason to mention also the name of Bernard Bolzano in this connection. Bolzano recognized the sufficiency of the condition in a work published in 1817. For another note about Bolzano see the remarks following the proof of Theorem 2–4 II. Augustin-Louis Cauchy (1789–1857) was the first to develop the theory of limits on a firm arithmetical basis. His discussion of what we now call the Cauchy condition appeared in his text, Cours d'Analyse, in 1821.

**PROBLEMS**

1. Suppose $a_n > 0$ and $a_{n+1} \leq a_n$ for each $n$, and suppose $a_n \to 0$. Let $\{x_n\}$ be defined by $x_1 = a_1, x_{n+1} = x_n + (-1)^n a_{n+1}$. Show that $\{x_n\}$ is a Cauchy sequence by showing that $|x_n - x_m| \leq a_m$ if $m < n$.
2. Suppose that $x_1 = a$, $x_2 = b$, and $x_{n+2} = \frac{1}{2}(x_n + x_{n+1})$ if $n \geq 1$. Show that $\{x_n\}$ is a Cauchy sequence by verifying that $|x_{m+1} - x_m| = \dfrac{|b - a|}{2^{m-1}}$ if $m \geq 1$, and that $|x_n - x_m| \leq |x_{m+1} - x_m|$ if $n > m$.
3. Let $\{x_n\}$ be a Cauchy sequence of real numbers. Define sets $L$ and $R$ as follows: $L$ is the set of all real numbers $y$ such that $y < x_n$ for all sufficiently large values of $n$; $R$ is the set of all real numbers $y$ such that $x_n \leq y$ for infinitely many values of $n$. Prove directly that $(L, R)$ is a section in the field of real numbers and that $x_n \to x$ if $x$ is the corresponding section number.
4. Suppose that $\{x_n\}$ is a Cauchy sequence of real numbers. Suppose it is known that a certain subsequence of $\{x_n\}$ converges to the finite limit $A$. Prove directly, without using the sufficiency part of Theorem 1–8 I, that $x_n \to A$.

## 1–9 The theorem on nested intervals

If $a$ and $b$ are points on the real line, with $a < b$, the set of all points $x$ such that $a \leq x \leq b$ is called the *finite closed interval* with ends $a$, $b$. Sometimes we denote this set by $[a, b]$. Note the use of square brackets. By contrast we denote the set of all $x$ such that $a < x < b$ by $(a, b)$, using ordinary parentheses. This set $(a, b)$ is called an *open* interval. The uses of the words "closed" and "open" here are particular cases of general usages of these words, to be more fully explained in Chapter 2.

The further notations

$$(a, b] = \{x : a < x \leq b\}, \qquad [a, b) = \{x : a \leq x < b\}$$

are also used at times.

Now let us suppose that we have a sequence of finite closed intervals, the $n$th interval being denoted by $I_n = [a_n, b_n]$. Let us suppose that $I_2 \subset I_1$, $I_3 \subset I_2$, and so on. That is, we suppose $a_n < b_n$ and

(1) $$a_1 \leq a_2 \leq a_3 \leq \cdots, \qquad b_1 \geq b_2 \geq b_3 \geq \cdots.$$

Finally, we suppose that the length of $I_n$ converges to 0 as $n \to \infty$. That is, we suppose

(2) $$b_n - a_n \to 0.$$

When all these conditions are satisfied we say that the sequence of intervals is a *nest*. We shall find that the concept of a nest is very useful in the proofs of some important theorems about the real line and about Euclidean space of higher dimensionality. The basic device is what we shall refer to as "the nested intervals theorem," which we now state and prove.

THEOREM 1–9 I. *Let $I_1, I_2, I_3, \ldots$ be finite closed intervals forming a nest on the real line. Then, the intersection of all the $I_n$'s consists of a single point.*

*Proof.* Let $I_n = [a_n, b_n]$. Then each of the sequences $\{a_n\}$, $\{b_n\}$ is bounded and monotonic, as a result of the fact that we have a nest. Hence, each sequence is convergent. Suppose $a_n \to a$, $b_n \to b$. Then $a_n \leq a$, $b \leq b_n$. We also know that $a_m < b_n$ for every $m$ and every $n$, and from this we conclude $a \leq b$. We must have $a = b$, for with $a_n \leq a < b \leq b_n$, it would be impossible to have $b_n - a_n \to 0$. Consequently, $a_n \leq a \leq b_n$ for every $n$. This means that

$$a \in \bigcap_{n=1}^{\infty} I_n.$$

There cannot be *more* than one point in the intersection of all the $I_n$'s, for if there were two points, a distance $d$ apart, where $d > 0$, this would mean that $b_n - a_n \geq d$ for every $n$, contrary to the fact that $b_n - a_n \to 0$.

## PROBLEMS

1. Refer to the discussion of completeness in Section 1–0, where Properties 1, 2, 3, 4 of an ordered field are defined.

(a) Show that Property 3 implies Property 4 ($3 \to 4$). [*Suggestion.* If $\{I_n\}$ is a nest in the field $F$, with $I_n = [a_n, b_n]$, show that $\{a_n\}$ is a Cauchy sequence and that $\lim a_n \in I_k$ for every $k$.]

(b) Show that $4 \to 2$. [*Suggestion.* Given a set $S$ with $a \in S$ and $x \leq b$ for each $x \in S$ (where $a < b$), let $a_1 = a$, $b_1 = b$, $I_1 = [a_1, b_1]$. Bisect $I_1$, and choose $I_2$ as the left-hand closed subinterval if the midpoint of $I_1$ is an upper bound of $S$. Otherwise let $I_2$ be the right-hand closed subinterval. Repeat the bisection process and obtain a nest $\{I_n\}$ with $I_n = [a_n, b_n]$, $I_n \cap S \neq \varnothing$ for each $n$, and each $b_n$ an upper bound of $S$. In showing that $\{I_n\}$ is a nest, one needs to know that $2^{-n} \to 0$. To show this, prove by induction that $n < 2^n$ and use property 4(a).]

(c) Show that $4 \to 3$ by using an argument based on repeated bisection of intervals.

2. Suppose that $a_1$ and $b_1$ are given, with $0 < a_1 < b_1$. Define $\{a_n\}$ and $\{b_n\}$ by

$$a_{n+1} = \sqrt{a_n b_n}, \qquad b_{n+1} = \tfrac{1}{2}(a_n + b_n), \qquad n \geq 1.$$

Show that if $I_n = [a_n, b_n]$, then $\{I_n\}$ is a nest. $\left[\textit{Suggestion.}\right.$ It may be shown that $a_n < a_{n+1} < b_1$, $a_1 < b_{n+1} < b_n$, and $0 < b_{n+1} - a_{n+1} < \dfrac{b_1 - a_1}{2^n}$.$\left.\right]$

## SUGGESTED READING FOR CHAPTER 1

BIRKHOFF [1], Chapter 10, for Boolean algebra and reference to work of Boole.
BIRKHOFF and MACLANE [1], Chapters 2, 4.
DIEUDONNÉ [1], Chapters 1, 2.
GRAVES [1], Chapter 2.
KNOPP [1], Chapter 1 (interesting for historical notes and references).
LANDAU [1] or [2], Chapters 3, 4.
MCSHANE and BOTTS [1], Chapter 1.
TAYLOR [1], Section 1.62 and Chapter 2.
VAN DER WAERDEN [1], Vol. 1, Chapter 9, especially Sections 66, 67.
WILDER [1], Chapter 3, especially Sections 4, 5, 6.

CHAPTER TWO

# Euclidean Space. Topology and Continuous Functions

## 2–0 Introduction

There are various possible ways of introducing the concept of a Euclidean space of some given dimension $k$, where $k$ is a positive integer. One may use a postulational approach, and define a Euclidean space abstractly by axioms. But a concrete example of a Euclidean space can be constructed with the aid of the real number system, and since it is a fact that any two realizations of abstract Euclidean space of a given dimension are isomorphic, we shall in this chapter discuss a standard model of Euclidean space of $k$-dimensions; we denote it by $R^k$. The elements of this space are ordered sets of $k$ real numbers. For example, if $k = 3$, an element $x$ of the Euclidean 3-dimensional space $R^3$ is an ordered triple $x = (\xi_1, \xi_2, \xi_3)$, where $\xi_1, \xi_2, \xi_3$ are real numbers. The order of the numbers is significant. That is, we regard (1, 4, 7) as different from (4, 1, 7); each of the 6 permutations of the numbers 1, 4, 7 gives us a separate element. The elements are called points.

One of the main concerns of analysis is with functions—with properties of functions and with operations that can be performed on functions. A function of $k$ real variables can be thought of as a function of a variable point in the Euclidean space $R^k$. It turns out in studying functions that many of the essential things do not depend on the number of variables. Such an important concept as continuity, for instance, can be defined and analyzed for a function of a variable point in Euclidean space without reference to the dimensionality of the space. In fact, it is one of the important discoveries of twentieth century mathematics that the concept of space itself can be vastly and usefully generalized, and that we do not need nearly all of the rather special structure of Euclidean space to support a fruitful study of functions.

The student of modern analysis finds it necessary at an early stage in his work to become acquainted with general topological notions. For economy of time and also for better understanding of what is essential, say in the study of continuous functions, but also in many other matters, it is desirable for a student to progress rapidly to the use of the concepts of metric spaces, Hausdorff spaces, and general topological spaces. It is the plan of this book to introduce the student to the concepts of general topology at first in connection with the study of the topology of Euclidean space. By a suitable method of exposition the definitions, theorems, and proofs are presented in a form which makes it easily possible to turn from the concrete situation of Euclidean space to the corresponding abstract situation. The topology of $R^k$ is introduced by way of the metric in $R^k$, but to a large extent the development is made in a way which does not really depend on the Euclidean character of the space, or even on its metric character. Thus, when the fundamental ideas about abstract spaces, as such, are developed in Chapter 3, it can be seen that many of the methods are exactly those which have already become familiar in Chapter 2; it is largely just a matter of adopting a more general point of view. It has been the author's experience that students progress more rapidly and with greater appreciation in Chapter 3 if they have previously studied general topological notions in the specific context of Euclidean space, as in Chapter 2. There are, of course, certain things which are specifically associated with the particular nature of Euclidean spaces. Among the very special things, we mention the structure of open sets in $R$ (Theorem 2–3 IV) and the Cantor ternary set in $[0, 1]$ (see Section 2–10).

## 2–1 The space $R^k$

The real Euclidean space $R^k$ is a collection of certain elements, called points, together with a certain mathematical structure which is created by making certain definitions. A point in $R^k$ is an ordered set of $k$ real numbers $\xi_1, \xi_2, \ldots, \xi_k$. If $k = 1$, $R^1$ is just the same as $R$, the class of all real numbers. We often find it convenient to designate a point by a single symbol: $x = (\xi_1, \ldots, \xi_k)$. Other letters may be used, of course: $a = (\alpha_1, \ldots, \alpha_k)$, $b = (\beta_1, \ldots, \beta_k)$, $y = (\eta_1, \ldots, \eta_k)$, and so on. Between each two points $x, y$ in $R^k$ there is defined to be a numerical distance:

(1) $$D(x, y) = [(\xi_1 - \eta_1)^2 + \cdots + (\xi_k - \eta_k)^2]^{1/2}.$$

We observe the following properties:

(2) $$D(x, y) = 0 \quad \text{is equivalent to} \quad x = y;$$

(3) $$D(x, y) = D(y, x);$$

(4) $$D(x, y) \leq D(x, a) + D(a, y).$$

The correctness of (2) and (3) is evident. In order to prove that (4) is correct one must first prove some simpler inequalities.

Lemma 2–1 I. *(Cauchy's Inequality) For any* $(\alpha_1, \ldots, \alpha_k)$ *and* $(\beta_1, \ldots, \beta_k)$ *we have*

(5) $$\left|\sum_{i=1}^{k} \alpha_i\beta_i\right| \leq \left(\sum_{i=1}^{k} \alpha_i^2\right)^{1/2} \left(\sum_{i=1}^{k} \beta_i^2\right)^{1/2}.$$

*Proof.* Let

$$A = \left(\sum_{i=1}^{k} \alpha_i^2\right)^{1/2}, \qquad B = \left(\sum_{i=1}^{k} \beta_i^2\right)^{1/2},$$

and let $u = |\alpha_i|/A$, $v = |\beta_i|/B$. Since $(u - v)^2 = u^2 + v^2 - 2uv \geq 0$, we evidently have

$$2uv \leq u^2 + v^2,$$

or

$$2\frac{|\alpha_i\beta_i|}{AB} \leq \frac{\alpha_i^2}{A^2} + \frac{\beta_i^2}{B^2}.$$

When we add these results for $i = 1, \ldots, k$ and take note of the definitions of $A$ and $B$ we see that

$$2 \sum_i |\alpha_i \beta_i| \leq 2AB.$$

Therefore

$$\left| \sum_i \alpha_i \beta_i \right| \leq \sum_i |\alpha_i \beta_i| \leq AB.$$

This result is the same as (5).

Next, we apply Cauchy's inequality to prove another important inequality.

LEMMA 2–1 II. *For any* $(\xi_1, \ldots, \xi_k)$ *and* $(\eta_1, \ldots, \eta_k)$ *we have*

$$\left[ \sum_{i=1}^{k} (\xi_i + \eta_i)^2 \right]^{1/2} \leq \left[ \sum_{i=1}^{k} \xi_i^2 \right]^{1/2} + \left[ \sum_{i=1}^{k} \eta_i^2 \right]^{1/2} \tag{6}$$

*Proof.* We can write

$$(\xi_i + \eta_i)^2 = |\xi_i + \eta_i| \, |\xi_i + \eta_i| \leq |\xi_i| \, |\xi_i + \eta_i| + |\eta_i| \, |\xi_i + \eta_i|.$$

Adding, we obtain

$$\sum_i (\xi_i + \eta_i)^2 \leq \sum_i |\xi_i| \, |\xi_i + \eta_i| + \sum_i |\eta_i| \, |\xi_i + \eta_i|.$$

Now we apply Cauchy's inequality to the sums on the right:

$$\sum_i |\xi_i| \, |\xi_i + \eta_i| \leq \left( \sum_i \xi_i^2 \right)^{1/2} \left[ \sum_i (\xi_i + \eta_i)^2 \right]^{1/2},$$

$$\sum_i |\eta_i| \, |\xi_i + \eta_i| \leq \left( \sum_i \eta_i^2 \right)^{1/2} \left[ \sum_i (\xi_i + \eta_i)^2 \right]^{1/2}.$$

Therefore

$$\sum_i (\xi_i + \eta_i)^2 \leq \left[ \left( \sum_i \xi_i^2 \right)^{1/2} + \left( \sum_i \eta_i^2 \right)^{1/2} \right] \left[ \sum_i (\xi_i + \eta_i)^2 \right]^{1/2}.$$

From this result we at once infer the truth of (6), by a simple argument which we leave to the student. (The case in which $\xi_i + \eta_i = 0$ for each $i$ must be considered separately; the truth of (6) is evident in this case.)

We can now prove the inequality (4), which is called the *triangular inequality* for distances. If we think of the three points $x, y, a$ as the vertices of a triangle, observe that (4) asserts that the length of the side $xy$ is not larger than the sum of the lengths of $xa$ and $ay$ (see Figure 4).

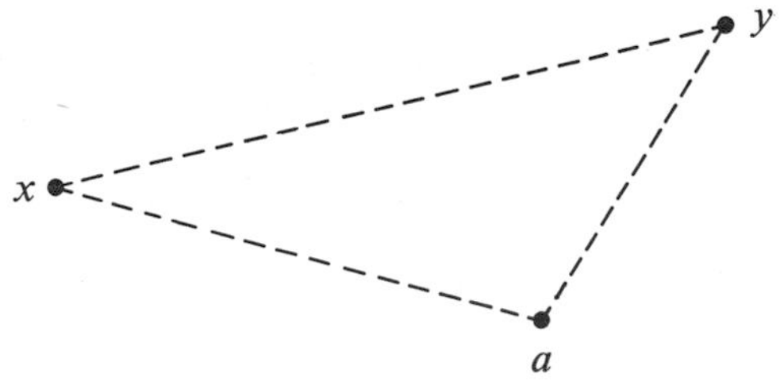


FIGURE 4

We are *proving* this inequality, however, not merely taking it as true on grounds of geometric intuition. Moreover, it is true for all possible choices of $x$, $y$, and $a$. Now, to prove it, we must look at the formulas for $D(x, a)$ and $D(a, y)$, comparable to the formula (1) for $D(x, y)$. We can write

$$\xi_i - \eta_i = (\xi_i - \alpha_i) + (\alpha_i - \eta_i).$$

If we apply (6), putting $\xi_i - \alpha_i$ in place of $\xi_i$ and $\alpha_i - \eta_i$ in place of $\eta_i$, we see that

$$\left[\sum_{i=1}^{k} (\xi_i - \eta_i)^2\right]^{1/2} \leq \left[\sum_{i=1}^{k} (\xi_i - \alpha_i)^2\right]^{1/2} + \left[\sum_{i=1}^{k} (\alpha_i - \eta_i)^2\right]^{1/2}$$

This is precisely the inequality (4) in a different notation.

## $R^k$ IS A METRIC SPACE

The fact that the distance, as defined in (1), satisfies the conditions (2), (3), and (4) means that $R^k$ is what is called *a metric space*. The general notion of a metric space is considered in Section 3–6. The distance function $D$ is called *the metric* for $R^k$.

## $R^k$ AS A VECTOR SPACE

The essential character of the space $R^k$ stems from two things: (1) It has the algebraic structure of what is known technically in algebra as a *k-dimensional real vector space*. (2) It has a very particular kind of structure as a metric space, stemming from the particular way in which the metric is defined. It is the particular character of the algebraic and metrical structure of $R^k$ that permits us to develop the ideas of Euclidean geometry for the space $R^k$. The algebraic structure permits us to introduce such notions as "a straight line," "a set of linearly independent vectors," "a plane of specified dimension $r$," and so on. The metrical structure permits us (among other things) to talk about perpendicularity, which is a notion of central importance in Euclidean geometry.

We shall now explain what is meant by saying that $R^k$ is a real vector space. When this terminology from modern algebra is used, the elements of $R^k$ are sometimes called *vectors*. Thus, we may speak either of "the point $x$" or of "the vector $x$"; *the same thing is meant in both cases*. A student who has become accustomed to the rather physical way of thinking of a vector as a line segment with an arrowhead marked at one end of the segment must now take care. We are making our own definitions and our own logical development as we proceed. Nothing from the classical "vector analysis" of physics and applied mathematics is presupposed here. However, what we say here, with $k = 3$, is consistent with ordinary vector analysis.

If $x = (\xi_1, \ldots, \xi_k)$ and $y = (\eta_1, \ldots, \eta_k)$ are elements of $R^k$, we define another element of $R^k$, denoted by $x + y$ and called the sum of $x$ and $y$, by

$$x + y = (\xi_1 + \eta_1, \ldots, \xi_k + \eta_k). \tag{7}$$

We also define multiplication of $x$ by a real number $\alpha$. The product is denoted by $\alpha x$ or $\alpha \cdot x$, and is, by definition,

$$\alpha x = (\alpha\xi_1, \ldots, \alpha\xi_k). \tag{8}$$

For convenience we usually write $-x$ in place of $-1 \cdot x$.

The element $(0, 0, \ldots, 0)$ of $R^k$ is denoted by the same symbol 0 as is used for the zero of the real number system. Experience shows that as soon as a person gets accustomed to the ideas involved here in thinking of $R^k$, no serious ambiguity or confusion need arise from the fact that 0 can have different meanings in different contexts.

We observe the following algebraic laws governing sums and products:

$$\text{(9)} \qquad \begin{cases} x + y = y + x, \\ x + (y + z) = (x + y) + z, \\ x + 0 = x, \\ x + (-x) = 0, \end{cases}$$

$$\text{(10)} \qquad \begin{cases} \alpha(x + y) = \alpha x + \alpha y, \\ (\alpha + \beta)x = \alpha x + \beta x, \\ \alpha(\beta x) = (\alpha\beta)x, \\ 1 \cdot x = x, \\ 0 \cdot x = 0. \end{cases}$$

It is a routine matter to check the validity of these laws, and we leave verification to the student.

It is because of the validity of the two sets of laws (9) and (10) that $R^k$ is called a vector space. It is called a *real* vector space because the admissible multipliers $\alpha$ in (8) are from the field of real numbers. In modern algebra there are vector spaces of other kinds; for instance, there are vector spaces in which the multipliers may be complex numbers.

The laws (9) and (10) have some familiar consequences. As rules of algebra, all of these laws are familiar, and we shall not linger over them. See, in particular, Problem 1.

## THE INNER PRODUCT AND THE NORM IN $R^k$

In general we do not define a multiplication of two vectors to yield another vector, but we *do* define a sort of multiplication of two vectors to yield a real number as a result. We define the *inner product* (also called dot-product) of $x$ and $y$ as follows, denoting it by $\langle x, y \rangle$ or $x \cdot y$:

$$\text{(11)} \qquad \langle x, y \rangle = x \cdot y = \sum_{i=1}^{k} \xi_i \eta_i.$$

Here, $x = (\xi_1, \ldots, \xi_k)$ and $y = (\eta_1, \ldots, \eta_k)$. Observe the rules governing calculations with inner products:

$$\text{(12)} \qquad \begin{cases} x \cdot y = y \cdot x, \\ x \cdot (y + z) = x \cdot y + x \cdot z, \\ (\alpha x) \cdot y = \alpha(x \cdot y), \\ x \cdot x \geq 0, \\ x \cdot x = 0 \quad \text{if and only if} \quad x = 0. \end{cases}$$

The vector $x = (\xi_1, \ldots, \xi_k)$ has associated with it the number $\sqrt{x \cdot x}$ (the nonnegative square root is understood). We call this quantity the *norm* of $x$, and denote it by $\|x\|$:

$$\|x\| = \sqrt{x \cdot x} = (\xi_1^2 + \cdots + \xi_k^2)^{1/2}. \tag{13}$$

Observe that there is a relation between distance and norm:

$$D(x, y) = \|x - y\|. \tag{14}$$

Verification of this is immediate, by inspection of (1), (11), and (13). In particular, $D(x, 0) = \|x\|$, so that $\|x\|$ is the distance between the vectors $x$ and 0. Sometimes we refer to $\|x\|$ as the length of the vector $x$.

Observe that Cauchy's inequality (see Lemma 2–1 I) can be expressed in the form

$$|x \cdot y| \leq \|x\| \cdot \|y\|. \tag{15}$$

The following facts about the norm are important:

$$\|x + y\| \leq \|x\| + \|y\|, \tag{16}$$

$$\|\alpha x\| = |\alpha| \cdot \|x\|, \tag{17}$$

$$\|x\| = 0 \quad \text{is equivalent to} \quad x = 0. \tag{18}$$

The inequality (16) is merely the result (6) from Lemma 2–1 II in a different notation. Properties (17) and (18) follow at once from (12) and (13).

The norm of $x$ is much like the absolute value of a number; this is evident from (16)–(18). In particular, when $k = 1$, an element of $R^k$ is determined by a single real number, and $\|x\|$ is just the absolute value of $x$.

## ORTHOGONALITY

Two vectors $x$ and $y$ are said to be *orthogonal* to each other if $x \cdot y = 0$. Note that $0 \cdot y = 0$ for any $y$, so that 0 and any vector are orthogonal.

*Example 1.* In $R^k$ let $e_1 = (1, 0, \ldots, 0)$, $e_2 = (0, 1, 0, \ldots, 0), \ldots, e_k = (0, \ldots, 0, 1)$. That is, let $e_j$ be that element of $R^k$ which has 1 in the $j$th position and 0 in each of the other positions. Then $e_1$ is orthogonal to each of $e_2, \ldots, e_k$, and in fact $e_i$ and $e_j$ are orthogonal if $i \neq j$. Since $\|e_j\| = 1$ for each $j$, we say that $e_j$ is a *unit vector*. Hence, $e_1, \ldots, e_k$ is a set of $k$ mutually perpendicular (orthogonal) unit vectors. Observe that any $x = (\xi_1, \ldots, \xi_k)$ in $R^k$ can be expressed in the form

$$x = \xi_1 e_1 + \cdots + \xi_k e_k. \tag{19}$$

That is, each element of $R^k$ can be expressed as a linear combination of the vectors $e_1, \ldots, e_k$. The basic reason why we say that $R^k$ is $k$-dimensional is found in (19). But our formal definition of dimensionality is yet to be formulated (in Section 2–2).

We have now completed the definitions which are necessary to develop in detail the discussion of $R^k$ as a Euclidean space. This is not a book on geometry, and therefore not many theorems specifically relating to Euclidean geometry will find a place in it. A few further definitions, of geometric objects such as lines, planes, and hyperplanes, will be found in Section 2–2. For the most part we shall be interested in properties of $R^k$ which derive from the fact that it is a finite-dimensional vector space with a metric given by

$D(x, y) = \|x - y\|$. Insofar as possible we shall develop the ideas and make the exposition in a form which does not refer explicitly to the value of $k$ or to the numbers $\xi_1, \ldots, \xi_k$ which compose the element $x$. This policy makes the notation easier and tends to make our thinking less cluttered with nonessentials.

### PROBLEMS

1. The following "cancellation laws" are consequences of (9) and (10):
 (a) $x + y = x + z$ implies $y = z$,
 (b) $\alpha x = \alpha y$ and $\alpha \neq 0$ imply $x = y$,
 (c) $\alpha x = \beta x$ and $x \neq 0$ imply $\alpha = \beta$.
Make the deductions of (a), (b), and (c) from (9) and (10).
2. Deduce from (16) and (17) that

$$\big|\|x\| - \|y\|\big| \leq \|x + y\|.$$

Begin by observing that $x = (x + y) + (-y)$.
3. Use (12) and (13) to show that $\|x + y\|^2 = \|x\|^2 + \|y\|^2$ if $x$ and $y$ are orthogonal.
4. Show from (12) and (13) that

$$\|x + y\|^2 + \|x - y\|^2 = 2(\|x\|^2 + \|y\|^2).$$

5. Let $u$ be a vector in $R^k$ such that $\|u\| = 1$, and let $x$ be an arbitrary vector in $R^k$. Show that there is a unique way to express $x$ as a sum of a real multiple of $u$ and a vector orthogonal to $u$, and that this expression of $x$ is

$$x = (x \cdot u)u + [x - (x \cdot u)u].$$

Show also that $t = (x \cdot u)$ is the value of $t$ for which $\|x - tu\|^2$ is least.

## 2–2 Linear configurations in $R^k$

Let $x_1, \ldots, x_n$ be some set of $n$ vectors in $R^k$. We say that these vectors are *linearly dependent* if there exists a set of real numbers $\alpha_1, \ldots, \alpha_n$, *not all zero*, such that

(1)
$$\alpha_1 x_1 + \cdots + \alpha_n x_n = 0.$$

This means, in effect, that at least one of the $x_i$'s can be expressed as a linear combination of the others. For instance, if $\alpha_n \neq 0$, we can write

$$x_n = \beta_1 x_1 + \cdots + \beta_{n-1} x_{n-1},$$

where

$$\beta_i = -\frac{\alpha_i}{\alpha_n}.$$

If the vectors $x_1, \ldots, x_n$ are not linearly dependent, we say that they are *linearly independent*.

*Example 1.* Let $e_1 = (1, 0, 0, \ldots, 0)$, $e_2 = (0, 1, 0, \ldots, 0)$, and so on. Then $e_1, \ldots, e_k$ are linearly independent. But if $x$ is any vector, $x$ can be expressed as a linear combination of $e_1, e_2, \ldots, e_k$, as we see by (19) in Section 2–1. Hence, $e_1, \ldots, e_k, x$ is a linearly dependent set.

It can be proved that if $x_1, \ldots, x_n$ is a linearly independent set of vectors in $R^k$, then $n$ cannot exceed $k$. This fact, together with the fact that we can have as many as $k$ linearly independent vectors, is the reason for saying that $R^k$ has dimension $k$. Students who wish to read more about vector spaces, linear independence, and dimensionality, should consult a text on abstract algebra. There is also a brief account of the essentials in Section 1.1 of the author's book *Introduction to Functional Analysis* (A. E. Taylor [2]).

## SUBSPACES OF $R^k$

A nonempty subset $M$ of $R^k$ is called a subspace if it contains all the linear combinations $\alpha x + \beta y$ ($\alpha$ and $\beta$ arbitrary) whenever it contains $x$ and $y$. The whole of $R^k$ is itself a subspace; so is the set consisting of the single vector 0.

*Example 2.* Let $M$ consist of all multiples of a single nonzero vector $u$. Then $M$ is a subspace. In this case any set of two or more vectors from $M$ is linearly dependent, but the set consisting of the single vector $u$ is a linearly independent set.

*Example 3.* Suppose $k \geq 2$, and let $x_1$, $x_2$ be any two vectors in $R^k$. Let $M$ consist of all the linear combinations of $x_1$ and $x_2$, that is, of all elements of the form $\alpha x_1 + \beta x_2$, where $\alpha$ and $\beta$ are real numbers. Then $M$ is a subspace, and any three or more vectors from $M$ form a linearly dependent set. The proof of this fact can be given easily by using the fact (familiar from algebra) that a system of two homogeneous linear equations in three unknowns always has a solution in which the values of the unknowns are not all 0 (that is, at least one unknown has a value not 0).

When $M$ is a subspace of $R^k$ containing at least one nonzero vector, it turns out that there is a unique positive integer $n$ such that all sets of more than $n$ elements from $M$ are linearly dependent, whereas some set of exactly $n$ elements is linearly independent. This number $n$ is called the dimension of $M$. If $M$ is not all of $R^k$, then necessarily $n < k$; if $M = R^k$, then $n = k$. When $M$ is an $n$-dimensional subspace of $R^k$, with $1 \leq n < k$, it can be shown that $M$ is exactly like the Euclidean space $R^n$, in the following sense: It is possible to find in $M$, $n$ linearly independent mutually orthogonal vectors $a_1, \ldots, a_n$, each of unit length, such that every $x$ in $M$ has a unique representation

$$x = \alpha_1 a_1 + \cdots + \alpha_n a_n.$$

If we then set up the correspondence

$$x \leftrightarrow (\alpha_1, \ldots, \alpha_n), \tag{2}$$

we obtain a one-to-one correspondence between the elements of $M$ and the elements of $R^n$. This correspondence is an algebraic isomorphism between $M$ and $R^n$, and the metric structure of $M$ is an exact copy of the metric structure of $R^n$. That is, if $y$ is in $M$ and $y \leftrightarrow (\beta_1, \ldots, \beta_n)$, then the distance between $x$ and $y$ (which are points in $R^k$) is the same as the distance between $(\alpha_1, \ldots, \alpha_n)$ and $(\beta_1, \ldots, \beta_n)$:

$$\|x - y\| = [(\alpha_1 - \beta_1)^2 + \cdots + (\alpha_n - \beta_n)^2]^{1/2}.$$

When the vectors $a_1, \ldots, a_n$ have been found and the correspondence (2) has been established, we say that we have "set up a Euclidean coordinate system" in $M$. The vectors $a_1, \ldots, a_n$ form the basis of the system, and the numbers $\alpha_1, \ldots, \alpha_n$ are called the coordinates of $x$ relative to this basis. The basis is not unique.

In the case of $R^k$ itself the vectors $e_1, \ldots, e_k$ (introduced in Example 1, Section 2–1) form the basis of the standard coordinate system in $R^k$, and, if $x = (\xi_1, \ldots, \xi_k)$, the numbers $\xi_1, \ldots, \xi_k$ are the coordinates of $x$ relative to this standard basis.

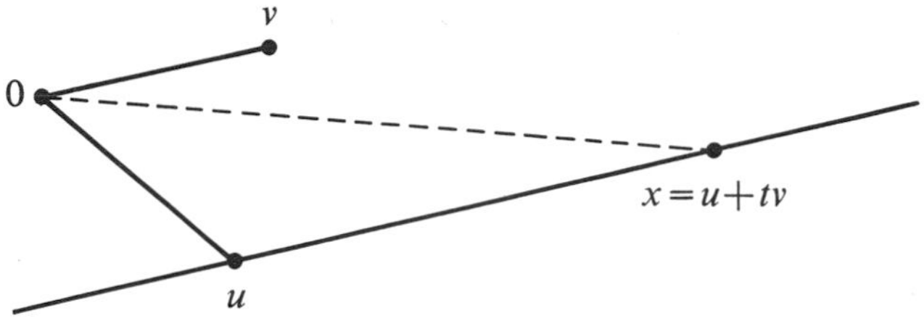


FIGURE 5

## STRAIGHT LINES

By a *straight line* in $R^k$ we mean a set the totality of whose vectors can be represented in the form

(3) $$x = u + tv,$$

where $u$ and $v$ are fixed vectors (with $v \neq 0$) and $t$ is allowed to take on all possible real values.

If $u = 0$ or if $u$ is a multiple of $v$, the line represented in (3) is the one-dimensional subspace consisting of all multiples of $v$. If $u$ and $v$ are linearly independent, the line represented by (3) is not a subspace of $R^k$. However, in this case the line lies in the two-dimensional subspace of $R^k$ consisting of all vectors of the form $\alpha u + \beta v$, where $\alpha$ and $\beta$ can be assigned all possible real values.

The line represented by (3) might be described intuitively as "the line through $u$ parallel to the direction of $v$." Different lines with the same direction are called parallel. All nonzero multiples of the vector $v$ are regarded as defining the same direction. (We are not now distinguishing between $v$ and $-v$ as far as direction is concerned.) The visualization of the line in the plane of $u$ and $v$ is shown in Figure 5. Equation (3) is really just the familiar parametric representation of a line, as used in standard vector treatments of geometry.

By confining $t$ to a finite closed interval of the real number scale, we obtain a part of the line called a *finite closed line segment*.

Two distinct points in $R^k$ determine a unique straight line—the line through these two points. If $x_1$ and $x_2$ are the points, the parametric representation of the line is

(4) $$x = (1 - t)x_1 + tx_2.$$

The line segment joining $x_1$ to $x_2$ is obtained from (4) by restricting $t$ to the interval [0, 1]. From $t < 0$ and $t > 1$ we obtain the other parts of the complete line. See Figure 6.

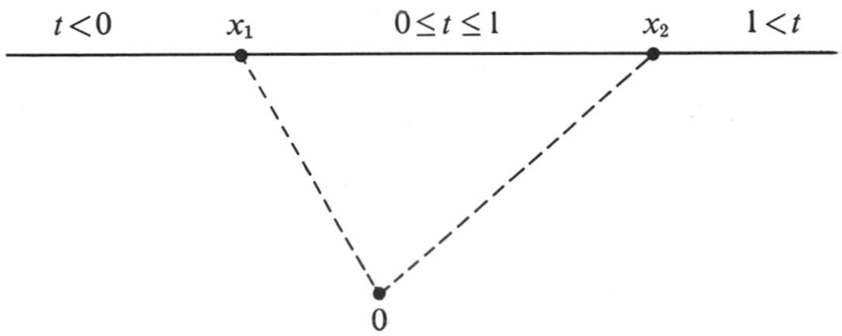


FIGURE 6

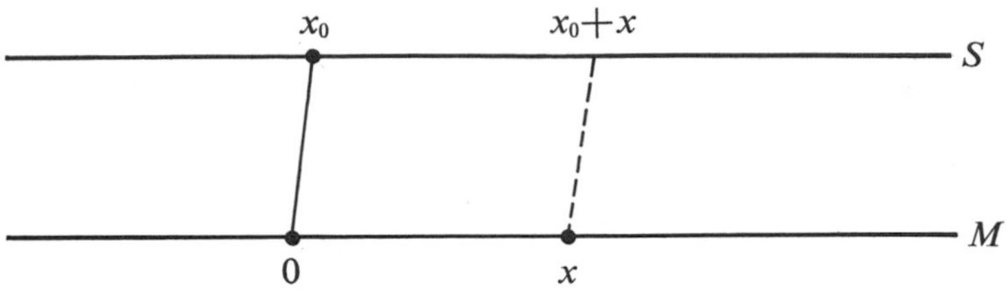


FIGURE 7

## PLANES AND HYPERPLANES

The one-dimensional Euclidean space $R^1$ is the real line. The two-dimensional Euclidean space $R^2$ is a model of what is called a "Euclidean plane." According to what was said earlier, if $k > 1$ and $M$ is an $n$-dimensional subspace of $R^k$, with $1 \leq n < k$, then $M$ is metrically and algebraically an exact copy of $R^n$. That is, after choosing a set of $n$ mutually orthogonal unit vectors to establish a coordinate system in $M$, we can effectively think of $M$ as if it were $R^n$. In particular every one-dimensional subspace of $R^k$ is a copy of the real line, and every two-dimensional subspace is a Euclidean plane.

Suppose $M$ is a subspace of $R^k$, let $x_0$ be an element of $R^k$ not in $M$, and let $S$ be the set of all elements obtained by adding $x_0$ to the various elements of $M$ (see Figure 7). Then $S$ is called a *translation* of $M$. If $M$ is a straight line, so is $S$. If $M$ is $n$-dimensional, where $1 \leq n < k$, we call both $M$ and $S$ $n$-dimensional planes in $R^k$, and we say that $S$ is parallel to $M$. Also, any two different translations of $M$ are said to be parallel. This use of the word "plane" is a generalized usage, since the dimension $n$ need not be 2. Thus, a "plane" of dimension 1 is a line. In the particular case when $n = k - 1$ we often use the term *hyperplane* instead of *plane*, especially when $n > 2$.

An important characteristic of hyperplanes is this: The set of all points $x = (\xi_1, \ldots, \xi_k)$ which satisfy a single linear equation of the form

$$\alpha_1\xi_1 + \cdots + \alpha_k\xi_k = \beta, \tag{5}$$

where $\alpha_1, \ldots, \alpha_k$ and $\beta$ are fixed and the $\alpha_i$'s are not all 0, is a hyperplane in $R^k$. It contains the origin if and only if $\beta = 0$. Conversely, every hyperplane in $R^k$ can be represented by an equation of the type (5). In the case $k = 3$ the hyperplanes are two-dimensional planes, and (5) is the familiar type of equation for a plane in the study of analytic geometry in $R^3$.

In $R^k$ the hyperplanes defined by setting one coordinate equal to 0 (for example, $\xi_1 = 0$) are called *coordinate hyperplanes.*

## PROBLEMS

1. Which of the following sets in $R^k$ are subspaces? Which are hyperplanes? Which are planes but not subspaces?
   (a) The set of all $x = (\xi_1, \ldots, \xi_k)$ with either $\xi_1 = 0$ or $\xi_2 = 0$.
   (b) The set of all $x$ with $\xi_1 = \xi_k + 1$.
   (c) The set of all $x$ with $\xi_1 + \cdots + \xi_k = 0$.
   (d) The set of all $x$ in $R^4$ with $\xi_2 = \xi_3$ and $\xi_1 + \xi_4 = 0$.
   (e) The set of all $x$ in $R^4$ with $\xi_3 = 0$ and $\xi_2 = 1$.

2. If $x_1, \ldots, x_n$ are linearly independent vectors in $R^k$ and if $y = c_1x_1 + \cdots + c_nx_n$, with $c_n \neq 0$, prove that (a) $x_1, \ldots, x_{n-1}, y$ are linearly independent, and (b) any linear combination of $x_1, \ldots, x_n$ is also a linear combination of $x_1, \ldots, x_{n-1}$ and $y$.

3. If $M$ is the linear subspace of $R^3$ formed by all linear combinations of the vectors (1, 1, 0) and (0, 1, 1), find $\alpha, \beta, \gamma$ so that one can describe $M$ as the subspace of all $x = (\xi_1, \xi_2, \xi_3)$ such that $\alpha\xi_1 + \beta\xi_2 + \gamma\xi_3 = 0$.

4. If $M$ is the subspace of $R^3$ consisting of all $x = (\xi_1, \xi_2, \xi_3)$ such that $2\xi_1 - \xi_2 = 0$ and $2\xi_1 + \xi_2 = 2\xi_3$, show that $M$ is isomorphic to $R^1$ by showing that $M$ can be expressed as the set of all multiples of the vector $(\frac{1}{3}, \frac{2}{3}, \frac{2}{3})$. Does the isomorphism preserve metrical structure?

5. Set up an isomorphism between $R^2$ and the subspace of $M$ of $R^4$ consisting of all $x = (\xi_1, \xi_2, \xi_3, \xi_4)$ such that $\xi_1 + \xi_2 = 0$ and $\xi_3 - \xi_4 = 0$. Arrange the isomorphism so that the correspondence between $M$ and $R^2$ preserves metrical structure. [*Suggestion.* Choose a basis in $M$ of mutually orthogonal unit vectors of the form $(a, -a, b, b)$, $(b, -b, -a, -a)$.]

6. Suppose $a_1, \ldots, a_n$ are unit vectors in $R^k$ which are mutually orthogonal, that is, $\langle a_i, a_j \rangle = 0$ if $i \neq j$. Let

$$x = \sum_{i=1}^{n} \alpha_i a_i, \qquad y = \sum_{i=1}^{n} \beta_i a_i$$

and use the rules governing inner products ((12) in Section 2–1) to show that

$$\|x - y\| = \left[\sum_{i=1}^{n} (\alpha_i - \beta_i)^2\right]^{1/2}.$$

## 2–3 The topology of $R^k$

In modern mathematics the word "topology" is used in at least two senses. In geometry a "space" is a collection of elements together with some kind of mathematical structure governed by axioms. To specify a "topological structure" for a space is to specify a certain special class of subsets of elements, subject to certain axioms. These particular subsets are called "open sets." The collection of all the open sets forms what is called "the topology" of the space. Here, then, is one of the meanings of the word "topology." A more explicit and concrete realization of what is entailed in talking about the topology of a space will be developed as we proceed with the discussion of the topology of $R^k$.

A second meaning of the word "topology" is the one which is involved when we speak about topology as a branch of geometry. Topology is the study of those properties of spaces which depend only on their topologies and not on other structural features of the spaces. Topology in the general sense developed from attempts to resolve various problems which arose in analysis and in the study of particular geometric questions.

One of our primary interests in topology comes from the fact that considerations of topology are central in the study of continuous functions. Also, as we shall see somewhat later in this book, there are important connections between topology and the theory of Lebesgue measure and integration.

### THE TOPOLOGY OF THE REAL LINE

Let us begin with the topology of $R (= R^1)$. After a certain amount of discussion of this, we shall proceed to discuss the topology of $R^k$, and the work will be conducted with as little reference as possible to the value of $k$.

Suppose $S$ is a set of points on the real line. We shall call $S$ an *open set* if to each $x_0 \in S$ there corresponds some $\epsilon > 0$ such that $x \in S$ whenever $|x - x_0| < \epsilon$.

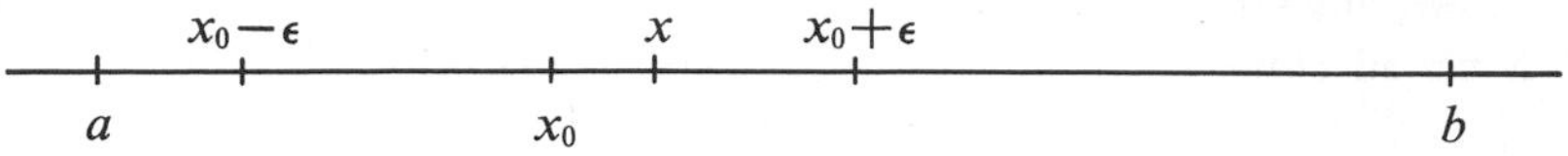


FIGURE 8

*Example 1.* If $a < b$ and $S = \{x : a < x < b\}$, then $S$ is an open set. We call it "the open interval $(a, b)$" (see Section 1–9). To verify that $S$ really is open, suppose $x_0 \in S$ and let $\epsilon$ be any positive number not larger than the smaller of the numbers $x_0 - a$, $b - x_0$. Then $|x - x_0| < \epsilon$ implies $a < x < b$ (see Figure 8).

*Example 2.* Let $S_n = \left\{x : \frac{1}{n+1} < x < \frac{1}{n}\right\}$. Consider any finite or infinite number of the sets $S_1, S_2, S_3, \ldots$, and form the union of all the $S_n$'s so selected, for example,

$$S = S_1 \cup S_5,$$

$$T = \text{union of all the } S_n\text{'s} \qquad (n = 1, 2, 3, \ldots),$$

$$U = \text{union of } S_1, S_3, S_5, S_7, \ldots.$$

Each of the unions so formed is an open set.

The foregoing example illustrates a general principle about open sets in $R$: *If we are given any number of open sets, and if $S$ is the set which is the union of all the given sets, then $S$ is an open set.* In other words, a set formed as the union of open sets is itself open. It does not matter how many sets are involved; the number may even be uncountably infinite. The proof should be thought through by the reader. It involves nothing more than consideration of the definition of an open set and of the definition of the union of a collection of sets.

When we consider intersections of open sets, the situation here is different. *The intersection of a finite number of open sets is again an open set, but the intersection of an infinite number of open sets need not be open* (though of course it *may* be in particular cases). We leave it to the reader to prove this statement, and to perceive why the proof does not apply to the case of an infinite number of sets.

*Example 3.* Let $S_n = \left\{x : |x| < 1 + \frac{1}{n}\right\}$, and let $S$ be the intersection of the countable collection of sets $S_1, S_2, \ldots$. Then each $S_n$ is open, but $S$ is not open. The reader should see that $S = \{x : |x| \leq 1\}$.

At this point we make two further observations about open sets in $R$. *The entire space $R$ is obviously an open set. The empty set is open.* The latter assertion is true because the condition for being open is satisfied vacuously: if $S = \varnothing$, then the situation $x_0 \in S$ never arises and hence no corresponding $\epsilon$ need be found.

## CLOSED SETS IN $R$

In the study of topology the notion of "open set" is used to develop several correlative notions, the most immediate of which are the notions "closed set" and "accumulation point of a set." We proceed to consider these notions.

We are considering sets $S$, where $S \subset R$. The complement of $S$, we recall, is $S^{\sim} = R - S$. The set $S$ is called *closed* if $S^{\sim}$ is open. A student must guard carefully against misconceptions arising from the differences between colloquial language and precise technical language. To say that a set is closed is *not the same* as saying that the set is not open. A set may be neither open nor closed; also, a set may be both open and closed.

*Example 4.* The set $S = \{x : 1 \leq x < 2\}$ is neither open nor closed. It is not open, because $1 \in S$ and yet there is no $\epsilon > 0$ such that $x \in S$ whenever $|x - 1| < \epsilon$. The complement is $S^{\sim} = \{x : x < 1 \text{ or } 2 \leq x\}$. Hence, $2 \in S^{\sim}$, and because of this it is readily seen that $S^{\sim}$ is not open. Therefore $S$ is not closed.

*Example 5.* The empty set $\varnothing$ and the set $R$ are both open. Since each is the complement of the other, both are also closed. It turns out, however, that no other sets in $R$ are both open and closed. This is a fact traceable to certain special properties of $R$. There will be a discussion of this later (see Section 2–8, after proof of Theorem 2–8 I).

*Example 6.* A set consisting of a single point, or of any finite number of points, is closed.

*Example 7.* If $a$ and $b$ are in $R$ and $a < b$, the set $\{x : a \leq x \leq b\}$ is closed. We call it "the closed interval $[a, b]$."

The facts about unions and intersections of open sets have their counterparts for closed sets, but the roles of unions and intersections are reversed, as a result of the rules of complementation (see (1) and (2) in Section 1–2). The formal statements are:

*The intersection of any number of closed sets is closed.*
*The union of any finite number of closed sets is closed.*

*Example 8.* Let $S_n = \left\{x : \dfrac{1}{n} \leq x\right\}$. Then $S_n$ is closed, but the union of the sets $S_1, S_2, \ldots$ is not closed. This union is the set $\{x : 0 < x\}$.

## ACCUMULATION POINTS IN $R$

Closely related to the concept of a closed set is the concept of an accumulation point of a set. If $S \subset R$, and if $y \in R$, we call $y$ *an accumulation point* of $S$ if the following is true: whenever $V$ is an open set and $y \in V$, then $V \cap S$ contains at least one point $x$ of $S$ such that $x \neq y$. If we use $\{y\}$ to denote the set whose only element is $y$, then the foregoing condition can be restated as follows: Whenever $V$ is an open set and $y \in V$, then $V \cap S - \{y\}$ is not empty.

An accumulation point of $S$ need not be a member of $S$.

The set consisting of all the points of accumulation of $S$ is called *the derived set* of $S$. We denote it by $S'$.

*Example 9.* Let $S$ consist of all the rational points on the real line. Then $S'$ is the set of *all* points on the line.

*Example 10.* Let $S$ consist of all the points of the type $\dfrac{1}{n} + \dfrac{1}{m}$, where $m$ and $n$ can be any positive integers, except that $m > n(n - 1)$ if $n > 1$. Then $S'$ is the set consisting of the points $0, 1, \frac{1}{2}, \frac{1}{3}, \frac{1}{4}, \ldots$.

Let $S$ be a nonempty set in $R$ having the number $M$ as least upper bound, and suppose that $M$ is not a member of $S$. Then $M \in S'$. For, if $\epsilon > 0$, there must exist some point $x$ in $S$ such that $M - \epsilon < x < M$. The fact that this is true for each $\epsilon > 0$ clearly implies that $M \in S'$.

Suppose a set $S$ has the property that $S' \subset S$ (every accumulation point of $S$ is actually in the set $S$). This implies that $S$ is a closed set, or, what is the same thing, that the complement $S^{\sim}$ is an open set. The proof is as follows: Let $x$ be any point of $S^{\sim}$. Then, since $S' \subset S$, $x$ is not in $S'$. The fact that $x$ is not an accumulation point of $S$ means that there is some open set $V$ such that $x \in V$ and such that no point of $S$ is in $V$. But then $V \subset S^{\sim}$. But, since $x \in V$ and $V$ is open, there must be some open interval contained in $V$ (and hence in $S^{\sim}$) and having its center at $x$. This, however, means that $S^{\sim}$ is open.

In the foregoing paragraph we have demonstrated that, if $S' \subset S$, then $S$ is closed. The converse proposition is also true. That is, if $S$ is closed it follows that $S' \subset S$. We prove this by showing that if $S$ is closed and $x \in S^{\sim}$, $x$ cannot be a point of accumulation of $S$ (so that all points of $S'$ must be in $S$). In fact, if $S$ is closed, $S^{\sim}$ is open, and from $x \in S^{\sim}$ we infer that $x$ cannot be an accumulation point of $S$ (because $S \cap S^{\sim} = \varnothing$).

We have now proved that a set $S$ is closed if and only if $S' \subset S$. The discussion has all been in the context of the topology of the real line. Presently we shall discuss the topology of $R^k$, and then we shall find that the foregoing arguments apply without essential change to prove the corresponding proposition in $R^k$. The proposition will then be formally recorded as a theorem.

## OPEN SETS IN $R^k$

We shall now define and discuss open sets, closed sets, and points of accumulation in $R^k$. In order to do so we first define the concept "spherical neighborhood of a point" in $R^k$. If $\epsilon > 0$, and if $x_0$ is a point in $R^k$, let $S(x_0; \epsilon)$ denote the set of all points $x$ in $R^k$ for which $D(x, x_0) < \epsilon$. Since $D(x, x_0) = \|x - x_0\|$, we can also write

$$S(x_0; \epsilon) = \{x : \|x - x_0\| < \epsilon\}.$$

The set $S(x_0; \epsilon)$ is called *the spherical neighborhood of* $x_0$, *of radius* $\epsilon$. We call $x_0$ the *center* of $S(x_0; \epsilon)$. The word "sphere" has a generalized meaning. If $k = 1$, $S(x_0; \epsilon)$ is the open interval in $R$ of length $2\epsilon$ with $x_0$ as its midpoint. If $k = 2$, $S(x_0; \epsilon)$ is a circular disk (the circumference excluded).

Now, let $T$ be any point set in $R^k$. We call $T$ an open set if to each point $x$ in $T$ corresponds some spherical neighborhood of the point, say $S(x; \epsilon)$, such that $S(x; \epsilon) \subset T$.

*Example 11.* A spherical neighborhood of a point is an open set. To see this, suppose the spherical neighborhood in question is $S(x_0; r)$. If $x \in S(x_0; r)$, we have to find a positive $\epsilon$ such that $S(x; \epsilon) \subset S(x_0; r)$. Let us choose $\epsilon = r - \|x - x_0\|$. Then $\epsilon > 0$, because the inequality $\|x - x_0\| < r$ expresses the fact that $x \in S(x_0; r)$. Now suppose $y \in S(x; \epsilon)$, that is, $\|y - x\| < \epsilon$. Then

$$y - x_0 = (y - x) + (x - x_0),$$

and so, by the triangular inequality,

$$\|y - x_0\| \leq \|y - x\| + \|x - x_0\| < \epsilon + \|x - x_0\| = r.$$

This shows that $y \in S(x_0; r)$, as required.

THEOREM 2–3 I. *The union of any number of open sets is an open set.*

This important proposition has already been mentioned for the case of $R$. The proof is achieved directly by considering the basic definitions.

THEOREM 2–3 II. *The intersection of any finite number of open sets is an open set.*

The proof here depends upon the fact that in a finite set of positive real numbers there is a smallest one. This is not true for infinite sets. It can happen that the intersection of infinitely many open sets is not open. The student may readily think of a case, for instance, where the intersection consists of a single point.

## CLOSED SETS IN $R^k$

For a subset $S$ of $R^k$ the complementary set $S^\sim$ is $S^\sim = R^k - S$. We call $S$ closed if $S^\sim$ is open. This definition has the same verbal form as the definition of closed sets on the real line. As before, the empty set $\varnothing$ is both open and closed. The same is true of $R^k$ itself. A set may be neither open nor closed.

*Example 12.* In the space $R^2$ consider the set of all points $x = (\xi_1, \xi_2)$ such that $\xi_1 \geq 0$ and $\xi_2 > \xi_1$. It is neither open nor closed. If the conditions are changed to $\xi_1 \geq 0$ and $\xi_2 \geq \xi_1$, we get a closed set. If the conditions are changed to $\xi_1 > 0$ and $\xi_2 > \xi_1$, we get an open set. The student should verify these assertions.

## ACCUMULATION POINTS IN $R^k$

If $S \subset R^k$, we say that $y$ is an accumulation point of $S$ provided that every open set which contains $y$ intersects $S$ in at least one point different from $y$. Note that nothing is specified about whether or not $y$ is in $S$. If $y$ is an accumulation point of $S$, every open set $U$ which contains $y$ must in fact contain an infinite number of points of $S$. We can see this as follows. Let $y_1$ be a point of $S$ in $U - \{y\}$. Write $U_1 = U$, and let $U_2$ be an open set containing $y$ but not $y_1$ ($U_2$ can be a spherical neighborhood of $y$ with a radius less than $D(y_1, y)$). Let $y_2$ be a point of $S$ in $U_2 - \{y\}$. Proceed in this way, obtaining at each step a point $y_n$ of $S$ in $U_n - \{y\}$, where $U_n$ is an open set which contains $y$ but not $y_{n-1}$. Then all of the points $y_1, y_2, \ldots$ are in $S \cap U$.

The set of all accumulation points of $S$ is denoted by $S'$ and called the derived set of $S$. We then have the following basic theorem:

THEOREM 2–3 III. *A set $S$ in $R^k$ is closed if and only if $S' \subset S$.*

This has already been proved (see the text immediately after Example 10 of this section) for the case $k = 1$. The argument in the general case is not essentially different; we have only to substitute appropriate references to spherical neighborhoods in place of the earlier references to open intervals centered at certain points. We leave it for the reader to check the proof through with these changes.

It is possible, after a preliminary observation, to give an exposition of the proof of Theorem 2–3 III without any explicit reference to the value of $k$, or to spherical neighborhoods. The observation is this. *Suppose a set $S$ in $R^k$ has the following property: if $x \in S$, there exists an open set $U$ such that $x \in U$ and $U \in S$. Then $S$ is open.* This conclusion comes immediately by using the definition of an open set.

## THE CLOSURE OF A SET

The set $S \cup S'$ is called the *closure* of $S$, and denoted by $\bar{S}$:

$$\bar{S} = S \cup S'. \tag{1}$$

There are a number of useful assertions which can be made about $\bar{S}$:

The set $\bar{S}$ is closed.

The set $\bar{S}$ is the intersection of all closed sets which contain $S$.

The set $S$ is closed if and only if $S = \bar{S}$.

A point $x$ is in $\bar{S}$ if and only if every open set which contains $x$ also contains a point of $S$.

The proofs of these assertions are left as problems.

## THE BOUNDARY OF A SET

For technical purposes we define the boundary of an arbitrary set, even though in many applications our interest in the boundary is in cases where the set is open or is the closure of an open set. The boundary of $S$ is denoted by $\beta(S)$ and is defined by

$$\beta(S) = \bar{S} \cap \overline{(S^{\sim})}. \tag{2}$$

That is, $x$ is a boundary point of $S$ if and only if it is simultaneously in the closures of $S$ and $S^{\sim}$. We shall presently encounter another way of expressing $\beta(S)$.

## THE INTERIOR OF A SET

A point $x$ is said to be an *interior point* of $S$ if there exists an open set $V$ such that $x \in V$ and $V \subset S$. The aggregate of all interior points of $S$ is called *the interior* of $S$, and denoted by $S^o$. Concerning $S^o$ we have the following assertions; the proofs are left as problems.

The set $S^o$ is open.

The set $S^o$ is the union of all the open subsets of $S$.

The set $S$ is open if and only if $S = S^o$.

There is a connection between the interior and the boundary, as shown in the following formula:

$$\beta(S) = \bar{S} - S^o. \tag{3}$$

For the proof of (3) see Problem 7.

In case $S$ is open, we have the formula

$$\beta(S) = \bar{S} - S \qquad \text{(when } S \text{ is open).} \tag{4}$$

## NEIGHBORHOODS

By a *neighborhood* of a point $x$ in $R^k$ we shall mean an open set containing $x$. We have already used the term "spherical neighborhood of a point." It was shown that a spherical neighborhood is an open set; hence a spherical neighborhood is a particular kind of neighborhood as we have just defined that term.

In some current mathematical literature the word neighborhood has a slightly different meaning: any set of which $x$ is an interior point is called a neighborhood of $x$. We shall not follow this usage, however.

It is of interest to observe that in our definition of the topology of $R^k$ we made use of a certain special family of sets: the family of all possible spherical neighborhoods of all possible points. These spherical neighborhoods illustrate the concept of "a basis of neighborhoods." Let $\mathscr{B}_x$ be a family of open sets, each one of which is a neighborhood of $x$. We call $\mathscr{B}_x$ a *basis of neighborhoods at* $x$ if to each neighborhood $U$ of $x$ there corresponds some $B \in \mathscr{B}_x$ such that $B \subset U$. If $\mathscr{B}$ is a family of open sets such that to each $x \in R^k$ corresponds at least one subfamily $\mathscr{B}_x$ of $\mathscr{B}$ such that $\mathscr{B}_x$ is a basis of neighborhoods at $x$, then $\mathscr{B}$ is called a basis of neighborhoods for $R^k$.

There are many ways of selecting a basis of neighborhoods at a given point $x$. The set of *all* spherical neighborhoods of $x$ is one possible basis. Or, we might select only the spherical neighborhoods of $x$ with all possible rational numbers as radii. Still another choice would be to choose just the spherical neighborhoods of $x$ with radii $1, \frac{1}{2}, \frac{1}{3}, \ldots, \frac{1}{n}, \ldots$ (all positive integers $n$). There are times when it is advantageous to know that a basis of neighborhoods for $R^k$ can be chosen in such a way that it consists of a certain countably infinite family of open sets. We shall return to this matter at an appropriate place in the text. See Theorem 2–5 I.

## OPEN BOXES IN $R^k$

Let $a = (\alpha_1, \ldots, \alpha_k)$ be a point in $R^k$, and suppose that $\epsilon_1, \ldots, \epsilon_k$ are positive numbers. Consider the aggregate of all points $x = (\xi_1, \ldots, \xi_k)$ in $R^k$ which satisfy the inequalities

$$(5) \qquad \begin{cases} |\xi_1 - \alpha_1| < \epsilon_1, \\ |\xi_2 - \alpha_2| < \epsilon_2, \\ \quad \cdots \\ |\xi_k - \alpha_k| < \epsilon_k. \end{cases}$$

This aggregate of points is an open set; we call it an *open box* with center at $a$. For the special case $k = 1$ this is simply the open interval of length $2\epsilon_1$, with center at $\alpha_1$. In the case $k = 2$ the open box is the interior of a rectangle, as shown in Figure 9, and in the case $k = 3$ the open box under discussion is the interior of a rectangular parallelepiped bounded by the three pairs of parallel planes $\xi_i = \alpha_i \pm \epsilon_i$, $i = 1, 2, 3$.

In the general case $\xi_i = \alpha_i + \epsilon_i$ and $\xi_i = \alpha_i - \epsilon_i$ define parallel hyperplanes (parallel to the coordinate hyperplane $\xi_i = 0$). The set of points $x$ for which $\alpha_i - \epsilon_i < \xi_i < \alpha_i + \epsilon_i$ (or, what is the same thing, $|\xi_i - \alpha_i| < \epsilon_i$) is the set of points *between* the two parallel hyperplanes. This is an open set. The open box defined by (5) is the intersection of the $k$ open sets formed in this way, one set between each pair of parallel hyperplanes.

Hereafter, whenever we refer to open boxes we take it for granted (unless there is explicit mention to the contrary) that the boxes are formed in the manner here described, using hyperplanes parallel to coordinate hyperplanes.

In Chapter 4 we shall speak of open boxes as *open intervals*, even when $k > 1$.

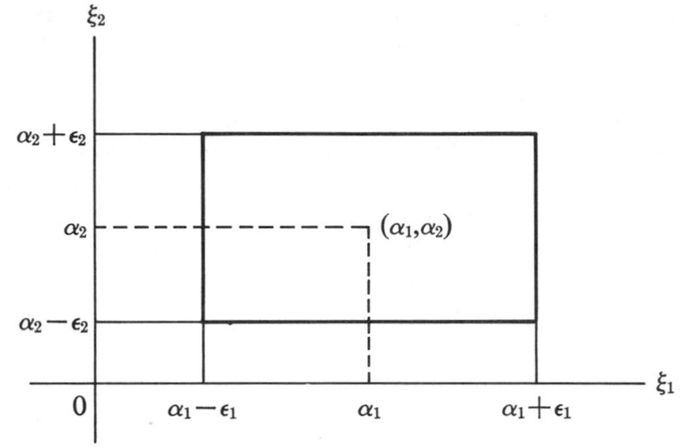


FIGURE 9

The open box defined by (5) is contained in the open sphere $S(a; \epsilon)$ if $\epsilon$ is defined by

$$\epsilon = (\epsilon_1^2 + \epsilon_2^2 + \cdots + \epsilon_k^2)^{1/2}.$$

On the other hand, the open box (5) contains the open sphere $S(a; \delta)$ if $\delta$ is defined as the smallest of the numbers $\epsilon_1, \ldots, \epsilon_k$. For the case $k = 2$ the situation is illustrated in Figure 10.

It is now evident that the set of all open boxes centered at a given point is a basis of neighborhoods at that point. We still get a basis if we take only those boxes for which $\epsilon_1, \ldots, \epsilon_k$ are all the same for any one box (thus giving us squares if $k = 2$, cubes if $k = 3$, and so on.)

We could have used open boxes instead of spherical neighborhoods in defining the notion of an open set. That is, a set $S$ is open if and only if to each $x$ in $S$ corresponds some open box $B$ with center at $x$ such that $B \subset S$. In fact *any* basis of neighborhoods can be used. That is, if $\mathscr{B}$ is a basis of neighborhoods for $R^k$, a set $S$ in $R^k$ is open if and only if to each $x$ in $S$ corresponds some $B \in \mathscr{B}$ such that $B$ is a neighborhood of $x$ and $B \subset S$.

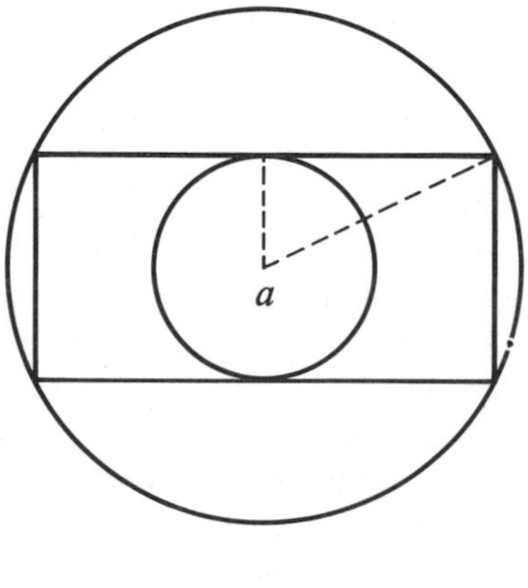


FIGURE 10

## $F_\sigma$'s AND $G_\delta$'s

A set is called an $F_\sigma$ set if it is expressible as $\bigcup_n E_n$, where $E_1, E_2, \ldots$ are closed sets. A set is called a $G_\delta$ set if it is expressible as $\bigcap_n E_n$, where $E_1, E_2, \ldots$ are open sets. We shall not have much need to employ the notions of $F_\sigma$ and $G_\delta$ sets.

## THE STRUCTURE OF OPEN SETS IN $R$

The nature of open sets in $R$ is made explicit by the following theorem, which has no counterpart for open sets in $R^k$ when $k \geq 2$.

THEOREM 2–3 IV. *If $E$ is an open set in $R$ such that $E \neq \varnothing$ and $E \neq R$, $E$ can be expressed as a countable (possibly finite) union of disjoint sets $E_1, E_2, \ldots,$ where each $E_n$ is a nonempty open set of one of the following types:*

(i) *a finite open interval $\{x : a < x < b\}$,*
(ii) *a left-semiinfinite open interval $\{x : x < b\}$, where $b \in R$,*
(iii) *a right-semiinfinite open interval $\{x : a < x\}$, where $a \in R$.*

*Proof.* If $x \in E$, consider the set (clearly nonempty since $E$ is open) of all real numbers $u$ such that $u < x$ and such that $t \in E$ if $u < t \leq x$. Let $a(x)$ be the greatest lower bound (in $R^*$) of this set. Consider likewise the set of all real numbers $v$ such that $x < v$ and such that $t \in E$ if $x \leq t < v$. Let $b(x)$ be the least upper bound (in $R^*$) of this set. Evidently $a(x) < b(x)$. We cannot have $a(x) = -\infty$ and $b(x) = +\infty$ for the same $x$, for this would imply $E = R$. Let $I(x) = \{t : a(x) < t < b(x)\}$. Then $I(x)$ is a set of one of the three specified types, and $I(x) \subset E$, as can readily be seen. If $x$ and $y$ are distinct points of $E$, we must have either $I(x) = I(y)$ or $I(x) \cap I(y) = \varnothing$. This follows from the way in which the sets $I(x)$ are defined. We leave verification to the reader. Since each $I(x)$ must contain a rational point, it follows that the number of distinct $I(x)$'s is countable. If $E_1, E_2, \ldots$ is a listing of the distinct $I(x)$'s, we have $E = \bigcup_n E_n$.

## PROBLEMS

1. Prove, for an arbitrary set $S$ in $R^k$, that
   (a) $\bar{S}$ is closed.
   (b) $\bar{S}$ is the intersection of all closed sets $A$ such that $S \subset A$;
   (c) $S$ is closed if and only if $S = \bar{S}$;
   (d) $x \in \bar{S}$ if and only if $A$ an open set and $x \in A$ together imply $A \cap S \neq \varnothing$.
2. (a) Is it always true that $\overline{(A \cup B)} = \bar{A} \cup \bar{B}$?
   (b) Is it always true that $\overline{(A \cap B)} = \bar{A} \cap \bar{B}$?
3. (a) Suppose $S$ is closed. Exhibit $S$ as $\bigcap_n A_n$, where each $A_n$ is open and $A_{n+1} \subset A_n$.
   (b) Suppose $S$ is open. Exhibit $S$ as $\bigcup_n A_n$, where each $A_n$ is closed and $A_n \subset A_{n+1}$.
4. If $A$ is open and $B$ is arbitrary, show that $A \cap \bar{B} \subset \overline{(A \cap B)}$. Show that this is not true in general if $A$ is not open. In particular, it can happen with very simple sets in $R$ that $\overline{(A \cap B)}$ is a proper subset of $A \cap \bar{B}$.

5. Prove, for an arbitrary set $S$ in $R^k$, that
   (a) $S^o$ is open;
   (b) $S^o$ is the union of all the open sets $A$ such that $A \subset S$;
   (c) $S$ is open if and only if $S = S^o$.
6. Show that $A \subset (\bar{A})^o$ if $A$ is open.
7. Prove that $(S^o)^\sim = \overline{(S^\sim)}$, and observe that when this is combined with (2) we get (3).
8. Prove that $S - \beta(S) = S^o$. Begin by showing that $[\beta(S)]^\sim = (\bar{S})^\sim \cup S^o$.
9. (a) Does $A \subset B$ imply that $\beta(A) \subset \beta(B)$?
   (b) Show that $\beta(\bar{A}) \subset \beta(A)$.
   (c) Show that $\beta(A^o) \subset \beta(A)$.
10. Show that $\beta(A \cup B) = \beta(A) \cup \beta(B)$ if $\bar{A} \cap \bar{B} = \varnothing$.
11. Prove in detail the assertion, in the proof of Theorem 2–3 IV, that if $x \neq y$ and $I(x) \cap I(y) \neq \varnothing$, then $I(x) = I(y)$.
12. Is the following assertion true (as a partial counterpart to Theorem 2–3 IV)? "Every bounded open set in $R^2$ can be expressed as a countable union of disjoint open boxes." Explain.

## 2–4 Nests, points of accumulation, and convergent sequences

Some point sets have accumulation points; others do not. A finite set has no points of accumulation. An infinite set may have no accumulation points. For instance, in $R$ the set of all integers (positive, negative, and zero) has no accumulation points. There is, however, an important theorem to the effect that if a point set has infinitely many members *and is bounded*, then it must have at least one accumulation point. This theorem and some of its consequences form the subject of the present section. To begin with, we must explain what it means for a set to be bounded.

A set $S$ in $R^k$ is called *bounded* if it is contained in some open sphere, that is, if there is some point $x_0$ in $R^k$ and some $r > 0$ such that $D(x, x_0) < r$ for each $x$ in $S$. Any set which is contained in an open sphere is also contained in an open box, and vice versa. Hence a set $S$ is bounded if and only if it is contained in some open box. There are still other useful ways of specifying that a set be bounded. For instance, $S$ is bounded if and only if the set of norms $\|x\|$ (obtained as $x$ varies over $S$) is a bounded set of real numbers, that is, if and only if there is some real number $M$ such that $\|x\| \leq M$ for each $x$ in $S$. Since

$$\|x\| = (\xi_1^2 + \cdots + \xi_k^2)^{1/2} \leq \sqrt{k} \max_i |\xi_i|$$

when $x = (\xi_1, \ldots, \xi_k)$, we see that $S$ is bounded if and only if there is a real constant $C$ such that $|\xi_i| \leq C$ for each $i$ ($i = 1, 2, \ldots, k$) and each $x$ in $S$.

### NESTS IN $R^k$

We shall develop an extension of Theorem 1–9 I for Euclidean spaces of dimension higher than one. In place of nests of closed intervals we shall have nests of closed boxes. We defined the notion of an open box in Section 2–3. Suppose $\alpha_1 < \beta_1, \alpha_2 < \beta_2, \ldots, \alpha_k < \beta_k$. Then the set of all $x = (\xi_1, \ldots, \xi_k)$ such that

$$\alpha_i < \xi_i < \beta_i \qquad i = 1, \ldots, k \tag{1}$$

is an open box. Its center is the point for which

$$\xi_i = \tfrac{1}{2}(\alpha_i + \beta_i) \qquad i = 1, \ldots, k.$$

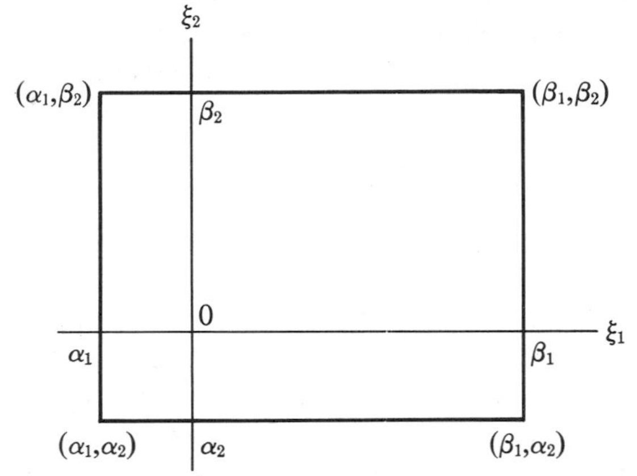


FIGURE 11

The set of all $x$ such that

(2) $$\alpha_i \leq \xi_i \leq \beta_i \qquad i = 1, \ldots, k$$

is the closure of the foregoing open box. We call it a *closed box*. The situation for $k = 2$ is shown in Figure 11. The closed box has corners at the points $(\alpha_1, \alpha_2)$, $(\beta_1, \alpha_2)$, $(\beta_1, \beta_2)$, $(\alpha_1, \beta_2)$, and consists of all points *inside or on* the rectangle with these four points as vertices.

By the *diameter* of the closed box defined by (2) we mean the number

$$[(\beta_1 - \alpha_1)^2 + \cdots + (\beta_k - \alpha_k)^2]^{1/2}.$$

This the greatest distance apart which two points can be if they are both in the box. If $B$ denotes the closed box, we denote its diameter by diam $(B)$.

Now let us suppose we have a sequence $\{B_n\}$ of closed boxes in $R^k$, such that $B_1 \supset B_2 \supset B_3 \supset \cdots$, that is, $B_{n+1}$ is contained in $B_n$ if $n = 1, 2, \ldots$. Furthermore, suppose that diam $(B_n) \to 0$ as $n \to \infty$. Then the sequence of closed boxes is called a *nest in* $R^k$.

THEOREM 2–4 I. *If $\{B_n\}$ is a nest in $R^k$, the intersection of all $B_n$'s consists of a single point.*

*Proof.* We make use of the theorem of nested intervals (Theorem 1–9 I), which is the special case $k = 1$ of our present theorem. Suppose the box $B_n$ is defined by the inequalities

(3) $$\alpha_i^{(n)} \leq \xi_i \leq \beta_i^{(n)}, \qquad i = 1, \ldots, k.$$

For a fixed $i$ the real numbers $\xi_i$ which satisfy (3) form a closed interval $I_i^{(n)}$ on the real line. We call this interval the *projection* of the box $B_n$ on the $i$th coordinate axis. (For example, in Figure 11, the projection of the rectangle on the $\xi_1$ axis is the interval $[\alpha_1, \beta_1]$, and the projection of the rectangle on the $\xi_2$ axis is the interval $[\alpha_2, \beta_2]$.) Now, the fact that $B_{n+1} \subset B_n$ means that $I_i^{(n+1)} \subset I_i^{(n)}$ for each $i$. We observe, also, that $\beta_i^{(n)} - \alpha_i^{(n)} <$ diam $(B_n)$. Hence, the length of $I_i^{(n)}$ approaches 0 as $n \to \infty$. It now follows that $\{I_i^{(n)}\}$ is a nest of closed intervals for each fixed $i$ $(i = 1, \ldots, k)$. Hence, by Theorem 1–9 I, there is a unique real number $\xi_i$ such that $\xi_i \in I_i^{(n)}$ for every $n$. In this way we obtain a point $x = (\xi_1, \ldots, \xi_k)$ which belongs to $B_n$ for every $n$. There cannot be more than one such point, for if there were two, they would be a certain positive distance apart, say $\delta$. But then diam $(B_n) < \delta$ when $n$ is sufficiently large, and this would make it impossible for the two points both to be in $B_n$.

### THE FUNDAMENTAL THEOREM ON POINTS OF ACCUMULATION

THEOREM 2–4 II. *Suppose $S$ is a bounded, infinite point set in $R^k$. Then there is at least one point of accumulation of $S$.*

*Proof.* For the sake of greater ease in making the proof comprehensible, we shall write out the argument for the case $k = 2$. The same general principle applies for all values of $k$.

Since $S$ is bounded, there is certainly some closed box $B$ such that $S \subset B$. (In the case $k = 2$, we recall, a box is rectangular.) Now let us divide $B$ into four equal parts by two lines drawn through its center, one parallel to each coordinate axis (see Figure 12). In this

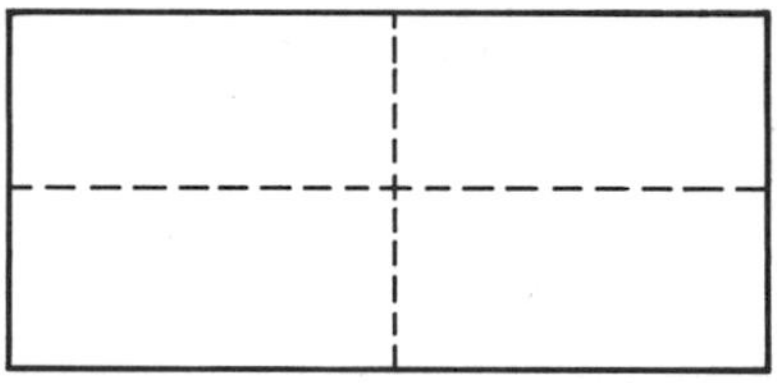

FIGURE 12

way we get four closed boxes whose union is $B$. Since $S$ is an infinite set, *at least one* of these four closed boxes must contain an infinite number of points of $S$. Perhaps more than one of the four boxes has this property. At any rate, let us denote by $B_2$ a certain one of the four boxes, so chosen that it does contain an infinite number of points of $S$, and chosen according to some unambiguous procedure in case more than one of the boxes contains infinitely many points of $S$. (We could agree, for example, to choose $B_2$ so that all the coordinates of its upper right-hand corner are as large as possible, consistent with the other requirement on $B_2$.) Let us now denote $B$ itself by $B_1$. Next, we repeat the procedure by which $B_2$ was derived from $B_1$, applying the procedure this time to get $B_3$ from $B_2$; $B_3$ will be a certain one of four parts into which $B_2$ is divided. The procedure can be repeated indefinitely, and we obtain a sequence $\{B_n\}$ of closed boxes, each $B_n$ containing infinitely many points of $S$, and $B_{n+1}$ obtained as a certain one of four equal parts of $B_n$. The procedure insures that

$$\text{diam}\,(B_{n+1}) = \frac{1}{2}\,\text{diam}\,(B_n),$$

and hence

$$\text{diam}\,(B_n) = \frac{1}{2^{n-1}}\,\text{diam}\,(B_1)$$

if $n \geq 1$. Evidently, then $\{B_n\}$ is a nest in $R^k$. Let $x_0$ be the unique point in the intersection of all the $B_n$'s (existence guaranteed by Theorem 2–4 I). This point $x_0$ is an accumulation point of $S$. For, if an open sphere $S(x_0; \epsilon)$ of center $x_0$ and radius $\epsilon$ is given, we shall have diam $(B_n) < \epsilon$ when $n$ is large enough. Hence, for such values of $n$, $B_n \subset S(x_0; \epsilon)$, because $x_0 \in B_n$. But $B_n$ contains infinitely many points of $S$; hence certainly $S(x_0; \epsilon)$ contains points of $S$ distinct from $x_0$. This makes $x_0$ an accumulation point of $S$.

We leave it for the student to adapt this method of proof to values of $k$ other than 2. For clear intuitive comprehension the cases $k = 1, 3$ should be considered first.

Theorem 2–4 II is quite generally referred to as "the Bolzano-Weierstrass theorem." Karl Weierstrass (1815–1897) was one of the pioneers in the study of the theory of sets of points in connection with investigations of the properties of functions. Bernard Bolzano (1781–1848) made early and important contributions to the study of continuous functions and other fundamental topics in analysis. The precise historical reasons for naming Theorem 2–4 II after both Bolzano and Weierstrass are not clear. Some of the ideas that underlie the theorem are present in Bolzano's work. The theorem itself apparently should be attributed to Weierstrass.

## SEQUENCES OF POINTS IN $R^k$

We discussed real sequences in Section 1–6. Now we shall consider sequences of points in $R^k$. Such a sequence is the same as a real sequence if $k = 1$. The definition of a sequence in $R^k$ is the same as the definition of a real sequence in Section 1–6, except that now $x$ will refer to a point in $R^k$ instead of to a real number. As before, the sequence with elements

$$(1, x_1), (2, x_2), (3, x_3), \ldots$$

will for brevity be denoted by $\{x_n\}$.

We emphasize that a sequence in $R^k$ is not the same as a point set in $R^k$.

A sequence $\{x_n\}$ is called *bounded* if the set of norms $\|x_n\|$ is bounded, that is, if there is some real $M$ such that $\|x_n\| \leq M$ for every $n$.

The sequence $\{x_n\}$ is called *convergent* if there is a point $x$ in $R^k$ such that $\|x_n - x\| \to 0$ as $n \to \infty$. The point $x$ is then called the *limit* of the sequence, and the sequence is said to *converge* to $x$. A sequence cannot converge to two different limits. This is apparent from an equivalent restatement of the definition of convergence; *the sequence $\{x_n\}$ converges to $x$ if every open sphere with center at $x$ contains all the $x_n$'s from a certain $n$ onward.*

The fact that $\{x_n\}$ converges to $x$ is indicated by writing

$$\lim_{n\to\infty} x_n = x, \qquad \text{or} \qquad x_n \to x.$$

A convergent sequence is necessarily bounded.

An important relation between convergent sequences and points of accumulation is indicated in the next theorem.

THEOREM 2–4 III. *Let $y$ be an accumulation point of the set $S$ in $R^k$. Then there exists a sequence $\{x_n\}$ such that each $x_n$ is in $S$, $x_n \to y$, and the points $x_1, x_2, x_3, \ldots$ are all distinct.*

*Proof.* Let $U_1$ be the open sphere of radius 1 with center $y$. In $U_1$ there must be a point of $S$ distinct from $y$. Select such a point and call it $x_1$. Let $U_2$ be the open sphere with center $y$ and radius equal to the smaller of the numbers $1/2$, $\|x_1 - y\|$. In $U_2$ there must be a point of $S$ distinct from $y$. Select such a point and call it $x_2$. Observe that $x_2 \neq x_1$. Let $U_3$ be the open sphere with center $y$ and radius equal to the smaller of the numbers $1/3$, $\|x_2 - y\|$. We continue in the manner indicated, obtaining a sequence $\{x_n\}$ of distinct points of $S$ such that $\|x_n - y\| < \frac{1}{n}$, whence certainly $x_n \to y$.

The notion of a subsequence, as defined in Section 1–6 in connection with real sequences, can be carried over at once to sequences in $R^k$. The following extremely useful consequence of the Bolzano-Weierstrass theorem entails the consideration of subsequences.

THEOREM 2–4 IV. *If $\{x_n\}$ is a bounded sequence, it contains a convergent subsequence.*

*Proof.* We divide the proof into two cases. Let $S$ be the set of distinct points of $R^k$ represented in the terms $x_1, x_2, x_3, \ldots$.

*Case 1. S is a finite set.* In this case some point of $S$ recurs infinitely often in the sequence, and we can select a certain subsequence $x_{n_1}, x_{n_2}, x_{n_3}, \ldots$, all the terms of which are the same, say equal to $y$. Then certainly the subsequence converges to $y$. This disposes of Case 1.

*Case 2. S is an infinite set.* In this case Theorem 2–4 II guarantees that $S$ has a point of accumulation $y$, because the sequence is bounded, by hypothesis. By Theorem 2–4 III we can then choose a sequence of distinct points from $S$ so that the sequence converges to $y$. Now, a sequence of distinct points chosen from $S$ will be representable in the form $x_{n_1}, x_{n_2}, x_{n_3}, \ldots$, where each $n_k$ is a positive integer and $n_i \neq n_j$ if $i \neq j$. It may be, however, that $n_1, n_2, n_3, \ldots$ is not an *increasing* sequence of integers. However, since the $n_k$'s are all distinct, we can obtain an increasing sequence by proper selection. That is, let $p_1 = n_1$, $p_2 =$ the first $n_i > p_1$, $p_3 =$ the first $n_i > p_2$, and so on. Then $x_{p_1}, x_{p_2}, x_{p_3}, \ldots$ is genuinely a subsequence of $\{x_n\}$, and it converges to $y$.

## CAUCHY'S CONVERGENCE CONDITION

In Section 1–8 we stated a necessary and sufficient condition for a real sequence to be convergent. The proof given there employed the concepts of limit superior and limit inferior. These concepts have no counterpart for sequences in $R^k$ when $k > 1$. But Theorem 1–8 I does have a counterpart for sequences in $R^k$; the statement of the theorem for $R^k$ is the same as for $R$, except that we write $\|x_n - x_m\|$ in place of $|x_n - x_m|$ (norms in place of absolute values). We can now give a proof for the $R^k$ version of the theorem which applies equally well when $k = 1$. Here is the statement of the theorem.

THEOREM 2–4 V. *If $\{x_n\}$ is a sequence in $R^k$, in order that it be convergent it is necessary and sufficient that to each $\epsilon > 0$ correspond some positive integer $N$ such that $\|x_n - x_m\| < \epsilon$ whenever $N \leq m$ and $N \leq n$.*

*Proof.* The proof of the necessity of the condition is exactly like the proof when $k = 1$; see Section 1–8. The proof of the sufficiency of the condition begins, as before, with an argument to show that the sequence is bounded. By hypothesis there is some positive integer $N$ such that $\|x_n - x_N\| < 1$ if $N \leq n$. Now certainly, for all $m$,

$$\|x_m\| \leq \|x_m - x_N\| + \|x_N\|.$$

Hence, if $M$ is the largest of the numbers $1, \|x_1 - x_N\|, \ldots, \|x_{N-1} - x_N\|$, we certainly have

$$\|x_m\| \leq M + \|x_N\|$$

for all values of $m$. We can now apply Theorem 2–4 IV to assert that the sequence $\{x_n\}$ contains a convergent subsequence, say $x_{n_1}, x_{n_2}, x_{n_3}, \ldots$, with a limit $x$. To conclude the proof we now prove that the original sequence converges to $x$. Supposing an arbitrary positive $\epsilon$ is given, our hypothesis that the sequence satisfies the Cauchy condition (see the comment in the sufficiency proof for Theorem 1–8 I) enables us to assert the existence of an integer $N'$ such that $\|x_m - x_n\| < \frac{\epsilon}{2}$ if $N' \leq m$ and $N' \leq n$. Now, since the subsequence converges to $x$, we can choose an index $n_i$ large enough to insure both

$$N' \leq n_i \quad \text{and} \quad \|x_{n_i} - x\| < \frac{\epsilon}{2}.$$

Then, if $n \geq N'$, we have

$$\|x_n - x\| \leq \|x_n - x_{n_i}\| + \|x_{n_i} - x\| < \frac{\epsilon}{2} + \frac{\epsilon}{2} = \epsilon.$$

This completes the proof.

### PROBLEMS

1. Prove that if $x_n \to x$, then every subsequence of $\{x_n\}$ is convergent to $x$.
2. Let $x_n = (\xi_{1n}, \ldots, \xi_{kn})$ and $x = (\xi_1, \ldots, \xi_k)$. Show that $x_n \to x$ if and only if $\lim_{n\to\infty} \xi_{in} = \xi_i$ when $i = 1, 2, \ldots, k$.
3. Suppose that $x_n \to x$, and that $S$ is a set such that $x_n \in S$ for each $n$. Prove that $x \in \bar{S}$.
4. Suppose that $\{x_n\}$ is a given sequence in $R^k$. Let $y_n = x_{2n}$, $z_n = x_{2n+1}$, $w_n = x_{5n}$.
   (a) Prove that if $y_n \to y$ and $z_n \to z$, then $\{x_n\}$ is convergent if and only if $y = z$.
   (b) Suppose that $y_n \to y$, $z_n \to z$, and $w_n \to w$. Show that $\{x_n\}$ is convergent.
5. Construct a sequence $\{x_n\}$ in $R^2$ such that if $S$ is the set of all the $x_n$'s, then $S' = A \cup B$, where $A = \{(\xi, \eta) : \xi = 0, 0 \leq \eta \leq 1\}$ and $B = \{(\xi, \eta) : 0 \leq \xi \leq 1, \eta = 0\}$, and further such that the $x_n$'s are all distinct and inside the square with vertices (0, 0), (0, 1), (1, 1), (1, 0).

## 2–5 Covering theorems

In this section we deal with the concept of *an open covering of a set*. Let $S$ be a set in $R^k$, and let $\mathscr{F}$ be a family of open sets from $R^k$. We call $\mathscr{F}$ an open covering of $S$ if $S$ is contained in the union of all of the members of $\mathscr{F}$. We require, in other words, that each point of $S$ be contained in at least one of the open sets of the family $\mathscr{F}$. The usefulness of this concept will be evident in due course, from the theorems we prove and the applications we make of these theorems.

*Example 1.* Let $S$ be any nonempty set in $R^k$. Corresponding to each point $x$ in $S$ let us select some one neighborhood of $x$, and denote it by $U_x$. Let $\mathscr{F}$ be the family of all the sets $U_x$. Then $\mathscr{F}$ is an open covering of $S$.

*Example 2.* Consider the case $k = 1$. Let $S$ be the closed interval $[-1, 1]$ in $R$. Consider the family $\mathscr{F}$ of all open intervals $(r - \frac{1}{4}, r + \frac{1}{4})$, where $r$ varies over the set of all *rational* numbers belonging to $S$. Then $\mathscr{F}$ is an open covering of $S$. To see this it is sufficient to observe that if $x$ is an irrational member of $S$, there exists a rational member $r$ of $S$ such that $|x - r| < \frac{1}{4}$ (see Theorem 1–4 II).

There is no difficulty in constructing many open coverings of any given set. For instance, the entire space $R^k$ is an open set, and it is an open covering of any set whatsoever in $R^k$. Or, let $\mathscr{F}$ be the countable family of open spheres $S(0; n)$ (center at the origin, radius $n$), with $n = 1, 2, 3, \ldots$. Then $\mathscr{F}$ is an open covering of any specified set.

As it turns out, the interesting and useful thing to consider about open coverings is the following question: Supposing we are given a set $S$ and a certain open covering $\mathscr{F}$ of this set.

What can be said about the possibility of using only a part of the family $\mathscr{F}$ and nevertheless maintaining an open covering of $S$? If, for example, $\mathscr{F}$ consists of infinitely many open sets, can we perhaps cover $S$ with merely a finite number of these sets? Or, supposing that the family $\mathscr{F}$ is *uncountably* infinite, will some *countable* subset of $\mathscr{F}$ suffice to cover $S$? In order to investigate ways of answering these questions we need some preliminary results not directly concerned with open coverings.

## A COUNTABLE BASIS OF NEIGHBORHOODS FOR $R^k$

In Section 2–3 we mentioned the desirability of knowing that there exists a countable basis of neighborhoods for $R^k$. The time has now come when we need to make use of this fact, so we shall show how to construct such a countable basis of neighborhoods.

THEOREM 2–5 I. *It is possible to form a countable family $\mathscr{F}$ of open sets in $R^k$ with the following property: given any point $x$ and any open set $U$ containing $x$, there exists an open set $V$ from the family $\mathscr{F}$ such that $x \in V$ and $V \subset U$.*

*Proof.* Let $\mathscr{F}$ be the family of all those open spherical neighborhoods in $R^k$ which have rational radii and whose centers have rational coordinates. This family is countably infinite (a fact which we shall discuss in more detail at the end of the proof), and we shall show that it has the property claimed in the theorem. Suppose a point $x$ and one of its neighborhoods $U$ are given. Let $S$ be an open sphere of radius $\epsilon$ with center at $x$ such that $S \subset U$. Let $T$ be the open sphere with center $x$ and radius $\frac{\epsilon}{2}$. Choose a point $y$ in $T$ such that $y$ has rational coordinates. Let $r$ be a rational number such that

$$\|x - y\| < r < \frac{\epsilon}{2},$$

and let $V$ be the open sphere with center $y$ and radius $r$. Then $V \in \mathscr{F}$. The fact that $\|x - y\| < r$ implies that $x \in V$. To show that $V \subset U$, suppose $z \in V$. Then

$$\|z - x\| \leq \|z - y\| + \|y - x\| < r + r < \epsilon,$$

and consequently $z \in S$. That is, $V \subset S$. But $S \subset U$, and hence $V \subset U$. This finishes the proof.

There are two matters which deserve more comment. In the first place, the proof that $\mathscr{F}$ is a countably infinite family goes as follows: It suffices to prove that the set of all points in $R^k$ with rational coordinates is countable, for then the set of all spheres with rational radii and centers having rational coordinates is countable, by the argument given in Section 1–4 to show that a countable union of countable sets is a countable set. Now, to prove that the set of all points in $R^k$ with rational coordinates is countable, the argument goes by induction on $k$. The assertion is correct for $k = 1$, because we know that the set of real rational numbers is countable. The induction step is then made by using once more the fact that a countable union of countable sets is countable. (A point $(\xi_1, \ldots, \xi_k)$ in $R^k$ with rational coordinates is thought of as a pair $(P, \xi_k)$, where $P$ is a point of $R^{k-1}$ with rational coordinates. We then enumerate the $P$'s and the $\xi_k$'s and so display all the $(P, \xi_k)$'s as a countable set of countable sets.)

The other matter in the proof of Theorem 2–5 I which requires comment is this: Within any neighborhood of any point in $R^k$ there is a point with rational coordinates. This is an obvious consequence of the fact that between any two real numbers there is a rational number, together with the fact that the open boxes form a basis of neighborhoods in $R^k$.

## THE CANTOR INTERSECTION THEOREM

Presently we shall need the following theorem.

THEOREM 2–5 II. *Let $\{S_n\}$ be a sequence of nonempty, bounded, and closed sets in $R^k$ such that $S_{n+1} \subset S_n$ for each n. Then the intersection of all the $S_n$'s is not empty.*

*Proof.* Form a sequence $\{x_n\}$ by selecting $x_n$ so that $x_n \in S_n$ for each $n$. Then all the points $x_n$ are in $S_1$, which is a bounded set. Hence the sequence $\{x_n\}$ is bounded. It therefore contains a convergent subsequence, with some limit $x$ (Theorem 2–4 IV). We assert that $x \in S_n$ for each $n$. In fact, if the convergent subsequence is $x_{n_1}, x_{n_2}, \ldots$, and if $n$ is any positive integer, we certainly have $n_i > n$ if $i$ is large enough. But then, for such sufficiently large values of $i$, we have $x_{n_i} \in S_{n_i} \subset S_n$ because of the inclusion relations among the given sets. Now $S_n$ is a closed set. Hence it contains the limit $x$ of the convergent subsequence, because all but a finite number of terms of the subsequence belong to $S_n$. The principle used here is this: If the terms of the convergent sequence $\{y_n\}$ are in a set $T$, the limit $y$ of the sequence belongs to the closure $\bar{T}$ (see Problem 3, Section 2–4). The proof is now complete.

Theorem 2 5 II is named "the Cantor Intersection Theorem" because it embodies essentially a result proved by Georg Cantor in 1880. Cantor (1845–1918) contributed greatly to the foundations of analysis by his work in set theory; he was a true innovator in his studies of the infinite in mathematics. Many surprising discoveries and curious examples are due to Cantor. We shall meet his name again in Section 2–10.

We now return to the subject of open coverings. Our first result is a theorem due to E. Lindelöf (1870–1946). The theorem dates from 1903.

THEOREM 2–5 III. *Let $\mathscr{F}$ be an arbitrary open covering of an arbitrary set $S$ in $R^k$ Then there exists a countable subfamily of $\mathscr{F}$ which also covers $S$.*

*Proof.* We may certainly assume that $S$ is nonempty, for it is clear that any family of open sets is an open covering of the empty set. We remind the reader that countable means "either finite or countably infinite." In the proof we make use of Theorem 2–5 I. Let $V_1, V_2, \ldots$ be a countable family of open sets forming a basis of neighborhoods for $R^k$, as guaranteed by the theorem just mentioned. Now consider any particular $V_n$. If there is a set $U$ in $\mathscr{F}$ such that $V_n \subset U$, select one such $U$ and call it $U_n$. We do not claim that for every $n$ there *is* such a $U$, but those indices $n$ for which a $U_n$ can be chosen certainly form a countable set (and not an *empty* set, as we shall presently see). We claim that these $U_n$'s form an open covering of $S$. In fact, suppose $x \in S$. Then, since $\mathscr{F}$ is an open covering of $S$, there exists a set $U$ in $\mathscr{F}$ such that $x \in U$. The fact that the $V_n$'s form a basis of neighborhoods now insures the existence of some $V_n$ such that $x \in V_n$ and $V_n \subset U$. There is for this $n$, accordingly, one of the chosen sets $U_n$ in $\mathscr{F}$ such that $V_n \subset U_n$. Consequently $x \in U_n$. This completes the proof that the $U_n$'s form a covering of $S$.

## THE BOREL COVERING THEOREM

The foregoing theorem answers one of the questions raised prior to the discussion of Theorem 2–5 I. We now turn to this question: Are there any general circumstances under which we can assert that, if a set $S$ possesses an open covering $\mathcal{F}$, then some finite number of members of $\mathcal{F}$ will suffice to cover $S$? This can obviously be asserted if $S$ is a finite set. But it is not possible to make the assertion without some restriction on $S$. This is shown by the following example.

*Example 3.* Let $S$ be the set $\{x : 0 \leq x < 1\}$ in $R$. Let open intervals $U_1, U_2, \ldots$ in $R$ be defined as follows:

$$U_1 = \left\{x : -\frac{1}{2} < x < \frac{1}{2}\right\}$$

$$U_2 = \left\{x : \frac{1}{3} < x < \frac{2}{3}\right\}$$

$$\cdots$$

$$U_n = \left\{x : \frac{n-1}{n+1} < x < \frac{n}{n+1}\right\} \qquad (n > 1)$$

$$\cdots$$

Let $\mathcal{F}$ be the family of all the $U_n$'s. Then $\mathcal{F}$ is an open covering of $S$, but no finite number of the $U_n$'s will suffice to cover $S$. We leave verification of these assertions to the reader.

The following theorem shows what can be achieved if $S$ is closed and bounded.

THEOREM 2–5 IV. *Suppose that $\mathcal{F}$ is an open covering of the set $S$ in $R^k$, and suppose that $S$ is both closed and bounded. Then some finite number of the sets in $\mathcal{F}$ will suffice to cover $S$.*

*Proof.* Because of Theorem 2–5 III there exists a countable set $U_1, U_2, \ldots$ of members of $\mathcal{F}$ such that the $U_n$'s form an open covering of $S$. If this countable set should in fact be finite, there would be nothing more to prove. Hence we assume the set of $U_n$'s is countably infinite. Now let

$$V_n = U_1 \cup U_2 \cup \cdots \cup U_n, \qquad S_n = S \cap V_n^{\sim}.$$

The set $V_n$ is open, and its complement $V_n^{\sim}$ is closed. Since $S$ is closed and bounded, it follows that $S_n$ also is closed and bounded. Clearly $V_n \subset V_{n+1}$, and so, since the inclusion relation is reversed when we take complements, we see that $S_{n+1} \subset S_n$. There are now two alternatives: either some $S_n$ is an empty set, or no $S_n$ is empty. In the first case suppose that $S_N$ is empty. This means that no point of $S$ is in $V_N^{\sim}$, and hence that $S \subset V_N$. But then the sets $U_1, \ldots, U_N$ form a finite open covering of $S$. We thus reach the desired conclusion in the first case. If, on the other hand, no $S_n$ is empty, then the $S_n$'s satisfy the conditions of Cantor's intersection theorem (Theorem 2–5 II), and hence there exists a point $x$ belonging to each of the $S_n$'s. This implies both $x \in S$ and $x \notin V_n$ for each $n$. But, since the $U_n$'s cover $S$, there is some $n$ for which $x \in U_n$. Certainly, then, we also have $x \in V_n$. But, as we know, $x \notin V_n$. We have now reached a contradiction in the second case, so it is impossible for every $S_n$ to be nonempty. This completes the proof.

Theorem 2–5 IV is known variously as the Borel-Lebesgue theorem, the Heine-Borel theorem, and the Borel covering theorem. The first formal statement of the theorem is due to

Émile Borel (1871–1956) in 1895. The reason for attaching Heine's name is that Eduard Heine (1821–1881) used the underlying idea in 1872 in proving the theorem that a real function which is continuous on a finite closed interval is in fact uniformly continuous. In Borel's original formulation and proof of the theorem he assumed that the given open covering was by a denumerable family, and showed that a finite subfamily would suffice. Moreover, the concern was with sets in $R$ (the one-dimensional case). Henri Lebesgue (1875–1943) gets his name attached to the Borel theorem because he eliminated the restriction to denumerable coverings. His proof was first published in his book, *Leçons sur l'intégration*, in 1904. (Lebesgue [2].) There has been some controversy as to priority. The proofs of Borel and Lebesgue were quite unlike the proof given here.

The Borel theorem has been studied intensively, and there are many extensions and generalizations of it. The central idea of the Borel theorem has played a very important part in the development of the theory of topologies of spaces more general than Euclidean space. For an interesting account with many references see the survey article [2] of T. H. Hildebrandt.

**PROBLEMS**

1. Here is an indication of one of the classical proofs of Theorem 2–5 IV for the case $k = 1$: Suppose $S$ a closed and bounded set in $R$; it is then contained in some finite closed interval $[a, b]$. Let $\mathscr{F}$ be an open covering of $S$, but suppose that no finite number of the sets in $\mathscr{F}$ will suffice to cover $S$. Bisect $[a, b]$. Then for at least one of the two closed subintervals, the part of $S$ in that subinterval cannot be covered by a finite number of the members of $\mathscr{F}$. Choose such a subinterval, bisect it, and continue the process, thus obtaining a nest. Then deduce a contradiction. This argument can be adapted to $R^k$ for every $k$.

2. Let $T$ be a closed and bounded set in $R^k$, and let $\mathscr{F}$ be an open covering of $T$. Then there exists a $\delta > 0$ such that for each $x$ in $T$ the open sphere $S(x; \delta)$ is contained in some member of $\mathscr{F}$. To prove this, assume the contrary, and observe then that to each positive integer $n$ corresponds a point $x_n$ in $T$ such that the open sphere $S\left(x_n; \frac{1}{n}\right)$ fails to lie wholly in any member of $\mathscr{F}$. Use Theorem 2–4 IV to deduce a contradiction.

## 2–6 Compactness

The term "compact" was introduced into mathematics in 1904 by Maurice Fréchet (1878– ). Subsequently, in 1906, he introduced an alternative definition of the term "compact," equivalent to his original definition under certain conditions. Fréchet was working in a much more general framework of ideas than we are in our present discussion of the topology of $R^k$, but according to his 1906 definition a set $S$ in $R^k$ would be called compact if every infinite subset of $S$ has at least one point of accumulation (which need not be in $S$, however). Fréchet's work implied the following in $R^k$: Suppose $S$ is compact in the sense just defined. Let $\{S_n\}$ be a sequence of nonempty closed sets such that $S_n \subset S$ and $S_{n+1} \subset S_n$ for each $n$. Then the intersection of all the $S_n$'s is not empty. Conversely, if this proposition is correct for a fixed set $S$, no matter how the sequence $\{S_n\}$ of the specified sort is selected, then $S$ is compact in Fréchet's sense. This characterization of compact sets was that used as the definition in 1904.

Fréchet's definition of compactness was used quite generally for more than thirty years, and it is still used by some mathematicians. However, the prevailing contemporary definition of compactness in America and western Europe, though closely related to Fréchet's definition, is not identical with it. For this reason one must be very careful in reading about compactness in mathematical books and periodicals. The lack of uniformity in terminology is regrettable, but it is a troublesome fact which must be faced.

Our definition of compactness (conforming to prevailing usage) will now be given. Hereafter all references to compactness will imply the use of the definition we give.

A set $S$ in $R^k$ is called *compact* if in every family $\mathscr{F}$ forming an open covering of $S$ there is some finite subfamily which also covers $S$.

It should be pointed out that the term *bicompact* is used in the Soviet Union with the same meaning that we have just now defined for *compact*. The term "bicompact" was originally introduced and widely used at a time when the word "compact" was generally used in Fréchet's sense. Later, "compact" and "bicompact" came to have the same meaning, and the term "bicompact" was generally dropped by American and French authors.

We know, by the Borel theorem, that any closed and bounded set in $R^k$ is compact. The converse is also true, as we shall show.

THEOREM 2–6 I. *If $S$ is a compact set in $R^k$, then $S$ is closed and bounded.*

*Proof.* The proof that $S$ is bounded is very simple. Select any one point in $R^k$, say $x_0$. Consider the family of open spheres $S(x_0; n)$ (center $x_0$, radius $n$), $n = 1, 2, \ldots$. If $x \in S$ we can choose $n$ so that $n > D(x_0, x)$. Then $x \in S(x_0; n)$. Hence the family of spheres covers $S$. Since $S$ is compact it follows that some finite family $S(x_0; 1), \ldots, S(x_0; N)$ covers $S$. But then we actually have $S \subset S(x_0; N)$, so that $S$ is bounded.

There are many ways to prove that a compact set in $R^k$ is closed. Here is one proof, chosen because of its applicability in a much more general orbit of ideas (see Theorem 3–3 I). We shall show that $S' \subset S$ if $S$ is compact. By Theorem 2–3 III this will imply that $S$ is closed. Now suppose that $x$ is not in $S$. For each $y$ in $S$ choose a neighborhood of $y$, call it $U_y$, and a corresponding neighborhood of $x$, call it $V_y$, in such a way that $U_y \cap V_y = \varnothing$. The family of all the $U_y$'s (as $y$ varies over $S$) is an open covering of $S$. Since $S$ is compact, some finite set of the $U_y$'s will suffice to cover $S$. For convenience of notation let the finite number of $U_y$'s be $U_1, \ldots, U_n$, with $U_i$ being the $U_y$ associated with a certain $y_i$. Let the corresponding $V_y$ be denoted by $V_i$. Let $U = U_1 \cup \cdots \cup U_n$, $V = V_1 \cap \cdots \cap V_n$. Then $S \subset U$, $U \cap V = \varnothing$, and hence no point of $S$ is in $V$. But $V$ is a neighborhood of $x$. Thus $x$ cannot be in $S'$. This proves that $S^\sim \subset (S')^\sim$, which is equivalent to $S' \subset S$. Thus the proof is complete.

The next theorem shows the relation between compactness, as we have defined it, and Fréchet's 1906 version of the concept.

THEOREM 2–6 II. (a) *If $T$ is a compact set in $R^k$, and if $S$ is an infinite subset of $T$, then $S' \cap T$ is not empty.*

(b) *If $T$ is a set in $R^k$ such that $S' \cap T \neq \varnothing$ whenever $S$ is an infinite subset of $T$, then $T$ is compact.*

We have separated the theorem into two distinct propositions, one of which is the converse of the other. We have deliberately arranged the proofs so they are valid in contexts more general than that of the Euclidean space $R^k$.

*Proof of* (a). Suppose $S$ is a subset of $T$ such that $S' \cap T = \varnothing$. Then to each $x$ in $T$ corresponds a neighborhood $U$ of $x$ such that $U \cap S$ is either empty or consists of $x$ alone. As $x$ varies over $T$ these $U$'s form an open covering of $T$. Hence a finite number of them suffice, say $U_1, \ldots, U_n$. Then $S \subset U_1 \cup \cdots \cup U_n$, and there is at most one point of $S$ in each $U_i$. Thus $S$ is a finite set. It follows that $S' \cap T$ cannot be empty if $S$ is an infinite subset of $T$.

*Proof of* (b). We make the hypothesis on $T$ as in the statement of proposition (b). As a first step we shall show the existence of a countable family $\mathscr{U}$ of open spheres in $R^k$ such that, for each $x \in T$, the family $\mathscr{U}$ contains a basis of neighborhoods at $x$.

We argue as follows: Corresponding to each positive integer $n$ there is some positive integer $N$ and a set of points $x_1, \ldots, x_N$ in $T$ such that the collection of open spheres $S\left(x_1; \frac{1}{n}\right), \ldots, S\left(x_N; \frac{1}{n}\right)$ covers $T$. If this were not so there would be some $n$ such that, no matter how any finite number of points $x_1, \ldots, x_N$ are chosen in $T$, the set of open spheres of radii $\frac{1}{n}$ with centers at $x_1, \ldots, x_N$ will fail to cover $T$. This would then permit us, starting with any $x_1$ in $T$, to select points $x_2, x_3, \ldots$ in $T$ successively in such a way that $D(x_i, x_j) \geq \frac{1}{n}$ if $i \neq j$. But then the infinite set consisting of $x_1, x_2, x_3, \ldots$ could not have any accumulation point, in contradiction to the property assumed for $T$.

We now resume the main line of the argument. Using the assertion made at the beginning of the preceding paragraph, we take $n$ successively equal to $1, 2, 3, \ldots$ and get the finite number of open spheres in each case. All of these spheres together form a countable family, which we denote by $\mathscr{U}$. We have to show that if $x \in T$, $\mathscr{U}$ contains a basis of neighborhoods at $x$. For this we must show that if $V$ is any open sphere with center at $x$, there is some $U$ in $\mathscr{U}$ such that $x \in U$ and $U \subset V$. Let $\epsilon$ be the radius of $V$, and choose the positive integer $n$ so that $\frac{1}{n} < \frac{\epsilon}{2}$. By what has been shown, there is some member $U$ of $\mathscr{U}$, $U$ being a sphere of radius $\frac{1}{n}$ with some center $y$ in $T$, such that $x \in U$. If $z \in U$ we have, $D(z, x) \leq D(z, y) + D(y, x) < \frac{1}{n} + \frac{1}{n} < \epsilon$. This means that $z \in V$. Thus $U \subset V$, and the first main step of the proof is finished.

Now, to prove that $T$ is compact, let $\mathscr{F}$ be any open covering of $T$. Just as in the proof of Theorem 2–5 III we can select a countable subfamily of $\mathscr{F}$ which is still an open covering of $T$. We use the countable family $\mathscr{U}$ here just as the countable family of $V_n$'s was used in the proof of Theorem 2–5 III. Hence, let $W_1, W_2, \ldots$ be a countable subfamily of $\mathscr{F}$ covering $T$. We claim that, for some $n$, $T$ is covered by $W_1, \ldots, W_n$. If this were not so, there would exist, for each $n$, a point $x_n$ in $T$ but not in $W_1 \cup \cdots \cup W_n$. The number of distinct points among the $x_n$'s must necessarily be infinite, and hence there must be an accumulation point, say $y$, of the $x_n$'s, with $y \in T$. Then $y \in W_N$ for some $N$, and also $x_n \in W_N$ for infinitely many indices $n$, in particular for some $n > N$. But now we have a contradiction, for $x_n$ is not in $W_1 \cup \cdots \cup W_n$. Thus, finally, we complete the proof of (b).

## PROBLEMS

1. Let $S$ be a compact set in $R^k$. Prove that $S$ is closed, starting as follows: Assume $x_0 \in S^{\sim}$. Let $V_n = \left\{x : D(x, x_0) > \frac{1}{n}\right\}$, $n = 1, 2, \ldots$. Use the compactness of $S$ to deduce that $S \subset V_N$ for some $N$. But then $S \cap \left\{x : D(x, x_0) < \frac{1}{N}\right\} = \varnothing$. Finish the argument.

2. Give an alternative proof of Theorem 2–6 II (a), using Theorems 2–6 I and 2–4 II. Observe that $S \subset T$ implies $S' \subset T'$. Why is $T' \subset T$ here ?

3. Give an alternative proof of Theorem 2–6 II (b) by showing that, under the given conditions, $T$ is closed and bounded.

## 2–7 Functions. Continuity

In elementary calculus the word "function" is ordinarily used to mean a function with real numbers as values. Moreover, these functions usually depend on one real variable (in the case of ordinary differentiation and integration), or on two or more real variables (in the case of partial differentiation and multiple integration). We now wish to study the function concept, and especially the character of continuous functions, from a general point of view. From this point of view there is no basic difference between functions of one variable and functions of several variables. Also, there is no reason to confine attention to functions with real values. In the study of complex analysis (the classical theory of analytic functions of a complex variable) the functions considered have complex values and depend on a complex variable. If we write $w = f(z)$ to express such a functional dependence, we can regard $z$ and $w$ as points in the Euclidean plane $R^2$. To forestall misunderstanding or criticism, we must be clear that we are not asserting that $R^2$ and the complex plane are identical as mathematical structures. We can perform the multiplication of two complex numbers, whereas we have not defined this multiplication between two elements of $R^2$. The complex plane is in fact a mathematical structure obtained by imposing on $R^2$ some additional structure. The standard topology of the complex plane is just the topology we have given to $R^2$; it is this topology which is used in complex analytic function-theory.

Our general point of view is going to lead us to consider relations of the form $y = f(x)$, where $x$ varies over some set $\mathscr{D}$ in the Euclidean space $R^k$ of $k$ dimensions and the "value" $y$ is a point in the Euclidean space $R^l$ of $l$ dimensions. When $k = l = 1$ we have the familiar case of a real-valued function of a real variable. If $k = 2$ and $l = 1$ we have a real-valued function of 2 real variables. In the general case suppose we express $x$ and $y$ in terms of their coordinates:

$$x = (\xi_1, \ldots, \xi_k), \qquad y = (\eta_1, \ldots, \eta_l).$$

Then, if $y$ is a function of $x$, say $y = f(x)$, this implies that each of the coordinates $\eta_1, \ldots, \eta_l$ is a real-valued function of $\xi_1, \ldots, \xi_k$. In functional notation, then,

$$\begin{cases} \eta_1 = f_1(\xi_1, \ldots, \xi_k), \\ \eta_2 = f_2(\xi_1, \ldots, \xi_k), \\ \quad \cdots \\ \eta_l = f_l(\xi_1, \ldots, \xi_k). \end{cases} \tag{1}$$

Thus, the "$R^l$-valued function" $f$ can actually be identified with the collection of $l$ real-valued functions $f_1, \ldots, f_l$, each of which is a function of $k$ real variables. There is manifestly an advantage in studying the single entity $f$ if in so doing we can accomplish the same purpose as we would in studying $f_1, \ldots, f_l$ as separate entities. This economy can in fact be realized if we confine attention to certain properties of the functions, and continuity is one of these properties. In what follows, then, we study functions defined on a certain set in $R^k$ and having values which are points in $R^l$.

## THE GENERAL FUNCTION CONCEPT

The most suitable way to define what is meant by a function involves the concept of a certain kind of subset of the product of two sets. To fix the ideas, and concentrate on the situation in which we are interested, we define the Cartesian *product* of $R^k$ and $R^l$ as the set of all pairs $(x, y)$, with $x$ a point in $R^k$ and $y$ a point in $R^l$. The collection of all such pairs is denoted by $R^k \times R^l$. Now suppose we have a certain nonempty subset of $R^k \times R^l$ with the following property: if $(x, y)$ is in this subset, there is no other member of the subset having the same first element $x$. Or, in other words, if $(x_1, y_1)$ and $(x_2, y_2)$ are in the subset, and if $x_1 = x_2$, then also $y_1 = y_2$. Such a subset of $R^k \times R^l$ is called a *function* with *domain* in $R^k$ and *range* in $R^l$. If $f$ is the function, the domain $\mathscr{D}$ of $f$ is defined to be the set of all elements $x$ of $R^k$ for which there is a $y$ such that $(x, y) \in f$. Likewise, the range $\mathscr{R}$ of $f$ is defined to be the set of all elements $y$ of $R^l$ for which there is an $x$ such that $(x, y) \in f$.

This definition of a function shows that, when $(x, y) \in f$, $y$ is uniquely determined by $x$. Hence we could, alternatively, speak of *a law of correspondence* whereby to each $x$ in $\mathscr{D}$ is assigned a unique corresponding $y$ in $\mathscr{R}$. This shows the relation of our present definition of a function to the older customary definition of a function as a certain law of correspondence. One essential feature is that we insist from the outset on "single-valuedness" of the function.

We shall follow the usual practices of functional notation, and write $y = f(x)$ when $(x, y) \in f$.

Here are some further matters of functional notation:

Suppose we are considering two sets $\mathscr{D}$, $S$, and a function $f$ with domain $\mathscr{D}$ and range *in* (perhaps, but not necessarily, equal to) $S$. We sometimes abbreviate this by saying "consider the function $f : \mathscr{D} \to S$."

Sometimes we indicate the definition of a function without using a symbol for the function, by the following device. Instead of writing "the function $f$ defined by $f(x) = \sin x$," we may write "the function $x \to \sin x$." The arrow here indicates the idea of the correspondence; the functional value corresponding to $x$ is $\sin x$. The domain of the function must of course be made clear in some way.

*Example 1.* Let $k = 2$, $l = 3$. Let $\mathscr{D}$ be all of $R^2$, and let the function $f$ consist of all pairs $(x, y)$ with $x = (\xi_1, \xi_2)$, $y = (\xi_1 \xi_2, \xi_1 + \xi_2, \xi_1^2 + \xi_2^2)$. In this case, if $y = (\eta_1, \eta_2, \eta_3)$, we can write

$$\eta_1 = \xi_1\xi_2, \qquad \eta_2 = \xi_1 + \xi_2, \qquad \eta_3 = \xi_1^2 + \xi_2^2. \tag{2}$$

These equations (2) are what equations (1) become for the present case. We can think of the function as a mapping of the plane $R^2$ into a part of $R^3$. The range of the function can be visualized as the surface of which (2) are the parametric equations (with $\xi_1$, $\xi_2$ as parameters).

*Example 2.* Let $k = 3$, $l = 2$. Let $\mathscr{D}$ be the set of points $(\xi_1, \xi_2, \xi_3)$ for which

$$\xi_1^2 + \xi_2^2 + (\xi_3 - \tfrac{1}{2})^2 = \tfrac{1}{4}, \tag{3}$$

with the exception of the point $(0, 0, 1)$. Let the function be defined by the equations

$$\eta_1 = \frac{\xi_1}{1 - \xi_3}, \qquad \eta_2 = \frac{\xi_2}{1 - \xi_3}. \tag{4}$$

That is, let the function consist of all pairs $(x, y)$, where $x = (\xi_1, \xi_2, \xi_3)$ and $y$ is given by (4).

We have here a function which maps all except one point of the sphere (3) in $R^3$ stereographically onto the whole plane $R^2$ (so that the range $\mathscr{R}$ in this case is $R^2$). We shall not go into the details about stereographic projection.

*Example 3.* Let $k = 3, l = 3$. Let $\mathscr{D}$ be the set of all $x$ in $R^3$ for which $\xi_1^2 + \xi_2^2 + \xi_3^2 \geq 1$, and let the function $f$ make $y = (\eta_1, \eta_2, \eta_3)$ correspond to $x = (\xi_1, \xi_2, \xi_3)$, where

$$\eta_1 = \frac{\xi_1}{r^2}, \qquad \eta_2 = \frac{\xi_2}{r^2}, \qquad \eta_3 = \frac{\xi_3}{r^2} \tag{5}$$

and $r^2 = \xi_1^2 + \xi_2^2 + \xi_3^2$. In this case the range of $f$ consists of all points $y$ for which $0 < \eta_1^2 + \eta_2^2 + \eta_3^2 \leq 1$. The function defines an inversive mapping of part of $R^3$ into another part of $R^3$. Our specification of $\mathscr{D}$ was made arbitrarily. We could have taken $\mathscr{D}$ to consist of all of $R^3$ except the point (0, 0, 0). In that case the range $\mathscr{R}$ would have been the same as $\mathscr{D}$.

## INVERSE FUNCTIONS

Suppose $f$ is a function with domain $\mathscr{D}$ in $R^k$ and range $\mathscr{R}$ in $R^l$. This function is a certain subset of $R^k \times R^l$. Now suppose we look at the pairs $(x, y)$ forming the function. If we reverse the order of $x$ and $y$, we get a certain set of pairs $(y, x)$ from the product $R^l \times R^k$. This subset of $R^l \times R^k$ *may* satisfy the condition for being a function with domain in $R^l$ and range in $R^k$. This condition is that no two different pairs shall have the same first element $y$. When this condition is satisfied, the function, consisting of all the pairs $(y, x)$ for which $(x, y) \in f$, is called *the inverse of f*, and denoted by $f^{-1}$.

It will be seen that $f^{-1}$ is defined if and only if the correspondence indicated by writing $y = f(x)$ is a one-to-one correspondence between the domain $\mathscr{D}$ of $f$ and the range $\mathscr{R}$ of $f$. One aspect of this correspondence is then described by saying that $f$ maps $x$ into $y$, or that $f$ maps $\mathscr{D}$ onto $\mathscr{R}$; the other aspect of the correspondence is described by saying that $f^{-1}$ maps $y$ into $x$, or that $f^{-1}$ maps $\mathscr{R}$ onto $\mathscr{D}$. The domain of $f^{-1}$ is $\mathscr{R}$, and its range is $\mathscr{D}$.

## IMAGES AND INVERSE IMAGES

For many purposes, especially to aid in thinking and expressing intuitive notions when we deal with functions, the concept of a function as a mapping is useful. If $f$ is a function with domain $\mathscr{D}$ and range $\mathscr{R}$, we think of $f$ as an agent that transports (maps) a point $x$ of $\mathscr{D}$ into a point $y$ of $\mathscr{R}$ (see Figure 13). We call $y$ (or $f(x)$) the *image* of $x$ under (or by) the mapping $f$. If $S$ is a subset of $\mathscr{D}$, the aggregate of the images $f(x)$ corresponding to all points $x$ of $S$

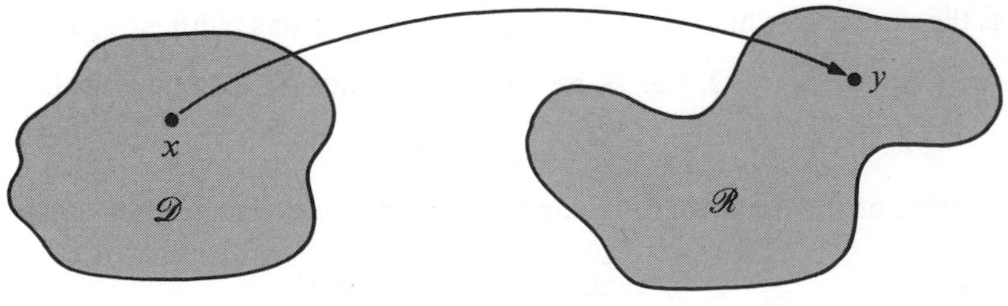


FIGURE 13

is called the image of $S$, and denoted by $f(S)$. Thus, in particular, $\mathscr{R} = f(\mathscr{D})$. Since $f(S) = \{y : y = f(x) \text{ for some } x \in S\}$, we see that $f(\varnothing) = \varnothing$.

If $T$ is a nonempty subset of $\mathscr{R}$, each point of $T$ is the image of one or more points in $\mathscr{D}$ (of just *one* point if the mapping is one-to-one). The set of *all* points $x$ in $\mathscr{D}$ such that $f(x) \in T$ is called the *inverse image* of $T$ under the mapping $f$. *We denote it by* $f^{-1}(T)$, *even though the mapping may not be one-to-one*. That is, we may use the notation $f^{-1}(T)$ even when the inverse function $f^{-1}$ is not defined. Of course, if $f^{-1}$ *is* defined, $f^{-1}(T)$ is the same as the image of $T$ under the mapping $f^{-1}$. The notation $f^{-1}(T)$ may also be used when $T = \varnothing$ if we express our general definition in the form $f^{-1}(T) = \{x : x \in \mathscr{D} \text{ and } f(x) \in T\}$. Observe that $f^{-1}(\varnothing) = \varnothing$.

## ONTO AND INTO MAPPINGS

There is a fairly standard technical usage of the words *onto* and *into* in connection with functions. Let $f$ have its domain $\mathscr{D}$ in $R^k$ and its range $\mathscr{R}$ in $R^l$. Let $S$ be a subset of $\mathscr{D}$ (perhaps all of $\mathscr{D}$). Then $f(S)$ is a subset of $\mathscr{R}$. We say that $f$ maps $S$ *onto* $f(S)$. But, if $T$ is any set in $R^l$ such that $f(S) \subset T$, we say that $f$ maps $S$ *into* $T$. The distinction is that $f(S)$ is precisely the set of all the images (under $f$) of points of $S$, whereas $T$ includes all the image points, but may also include other points as well. Thus, a real-valued function $f$ whose domain is $R^2$, is a mapping of $R^2$ *into* $R$. It is a mapping *onto* $R$ if and only if every real number occurs as a value of $f(x)$ for some $x$ in $R^2$.

## CONTINUITY

We have now cleared away the preliminaries of definition and notation, and we come to the discussion of continuity. Let $f$ be a function with domain $\mathscr{D}$ in $R^k$ and range $\mathscr{R}$ in $R^l$. Suppose $x_0$ is a point of $\mathscr{D}$. Then $f$ is said to be continuous at $x_0$ if to each neighborhood $U$ of $f(x_0)$ corresponds some neighborhood $V$ of $x_0$ such that $f(x) \in U$ whenever $x \in V \cap \mathscr{D}$. We say that $f$ is continuous on $\mathscr{D}$ if it is continuous at each point of $\mathscr{D}$.

The definition of continuity at $x_0$ can also be stated as follows: $f$ is continuous at $x_0$ if to each neighborhood $U$ of $f(x_0)$ corresponds some neighborhood $V$ of $x_0$ such that $f(V \cap \mathscr{D}) \subset U \cap \mathscr{R}$.

Because of the fact that the family of all open spheres forms a basis of neighborhoods, we obtain the following criterion for continuity: *$f$ is continuous at $x_0$ if and only if to each positive number $\epsilon$ corresponds some positive number $\delta$ such that $D[f(x), f(x_0)] < \epsilon$ whenever $x$ is in $\mathscr{D}$ and $D(x, x_0) < \delta$.* Here we use the same symbol $D$ for the distance functions in $R^l$ and $R^k$, respectively.

In the definition of continuity we have placed no restriction whatever on the nature of the domain $\mathscr{D}$ of the function $f$. It may happen, in particular, that $x_0$ is an *isolated* point of $\mathscr{D}$. That is, there may be some neighborhood of $x_0$ which contains no points of $\mathscr{D}$ except $x_0$ itself. In other words, $x_0$ may not be an accumulation point of $\mathscr{D}$. In this case, the function $f$ is certainly continuous at $x_0$, regardless of how it is defined at the other points of $\mathscr{D}$. But, if $x_0$ *is* an accumulation point of $\mathscr{D}$, and if $\{x_n\}$ is a sequence of points of $\mathscr{D}$ such that $x_n \to x_0$, the continuity of $f$ at $x_0$ has as a consequence that $f(x_n) \to f(x_0)$. In fact, we have the following theorem:

THEOREM 2–7 I. *Let $f$ be a function with domain $\mathscr{D}$ in $R^k$ and range $\mathscr{R}$ in $R^l$. Then, if*

*$x \in \mathscr{D}$, $f$ is continuous at $x$ if and only if $f(x_n) \to f(x)$ whenever $\{x_n\}$ is a sequence of points in $\mathscr{D}$ such that $x_n \to x$.*

We leave the proof of this theorem to the student.

## HOMEOMORPHISM

If $f$ is a function with domain $\mathscr{D}$ and range $\mathscr{R}$ such that the inverse function $f^{-1}$ exists, and such that both $f$ and $f^{-1}$ are continuous on their domains of definition, we call $f$ an homeomorphism. Then $f^{-1}$ is also an homeomorphism, of course. The sets $\mathscr{D}$ and $\mathscr{R}$ are said to be *homeomorphic*. Sometimes we describe $f$ as an *homeomorphic mapping* of $\mathscr{D}$ onto $\mathscr{R}$, and we call $\mathscr{R}$ an *homeomorphic image* of $\mathscr{D}$.

It can happen that $f$ is continuous on $\mathscr{D}$ and that $f^{-1}$ exists, yet $f$ is not an homeomorphism. That is, $f^{-1}$ may be discontinuous. See Problem 3.

## CONTINUITY AND COMPACTNESS

One of the most important theorems about continuous functions has to do with the image of a compact set.

THEOREM 2–7 II. *If $f$ is continuous on its domain $\mathscr{D}$, and if $\mathscr{D}$ is compact, then the range $\mathscr{R}$ (which is the image of $\mathscr{D}$) is compact.*

*Proof.* Let $\mathscr{F}$ be any open covering of $\mathscr{R}$. We have to show the existence of a finite subfamily of $\mathscr{F}$ which is a covering of $\mathscr{R}$. We proceed as follows: To each point $x$ in $\mathscr{D}$ corresponds some $U$ in $\mathscr{F}$ such that $f(x) \in U$, because $\mathscr{F}$ is a covering of $\mathscr{R}$. Then, since $f$ is continuous at $x$, there is some neighborhood $V$ of $x$ such that $f(V \cap \mathscr{D}) \subset U$. In this way we associate a definite $U$ and a definite $V$ with each $x$. Now, the family of all the $V$'s is an open covering of $\mathscr{D}$, and since $\mathscr{D}$ is compact, there is some finite set of the $V$'s which is a covering of $\mathscr{D}$. Thus we arrive at this finite set of $V$'s, say $V_1, \ldots, V_n$, and a corresponding set of $U$'s, say $U_1, \ldots, U_n$, such that $f(V_i \cap \mathscr{D}) \subset U_i$. It is then seen at once that each $y$ in $\mathscr{R}$ is in some one of the $U_i$'s, because $y = f(x)$ for some $x$ in $\mathscr{D}$, and $x$ must be in a certain $V_i$. Hence the finite set $U_1, \ldots, U_n$ is a covering of $\mathscr{R}$.

It may happen that $f$ is not continuous on all of its domain $\mathscr{D}$, but *is* continuous at each point of some compact subset $S$ contained in $\mathscr{D}$. In that case we can assert that the image set $f(S)$ is compact. For, we can restrict our attention to $S$, ignoring points of $\mathscr{D} - S$. From this point of view the domain of the restricted function is $S$ and the restricted function agrees with the original one on $S$; we can then apply Theorem 2–7 II. In order to conclude that $f(S)$ is compact, *it is sufficient to assume that the restricted function is continuous on its domain $S$.* This may sometimes be the case, even when the unrestricted function fails to be continuous at some points of $S$.

*Example 4.* Let us consider the following function $f$ with domain and range both in the space $R$. Let $\mathscr{D} = \{x : 0 < x < 3\}$, and define $f$ by $f(x) = 2$ if $0 < x < 1$, $f(x) = 2 - x$ if $1 \leq x \leq 2$, $f(x) = 1$ if $2 < x < 3$. See Figure 14. Let $S = \{x : 1 \leq x \leq 2\}$. The restricted function in this case has domain $S$ and is continuous on $S$. But the unrestricted function is discontinuous at $x = 1$ and $x = 2$.

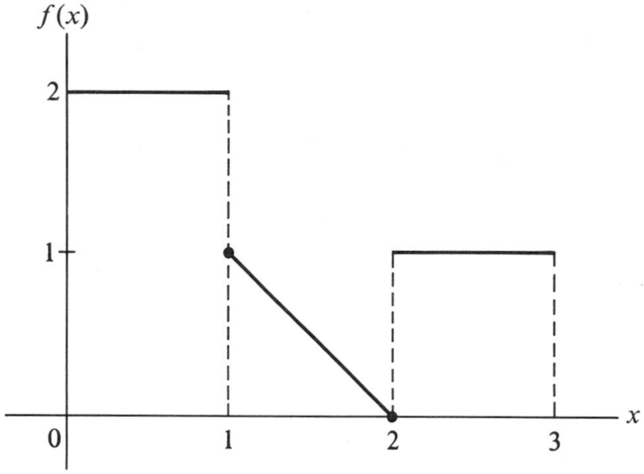


FIGURE 14

Theorem 2–7 II, along with the fact that a set in Euclidean space is compact if and only if it is both closed and bounded, has some direct implications which are sufficiently important to be given special mention.

THEOREM 2–7 III. *If $S$ is a compact set on which the function $f$ is continuous when $S$ is regarded as its domain, then the image set $f(S)$ is bounded, and hence*

$$\sup_{x \in S} \|f(x)\| < \infty.$$

Next, consider the particular case of a continuous real-valued function with a compact domain. Then the range is a compact set in $R$. As we know, a bounded, nonempty set of real numbers has both a least upper bound and a greatest lower bound. Now, let the greatest lower bound of the range of $f$ be $m$, and let the least upper bound be $M$. Since the range is closed, these bounds must actually be in the range. Hence there is some point $x$ for which $f(x) = m$; likewise, the value $M$ is actually attained by $f$ at some point. We summarize:

THEOREM 2–7 IV. *If $S$ is a compact set on which the real-valued function $f$ is continuous when $S$ is regarded as its domain, then $f$ attains absolute minimum and maximum values $m$, $M$, respectively, at certain points of $S$.*

## UNIFORM CONTINUITY

One of the important applications of the compactness concept is in proving a certain theorem about *uniform* continuity. Let $f$ be a function with domain in $R^k$ and range in $R^l$. Let $S$ be the domain of $f$. We say that $f$ is *uniformly continuous* on $S$ if for each $\epsilon > 0$ there is some corresponding $\delta > 0$ such that $D[f(x_1), f(x_2)] < \epsilon$ whenever $x_1$ and $x_2$ are in $S$ and $D(x_1, x_2) < \delta$. Here $D$ refers to distance between two points in the same Euclidean space.

Readers of this book have doubtless met the concept of uniform continuity before now. But we shall nevertheless emphasize the logical distinction between the two statements "$f$

is continuous at each point of $S$" and "$f$ is uniformly continuous on $S$." The first statement is expressed by saying that if a point $x_0$ in $S$ and a positive number $\epsilon$ are given, there is some positive number $\delta$ (and by implication it may depend on both $x_0$ and $\epsilon$) such that $D[f(x), f(x_0)] < \epsilon$ if $x$ is in $S$ and $D(x, x_0) < \delta$. In the definition of uniform continuity no point of $S$ is specified in advance. Instead, merely some positive $\epsilon$ is given; the corresponding $\delta$ then depends on $\epsilon$, *but not on any particular point of S.*

Let $f$ be continuous at each point $x_0$ of $S$. When $x_0$ and $\epsilon$ are specified, make a definite choice of $\delta$ so that $D[f(x), f(x_0)] < \epsilon$ if $x \in S$ and $D(x, x_0) < \delta$. This defines $\delta$ as a function of $x_0$ and $\epsilon$, say $\delta = F(x_0, \epsilon)$. If this function can be chosen in such a way that its values have a positive lower bound $h(\epsilon)$ when $\epsilon$ is kept fixed and $x_0$ varies over all of $S$, and if this state of affairs prevails for each positive $\epsilon$, then $f$ will be uniformly continuous on $S$, for it will be true that $D[f(x_1), f(x_2)] < \epsilon$ whenever $x_1$ and $x_2$ are in $S$ and $D(x_1, x_2) < h(\epsilon)$.

It is not difficult to illustrate cases in which $f$ is continuous at each point of $S$, but is not uniformly continuous on $S$. The reader should study the following examples.

*Example 5.* $f(x) = \dfrac{1}{x}$, $\quad S = \{x : 0 < x \leq 1\}$.

*Example 6.* $f(x) = x^2$, $\quad S = \{x : 1 \leq x\}$.

THEOREM 2–7 V. *Let $f$ have the compact set $S$ as its domain, and let $f$ be continuous at each point of $S$. Then $f$ is uniformly continuous on $S$.*

*Proof.* With an arbitrary positive $\epsilon$ given, let us assign to each $x$ in $S$ a positive number $r$, written as $r(x)$ to show its dependence on $x$, such that $D[f(y), f(x)] < \epsilon/2$ if $y \in S$ and $D(y, x) < r(x)$. Now let $U(x)$ be the open sphere with center $x$ and radius $\frac{1}{2}r(x)$. As $x$ varies over $S$ the spheres $U(x)$ form an open covering of $S$. By the compactness of $S$, some finite subfamily $U(x_1), \ldots, U(x_n)$ covers $S$. Let $\delta$ be the least of the numbers $\frac{1}{2}r(x_1), \ldots, \frac{1}{2}r(x_n)$. Now consider any pair of points $x, y$ in $S$ such that $D(x, y) < \delta$. Then $x \in U(x_i)$ for a certain index $i$, and

$$D(y, x_i) \leq D(y, x) + D(x, x_i) < \delta + \tfrac{1}{2}r(x_i) \leq r(x_i).$$

It follows that

$$D[f(y), f(x_i)] < \frac{\epsilon}{2} \quad \text{and} \quad D[f(x), f(x_i)] < \frac{\epsilon}{2},$$

so that

$$D[f(y), f(x)] \leq D[f(y), f(x_i)] + D[f(x_i), f(x)] < \epsilon.$$

This proves the uniform continuity, as required.

A critical student may ask at this juncture: "Of what use is it to know that a function is uniformly continuous on some set?" We are not going immediately into applications where this sort of knowledge is needed, but there will be numerous applications later in this book. See, for instance, the proofs of Theorems 9–3 I, 9–5 II, and 9–6 II. The earliest essential application of uniform continuity in calculus is in the proof that the sums approximating the value of a definite integral do actually converge to a limit in the case of the integral of a continuous real function of one real variable. Many later applications are similar in character to this.

## CONTINUITY OF FUNCTIONS OF TWO VARIABLES

There are occasions when we consider functions of two variables (or, also, of three or more variables). This is discussed systematically in Section 3–10 under the heading "continuity in product spaces." For the present we merely mention a few important special cases of continuous functions of two variables. We state the facts only; the relevant proofs can be worked out as illustrations of the ideas developed in Section 3–10.

The sum, $x + y$, of two vectors in $R^k$, can be thought of as the value of a function of two variables; this value is in $R^k$. The function is continuous. The topological expression of this continuity can be put in the following way: If $x_0$ and $y_0$ are given and if $U$ is any neighborhood of $x_0 + y_0$, there are neighborhoods $V$, $W$ of $x_0$, $y_0$, respectively, such that $x + y \in U$ if $x \in V$ and $y \in W$. An alternative expression of the continuity, using sequences, is this: If $x_n \to x$ and $y_n \to y$, then $x_n + y_n \to x + y$.

Likewise, the product $\alpha x$ of a number $\alpha$ and a vector $x$ is the value of a continuous function of two variables. Here one variable is from $R$, one from $R^k$, and the value of the function is in $R^k$.

The inner product $x \cdot y$ and the distance $D(x, y)$ furnish further examples of continuous functions of two variables.

## PROBLEMS

1. Suppose $f : \mathscr{D}_1 \to \mathscr{R}_1$ and $g : \mathscr{D}_2 \to \mathscr{R}_2$ are continuous, and that $\mathscr{R}_1 \subset \mathscr{D}_2$, where $\mathscr{D}_1 \subset R^k$, $\mathscr{D}_2 \subset R^l$, and $\mathscr{R}_2 \subset R^m$. Define $F(x) = g(f(x))$, $x \in \mathscr{D}_2$, so that $F : \mathscr{D}_1 \to R^m$.
   (a) Prove by direct use of the definitions that $F$ is continuous.
   (b) If $S \subset \mathscr{R}_2$, express $F^{-1}(S)$ by use of the symbols $g^{-1}, f^{-1}$.
2. (a) Prove Theorem 2–7 I.
   (b) Define $f : R^k \to R$ by $f(x) = \|x\|$. Show that $f$ is continuous.
3. Define $f$ as follows: $f(x) = x^{-1}$ if $x \geq 1$, $f(x) = x$ if $x \leq 0$. Is $f$ continuous? What is the range of $f$? What is $f^{-1}$? Is $f^{-1}$ continuous?
4. Suppose $\mathscr{D}$ is compact and $f : \mathscr{D} \to \mathscr{R}$ is continuous and one-to-one. Show that $f^{-1}$ is continuous.
5. Suppose $f : R^k \to R^l$ is given. Prove that $f$ is continuous on $R^k$ if and only if $f^{-1}(V)$ is an open set in $R^k$ whenever $V$ is an open set in $R^l$. Deduce from this that $f$ is continuous on $R^k$ if and only if $f^{-1}(T)$ is a closed set in $R^k$ whenever $T$ is a closed set in $R^l$. Deduce further that if $f : R^k \to R$ is continuous, the set $\{x : f(x) \leq c\}$ is closed for each choice of $c$ in $R$.
6. Let $G$ be a family of continuous functions $g, g : R^k \to R$. Suppose that $\sup_{g \in G} |g(x)| < +\infty$ for each $x$ in $R^k$. Prove the existence of a point $x_0$ and positive numbers $N, r$ such that $|g(x)| \leq N$ if $g \in G$ and $\|x - x_0\| \leq r$. [*Suggestion.* Let $A_n = \{x : |g(x)| \leq n \text{ if } g \in G\}$. Observe that $\bigcup_n A_n = R^k$ and prove that $A_n$ is a closed set. For the main result it is sufficient to prove that some $A_n$ contains a closed "spherical ball" $\{x : \|x - x_0\| \leq r\}$ with center $x_0$ and positive radius $r$. If this were not the case, then for each $n$ any closed spherical ball would contain another such ball whose intersection with $A_n$ is void. From this it would be possible to use Theorem 2–5 II and arrive at a contradiction. The reader should work out the complete argument.]
7. Suppose $f : R^k \to R$ is given. Let $S$ be the set of points at which $f$ is discontinuous. Show that $S$ is an $F_\sigma$ set, in the terminology of Section 2–3. [*Suggestion.* For given $\epsilon > 0$ let $S_\epsilon$ be the set of points $x$ such that every neighborhood of $x$ contains points $u, v$ such that $|f(u) - f(v)| \geq \epsilon$. Show that $S_\epsilon$ is closed, and that $S = \bigcup_n S_{1/n}$.]

## 2–8 Connected sets

One of the important theorems about continuous functions in elementary calculus is the "intermediate-value theorem," which asserts that if $f$ is continuous (real-valued, of course) at each point of a closed interval $[a, b]$ and has different values at the two ends of the interval (that is, if $f(a) \neq f(b)$), then every real number between $f(a)$ and $f(b)$ is in the range of $f$. This theorem can be generalized, and the generalization brings us into contact with the concept of a *connected set* of points.

The concept of a connected set occurs in an important way at a number of places in analysis. Connectedness is a vital matter, for example, in the theory of analytic continuation in complex analysis. It is also of crucial importance in the *principle of the maximum* for harmonic and subharmonic functions.

The uses of the idea of connectedness, in the early development of analysis, occurred in situations where open sets were the main concern. The intuitive idea then was that a set is to be regarded as "connected" if each two of its points can be joined by a curve which lies in the set. Another intuitive notion is that a "connected" set should be all in one piece; that is, it should not consist of two or more parts which are in some sense separated from each other. It is this idea which we make precise and use for the modern definition of connectedness.

Let us now consider two sets $S_1$, $S_2$ in the same Euclidean space $R^k$. We shall say that these sets are separated (from each other) if the following three conditions are satisfied:

(a) neither $S_1$ nor $S_2$ is empty;

(b) $S_1 \cap S_2$ is empty;

(c) $S_1' \cap S_2$ and $S_1 \cap S_2'$ are empty.

That is, the sets must be nonempty, they must not have any points in common, and neither may contain an accumulation point of the other.

*Example 1.* The sets (in $R$) $\{x : -1 \leq x < 0\}$ and $\{x : 0 < x \leq 1\}$ are separated, but the sets $\{x : -1 \leq x < 0\}$ and $\{x : 0 \leq x \leq 1\}$ are *not* separated. In the second case 0 is in one set and an accumulation point of the other.

The concept of connectedness will now be defined, using the idea of separated sets. A set $S$ will be called *connected* if it is not possible to express it as $S = A \cup B$, where $A$ and $B$ are separated. This means that, if we *do* break $S$ into two nonempty parts $A$ and $B$ having no points in common, then at least one of these sets must contain an accumulation point of the other.

### CONNECTED SETS IN $R$

It is very easy to describe the structure of connected sets in $R$. The situation for $R^k$ with $k > 1$ is much more complicated. On the real line, however, a set is connected if and only if there are no gaps in it—that is, if and only if the set always contains all the points in between any two points of the set. (We observe, by the way, that an empty set is connected, and so is a set consisting of a single point.) The formal statement of the "no gap" characterization of connected sets in $R$ is as follows:

THEOREM 2–8 I. *Let $S$ be a set in $R$.* (a) *If $S$ is connected, and if $a, b$ are in $S$ with $a < b$, then every point of $[a, b]$ is in $S$.* (b) *If $S$ has the property that every point of $[a, b]$ is in $S$ whenever $a$ and $b$ are in $S$ and $a < b$, then $S$ is connected.*

*Proof of* (a). Suppose $a < x_0 < b$, $a \in S$, $b \in S$, and $x_0 \notin S$. Let $A$ be the set of all points $x$ in $S$ such that $x < x_0$, and let $B$ be the set of all points $x$ in $S$ such that $x_0 < x$. Then, as may be proved by the reader, $S = A \cup B$ and $A$, $B$ are separated, so that $S$ is not connected. We leave this as a problem.

*Proof of* (b). Suppose $S$ is not connected, so that we can write $S = A \cup B$, where $A$ and $B$ are separated. Then there exists a point $a$ in $A$ and a point $b$ in $B$, and we can assume the notation is such that $a < b$. Let $T = [a, b]$, $A_1 = A \cap T$, $B_1 = B \cap T$. It is then easy to verify that $A_1$ and $B_1$ are separated, by virtue of the fact that $A$ and $B$ are separated. On the other hand, all of $T$ is in $S$, by virtue of the assumed property of $S$, as stated in the proposition (b). Hence, $T = A_1 \cup B_1$; we leave the easy verification of this to the reader. Now, let $c$ be the least upper bound of the set $A_1$. There are now two possibilities to consider: $c$ is either in $A_1$ or in $B_1$. In either case, certainly $c \leq b$. If $c \in A_1$, then $c < b$, and $B_1$ contains all points $x$ such that $c < x \leq b$. This, however, implies $c \in B_1'$, which is contradictory, because $A_1$ and $B_1$ are separated. The other possibility is that $c$ is in $B_1$. But then $c \in A_1'$, as a result of the fact that $c$ is the least upper bound of $A_1$, but not in $A_1$. Here again we encounter a contradiction of the fact that $A_1$ and $B_1$ are separated. The upshot of all this is that we must abandon the assumption that $S$ is not connected. The proof of the theorem is now complete.

It follows, as a special case of (b) in Theorem 2–8 I, that the entire real line $R$ is a connected set. As a consequence of this we can show that the only subsets of $R$ which are both open and closed are the empty set and $R$ itself. For, if $S$ is a subset of $R$ which is both open and closed, its complement $S^\sim$ is also both open and closed. If we then assume $S \neq \varnothing$ and $S \neq R$, it follows that $S$ and $S^\sim$ are separated sets with $R = S \cup S^\sim$, in contradiction to the fact that $R$ is connected.

## CONTINUITY AND CONNECTEDNESS

One of the basic facts about connected sets is that *the continuous image of a connected set is connected.* We state this formally as a theorem.

THEOREM 2–8 II. *Let $f$ be a function with domain $\mathscr{D}$ in $R^k$ and range $\mathscr{R}$ in $R^l$. Suppose that $f$ is continuous on $\mathscr{D}$, and that $\mathscr{D}$ is connected. Then $\mathscr{R}$ is connected.*

*Proof.* Suppose the contrary of the assertion of the theorem, so that $\mathscr{R} = A \cup B$, where $A$ and $B$ are separated. Let $A_0 = f^{-1}(A)$, $B_0 = f^{-1}(B)$. It is then evident that $A_0$ and $B_0$ are nonempty sets such that $\mathscr{D} = A_0 \cup B_0$ and $A_0 \cap B_0 = \varnothing$. We shall prove that $A_0 \cap B_0'$ and $A_0' \cap B_0$ are empty sets. This will contradict the fact that $\mathscr{D}$ is connected, and so the theorem will be proved.

Because of the symmetry of the situation it will be enough to prove that $A_0 \cap B_0' = \varnothing$. If this were not true there would exist a point $x_0$ in $A_0 \cap B_0'$. Let $y_0 = f(x_0)$. If $U$ is any neighborhood of $y_0$, there is some neighborhood $V$ of $x_0$ such that $f(V \cap \mathscr{D}) \subset U$ (because $f$ is continuous at $x_0$). Since $x_0 \in B_0'$, there exists a point $x_1$ distinct from $x_0$ and in $V \cap B_0$. Then $f(x_1) \in U \cap B$. We know that $f(x_0) \neq f(x_1)$, because $x_0 \in A_0$ implies $y_0 = f(x_0) \in A$, whereas $f(x_1) \in B$. We have thus shown that $y_0$ is an accumulation point of $B$, whence $A \cap B' \neq \varnothing$, in contradiction to the fact that $A$ and $B$ are separated. This finishes the proof.

The next theorem is the intermediate value theorem.

THEOREM 2–8 III. *Let $f$ be a real-valued function whose domain $\mathscr{D}$ is in $R^k$. Suppose that $\mathscr{D}$ is connected and that $f$ is continuous on $\mathscr{D}$. Then, if $y_1$ and $y_2$ are two distinct values assumed by the function, and if $y_1 < y < y_2$, there is some point $x$ in $\mathscr{D}$ such that $f(x) = y$.*

*Proof.* The range $\mathscr{R}$ is a connected set in $R$, by Theorem 2–8 II. Hence, if $y_1$ and $y_2$ are in $\mathscr{R}$, and $y_1 < y < y_2$, it follows by (a) in Theorem 2–8 I that $y$ is in $\mathscr{R}$, and this is what the theorem asserts.

## A THEOREM ON CONNECTEDNESS AND BOUNDARIES

The following theorem has many uses in analysis.

THEOREM 2–8 IV. *Let $S$ and $T$ be sets in $R^k$ such that $S$ is connected and intersects both $T$ and $T^\sim$ in at least one point each (that is, $S \cap T \neq \varnothing$, $S \cap T^\sim \neq \varnothing$). Then $S$ contains at least one point of the boundary of $T$ (that is, $S \cap \beta(T) \neq \varnothing$).*

We shall give two different proofs of this theorem. Each proof furnishes an occasion for displaying the usefulness of the distributive law of intersections and unions (see Section 1–2). We also have to refer back to some things we learned in Section 2–3 about the boundary of a set.

*First proof of Theorem* 2–8 IV. We begin by asserting that the whole of the space $R^k$ can be expressed as the union of three sets, as follows,

$$R^k = T^o \cup \beta(T) \cup (T^\sim)^o. \tag{1}$$

If a point $x$ is neither an interior point of $T$ nor an interior point of the complementary set $T^\sim$, then every neighborhood of $x$ contains a point of $T^\sim$ and also a point of $T$. This makes $x$ a boundary point of $T$, as we see from Section 2–3. Hence (1) is true. It follows by the distributive law that

$$S \cap R^k = S = [S \cap T^o] \cup [S \cap \beta(T)] \cup [S \cap (T^\sim)^o].$$

Now suppose that $x \in S \cap T$ and $y \in S \cap T^\sim$, but that $S \cap \beta(T) = \varnothing$. Let $A = S \cap T^o$, $B = S \cap (T^\sim)^o$. We see that $S = A \cup B$. Now, since $x$ is in $T$ but not in $\beta(T)$, it belongs to the interior of $T$, and so $x \in A$. Likewise $y \in B$. Clearly $A \cap B = \varnothing$, because $T^o$ and $(T^\sim)^o$ have no points in common. Next, we assert $A \cap B' = \varnothing$. For, if a point is in $A$, it is an interior point of $T$ and therefore a certain neighborhood of it lies wholly in $T$. This neighborhood cannot contain a point of $(T^\sim)^o$, and hence certainly not a point of $B$. Therefore $A \cap B' = \varnothing$. Likewise, $A' \cap B = \varnothing$. We have now proved that $A$ and $B$ are separated sets. Then $S = A \cup B$ contradicts the fact that $S$ is connected. We therefore must conclude that $S \cap \beta(T) \neq \varnothing$.

*Second proof of Theorem* 2–8 IV. This time we start from the defining formula $\beta(T) = \bar{T} \cap \overline{(T^\sim)}$ given in Section 2–3. Since $R^k = T \cup T^\sim$, we see that

$$\beta(T) = \{T \cap [\bar{T} \cap \overline{(T^\sim)}]\} \cup \{T^\sim \cap [\bar{T} \cap \overline{(T^\sim)}]\}.$$

Now, $T^{\sim} \cap [\bar{T} \cap \overline{(T^{\sim})}] = T^{\sim} \cap \bar{T} = T^{\sim} \cap (T \cup T') = (T^{\sim} \cap T) \cup (T^{\sim} \cap T') = T^{\sim} \cap T'$. This argument applies to any set $T$; if we replace $T$ by $T^{\sim}$ in the last result, we see that

$$T \cap [\overline{(T^{\sim})} \cap \bar{T}] = T \cap (T^{\sim})'.$$

From all of this we have the formula

$$\beta(T) = [T \cap (T^{\sim})'] \cup [T^{\sim} \cap T']. \tag{2}$$

Now let $A = S \cap T$, $B = S \cap T^{\sim}$, so that $S = A \cup B$ and $A \cap B = \varnothing$. By hypothesis $A \neq \varnothing$, $B \neq \varnothing$. Therefore, since $S$ is connected, $A$ and $B$ are not separated, and therefore

$$(A \cap B') \cup (A' \cap B) \neq \varnothing. \tag{3}$$

Now, since $A \subset T$, it follows that $A' \subset T'$. Likewise, $B' \subset (T^{\sim})'$. Thus

$$A' \cap B \subset T' \cap (S \cap T^{\sim}) = S \cap [T' \cap T^{\sim}],$$

and

$$A \cap B' \subset (S \cap T) \cap (T^{\sim})' = S \cap [T \cap (T^{\sim})'].$$

It now follows from (3) and the distributive law that

$$S \cap \{[T' \cap T^{\sim}] \cup [T \cap (T^{\sim})']\} \neq \varnothing.$$

In view of (2) this is the same as $S \cap \beta(T) \neq \varnothing$, so the proof is complete.

## AN APPLICATION TO SUBHARMONIC FUNCTIONS

We shall discuss an application of Theorem 2–8 IV. In doing so we are digressing far from the main line of development of this chapter.

For simplicity let us deal with $R^2$. What we have to say about subharmonic functions can easily be extended, with $R^k$ $(k > 2)$ in place of $R^2$. Let $f$ be a real-valued function whose domain is an open set $\mathscr{D}$ in $R^2$. Let $f$ be continuous on $\mathscr{D}$, and suppose that $f$ has the following property: to each point $x_0$ of $\mathscr{D}$ corresponds some positive number $\delta$ such that if $C$ is a circle with center $x_0$ and radius not exceeding $\delta$, $C$ and its interior lying in $\mathscr{D}$, then $f(x_0)$ does not exceed the average value of $f$ on $C$. Then $f$ is said to be *subharmonic* in $\mathscr{D}$. By the average value of $f$ on $C$ is meant the usual mean-value, calculated by an integral with respect to arc-length or angle:

$$\frac{1}{2\pi} \int_0^{2\pi} f(x_0 + re^{i\theta})\, d\theta. \tag{4}$$

In (4) we think of $x_0$ as a complex number, and $C$ is represented parametrically by $x = x_0 + re^{i\theta}$ (see Figure 15).

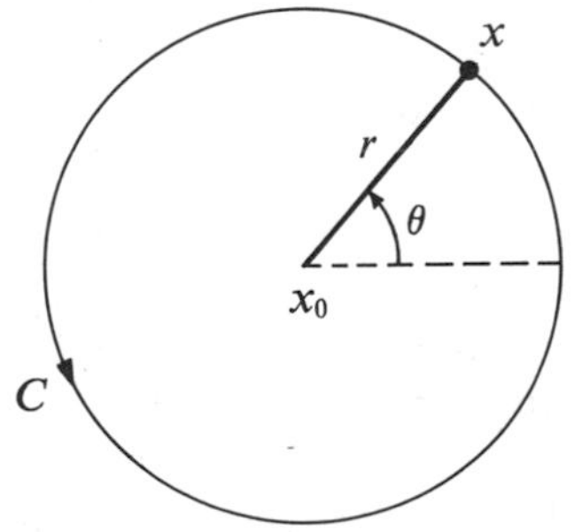


FIGURE 15

The function $f$ would be called *harmonic* in $\mathscr{D}$ if it were continuous, with continuous second partial derivatives satisfying

$$\frac{\partial^2 f}{\partial \xi_1^2} + \frac{\partial^2 f}{\partial \xi_2^2} = 0 \qquad [x = (\xi_1, \xi_2)]$$

at each point of $\mathscr{D}$. It is an important fact (which we shall not prove here) that a continuous function is harmonic if and only if it has the property that the mean-value integral in (4) is *equal* to $f(x_0)$ for each $x_0$ in $\mathscr{D}$ (with the same conditions on $C$ as before). In particular, then, a harmonic function is subharmonic.

We shall prove the following theorem:

*If $\mathscr{D}$ is a connected open set in $R^2$, and if $f$ is a real-valued continuous function with domain $\mathscr{D}$ which is subharmonic in $\mathscr{D}$, then $f$ cannot attain an absolute maximum value at any point of $\mathscr{D}$ except in one special case. This exceptional case is that in which $f$ has the same value at every point of $\mathscr{D}$.*

*Proof.* Let us rule out the exceptional case, and suppose there is some point $x_0$ in $\mathscr{D}$ such that $f(x) \leq f(x_0)$ for each $x$ in $\mathscr{D}$. By deducing a contradiction from this we shall prove the theorem. Let $T$ be the set of points $x$ in $\mathscr{D}$ at which $f(x) = f(x_0)$. Then $x_0 \in T$, but, since $f$ does not have the same value at all points of $\mathscr{D}$, there must also be a point of $\mathscr{D}$ in $T^{\sim}$. Then, since $\mathscr{D}$ is connected, Theorem 2–8 IV shows that there is a point $x_1$ of $\mathscr{D}$ in $\beta(T)$. This point $x_1$ must actually be in $T$ [that is, it must be that $f(x_1) = f(x_0)$], as a result of the fact that $f$ is continuous. If this were not true, we should have $f(x_1) < f(x_0)$, and continuity would entail the existence of a neighborhood of $x_1$ entirely in $\mathscr{D} \cap T^{\sim}$. Now, from $x_1 \in \beta(T)$ we can also conclude that there are points of $T^{\sim}$ inside any circle with center at $x_1$. Hence there exists a circle $C$ (with center $x_1$) which with its interior lies in $\mathscr{D}$, such that $f(x_1)$ does not exceed the average value of $f$ on $C$, and such that on $C$ there is a point $x_2$ of $T^{\sim}$. However, $f(x) \leq f(x_0)$ at each point $x$ on $C$, and $f(x_2) < f(x_0)$. Continuity of $f$ at $x_2$ assures us that there is an entire arc of $C$ on which the values of $f$ are strictly less than $f(x_0)$. Consequently, by familiar arguments about integrals, the average value of $f$ on $C$ must be less than $f(x_0)$. It follows that $f(x_1) < f(x_0)$. This contradicts the fact that $x_1$ is in $T$, and we are through.

## ARCWISE CONNECTEDNESS

By an *arc* in $R^k$ we mean a set in $R^k$ which is the homeomorphic image (see Section 2–7) of a compact interval $[a, b]$ in $R$. The images of the ends of the interval are called the ends of the arc.

In Section 2–2 we defined a finite closed line segment. If $x_1$ and $x_2$ are distinct points, and $f(t) = (1 - t)x_1 + tx_2$, $f$ maps $[0, 1]$ homeomorphically onto a line segment with ends $x_1, x_2$; therefore this line segment is an arc. See Problem 2.

By a *polygonal arc* in $R^k$ we mean a set consisting of the union of a finite number of finite closed line segments, say $L_1, \ldots, L_n$, such that $L_i$ and $L_{i+1}$ intersect in a single point which is an endpoint of each of them $(1 \leq i \leq n - 1)$, while $L_i \cap L_j = \varnothing$ if $i$ and $j$ differ by 2 or more. That is, $L_1, L_2, \ldots, L_n$ are joined successively, end-to-end, so as to form a "broken line" which does not intersect itself. See Figure 16. A polygonal arc is easily shown to be an arc in the sense already defined.

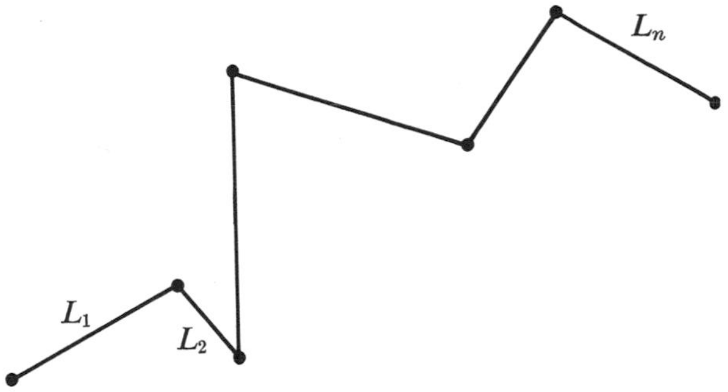


FIGURE 16

We come now to a theorem which shows that, if an open set is connected, it conforms to the original intuitive idea of a connected set.

THEOREM 2–8 V. *Let S be an open and connected set in $R^k$. Then, given any two distinct points x, y in S, there exists a polygonal arc lying in S and having x and y as its endpoints.*

*Proof.* The case $k = 1$ is covered by Theorem 2–8 I. Hence we can assume $k \geq 2$. Let $A$ consist of $x$ and all points $a$ in $S$ such that there exists a polygonal arc lying in $S$ with $x$ and $a$ as its end-points. We have to prove that $y$ is in $A$. We shall suppose the contrary and deduce a contradiction. Let $B = S - A$. Evidently $A \neq \varnothing$, $B \neq \varnothing$, $S = A \cup B$, $A \cap B = \varnothing$. The set $A$ is open. For suppose $a \in A$, and let $L_0$ denote the final segment (terminating at $a$) of a polygonal arc $L$ in $S$ from $x$ to $a$. Let $\delta$ be a positive number at least as small as the least of the perpendicular distances from $a$ to the segments (other than $L_0$) of $L$. Since $S$ is open there exists a spherical neighborhood with center at $a$, of radius less than $\delta$ and lying entirely in $S$ (see Figure 17). It is easily seen that all points of this spherical neighborhood are in $A$. A point on $L_0$ in the neighborhood is joined to $x$ by a polygonal arc in $S$ if we simply curtail $L_0$ appropriately; and a point in the neighborhood *not* on $L_0$ is joined to $x$ by a polygonal arc in $S$ if we simply use the polygonal arc from $x$ to $a$ and extend it by a segment of radius from $a$ to the point in question. See Figure 18. The fact that $A$ is open now insures that $A \cap B' = \varnothing$.

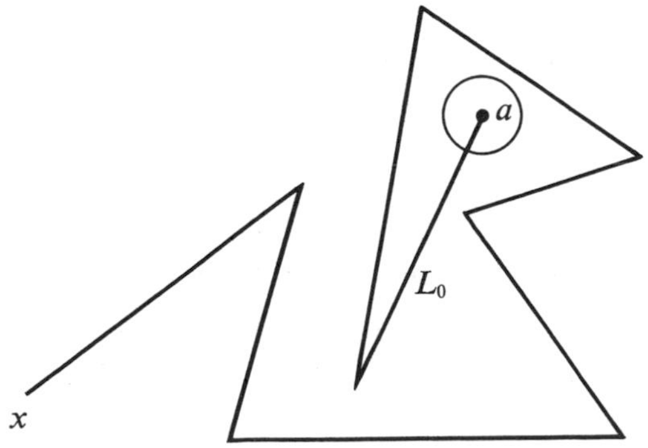


FIGURE 17

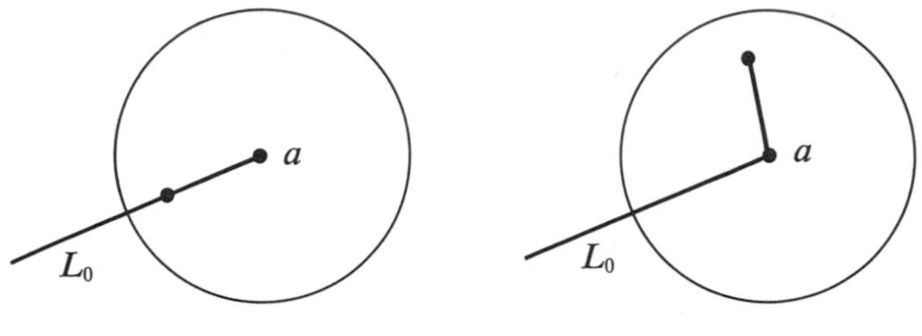


FIGURE 18

If we now prove that $A' \cap B = \varnothing$, $S$ will be expressed as the union of the separated sets $A$, $B$, contrary to the fact that $S$ is connected, and so we shall have completed our proof. Suppose then that $A' \cap B \neq \varnothing$, say $z \in A' \cap B$. Then $z \in S$, and there exists a spherical neighborhood of $z$ lying entirely in $S$. This neighborhood must contain a point $w$ in $A$, because $z \in A'$. There is then a polygonal arc $L$ in $S$ joining $x$ to $w$. Let $M$ be the line segment from $w$ to $z$ (ends included). Now $z$ is not on $L$, because $L \subset A$ and $z \in B$. The set $L \cap M$ is compact, and hence there is a point $y$ of $L \cap M$ at minimum distance from $z$. We then obtain a polygonal arc joining $x$ to $z$ by proceeding from $x$ along $L$ until we come to $y$, and then following the straight line segment from $y$ to $z$. But this means that $z \in A$, which is a contradiction. Hence we must conclude that $A' \cap B = \varnothing$, and the proof is complete.

A set $S$ is called *arcwise connected* if to each pair of distinct points in $S$ corresponds at least one arc lying in $S$ and having the two given points as its endpoints. From Theorem 2–8 V we see that a connected open set is arcwise connected. For the converse we do not need the set to be open, as we shall see presently. First we need the following result.

LEMMA 2–8 VI. *Suppose $S$ is a set with the property that, if $x$ and $y$ are in $S$, there exists a connected subset of $S$ which contains both $x$ and $y$. Then $S$ is connected.*

*Proof.* If we suppose $S$ is not connected, we can write $S = A \cup B$, where $A$ and $B$ are separated. Choose $x$ in $A$ and $y$ in $B$, and let $T$ be a connected subset of $S$ such that $x$ and $y$ are in $T$. Let $A_1 = A \cap T$, $B_1 = B \cap T$. Then, as is easily verified, $A_1$ and $B_1$ are separated. But $T = A_1 \cup B_1$, and this is a contradiction, since $T$ is connected. Thus the proof is complete.

It is now easy to prove the next theorem.

THEOREM 2–8 VII. *An arcwise connected set is connected.*

*Proof.* An arc is a connected set, by Theorem 2–8 II, for it is the homeomorphic image of a finite closed interval, which we know to be connected. The conclusion of our theorem now follows at once from Lemma 2–8 VI.

The space $R^k$ is evidently arcwise connected, for any two points in $R^k$ can be joined by a line segment, which is an arc. Hence, $R^k$ is connected.

### COMPONENTS OF A SET

If $S$ is a nonempty set in $R^k$, a subset $E$ of $S$ is called a *component* of $S$ if $E$ is connected and if $E$ is not a proper subset of a connected subset of $S$; $E$ is then maximal with respect to the property of being a connected subset of $S$. For example, if $S$ is the set in $R$ defined as the union of the open intervals $E_n = \left(\frac{1}{n+1}, \frac{1}{n}\right)$, $n = 1, 2, \ldots$ and the set $E_0$ consisting of the single point 0, then $E_0, E_1, E_2, \ldots$ are the components of $S$.

### PROBLEMS

1. (a) In the proof of Theorem 2–8 I(a) verify in detail that $A$ and $B$ are separated.
(b) In the proof of Theorem 2–8 I(b) verify in detail that $A_1$ and $B_1$ are separated.
Deduce that $T = A_1 \cup B_1$ by formal calculations, starting from the fact that $T \subset S$ and therefore $T = T \cap S$.

2. Let $x_0$ and $x_1$ be distinct points in $R^k$. The mapping $t \to (1 - t)x_1 + tx_2$, $0 \leq t \leq 1$, is a homeomorphism. Let $x = f(t) = (1 - t)x_1 + tx_2$, $0 \leq t \leq 1$. The continuity of $f$ is evident, and the mapping is one-to-one. Obtain a formula expressing explicitly the relation $t = f^{-1}(x)$, and use it to prove that $f^{-1}$ is continuous. [*Suggestion.* Compute $x \cdot x_1$ and $x \cdot x_2$ and notice that $(x_2 - x_1) \cdot x_1$ and $(x_2 - x_1) \cdot x_2$ are not both 0. (Why not?).]

3. Is it true that if $S_1$ and $S_2$ are connected, then $S_1 \cap S_2$ is connected?

4. Prove the following proposition: A set $S$ is connected if and only if there exists no continuous function $f: S \to R$ ($R$ the real line) such that $f(S)$ consists of exactly two points.

5. Prove that a connected set with more than one point is uncountably infinite.

6. Suppose that $S$ is a connected set. Prove that $\bar{S}$ is connected. More generally, prove that $T$ is connected if $S \subset T \subset \bar{S}$.

7. Prove that a component of a closed set is a closed set. Use Problem 6.

8. Let $\{S_\alpha\}$ be a family of connected sets such that $\bigcap_\alpha S_\alpha \neq \varnothing$. Prove that $\bigcup_\alpha S_\alpha$ is connected.

9. Let $\{S_\alpha\}$ be a family of connected sets, and let $T$ be a connected set. Suppose that $S_\alpha \cap T \neq \varnothing$ for each $\alpha$. Prove that $T \cup \bigcup_\alpha S_\alpha$ is connected.

## 2–9 Relative topologies

As a suitable prelude to this section the student should re-read the opening paragraphs of Section 2–3. We wish to explain now how the topology of $R^k$ induces a topology for any specified subset of $R^k$ when this subset is regarded as being a space. This sort of thing is useful in connection with the study of functions. If $f$ is a function with domain $\mathscr{D}$ in $R^k$ and range $\mathscr{R}$ in $R^l$, the continuity properties of $f$ may be examined without any regard whatsoever for the points of $R^k - \mathscr{D}$ and $R^l - \mathscr{R}$. Hence it is natural to develop suitable definitions and terminology for regarding each of the sets $\mathscr{D}$, $\mathscr{R}$ as a space by itself.

Suppose, then, that $H$ is an arbitrary nonempty subset of $R^k$. A subset $S$ of $H$ will be called *open relative to H*, or *open in H*, if there exists an open set $U$ in $R^k$ such that $S = U \cap H$. The *relative topology* of $H$ as a subset of $R^k$ (or, as we sometimes say, the topology of $H$ *induced by* the topology of $R^k$) is defined as the family of all the subsets of $H$ which are open relative to $H$.

There is a natural way in which we may regard $R^n$ as a subset of $R^k$ if $1 \leq n < k$. The usual topology of $R^n$ is then the relative topology of $R^n$ as a subset of $R^k$. We leave it to the reader to verify this. For simplicity think at first of $n = 1$ and $k = 2$ or 3.

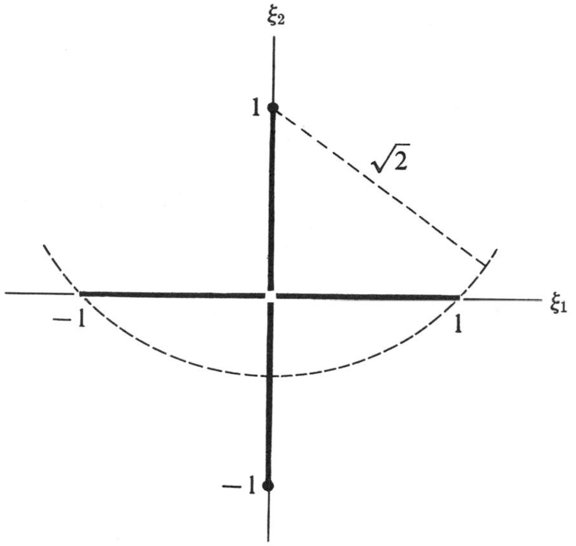


FIGURE 19

If $x_0 \in H$ and if $S(x_0; r)$ is the open sphere in $R^k$ with center $x_0$ and radius $r$, the intersection $S(x_0; r) \cap H$ will be called the open sphere in $H$ with center $x_0$ and radius $r$. This intersection may be very different in appearance from an open sphere in $R^k$, but just as with $S(x_0; r)$, the points of $S(x_0; r) \cap H$ can be characterized by an inequality:

$$S(x_0; r) \cap H = \{x : x \in H \quad \text{and} \quad D(x, x_0) < r\}.$$

This set may be finite; it may even turn out to be the set $\{x_0\}$ consisting of the single point $x_0$.

*Example 1.* With $R^2$ as the basic space let $H$ be the set of all points $x = (\xi_1, \xi_2)$ such that either $\xi_1 = 0$ and $0 < |\xi_2| \leq 1$ or $\xi_2 = 0$ and $0 < |\xi_1| < 1$ (see Figure 19). In this case the open sphere in $H$ with center (0, 1) and radius $\sqrt{2}$ contains all points of $H$ except the points for which $\xi_1 = 0$ and $-1 \leq \xi_2 \leq 1 - \sqrt{2}$. Each of the following subsets of $H$ is open:

$$\{x : \xi_2 = 0, 0 < \xi_1 < 1\}, \qquad \{x : \xi_2 = 0, -1 < \xi_1 < 0\},$$
$$\{x : \xi_1 = 0, 0 < \xi_2 \leq 1\}, \qquad \{x : \xi_1 = 0, -1 \leq \xi_2 < 0\}.$$

*Example 2.* With $R^2$ as the basic space, let

$$H = \{(\xi_1, \xi_2) : 0 < \xi_1 \leq 1, 0 \leq \xi_2 < 1, \xi_1^2 + \xi_2^2 \geq 1\}.$$

In this case the open sphere in $H$ with center (1, 0) and radius $\sqrt{2}$ is $H$ itself. See Figure 20.

Proceeding now with the general discussion, we observe that the following things are true about the relative topology of a set $H$:

The set $H$ itself is open relative to $H$.

The set $\varnothing$ is open relative to $H$.

The union of any number of relatively open sets is relatively open.

The intersection of any finite number of relatively open sets is relatively open.

To prove the last assertion, for instance, let the relatively open sets be $S_i = U_i \cap H$, $i = 1, \ldots, n$, where $U_i$ is an open set in $R^k$. Then $S_1 \cap \cdots \cap S_n = U \cap H$, where $U$ is an open set in $R^k$, because $U = U_1 \cap \cdots \cap U_n$.

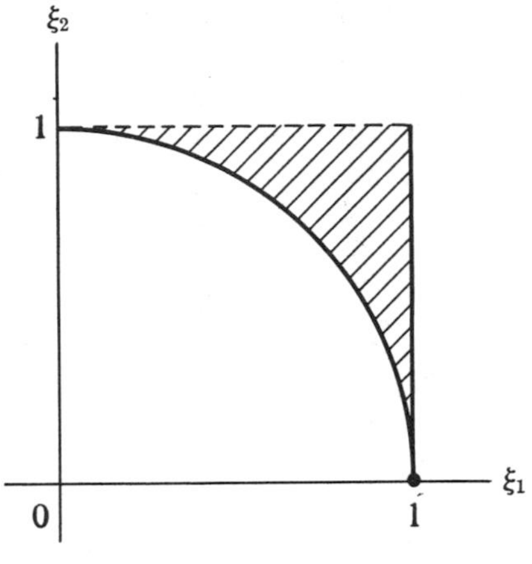


FIGURE 20

If $S \subset H$, the set $H - S$ is called the complement of $S$ relative to $H$. We call $S$ *closed in* $H$, or *closed relative to* $H$ if $H - S$ is open in $H$. Observe that this parallels exactly the definition of a closed set in $R^k$: a set $S$ in $R^k$ is called closed if $R^k - S$ is open. The same principle of parallelism is observed in making other definitions associated with the relative topology of $H$. If $S \subset H$ and $y \in H$, we call $y$ an accumulation point of $S$ in the relative topology if every relatively open subset of $H$ which contains $y$ also contains at least one point $x$ of $S$ such that $x \neq y$. The set of all such points is called the derived set of $S$ relative to $H$, and denoted by $(S')_{\text{rel}}$. The closure of $S$ relative to $H$, denoted by $(\bar{S})_{\text{rel}}$, is defined as

$$(\bar{S})_{\text{rel}} = S \cup (S')_{\text{rel}}.$$

We can also define the boundary of $S$ and the interior of $S$, relative to $H$. In all these things we proceed from $H$ and the relatively open subsets of $H$ just as we did in Section 2–3 with $R^k$ and the open subsets of $R^k$.

We note the following simple theorem:

THEOREM 2–9 I. *Suppose $S \subset H$ and let $S$ be such that to each $x \in S$ corresponds some relatively open set $V(x)$ such that $x \in V(x)$ and $V(x) \subset S$. Then $S$ is open relative to $H$.*

*Proof.* It is evident that the union of all the sets $V(x)$, as $x$ varies over $S$, is exactly $S$ (for it is contained in $S$ and contains each point of $S$). But then $S$, being a union of relatively open sets, is relatively open.

Theorem 2–3 III remains true in the context of relative topologies. That is, if $S \subset H$, $S$ is closed in $H$ if and only if $(S')_{\text{rel}} \subset S$. We leave the proof to the student.

A set which is closed in $H$ need not be closed in $R^k$. For instance, referring to Example 1 and Figure 19, we can see that the set $S = \{x : \xi_1 = 0, 0 < \xi_2 \leq 1\}$ is closed in $H$ but not closed in $R^2$. It fails to be closed in $R^2$ because the point $(0, 0)$ of $R^2$ is in $S'$ but not in $S$. But, since $(0, 0)$ is not in $H$, $(0, 0)$ is not in $(S')_{\text{rel}}$.

The foregoing remark brings us to an interesting observation. The set $S$ just mentioned is both open and closed in $H$, yet $S \neq \varnothing$ and $S \neq H$. Hence $S$ and $H - S$ are nonempty sets each of which is both open and closed in $H$. This is a state of affairs which cannot exist in the topology of $R^k$. As we remarked in Section 2–8, $R^k$ is connected. If $A$ and $B$ were nonempty sets such that $B = R^k - A$, with $A$ and $B$ each both open and closed, these sets would be separated, and there would be a contradiction of the fact that $R^k$ is connected. The fact that we can have $S$ and $H - S$ nonempty and both sets both open and closed relative to $H$ is traceable to the fact that the set $H$ itself is not a connected subset of $R^k$.

### CONTINUITY AND RELATIVE TOPOLOGY

Let $f$ be a function with domain $\mathscr{D}$ in $R^k$ and range $\mathscr{R}$ in $R^l$. The definition of continuity can be expressed very conveniently by using the relative topologies of $\mathscr{D}$ and $\mathscr{R}$. If $x \in \mathscr{D}$, a neighborhood of $x$ in the relative topology, which we shall call simply a relative neighborhood of $x$, is the intersection of $\mathscr{D}$ and an open set (of $R^k$) which contains $x$. Referring back to Section 2–7, we see that $f$ is continuous at a point $x_0 \in \mathscr{D}$ if and only if to each relative neighborhood $U$ of $f(x_0)$ (in $\mathscr{R}$) corresponds a relative neighborhood $V$ of $x_0$ such that $f(V) \subset U$. Or, to put the matter another way, $f$ is continuous at $x_0$ if and only if, for each relative neighborhood $U$ of $f(x_0)$, the inverse image $f^{-1}(U)$ contains a relative neighborhood of $x_0$. From this formulation of continuity it is easy to prove the following theorem.

THEOREM 2–9 II. *The function $f$ is continuous at each point of its domain $\mathscr{D}$ if and only if $f^{-1}(S)$ is open in $\mathscr{D}$ whenever $S$ is open in $\mathscr{R}$.*

*Proof.* Suppose $f^{-1}(S)$ is open in $\mathscr{D}$ whenever $S$ is open in $\mathscr{R}$. Suppose $x_0 \in \mathscr{D}$, and let $U$ be a relative neighborhood of $f(x_0)$. Then $f^{-1}(U)$ is open in $\mathscr{D}$. Since $x_0 \in f^{-1}(U)$, $f^{-1}(U)$ is a relative neighborhood of $x_0$; this shows that $f$ is continuous at $x_0$.

For the converse, suppose $f$ is continuous at each point of $\mathscr{D}$, and suppose $S$ is open in $\mathscr{R}$. We can assume $S \neq \varnothing$, because $f^{-1}(\varnothing) = \varnothing$. Suppose $x \in f^{-1}(S)$. Then $S$ is a relative neighborhood of $f(x)$, and hence $f^{-1}(S)$ must contain a relative neighborhood of $x$. This implies that $f^{-1}(S)$ is open in $\mathscr{D}$, by Theorem 2–9 I.

### PROBLEMS

1. Prove: Two subsets $A$ and $B$ of $H$, where $H \subset R^k$, are separated in the sense of the topology of $R^k$ if and only if they are separated in the sense of the relative topology of $H$. Therefore a subset $S$ of $H$ is connected in the sense of the topology of $R^k$ if and only if it is connected in the sense of the relative topology of $H$.
2. Prove: Two disjoint nonempty subsets $A$, $B$ of $R^k$ are separated if and only if each one is both open and closed in the relative topology of $A \cup B$.
3. Prove that $(S')_{\text{rel}} = S' \cap H$ and $(\bar{S})_{\text{rel}} = \bar{S} \cap H$.
4. Prove that $S \subset H$ and $H - S = U \cap H$ imply $S = H \cap U^{\sim}$, and hence that $S$ is closed in $H$ if and only if it is the intersection of $H$ and a closed subset of $R^k$.
5. Prove: If $H$ is closed in $R^k$ and $S$ is closed in $H$, then $S$ is closed in $R^k$. If $S \subset H$ and $S$ is closed in $R^k$, is $S$ closed in $H$?
6. If $f$ has domain $\mathscr{D}$ and range $\mathscr{R}$, and $S \subset \mathscr{R}$, show that $f^{-1}(\mathscr{R} - S) = \mathscr{D} - f^{-1}(S)$. Hence prove that $f$ is continuous on $\mathscr{D}$ if and only if $f^{-1}(T)$ is closed in $\mathscr{D}$ whenever $T$ is closed in $\mathscr{R}$.

## 2–10 Cantor's ternary set

The point set which is commonly known as Cantor's ternary set was exhibited by G. Cantor as an illustration of certain curious things which can occur with point sets on the real line. This set is so useful, as an illustrative example for many purposes, that we present it here.

The Cantor set, which we shall denote by $S_C[0, 1]$, is the part of $[0, 1]$ which is left after the removal of a certain specified countable collection of open intervals, which we shall now describe. We first remove the open interval $E_{11} = (1/3, 2/3)$, which is the interior of the middle one of three subintervals into which $[0, 1]$ is divided by the points $1/3$, $2/3$. Next, we divide each of the two remaining intervals, $[0, 1/3]$ and $[2/3, 1]$, into three equal parts and remove the interiors of the middle third in each case. The removed intervals are $E_{21} = (1/3^2, 2/3^2)$ and $E_{22} = (7/3^2, 8/3^2)$. There are now four intervals remaining. We divide each of these into three equal parts and remove the open middle third in each case. Denote these removed parts by $E_{31}, E_{32}, E_{33}, E_{34}$. Note that $E_{31} = (1/3^3, 2/3^3)$. We continue in this way. The numbers of intervals removed at successive stages are $2^0, 2^1, 2^2, \ldots,$ the $2^{n-1}$ intervals removed at the $n$th stage being $E_{ni}$ $(i = 1, 2, \ldots, 2^{n-1})$, with $E_{n1} = (1/3^n, 2/3^n)$. It is understood that the numbering $E_{n1}, E_{n2}, \ldots$ is in order from left to right on the line. The Cantor set is

$$S_C[0, 1] = [0, 1] - \bigcup_{n=1}^{\infty} E_n,$$

where

$$E_n = \bigcup_{i=1}^{2^{n-1}} E_{ni}.$$

For the present we make four observations about the Cantor set. (a) It is a closed set. (b) It contains no interior points. (c) Every point of the set is an accumulation point of the set. (d) The set is uncountably infinite. We leave it for the reader to verify the first three assertions. The following observation is helpful in connection with (b) and (c): If $x \in S_C[0, 1]$, then for no $N \geq 2$ is $x$ in $\bigcup_{n=1}^{N-1} E_n$. Therefore $x$ is in one of the closed intervals which is to be divided into thirds, and whose open middle third is $E_{Ni}$, for some $i$. This is true for every $N \geq 2$. The proof of (d) will be given in succeeding paragraphs.

To prove that $S_C[0, 1]$ is uncountably infinite, we prove first that each point $x$ of the Cantor set can be represented in exactly one way by a series of the form

$$x = \sum_{n=1}^{\infty} \frac{a_n}{3^n}, \tag{1}$$

where each $a_n$ is either 0 or 2, and that every number thus represented is in $S_C[0, 1]$.

There cannot be more than one such representation, for if

$$\sum_{n=1}^{\infty} \frac{a_n}{3^n} = \sum_{n=1}^{\infty} \frac{b_n}{3^n}. \tag{2}$$

where each $b_n$ also is either 0 or 2, we can show that $a_n = b_n$ for every $n$. In fact, if we suppose (2), where $a_n \neq b_n$ for some $n$, let $N$ be the smallest integer $n$ such that $a_n \neq b_n$. Then $|a_N - b_N| = 2$ and $|a_n - b_n| \leq 2$ for every $n$, so that we get the contradiction

$$0 = \left| \sum_{n=N}^{\infty} \frac{a_n - b_n}{3^n} \right| \geq \frac{1}{3^N}\left\{|a_N - b_N| - \sum_{n=N+1}^{\infty} \frac{|a_n - b_n|}{3^{n-N}}\right\}$$

$$\geq \frac{1}{3^N}\left\{2 - \sum_{n=1}^{\infty} \frac{2}{3^n}\right\} = \frac{1}{3^N}.$$

Now, just as with decimal representations, every $x$ in [0, 1] has a representation of the form (1), where each $a_n$ is either 0, 1, or 2; and each number thus represented is in [0, 1]. Representation in this general case is not always unique, however. For instance, $\frac{1}{3}$ has two representations, because

$$\frac{1}{3} = \sum_{n=2}^{\infty} \frac{2}{3^n}.$$

If we use the ternary system of place-values, we can symbolize the number $\sum_{n=1}^{\infty} \frac{a_n}{3^n}$ by $0.a_1a_2a_3 \ldots$. In this symbolism $1 = 0.222 \ldots$. Let us list the endpoints of some of the intervals $E_{ni}$ in this notation.

| | | | | |
|---|---|---|---|---|
| $E_{11}$ : 0.1 | or 0.022 . . . | and | 0.122 . . . | or 0.2 |
| $E_{21}$ : 0.01 | or 0.0022 . . . | and | 0.0122 . . . | or 0.02 |
| $E_{22}$ : 0.21 | or 0.2022 . . . | and | 0.2122 . . . | or 0.22 |
| $E_{31}$ : 0.001 | or 0.00022 . . . | and | 0.00122 . . . | or 0.002 |
| $E_{32}$ : 0.021 | or 0.02022 . . . | and | 0.02122 . . . | or 0.022 |
| $E_{33}$ : 0.201 | or 0.20022 . . . | and | 0.20122 . . . | or 0.202 |
| $E_{34}$ : 0.221 | or 0.22022 . . . | and | 0.22122 . . . | or 0.222 |
| . . . . | | | . . . . | |

After a bit of examination of the situation, the student can satisfy himself that a number symbolized by $0.a_1a_2 \ldots$ is in $E_{ni}$ for some $i$ if and only if $a_m$ is 0 or 2 if $m < n$, $a_n = 1$, with no restriction on $a_m$ for $m > n$ except that these $a_m$'s (all 0, 1, or 2) are neither all 0's nor all 2's. The claim made about the one-to-one correspondence between elements of $S_C[0, 1]$ and symbols of the form $0.a_1a_2 \ldots$ with each $a_n$ either 0 or 2 can now be justified easily. We leave details to the reader.

We can now show that $S_C[0, 1]$ is uncountably infinite. If we suppose the contrary and let $x_1, x_2, \ldots$ be an enumeration of $S_C[0, 1]$, each $x_i$ will have a unique canonical symbolization $x_i = 0.a_{1i}a_{2i}a_{3i} \ldots$. Let us select a sequence $\{b_n\}$ as follows: Each $b_n$ is 0 or 2, but $b_n \neq a_{nn}$. Then the number $x$ symbolized by $0.b_1b_2 \ldots$ is in $S_C[0, 1]$, but $x \neq x_i$ for each $i$. But this contradicts our assumption, and so the proof is complete.

## SUGGESTED READING FOR CHAPTER 2

BIRKHOFF and MACLANE [1], Chapter 7.
CARATHEODORY [1], Chapter 1.
FRÉCHET [1], pp. 66–72 and 190–195 for the concept of compactness.
GOFFMAN [1], Chapter 6, for the Cantor ternary set.
GRAVES [1], Chapter 3.
HALMOS [2], Chapter 1.
HILDEBRANDT [2], for the Borel theorem.
HOBSON [1], Vol. 1. Chapter 2 for general information on point sets and topology; p. 123 for Cantor's ternary set.
NATANSON [1], Vol. 1. Chapter 2.
NEWMAN [1], Chapters 1–4.
PAIGE and SWIFT [1], Chapters 1–4.
TAYLOR [2], Sections 1.1 and 1.2.

CHAPTER THREE

# Abstract Spaces

## 3–0 Introduction

Modern mathematics, roughly since 1900, has increasingly emphasized postulational method and a trend toward an abstract point of view. In algebra there has been the evolution of the systematic theories of groups, rings, fields, vector spaces, lattices, and so on—all stemming from postulational definitions of these various sorts of algebraic systems. These *abstract* conceptions of groups and other systems sprang from extensive familiarity with particular concrete examples of such systems.

In analysis there has likewise been a development of abstraction. We may discern two threads in this development. On one hand there is the incorporation into analysis of the abstract concepts of general topology, as these concepts have evolved from the earlier concrete studies of point sets in connection with the theory of limits and continuity and the more refined and intricate studies of real functions of a real variable. The concept of a topology for a space, liberated from its exclusive association with point sets on the real line or in Euclidean space of higher dimension, has now become an indispensable concept for the study of families of functions. On the other hand, the ideas of abstract algebra have permeated analysis; we find ourselves examining families of functions to see whether they can be regarded as groups or as vector spaces or rings. In the study of modern theories of integration, for instance, vector spaces of functions play an essential role.

Abstraction serves in at least two important ways in modern analysis. It permits us to simplify the exposition of important theories by stripping them of extraneous matter which may be present if we study these theories solely through the medium of particular concrete situations. Thus, for instance, many general theorems about continuous functions are best understood if they are presented in the context of general topology. It was for this reason that we discussed continuous functions as we did in Section 2–7, mainly without reference to the underlying Euclidean spaces, or to their dimensionality. Abstraction within appropriate bounds simplifies and clarifies. There must of course be suitable preparation for abstraction, by consideration of particular cases which exemplify the general and the abstract. After the discussion in Chapter 2 we shall find it both instructive and rather easy to proceed to a much more thoroughly abstract discussion of the parts of topology (including the topology of metric spaces) which are at the base of analysis. This program will be carried out in Chapter 3.

A second major function of abstraction is that of economizing intellectual effort in learning. Many mathematical ideas recur in different guises in various seemingly distinct subjects. Generalization by abstraction permits us to see the essential sameness of what at first appear to be distinct mathematical developments. The unifying power of abstraction makes it possible to comprehend as one a number of theories which were initially presented at the level of concrete specialization, and thus to master the general principles of these theories only once. Of course it remains important to learn the special features of particular mathematical developments—features not accounted for when one looks only at the larger and less detailed features which identify a certain development as a particular case of a grand abstraction.

In this chapter we shall give first of all an exposition of the elementary and basic things about topological spaces, about Hausdorff spaces in particular, and about metric spaces. In the later part of the chapter we discuss vector spaces, and especially normed linear spaces, Banach spaces, and Hilbert spaces. Our main interest is in being able to use elementary notions about such spaces in discussing families of functions and in presenting in a suitably general light some of the important parts of classical analysis (the Hilbert space aspect of the theory of Fourier series, for example).

Spaces of continuous functions are of particular significance for one aspect of the modern theory of integration; they also occupy a position of great importance in many other parts of modern analysis. The Stone-Weierstrass theorem (see Section 3–15), which deals with a certain class of spaces of continuous functions, is a superb example of the blending of the abstractions of topology and algebra to achieve a remarkable generalization of a classical and rather special theorem.

## 3–1 Topological spaces

Let $X$ be a nonempty collection of objects of unspecified nature; each of these objects is called an element of $X$. We shall denote elements by $x$, $y$, and so on. Let $\mathscr{T}$ be any family of subsets of $X$ which fulfills the following conditions (postulates):

(a) The empty set $\varnothing$ and $X$ itself belongs to $\mathscr{T}$;

(b) the union of any number of members of $\mathscr{T}$ (even an uncountable infinity of them) is again a member of $\mathscr{T}$;

(c) the intersection of any finite number of members of $\mathscr{T}$ is again a member of $\mathscr{T}$.

Such a family $\mathscr{T}$ is called *a topology* for $X$. The collection $X$, together with a specified topology for $X$, is called *a topological space*. The sets which belong to $\mathscr{T}$ are called *the open sets of* $X$ in this topology.

In the foregoing definition no conditions except those stated are placed on the open sets, and there is no implication that these open sets are selected by any particular method. Consequently, there are many ways of constructing examples of topological spaces. There are even many ways of constructing different topologies for the same given collection $X$.

*Example 1.* Let $X$ be the real line $R$, and let $\mathscr{T}$ be the family of *all* subsets of $X$. This family evidently satisfies the requirements for a topology. But it is clearly not the same as the topology defined for $R$ in Section 2–3.

We can define a topology for a perfectly arbitrary set in the manner of the foregoing example. Namely, let $\mathscr{T}$ be the family of all subsets of $X$. We call this *the discrete topology* for $X$. With this topology even a single point forms an open set.

*Example 2.* Let $X$ be any nonempty set in $R^k$. Let $\mathscr{T}$ be the family of all subsets of $X$ of the form $U \cap X$, where $U$ is an open set in $R^k$. Then $\mathscr{T}$ is a topology for $X$; it is the relative topology of $X$ induced by the standard topology of $R^k$, as described in Section 2–9.

*Example 3.* Let $X$ be the Euclidean plane $R^2$, but with a topology $\mathscr{S}$ defined as follows: a set $S$ in $X$ will belong to $\mathscr{S}$ if and only if there is a set $T$ in $R$, with $T$ open in the usual topology of $R$, such that $S$ consists of all points $x = (\xi_1, \xi_2)$ for which $\xi_1 \in T$, with no restriction on $\xi_2$. Thus, for example, if $T$ is the open interval (1, 2) on the $\xi_1$ axis, $S$ will consist of all points $(\xi_1, \xi_2)$ such that $1 < \xi_1 < 2$, regardless of the value of $\xi_2$. This gives a genuine topology $\mathscr{S}$ for the plane, but it is peculiar in certain ways, and is very different from the usual topology of $R^2$.

The following simple theorem is recorded so that we may make formal reference to it in future arguments.

THEOREM 3–1 I. *Let $S$ be a set in a topological space, and suppose $S$ is such that to each point $x$ in $S$ corresponds some open set $U$ such that $x \in U$ and $U \subset S$. Then $S$ is an open set.*

*Proof.* Let $T$ be the union of all the open subsets of $S$. Clearly $T \subset S$; also, $T$ is open, by postulate (b). On the other hand, $S \subset T$, because of the relation of $x$, $U$, and $S$ in the hypothesis about $S$, and the fact that $U$ is one of the sets of which $T$ is the union. Therefore $S = T$ and $S$ is open.

## RELATIVE TOPOLOGIES

The idea of a relative topology can be used in general; the procedure is the same as in Section 2–9. Suppose we are given a topology $\mathscr{T}$ for $X$. Let $Y$ be a proper subset of $X$, and consider the family $\mathscr{U}$ of all subsets of $Y$ of the form $U = Y \cap T$, where $T$ varies over $\mathscr{T}$. Then $\mathscr{U}$ is a topology for $Y$; we call it the relative topology for $Y$ induced by (or inherited from) $\mathscr{T}$.

## CLOSED SETS. CLOSURE OF A SET

If we are presented with a topological space $X$, with topology $\mathscr{T}$, we can develop the notions of closed set, point of accumulation, and so on, just as we did in discussing the space $R^k$ in Section 2–3. A subset $S$ of $X$ is called *closed* if the complementary set $S^\sim = X - S$ is open. Since $\varnothing$ and $X$ are open, they are also closed, for $\varnothing^\sim = X$ and $X^\sim = \varnothing$. From the postulates governing unions and intersections of open sets we deduce the following information about closed sets:

*Any intersection of closed sets is a closed set.*

*Any union of finitely many closed sets is a closed set.*

To prove the second one of these propositions, let $T_1, \ldots, T_n$ be closed sets. Then, by (1) in Section 1–2,

$$\left(\bigcup_{i=1}^{n} T_i\right)^\sim = \bigcap_{i=1}^{n} T_i^\sim.$$

But the finite intersection of the open sets $T_1^\sim, \ldots, T_n^\sim$ is open, and since it is the complement of the union of the $T_i$'s, this latter union must be closed. The proof of the proposition about the intersection of closed sets is similar.

If $S \subset X$, a point $y$ in $X$ is called an *accumulation point* of $S$ if every open set which contains $y$ also contains at least one point $x$ of $S$ such that $x \neq y$. The collection of all accumulation points of $S$ is denoted by $S'$ (*the derived set*), and the set $\bar{S} = S \cup S'$ is called the *closure* of $S$. If $\bar{S} = X$, we say that $S$ is *dense* in $X$.

The basic connection between points of accumulation and closed sets is the same as in Theorem 2–3 III. We restate it formally.

THEOREM 3–1 II. *A set $S$ in a topological space $X$ is closed if and only if $S' \subset S$.*

*Proof.* Suppose that $S$ is closed; then $S^{\sim}$ is open. We wish to show that $S' \subset S$, or equivalently, that $S^{\sim} \subset (S')^{\sim}$. Suppose that $x \in S^{\sim}$. Since $S^{\sim}$ is an open set which contains no points of $S$, the definition of an accumulation point shows that $x$ cannot be in $S'$. This is what we need to infer that $S^{\sim} \subset (S')^{\sim}$.

Now suppose that $S' \subset S$. We shall prove that $S^{\sim}$ is open, whence $S$ is closed. If $x \in S^{\sim}$, then $x$ is not in $S'$, and there must exist some open set $U$ such that $x \in U$ and $U$ contains no point of $S$. But then $U \subset S^{\sim}$. This implies that $S^{\sim}$ is open, by Theorem 3–1 I. Thus the theorem is proved.

In dealing with the closure of a set $S$, it is often convenient to make use of the following criterion: $x \in \bar{S}$ if and only if every open set $U$ which contains $x$ is such that $U \cap S \neq \varnothing$. Using this criterion, it is easy to prove that $(\bar{S})' \subset \bar{S}$, and hence that $\bar{S}$ is a closed set. The detailed reasoning on these issues is left to the student (see the Problems).

It should be pointed out that in a general abstract setting, if $y \in S'$, it is not necessarily true that every open set which contains $y$ contains infinitely many points of $S$. This contrasts with the situation in $R^k$, as elaborated in Section 2–3. What is needed to get back to the situation as it was in $R^k$ is the $T_1$-separation axiom. See Section 3–3, especially Problem 2(b).

## OTHER DEFINITIONS

In the case of an arbitrary topological space we make a number of further definitions exactly as in Chapter 2.

*Neighborhood of a point $x$: Any open set which contains $x$.*

*Basis of neighborhoods at $x$:* A family $\mathscr{B}_x$ of neighborhoods of $x$ such that if $U$ is *any* neighborhood of $x$, there is some $B \in \mathscr{B}_x$ such that $B \subset U$.

*Basis of neighborhoods for the space $X$:* A family $\mathscr{B}$ of open sets such that for each $x$ in $X$ there is a subfamily $\mathscr{B}_x$ of $\mathscr{B}$ such that $\mathscr{B}_x$ is a basis of neighborhoods at $x$. It is evident that $X$ is the union of all the members of $\mathscr{B}$.

*One set dense in another:* If $A$ and $B$ are subsets of $X$, we say that $A$ is dense in $B$ if $B \subset \bar{A}$. (In case $B = X$ this is the same as $X = \bar{A}$.) Observe that $A$ can be dense in $B$ even though $A$ is not a subset of $B$; in fact we may have $B \subset \bar{A}$ and $A \cap B = \varnothing$.

There is a concept of a set "dense-in-itself." See Problem 8, Section 3–2. There is some danger of confusion in terminology, because "$A$ is dense-in-itself" does not mean the same as "$A$ is dense in $A$."

*The boundary $\beta(S)$ of a set $S$:*

$$\beta(S) = \bar{S} \cap (\overline{S^{\sim}}). \tag{1}$$

*The interior $S^o$ of a set $S$:* $x \in S^o$ if there exists a neighborhood $U$ of $x$ such that $U \subset S$.
*Separated sets:* The sets $A$ and $B$ are separated if $A \neq \varnothing, B \neq \varnothing, A \cap B = \varnothing, A' \cap B = \varnothing$, $A \cap B' = \varnothing$.

*Connectedness:* A set $S$ is connected if it cannot be expressed as the union of two separated sets.

We point out that Theorem 2–8 IV, which deals with connectedness and boundaries, is perfectly general. The proofs which were given remain valid if we simply write $X$ in place of $R^k$ at each occurrence of the latter.

For later reference we point out some useful formulas involving the interior of sets. Since $\bar{S}$ is the intersection of all closed sets which contain $S$, $(\bar{S})^\sim$ is the union of all open sets which are contained in $S^\sim$. But this union is just the interior of $S^\sim$. Hence we have

$$(\bar{S})^\sim = (S^\sim)^0. \tag{2}$$

From this it follows that

$$\bar{S} = X \text{ is equivalent to } (S^\sim)^o = \varnothing. \tag{3}$$

This gives us an alternative expression of the condition that $S$ be dense in $X$.

## THE CARTESIAN PRODUCT OF TWO SPACES

If $X$ and $Y$ are two nonempty sets, their Cartesian product is the set $X \times Y$ of all ordered pairs $(x, y)$, where $x \in X$ and $y \in Y$. We distinguish between $X \times Y$ and $Y \times X$, although there is obviously a natural one-to-one correspondence between these two products.

If $X$ and $Y$ are topological spaces, there is a standard way of defining a topology for the product $X \times Y$. This topology is called the Cartesian product topology. It is discussed in Section 3–11. For the present we are not concerned with the topology of $X \times Y$.

## FUNCTIONS

Let $X$ and $Y$ be nonempty sets. A nonempty subset $f$ of $X \times Y$ is called a function with domain in $X$ and range in $Y$ if $f$ is such that when $(x, y) \in f$ and $(x, z) \in f$, then $y = z$. Thus, if $(x, y) \in f$, $y$ is uniquely determined by $x$, and we write $y = f(x)$. The set of all the $x$'s coming from elements $(x, y)$ of $f$ is called the domain $\mathscr{D}$ of $f$; the set of all the $f(x)$'s corresponding to all the $x$'s in $\mathscr{D}$ is called the range $\mathscr{R}$ of $f$.

As a convenient and brief way of referring to a function, we often speak of "a function $f : \mathscr{D} \to Y$." This exhibits the symbol for the function, the domain of the function, and the space in which the range lies. It can happen that $Y = \mathscr{R}$, but this is not implied by the notation $f : \mathscr{D} \to Y$.

If the set of all the pairs $(f(x), x)$, as $x$ varies over $\mathscr{D}$, is a function, we call it the function $f^{-1}$ inverse to $f$. Observe that it is a set in the Cartesian product $Y \times X$. Then we have $f^{-1} : \mathscr{R} \to X$.

The general usage as regards notation for inverse images is the same as was explained in Section 2–7.

We recall the distinctive use of the words "into" and "onto": If $f : X \to Y$ is given, we say that $f$ maps $X$ *into* $Y$. If $f(X) = Y$, we say that $f$ maps $X$ *onto* $Y$.

## CONTINUITY

Suppose we have a function $f : \mathscr{D} \to Y$, where $\mathscr{D} \subset X$, and $X$, $Y$ are topological spaces. If $x_0 \in \mathscr{D}$, we say that $f$ is continuous at $x_0$ if to each neighborhood $U$ of $f(x_0)$ in $Y$ corresponds some neighborhood $V$ of $x_0$ in $X$ such that $f(V \cap \mathscr{D}) \subset U$. This is exactly the way continuity was defined in Section 2–7, for the case in which $X$ and $Y$ are Euclidean spaces. As was explained in Section 2–9, the concept of continuity really depends only on the relative topologies induced in $\mathscr{D}$ and $\mathscr{R}$ respectively by the topologies of $X$ and $Y$. Hence, in discussing continuity, we may as well assume that $\mathscr{D} = X$ and $\mathscr{R} = Y$.

In our present very general situation, it is meaningless to talk of distance between points. Therefore we cannot use the classical $\epsilon$, $\delta$ formulation of the criterion for continuity. This formulation does have significance when $X$ and $Y$ are metric spaces, however (see Section 3–6).

The basic theorem which characterizes continuous functions is the following:

THEOREM 3–1 III. *Consider $f : X \to Y$, where $X$ and $Y$ are topological spaces, and the range of $f$ is all of $Y$. Then $f$ is a continuous mapping of $X$ onto $Y$ if and only if $f^{-1}(S)$ is open in $X$ whenever $S$ is open in $Y$.*

*Proof.* Exactly the same as the proof of Theorem 2–9 II, except that we have $X$ in place of $\mathscr{D}$ and $Y$ in place of $\mathscr{R}$.

The discussion of continuity and connectedness in Section 2–8 is general, as we see by examining Theorem 2–8 II and its proof. For the record we restate the main result:

THEOREM 3–1 IV. *The continuous image of a connected set is connected.*

It is possible to express the proof somewhat differently, using Theorem 3–1 III; see Problem 4.

## GENERATED TOPOLOGIES

Let $X$ be an arbitrary nonempty set, and let $Y$ be a topological space. Let $f$ be any function with domain $X$ and range all of $Y$. Since no topology is assumed for $X$, it is meaningless to inquire about continuity of $f$. But it is possible to define a topology for $X$ in such a way that $f$ becomes continuous. We merely define a subset $T$ of $X$ to be open if there is some open subset $S$ of $Y$ such that $f^{-1}(S) = T$. The class of all such $T$'s is indeed a topology for $X$, as we proceed to verify. In the first place,

$$f^{-1}(Y) = X \quad \text{and} \quad f^{-1}(\varnothing) = \varnothing,$$

and therefore $X$ and $\varnothing$ are open. If $\{S_\alpha\}$ is a family of sets in $Y$, we see that

$$\bigcup_\alpha f^{-1}(S_\alpha) = f^{-1}\left[\bigcup_\alpha S_\alpha\right], \qquad \bigcap_\alpha f^{-1}(S_\alpha) = f^{-1}\left[\bigcap_\alpha S_\alpha\right]. \tag{4}$$

We can use (4) to prove that the sets defined as open in $X$ have the correct properties as regards unions and intersections. Theorem 3–1 III shows that $f$ is rendered continuous by our definition of a topology for $X$.

The topology of Example 3 can be regarded as arising in this manner. Here we take $X = R^2$, $Y = R$, and $f$ maps $(\xi_1, \xi_2)$ into $\xi_1$.

There is also a method for constructing a topology by using several functions. The procedure is a bit more complicated than in the case of a single function, and it is better to consider first the general notion of a topology generated by a family of sets.

Suppose a given set $X$ has two topologies $\mathcal{S}_1$ and $\mathcal{S}_2$. Then $\mathcal{S}_1$ and $\mathcal{S}_2$ are collections whose elements are sets (subsets of $X$). We can consider the intersection $\mathcal{S}_1 \cap \mathcal{S}_2$, which is the collection of all subsets of $X$ which belong to both $\mathcal{S}_1$ and $\mathcal{S}_2$. The intersection $\mathcal{S}_1 \cap \mathcal{S}_2$ satisfies the conditions for being a topology for $X$; this is immediately evident as we examine the conditions. The same thing holds true when we consider the intersection of any number of topologies for $X$.

Now, suppose that $\mathcal{A}$ is any nonempty family of subsets of $X$. There certainly is a topology for $X$ which includes all the members of $\mathcal{A}$. The discrete topology is an example (it consists of *all* subsets of $X$). Hence, if we consider all topologies for $X$ which include the members of $\mathcal{A}$, the intersection of all these topologies is again a topology for $X$, and it includes the members of $\mathcal{A}$. We call it *the topology generated by* $\mathcal{A}$. The sets comprising this topology are $\varnothing$, $X$, all sets of the form $A_1 \cap A_2 \cap \cdots \cap A_n$ where each $A_i$ is from $\mathcal{A}$ and the integer $n$ is arbitrary (not fixed), and, finally, all sets which are obtained as unions of unrestrictedly many sets of this form $A_1 \cap \cdots \cap A_n$.

## THE MINIMAL TOPOLOGY RENDERING CERTAIN FUNCTIONS CONTINUOUS

Starting again with a given nonempty set $X$, let $\mathcal{F}$ be a nonempty family of functions, each function $f$ having domain $X$ and having as range a certain topological space (which may be different for different members of $\mathcal{F}$). For instance, $\mathcal{F}$ might consist of just two functions, one with range $R^2$ and one with range the closed interval $[0, 1]$ in $R$. But $\mathcal{F}$ could contain infinitely many functions. Now let $\mathcal{A}$ be the class of subsets of $X$ obtained as follows: each $A$ in $\mathcal{A}$ is the inverse image under some $f$ in $\mathcal{F}$ of an open set in its range, and $\mathcal{A}$ contains all possible such $A$'s. If we take the topology of $X$ generated by $\mathcal{A}$, it is evident that each of the functions in the family $\mathcal{F}$ becomes continuous on $X$. This topology is evidently *minimal* in the following sense: any topology for $X$ which renders every member of $\mathcal{F}$ continuous on $X$ must contain every one of the sets in $\mathcal{A}$, and hence must contain every one of the sets which make up the topology generated by $\mathcal{A}$.

## PROBLEMS

1. Show that $x \in \bar{S}$ if and only if every neighborhood $U$ of $x$ is such that $U \cap S \neq \varnothing$. Then show that $(\bar{S})' \subset \bar{S}$, thus proving that $\bar{S}$ is closed.
2. Prove that $\bar{S}$ is the intersection of all closed sets which contains $S$, and that $S^o$ is the union of all open subsets of $S$.
3. Explain why $\beta(S)$ is always a closed set.
4. Suppose $S \subset X$, where $X$ is a topological space.

(a) Let $S = A \cup B$, where $A \neq \varnothing, B \neq \varnothing, A \cap B = \varnothing$. Denote by $(B')_{\text{rel}}$ the set of accumulation points of $B$ in $S$, using the relative topology of $S$. Show that $(B')_{\text{rel}} = B' \cap S$, and likewise for $A'$. Deduce that

$$(B')_{\text{rel}} \cap A = B' \cap A \quad \text{and} \quad (A')_{\text{rel}} \cap B = A' \cap B.$$

Hence show that the notion of connectedness for $S$ is the same whether we use the topology of $X$ or the relative topology of $S$.

(b) Prove that a topological space $X$ is connected if and only if the only subsets of $X$ which are both open and closed are $\varnothing$ and $X$.

(c) Use (b) and Theorem 3–1 III to prove Theorem 3–1 IV. Note that you may consider $f: X \to Y$, where $X$ is connected and the range of $f$ is all of $Y$.

5. Suppose $A \subset B \subset X$, $X$ being the space. The closure of $A$ in the relative topology of $B$ is $A \cup (A' \cap B)$ (see Problem 4(a)). Show that $A$ is dense in $B$ (that is, that $B \subset \bar{A}$) if and only if $A \cup (A' \cap B) = B$.

## 3–2 Compactness and other properties

For the notion of compactness in general topology we use the same definition as that given in Section 2–6 for sets in Euclidean space. An *open covering* of the set $S$ in the topological space $X$ is a family $\mathscr{F}$ of open sets in $X$ such that $S$ is contained in the union of all the members of $\mathscr{F}$. The set $S$ is called *compact* if for each open covering $\mathscr{F}$ of $S$ there is some finite subfamily of $\mathscr{F}$ which covers $S$. It is at once evident that any finite set is compact. It can happen that $X$ itself is compact.

*Example 1.* Let $X$ be any nonempty closed and bounded set in $R^k$, and give $X$ the relative topology induced by the topology of $R^k$. Then $X$ is a compact space.

Let $X_0$ be a proper subset of an arbitrary topological space $X$, and let $\mathscr{T}_0$ be the relative topology for $X_0$ induced by the topology $\mathscr{T}$ of $X$. There are then two ways of considering the possibility that $X_0$ is compact, according to which of the topologies $\mathscr{T}$, $\mathscr{T}_0$ we use. *But, in fact, $X_0$ is compact as a subset of $X$, using the topology $\mathscr{T}$, if and only if $X_0$ is compact as a space, using the topology $\mathscr{T}_0$.*

In Euclidean space a compact set can be characterized as a set which is closed and bounded, but this characterization has no counterpart in general topology. For one thing, the concept of a bounded set is not meaningful in our present general situation, because it depends on the notion of distance between points. The concept of a bounded set is meaningful in metric spaces (to be defined in Section 3–6); but even there a closed and bounded set need not be compact. Compactness in metric spaces is discussed in Section 3–7.

### CONTINUOUS MAPPINGS OF COMPACT SETS

One of the most important things about compact sets is expressed in the following theorem:

THEOREM 3–2 I. *Let $f: X \to Y$ be a continuous mapping of the topological space $X$ into the topological space $Y$. Then, if $X$ is compact, the image $f(X)$ is compact.*

*Proof.* This is the same as Theorem 2–7 II, except that now the context is entirely general. The proof of Theorem 2–7 II is in fact general in form, and applies here. Let us reword the proof, using Theorem 3–1 III. We may as well assume that $f(X) = Y$. If $\mathscr{F}$ is an open covering of $Y$, the family of inverse images $f^{-1}(U)$, as $U$ varies over $\mathscr{F}$, is an open covering of $X$, because of the continuity. Hence, some finite set $f^{-1}(U_1), \ldots, f^{-1}(U_n)$ is an open covering of $X$. But this implies that $U_1, \ldots, U_n$ is an open covering of $Y$, and so $Y$ is compact.

### CLOSED SETS AND COMPACT SETS

One simple and important fact about compactness is stated in the following theorem.

THEOREM 3–2 II. *If $X$ is a compact topological space, each closed subset of $X$ is compact.*

*Proof.* Let $S$ be the closed subset. We may assume $S \neq \varnothing$, because we know that $\varnothing$ is compact. Now suppose $\mathscr{F}$ is an open covering of $S$. Let $\mathscr{G}$ be the family consisting of $X - S$ and the members of $\mathscr{F}$. Then $\mathscr{G}$ is an open covering of $X$, and so some finite number of members of $\mathscr{G}$ will serve to cover $X$. This finite covering must include at least one member of $\mathscr{F}$, because points of $S$ are not included in $X - S$. Let $U_1, \ldots, U_n$ be the members of $\mathscr{F}$ in this finite subcovering from $\mathscr{G}$. Then, since the only possible additional member of the finite subfamily of $\mathscr{G}$ is $X - S$, the finite family $U_1, \ldots, U_n$ is a covering of $S$. This proves that $S$ is compact.

A closed set need not be compact. Examples can be found in $R^k$.

As we know, a compact set in $R^k$ is closed. In fact, in a large and important class of topological spaces called Hausdorff spaces, compact sets are always closed (see Theorem 3–3 I). But in topological spaces which are not Hausdorff spaces it may occur that a set is compact without being closed; this is shown by the following example.

*Example 2.* Consider the space $X$ of Example 3 in Section 3–1. The points of $X$ are the points of $R^2$. As one possible basis of neighborhoods for $X$ we can take all the open strips of the form $\{x : a < \xi_1 < b, \xi_2 \text{ arbitrary}\}$, where $a, b$ are any two elements of $R$ such that $a < b$. The set $S$ of all points $x = (\xi_1, \xi_2)$ such that $0 \leq \xi_1 \leq 1$ and $\xi_2 = 0$ is compact in this space $X$, but is not closed. The closure of $S$, in fact, is composed of all points $x$ for which $0 \leq \xi_1 \leq 1$, with no restriction on $\xi_2$. Verification is left to the reader.

### COMPACTNESS AND POINTS OF ACCUMULATION

The relationship already pointed out for the space $R^k$ is quite general:

THEOREM 3–2 III. *If $T$ is a compact subset of the topological space $X$, every infinite subset of $T$ has an accumulation point in $T$.*

*Proof.* Just the same as the proof given in the special case when $X = R^k$. See Theorem 2–6 II (a).

In order to characterize compact sets by this requirement of the existence of points of accumulation, some restriction on the space is necessary. For the situation in metric spaces see Theorem 3–7 II.

### COMPACTNESS AND INTERSECTION PROPERTIES

For a family $\mathscr{S}$ of sets $S$ in $X$, we shall say that $\mathscr{S}$ has the *finite intersection property* if $\bigcap_{i=1}^{n} S_i \neq \varnothing$ for each finite collection $S_1, \ldots, S_n$ of members of $\mathscr{S}$. For brevity we call this "property $F$." The *void intersection property*, denoted here briefly as "property $V$," is defined as follows: $\mathscr{S}$ has property $V$ if the intersection of all the members of $\mathscr{S}$ is the empty set $\varnothing$.

If $P$ denotes a property, let $\sim P$ denote the negation of the property. That is, $\mathscr{S}$ has property $\sim P$ if $\mathscr{S}$ fails to have property $P$. To say that $\mathscr{S}$ has property $\sim F$ means that $\bigcap_{i=1}^{n} S_i = \varnothing$ for some finite collection $S_1, \ldots, S_n$ of elements of $\mathscr{S}$. To say that $\mathscr{S}$ has property $\sim V$ means that $\bigcap_{S \in \mathscr{S}} S \neq \varnothing$. After these definitions and remarks we can state the following theorem, which contains some convenient alternative characterizations of compactness.

THEOREM 3–2 IV. *Let $X$ be a topological space. Then*

(a) *$X$ is compact if and only if each family of closed sets in $X$ with property $V$ also has property $\sim F$.*

(b) *$X$ is compact if and only if each family of closed sets in $X$ with property $F$ also has property $\sim V$.*

(c) *If $\mathscr{S}$ is a family of sets $S$ in $X$, let $\overline{\mathscr{S}}$ denote the family of all the closures $\bar{S}$ of these sets. Then $X$ is compact if and only if $\overline{\mathscr{S}}$ has property $\sim V$ when $\mathscr{S}$ has property $F$.*

*Proof of* (a). Suppose $X$ is compact, and let $\mathscr{S}$ be a family of closed sets with property $V$. By complementation,

$$\bigcap_{S \in \mathscr{S}} S = \varnothing \quad \text{is equivalent to} \quad \bigcup_{S \in \mathscr{S}} S^{\sim} = X.$$

Thus the family of the open sets $S^{\sim}$ covers $X$, and the compactness implies that some finite subfamily $S_1^{\sim}, \ldots, S_n^{\sim}$ covers $X$. But

$$\bigcup_{i=1}^{n} S_i^{\sim} = X \quad \text{is equivalent to} \quad \bigcap_{i=1}^{n} S_i = \varnothing,$$

and so $\mathscr{S}$ has property $\sim F$.

The proof of the converse part of (a) is left to the reader.

Assertion (b) follows from (a) by the principle that "$A$ implies $B$" is equivalent to "not $B$ implies not $A$."

*Proof of* (c). In view of (b) and the fact that $S = \bar{S}$ if $S$ is closed, the "if" part of (c) is certainly true. The "only if" part also follows with the aid of (b), for if $\mathscr{S}$ is a family of sets with property $F$, it is obvious that $\overline{\mathscr{S}}$ is a family of closed sets with property $F$.

For a use of Theorem 3–2 IV see the proof of Theorem 3–11 I.

## REGULARITY

The topological space $X$ is called *regular* if whenever $U$ is a neighborhood of a point $x$, there is another neighborhood $V$ of $x$ such that $\bar{V} \subset U$. An instance of a space which is not regular is given in Example 1, Section 3–4. For more about regularity see Problem 4 and the discussion of $T_3$ spaces in Section 3–3.

## THE AXIOMS OF COUNTABILITY

The topological space $X$ is said to satisfy *the first axiom of countability* if there is a countable basis of neighborhoods at each point of $X$. This axiom is certainly satisfied in the topology of $R^k$, for we can take as a basis of neighborhoods at $x_0$ the family of open spheres $S(x_0; r)$ with center $x_0$ and arbitrary positive rational $r$ as radius.

For spaces which satisfy the first axiom of countability we have the following partial counterpart of Therem 2–4 III:

THEOREM 3–2 V. *Let $X$ be a topological space which satisfies the first axiom of countability. Let $S$ be a set in $X$, and $y$ an accumulation point of $S$. Then there exists a sequence $\{x_n\}$ of elements of $S$ such that $x_n \neq y$ for each $n$ and any given neighborhood of $y$ contains $x_n$ for all sufficiently large values of $n$.*

*Proof.* Let the sets $B_1, B_2, \ldots$ be a basis of neighborhoods at $y$. Let $U_n = B_1 \cap B_2 \cap \cdots \cap B_n$. Choose $x_n$ so that $x_n \in U_n \cap S$ and $x_n \neq y$. If $U$ is a neighborhood of $y$, there is some $N$ such that $B_N \subset U$. Then $U_n \subset U$ if $n \geq N$, and hence $x_n \in U$ if $n \geq N$. Observe that we do not claim that there are an infinite number of distinct $x_n$'s. But see Problem 3 in Section 3–3.

We can introduce the notion of a convergent sequence in a topological space, and then Theorem 3–2 V can be restated in terms of this notion. A sequence $\{x_n\}$ in $X$ is said to converge to $x$ (and we write $x_n \to x$) if to each neighborhood $U$ of $x$ corresponds some $N$ such that $x_n \in U$ if $N \leq n$. We say that $x$ is a limit of $\{x_n\}$. This notion is not very fruitful unless the limit is unique. To insure uniqueness of the limit we need some additional assumption about the nature of the space $X$. See Example 1, Section 3–3 and the remark, preceding Theorem 3–3 I, about the uniqueness of limits in Hausdorff spaces.

We say that $X$ satisfies *the second axiom of countability* if there is a countable basis of neighborhoods for the whole space $X$. A space which satisfies the second axiom of countability is also called *perfectly separable*. We know from Theorem 2–5 I that $R^k$ is perfectly separable.

The next theorem is known as Lindelöf's theorem.

THEOREM 3–2 VI. *Let $X$ be a perfectly separable space. Then, if $S$ is a set in $X$ and $\mathcal{F}$ is an open covering of $S$, there exists a countable subfamily of $\mathcal{F}$ which also covers $S$.*

*Proof.* This was stated as Theorem 2–5 III for the space $R^k$. The proof as there given applies to the general case, since it used no specific properties of $R^k$ other than the existence of a countable basis of neighborhoods for the space.

## SEPARABILITY

A space $X$ is called *separable* if there is a countable set $S$ in $X$ such that $\bar{S} = X$. This notion is related to, but not the same as, perfect separability. If $X$ is perfectly separable it is separable (see Problem 5). There exist separable spaces which are not perfectly separable. An instance will be found in Example 2 of Section 3–4. For the situation in a metric space see Problem 1, Section 3–6.

## HOMEOMORPHISMS

Two topological spaces $X$, $Y$ are said to be *homeomorphic* if there exists a function $f: X \to Y$ such that (1) the range of $f$ is all of $Y$, (2) the inverse function $f^{-1}$ exists, and (3) $f$ and $f^{-1}$ are continuous. The function $f$ thus establishes a one-to-one correspondence between the elements of $X$ and $Y$, and it also establishes a one-to-one correspondence between the class of all open sets in $X$ and the class of all open sets in $Y$. Such a mapping $f$ is called a homeomorphism.

The relation of homeomorphism is an equivalence relation; it divides the totality of all topological spaces into equivalence classes. The spaces in any one equivalence class may be said to be of the same topological type. A topological property of a space $X$ is a property which is shared by all spaces homeomorphic to $X$.

Many topological spaces can be formed by taking subsets of $R^k$ and using the induced relative topologies. Two spaces formed in this way may be homeomorphic and yet may present quite different geometric appearances. This is possible because many of the properties which a set may possess as a subset of Euclidean space are not topological properties when the set is viewed as a topological space. Boundedness, for instance, is not a topological property.

*Example 3.* The subsets of $R$ defined by $X = \{x : 0 \leq x < 1\}$, $Y = \{y : 0 \leq y\}$ are homeomorphic when their topologies are the relative topologies inherited from $R$. One possible homeomorphic mapping is defined by $y = f(x)$, where $f(x) = \dfrac{x}{1 - x}$. Another possibility is given by $f(x) = \tan \dfrac{\pi x}{2}$.

*Example 4.* This time we take $X$ and $Y$ as subsets of $R^2$, with the naturally induced topologies. Let $x = (\xi_1, \xi_2)$, $y = (\eta_1, \eta_2)$, and let

$$X = \{x : 0 < \xi_1^2 + \xi_2^2 < 1, \xi_1 > 0, \xi_2 > 0\},$$

$$Y = \{y : 1 < \eta_1^2 + \eta_2^2, \eta_2 > 0\}.$$

We can most easily describe a homeomorphic mapping of $X$ onto $Y$ by using polar coordinates: $(r, \theta)$ for $P$ in $X$, $(\rho, \phi)$ for $Q$ in $Y$. Let $\phi = 2\theta$, $\rho = r^{-2}$. We make the restrictions $0 < \theta < \dfrac{\pi}{2}$, $0 < r < 1$. See Figure 21.

In order to be sure that two given spaces $X$ and $Y$ are *not* homeomorphic, one must somehow show that there is no homeomorphic mapping on $X$ onto $Y$. This demonstration

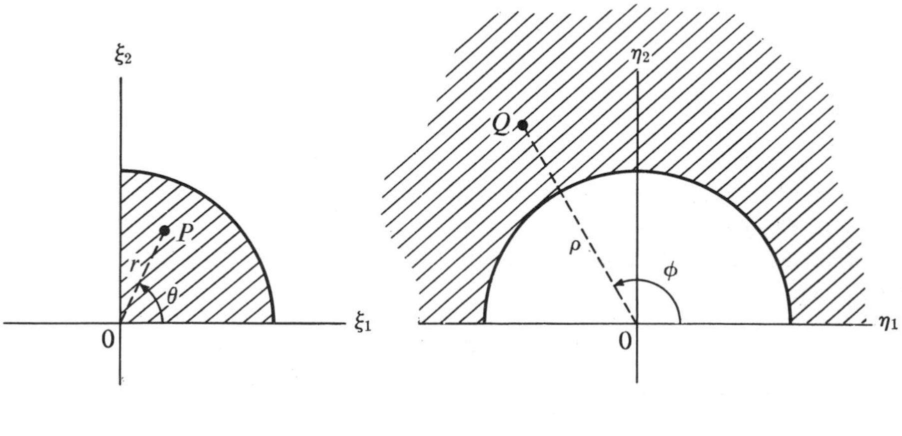


FIGURE 21

can be made if it can be recognized that one of the spaces possesses a topological property not shared by the other. For example, one space may be compact, and the other not, or one may be connected, and the other not. The following example uses an argument which derives from the recognition that one space $X$ contains a point whose relation to the space is unlike that of any point in $Y$ to the space $Y$.

*Example 5.* Let $X = \{x : 0 \leq x < 1\}$ and let $Y = R$. Use for $X$ the topology inherited from $R$. The point $x = 0$ appears to be unlike any point of $Y$ in its relation to the whole space. Suppose that there is a homeomorphic mapping $f$ of $X$ onto $Y$. Choose points $y_1$ and $y_2$ in $Y$ so that $y_1 < f(0) < y_2$, and let $f(x_i) = y_i$, $i = 1, 2$, where $x_i \in X$. Since $f$ is continuous and $X$ is connected, Theorem 2–8 III shows that there must be some point $x$ strictly between $x_1$ and $x_2$ such that $f(x) = f(0)$. The fact that $x$ is between $x_1$ and $x_2$ implies that $x \neq 0$. But then $f(x) = f(0)$ contradicts the fact that the mapping is one-to-one. Hence $X$ and $Y$ cannot be homeomorphic.

In the foregoing example we may recognize that $Y$ has the following property: if a single point is removed from $Y$, the resulting set is not connected. This is a topological property. But $X$ does not have this property, because $X - \{0\}$ is connected.

## PROBLEMS

1. Prove the assertion made about the identity of the two senses in which a subset $X_0$ of $X$ may be compact in the paragraph immediately following Example 1.
2. Use Theorem 3–2 IV(a) to give an alternative proof of Theorem 3–2 II. Use the relative topology of the closed subset.
3. Prove that the following properties of a space are topological properties:
   (a) Compactness;
   (b) connectedness;
   (c) $X - \{x\}$ is connected for each $x \in X$;
   (d) perfect separability;
   (e) separability;
   (f) $X = X'$;
   (g) regularity.
4. Prove that a topological space $X$ is regular if and only if to each point $x$ and each closed set $A$ such that $x \notin A$ there corresponds a pair of disjoint open sets $U$, $V$ such that $x \in U$ and $A \subset V$.
5. Prove that a perfectly separable space is separable.
6. Suppose $f : X \to Y$, where $f$ is continuous and such that $f(A)$ is closed in $Y$ if $A$ is closed in $X$. Prove that $f(\bar{S}) = \overline{f(S)}$ for each $S \subset X$. This applies in particular if $f$ is a homeomorphism of $X$ onto $Y$.
7. If $S \subset X$ and $f$ is a homeomorphic mapping of $X$ onto $Y$, show that $f(S') = \{f(S)\}'$.
8. A set $S \subset X$ is called dense-in-itself if $S \subset S'$. If $S$ is closed and dense-in-itself it is called *perfect*.
   (a) Suppose that $f : X \to Y$ is continuous and that $f^{-1}$ exists. Show that $f(S)$ is dense-in-itself if $S$ is.
   (b) Suppose that $S$ is perfect and that $f$ is a homeomorphism of $X$ onto $Y$. Show that $f(S)$ is perfect.
9. Suppose $f : X \to R$ is continuous, $X$ being a compact space. Prove that the values of $f$ are bounded, and that $f(x)$ attains both an absolute maximum and an absolute minimum value as $x$ varies over $X$.

## 3–3 Postulates of separation

In Euclidean space it is true that a set consisting of a single point is closed, that is, its complementary set is open. In other words, if $x$ and $y$ are distinct points, there exists a neighborhood of $y$ which does not contain $x$ (for example, the open sphere with center $y$ and radius any positive number not exceeding the distance from $x$ to $y$). But, if $X$ is an arbitrary topological space, there is nothing in the postulates which enables us to prove that a set consisting of a single point is closed.

*Example 1.* Consider the situation of Example 3 in Section 3–1, where $X$ is the plane $R^2$ with the topology for $X$ defined as follows: the open sets in $X$ are the inverse images $f^{-1}(T)$ of open sets $T$ in $R$ (with the usual topology for $R$), where $f$ is the mapping which sends $x = (\xi_1, \xi_2)$ into the number $\xi_1$ in $R$. In this space $X$, if $(\xi, \alpha)$ and $(\xi, \beta)$ are two distinct points with the same first coordinate, every neighborhood of either point contains the other. We have here the curious situation that if $S$ is the set consisting of a single point $x$, the closure $\bar{S}$ is the straight line through $x$ parallel to the $\xi_2$ axis. A further curiosity is that if $x = (0, \eta)$, with $\eta$ arbitrary, and if $x_n = (\xi_n, \eta_n)$, with $\eta_n$ arbitrary and $\xi_n \to 0$, then $x_n \to x$. Here is an example of a sequence which converges to infinitely many different limits.

### $T_1$ SPACES

A topological space $X$ is called a $T_1$ space if every set consisting of a single point is closed. An equivalent requirement is that if $x$ and $y$ are distinct points, some neighborhood of $y$ fails to contain $x$. The postulate that this is so is a particular example of what is often called a *separation axiom.* (We have some open set $U$ such that $y \in U$ and $x \notin U$, so that $U$ "separates" $y$ from $x$ in a certain sense.)

When the $T_1$-separation axiom is not satisfied, some curious things can occur.

*Example 2.* Let $X$ consist of three distinct elements, denoted by 1, 2, 3. We specify a topology for $X$ by declaring the class of open sets to consist of $\varnothing$, $X$, $\{1\}$, and $\{2, 3\}$. The reader can verify that this is indeed a topology. Moreover, $X$ is a regular space, for all the open sets are also closed. But $X$ is not a $T_1$ space, for the sets $\{2\}$, $\{3\}$ are not closed. If $S = \{2\}$, it is easy to verify that $S' = \{3\}$. Hence $S'$ is not closed. This is in contrast to the situation in a $T_1$ space. In such a space a derived set is always closed (see Problem 2(a)).

A few interesting propositions requiring the $T_1$-separation axiom for their proofs are given in the problems. This separation axiom is rather weak, however, and a great many propositions of importance in topology and its applications require a stronger separation axiom.

### $T_2$ SPACES

A topological space $X$ is called a $T_2$ space if for each pair of distinct points $x_1, x_2$ in $X$ there exists a pair of disjoint open sets $U_1, U_2$ with $U_i$ a neighborhood of $x_i (i = 1, 2)$. A $T_2$ space is commonly called a Hausdorff space, in honor of Felix Hausdorff (1868–1942), who used this separation axiom in his influential writings during the early development of the general theory of abstract point-set topology.

There are $T_1$ spaces which do not satisfy the $T_2$-separation axiom. For an example see Problem 1.

In a Hausdorff space convergent sequences have unique limits. That is, if $x_n \to x$ and $x_n \to y$, then $x = y$. The proof is left as a problem for the reader.

One of the important consequences of the $T_2$-separation axiom is the following theorem.

THEOREM 3–3 I. *In a Hausdorff space a compact subset of the space is always closed.*

This is proved by the argument used in connection with Theorem 2–6 I to prove that a compact set in $R^k$ is closed. This earlier proposition could have been proved in a variety of ways; the method selected applies *verbatim* in the present general context. The student should take note of the place in the proof where the Hausdorff separation axiom is used.

We pass now to another important theorem about Hausdorff spaces.

THEOREM 3–3 II. *If $S$ and $T$ are disjoint compact sets in a Hausdorff space $X$, there exist disjoint open sets $U$, $V$ such that $S \subset U$ and $T \subset V$.*

*Proof.* First of all we assert that the proposition is true in the special case when $T$ consists of a single point. The proof of this assertion will be found as part of the argument in the proof of Theorem 2–6 I (where $U$ is constructed as a union $U_1 \cup \cdots \cup$ and $U_n$ $V$ is constructed as an intersection $V_1 \cap \cdots \cap V_n$). Now, for the general case suppose $x \in T$. Then there exists a pair of disjoint open sets, say $A_x$ and $B_x$, such that $S \subset A_x$ and $x \in B_x$. As $x$ varies over $T$ the family of all the $B_x$'s covers $T$, and hence some finite number of them suffice to cover $T$. For convenience of typography let us denote this finite set of $B_x$'s, corresponding to $x_1, \ldots, x_n$, by $B_1, \ldots, B_n$, and denote the corresponding $A_x$'s by $A_1, \ldots, A_n$. Now let $U = A_1 \cap A_2 \cap \cdots \cap A_n$, $V = B_1 \cup \cdots \cup B_n$. Then $U$ and $V$ are disjoint open sets fulfilling the requirements of the theorem.

The next theorem formalizes an important principle which is often used in dealing with continuous functions. We recall that, if $S \subset X$ and $\bar{S} = X$, $S$ is said to be *dense in X*.

THEOREM 3–3 III. *Suppose $X$ and $Y$ are topological spaces, and that $Y$ is a Hausdorff space. Let $f$ and $g$ be continuous functions with $X$ as their common domain, their ranges being in $Y$. Suppose it is known that there is a set $S$ in $X$ such that $\bar{S} = X$ and $f(x) = g(x)$ when $x \in S$. Then we can conclude that $f$ and $g$ are the same function.*

*Proof.* Suppose, to the contrary, that there is some $x_0$ in $X$ for which $f(x_0) \neq g(x_0)$. Then, since $Y$ is a Hausdorff space, there must exist a pair $U$, $V$ of disjoint open sets in $Y$, $U$ containing $f(x_0)$ and $V$ containing $g(x_0)$. Then the set $f^{-1}(U) \cap g^{-1}(V)$ is a neighborhood of $x_0$, and hence must contain a point $x$ of $S$ (because $\bar{S} = X$). Then $f(x) \in U$ and $g(x) \in V$; since $U \cap V = \varnothing$ and $f(x) = g(x)$, we have a contradiction, so the proof is finished.

## $T_3$ SPACES

We defined the concept of regularity in Section 3–2. A $T_1$ space which is regular is called a $T_3$ space. The definition of regularity can be given a different but equivalent formulation which makes it clear that the requirement of regularity is a separation condition. *A topological space $X$ is regular if and only if to each point $x$ and each closed set $A$ such that $x \notin A$ there corresponds a pair of disjoint open sets $U$, $V$ such that $x \in U$ and $A \subset V$.* The proof of this is left to the reader (Problem 4, Section 3–2).

When a space is regular and also a $T_1$ space, the closed set $A$ in the foregoing statement may be chosen to consist of a single point. Thus we see that a $T_3$ space is certainly a Hausdorff space. For an instance of a $T_2$ space which is not a $T_3$ space, see Example 1 in Section 3–4.

### $T_4$ SPACES

A topological space $X$ is called *normal* if for each pair of disjoint closed sets $A$, $B$ in $X$ there exists a pair of disjoint open sets $U$, $V$ such that $A \subset U$ and $B \subset V$. A normal $T_1$ space is called a $T_4$ space. Such a space is clearly a $T_3$ space. There are, however, $T_3$ spaces which are not normal. See Example 2 in Section 3–4 and the further discussion of it in Section 3–9.

The concept of normality of a space was introduced by the Russian mathematician P. Urysohn (1898–1924). One of Urysohn's important contributions was the proof of the following proposition, which is widely known as *Urysohn's Lemma: If $S$ and $T$ are disjoint closed sets in a normal space $X$, it is possible to construct a real-valued continuous function $f$ with domain $X$ and with range contained in the closed interval* $[0, 1]$ *of the real line, such that $f(x) = 0$ if $x \in S$ and $f(x) = 1$ if $x \in T$.* We shall not give the proof of this theorem. For references see Dunford and Schwartz [1], p. 15, Hocking and Young [1], p. 57, Kelley [1], p. 115, Loomis [1], p. 6.

Although not all Hausdorff spaces are normal, we can assert the following:

THEOREM 3–3 IV. *A compact Hausdorff space is normal.*

*Proof.* We have only to cite the combination of Theorems 3–2 II, 3–3 II.

Another result in this direction was proved by A. Tychonoff (born in 1906), namely, *A perfectly separable $T_3$ space is normal.* See Problem 7.

### COMPLETE REGULARITY

The concept of regularity can be strengthened in a manner which is suggested by Urysohn's lemma. A topological space $X$ is called *completely regular* if, given a point $x_0$ and a closed set $A$ not containing $x_0$, there exists a continuous mapping $f : X \to [0, 1]$ such that $f(x_0) = 0$ and $f(x) = 1$ if $x \in A$. Such a space is regular, for if we let $U = \{x : f(x) < \frac{1}{2}\}$, $V = \{x : \frac{1}{2} < f(x)\}$, we see that $U$ and $V$ are disjoint open sets such that $x_0 \in U$ and $A \subset V$. By Urysohn's lemma it is clear that a $T_4$ space is completely regular.

There exist $T_3$ spaces which are not completely regular. In fact, in E. Hewitt [1] there is described a $T_3$ space on which each continuous, real-valued function is constant in value.

### PROBLEMS

1. Let $X$ be the set of all real numbers. Define a topology for $X$ by declaring a set $S$ in $X$ to be open if and only if either (a) $S = \varnothing$ or (b) $S^{\sim}$ is a countable set. Verify that $X$ is a $T_1$ space but not a $T_2$ space.

2. Here are two useful theorems about $T_1$ spaces; they are not true for arbitrary topological spaces. Prove them.

   (a) If $S \subset X$, where $X$ is a $T_1$ space, $S'$ is closed.

   (b) If $S \subset X$ and $X$ is a $T_1$ space, $y \in S'$ if and only if every neighborhood of $y$ contains infinitely many points of $S$. Consequently, $S' = \varnothing$ if $S$ is a finite set.

3. Let $X$ be a $T_1$ space which satisfies the first axiom of countability. Suppose $S \subset X$ and $y \in S'$. Prove that there exists a sequence $\{x_n\}$ in $S$ such that $x_n \to y$, $x_n \neq y$, and $x_1, x_2, \ldots$ are all different.

4. There exist $T_1$ spaces in which a compact set need not be closed (in contrast to Theorem 3–3 I). To show this, let $X$ be an infinite set, and let the topology of $X$ be defined to consist of the empty set and all sets $S$ such that $S^{\sim}$ is a finite set. Show that $X$ is a $T_1$ space but not a Hausdorff space. Show that every subset of $X$ is compact, but that $X$ contains a nonclosed set.

5. Suppose that $X$ is a compact space and that $Y$ is a Hausdorff space. Let $f: X \to Y$ be continuous. Show that $f(S)$ is closed if $S$ is a closed set in $X$. Hence show that $f$ is a homeomorphism of $X$ onto $f(X)$ if $f^{-1}$ exists.

6. Suppose that $Y$ is a $T_2$ space, that $f: X \to Y$ is continuous, and that $f^{-1}$ exists. Show that $X$ is a $T_2$ space.

7. Show that, if $A$ and $B$ are disjoint closed sets in a normal space $X$, there exist open sets $U$, $V$ such that $A \subset U$, $B \subset V$, and $\bar{U} \cap \bar{V} = \varnothing$.

8. A space $X$ is called *completely normal* if it is a $T_1$ space and if, whenever $A$ and $B$ are separated sets, there exist disjoint open sets $U$, $V$ with $A \subset U$ and $B \subset V$. It is clear that a completely normal space is a $T_4$ space. Prove that a perfectly separable $T_3$ space is completely normal.

## 3–4 Postulated neighborhood systems

It is often convenient to start from an alternative postulational approach in building a topological space. Let $X$ be a nonempty set of elements, and let $\mathcal{N}$ be a family of ordered pairs $(N, x)$, where $N$ is a subset of $X$ and $x$ is an element of $N$. We make no assumptions about the family $\mathcal{N}$ other than the following postulates:

1. To each $x$ in $X$ corresponds some subset $N$ of $X$ such that $(N, x) \in \mathcal{N}$.
2. If $(N_1, x)$ and $(N_2, x)$ are in $\mathcal{N}$, there exists an $(N_3, x)$ in $\mathcal{N}$ such that $N_3 \subset N_1 \cap N_2$.
3. If $(N_1, x_1) \in \mathcal{N}$ and $x_2 \in N_1$, there exists a subset $N_2$ of $X$ such that $(N_2, x_2) \in \mathcal{N}$ and $N_2 \subset N_1$.

Let us now define a subset $S$ of $X$ to be open if to each $x$ in $S$ corresponds some $(N, x)$ in $\mathcal{N}$ such that $N \subset S$. It follows by the first postulate that $\varnothing$ and $X$ are open. A union of open sets is open, as a direct consequence of the definition, and an intersection of finitely many open sets is open, as a consequence of the second postulate (and induction). Hence, on the basis of the first two postulates, we obtain a topology for $X$. The third postulate ensures that the sets $N$ occurring in the elements of $\mathcal{N}$ are open sets. It is clear that they form a basis of neighborhoods for $X$.

If $X$ is any topological space, we can get a system satisfying the foregoing set of postulates by taking for $\mathcal{N}$ the family of all pairs $(U, x)$ where $x$ is any element of $X$ and $U$ is any open set containing $x$. Or, alternatively, we may take for the $U$'s the members of any basis of neighborhoods at $x$.

To get separation properties in a topology which is developed from the foregoing postulate system we need some additional postulate. We get a $T_1$ space if we add the following postulate.

$T_1$: If $x_1$ and $x_2$ are distinct elements of $X$, there exists a subset $N$ containing $x_2$ but not $x_1$ such that $(N, x_2) \in \mathcal{N}$. To get a Hausdorff space we add, instead, the following postulate.

$T_2$: If $x_1$ and $x_2$ are distinct elements of $X$, there exist subsets $N_1$, $N_2$ of $X$ such that $(N_1, x_1) \in \mathcal{N}$, $(N_2, x_2) \in \mathcal{N}$, and $N_1 \cap N_2 = \varnothing$.

*Example 1.* For $X$ let us take the collection of all points in the Euclidean plane $R^2$. To get a family $\mathcal{N}$ let us associate with each $x$ in $X$ and each positive $\epsilon$ a set $N_\epsilon(x)$ defined as follows. If $x = (\xi_1, \xi_2)$, $N_\epsilon(x)$ consists of $x$ and all points $a = (\alpha_1, \alpha_2)$ such $\alpha_1 \neq \xi_1$ and $(\alpha_1 - \xi_1)^2 + (\alpha_2 - \xi_2)^2 < \epsilon^2$. Then $(N(x), x)$ is to be in $\mathcal{N}$. The geometrical condition defining $N_\epsilon(x)$ is that it consists of $x$ and all other points inside the circle of radius $\epsilon$ with center at $x$, except those on the diameter parallel to the $\xi_2$ axis. It is easy to verify that the postulates for a Hausdorff space are fulfilled by this specially constructed neighborhood system. The space is not regular, however. For instance, the set of points $(0, \xi)$ for which $0 < \xi \leq 1$ is a closed set $S$, but it is impossible to find disjoint open sets $U$, $V$ such that $S \subset U$ and $(0, 0) \in V$. We leave detailed verification to the reader. We have here a $T_2$ space which is not a $T_3$ space.

*Example 2.* Next we shall illustrate the existence of a $T_3$ space which is separable but not perfectly separable. Furthermore, the space is not normal. For $X$ we take the collection of all points $x = (\xi_1, \xi_2)$ in $R^2$. If $x$ is a point for which $\xi_2 \neq 0$, we take for $N_\epsilon(x)$ the set of those points $y$ whose Euclidean distance from $x$ is less than $\epsilon$, and we get all the corresponding members $(N_\epsilon(x), x)$ of $\mathcal{N}$ by assigning $\epsilon$ all possible positive values. If $x$ is a point $(\xi, 0)$, we again construct a family of pairs $(N_\epsilon(x), x)$; this time we take for $N_\epsilon(x)$ the set consisting of $x$ itself and all points inside either the circle of radius $\epsilon$ with center $(\xi, \epsilon)$ or the circle of radius $\epsilon$ with center $(\xi, -\epsilon)$. It is not hard to verify that the family $\mathcal{N}$ of all the pairs $(N_\epsilon(x), x)$ satisfies the postulates for a Hausdorff space. The space is regular (and therefore a $T_3$ space) for it is easy to verify that if $U$ is open and $x \in U$, we can find one of the special neighborhoods $N_\epsilon(x)$ whose closure lies in $U$. (The closure of $N_\epsilon(x)$, in this special topology, happens to be the same as the closure of $N_\epsilon(x)$ in the sense of the topology of the Euclidean plane $R^2$.)

We now observe that the space $X$ is separable. In fact, the set of points $x = (\xi_1, \xi_2)$ for which both $\xi_1$ and $\xi_2$ are rational and $\xi_2 \neq 0$ is a countable set which is dense in $X$. The space $X$ is *not* perfectly separable, however. The reasons for this lie in the peculiar nature of the neighborhoods $N_\epsilon(x)$ of points $x$ for which $\xi_2 = 0$. Such a neighborhood $N_\epsilon(x)$ contains no other point of the $\xi_1$ axis except the point $x$ itself. Hence, any basis of neighborhoods for the

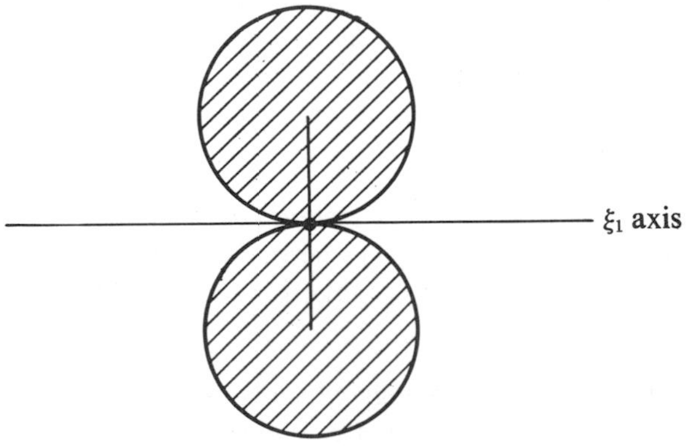


A neighborhood of the point $(\xi,0)$

FIGURE 22

whole space $X$ must contain at least as many different neighborhoods as there are different points on the $\xi_1$ axis, that is, as there are different real numbers. Since the set of all real numbers is uncountably infinite, it follows that a basis of neighborhoods for $X$ cannot be merely countable.

We shall see, later on, that this space $X$ is not normal (see Section 3–9).

**PROBLEMS**

1. Verify the assertions made in connection with Example 1.

2. Suppose $X = R^2$. Let $\mathscr{E}$ denote the ordinary topology of $R^2$ as the Euclidean plane. If $\epsilon > 0$ and $x = (\xi_1, \xi_2) \in X$, define $N_\epsilon(x)$ as the set consisting of $x$ and all points $(\alpha_1, \alpha_2)$ such that $\alpha_1 \neq \xi_1$, $\alpha_2 \neq \xi_2$, and $(\alpha_1 - \xi_1)^2 + (\alpha_2 - \xi_2)^2 < \epsilon^2$. Let $\mathscr{N}$ consist of all pairs $(N_\epsilon(x), x)$ as $\epsilon$ and $x$ vary. Show that $\mathscr{N}$ satisfies postulates 1, 2, 3, and $T_2$, so that we obtain a Hausdorff topology $\mathscr{T}$ for $X$. Show that if $S \in \mathscr{E}$ then $S \in \mathscr{T}$. For any subset $A$ of $X$ let $A^i$ denote its interior in the sense of the topology $\mathscr{E}$. If $S \in \mathscr{T}$ and $S \neq \varnothing$, show that $S^i \neq \varnothing$. Let $A$ be a set which lies on the union of a finite number of straight lines, each of one of the forms $\xi_1 =$ constant or $\xi_2 =$ constant. Show that $A' = \varnothing$, and hence that $A$ is closed in the sense of $\mathscr{T}$.

3. Define a topology for the real line $R$ as follows. If $\epsilon > 0$ and $x \in R$, let

$$N_\epsilon(x) = \{y : |y - x| < \epsilon \quad \text{and} \quad y \text{ irrational} \quad \text{if } y \neq x\}.$$

Let $\mathscr{N}$ consist of all pairs $(N_\epsilon(x), x)$ as $\epsilon$ and $x$ vary. Show that this definition yields a Hausdorff topology for $R$. Show that any set $S$ composed entirely of rational numbers has a void derived set.

4. Let $X$ be the class of all positive integers. If $x, y$ are relatively prime elements of $X$, let $N_{x,y}$ be the set consisting of $x, x + y, x + 2y, x + 3y, \ldots$. Let $\mathscr{N}$ consist of all the ordered pairs $(N_{x,y}, x)$. Show that postulates 1, 2, 3 of this section are satisfied. Thus a topology is determined for the class $X$. It may be shown that the topological space so defined is a connected Hausdorff space which is not regular. (See S. Golomb, A connected topology for the integers, *American Mathematical Monthly*, Vol. 66 (1959), pp. 663–665.) Nor is the space compact. There are some interesting connections between the topology of this space and various questions in number theory.

5. Let $\mathscr{F}$ be a family of sets $N$ in $X$ such that (a) the union of all the $N$'s is $X$ and (b) the intersection of any two members of $\mathscr{F}$ is a member of $\mathscr{F}$. Let $\mathscr{N}$ consist of all ordered pairs $(N, x)$ such that $x \in X$, $N \in \mathscr{F}$, and $x \in N$. Show that postulates 1, 2, 3 are satisfied.

## 3–5 Compactification. Local compactness

If $X$ is a noncompact topological space, it may be possible in various ways to make a new space $Y$ which is compact, which contains $X$ as a dense subset of $Y$, and which is such that the original topology of $X$ is identical with the relative topology of $X$ induced by the topology of $Y$. A space $Y$ related to $X$ in this way is called a *compactification* of $X$.

*Example 1.* The extended real number system $R^*$ can be viewed as a compactification of the space $R$. As we saw in Section 1–7, $R^*$ is composed of the elements of $R$ and the two additional elements $-\infty, +\infty$. Let us define a topology for $R^*$ in the following way, using the method of neighborhood systems as explained in Section 3–4. We make use of the total ordering of $R^*$. If $x \in R$, we take the corresponding pairs $(N, x) \in \mathscr{N}$ to be those given by $N = N_\epsilon(x) = \{t : x - \epsilon < t < x + \epsilon\}$, where $\epsilon$ can be any positive real number. If $x = +\infty$, we take pairs $(N, +\infty)$ with $N = N_a(+\infty) = \{t : a < t \leq +\infty\}$, where $a$ is any real number. If $x = -\infty$, we take pairs $(N, -\infty)$ with $N = N_a(-\infty) = \{t : -\infty \leq t < a\}$, where $a$ is any real number. Postulates 1–3 in Section 3–4 are satisfied, so we obtain a topology

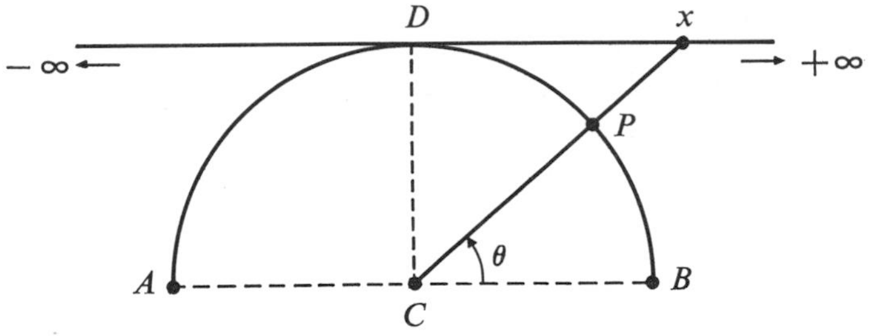


FIGURE 23

for $R^*$ in which all the $N$'s form a basis of neighborhoods. If $S \subset R$, then $S \subset R^*$ also, of course. We see from the foregoing definition that a subset $S$ of $R$ is open in the topology of $R^*$ if and only if $S$ is open in the topology of $R$, as defined in Section 2–3. Moreover, any open set in $R^*$ remains open if we delete from it either or both of the points $\pm\infty$. It is then clear that the relative topology of $R$ induced by that of $R^*$ is just the usual topology of $R$. Obviously $R$ is dense in $R^*$. Also, obviously, $R^*$ is a Hausdorff space. Finally, $R^*$ is compact. For, suppose $\mathscr{U}$ is an open covering of $R^*$. Then some $U_1 \in \mathscr{U}$ contains $-\infty$, and also contains a set $N_a(-\infty)$; also, some $U_2 \in \mathscr{U}$ contains $+\infty$, and also contains a set $N_b(+\infty)$. If $b < a$, the two sets $U_1$, $U_2$ cover $R^*$. If $a \leq b$, $U_1$ and $U_2$ cover all of $R^*$ except perhaps the points of the compact set $\{x : a \leq x \leq b\}$. Since a finite number of the elements of $\mathscr{U}$ will suffice to cover this set, it is clear that a finite subfamily from $\mathscr{U}$ covers $R^*$; hence $R^*$ is compact.

We can construct a "topological model" of $R^*$ as follows. Draw a semicircular arc $ADB$ with center $C$, tangent to the $x$ axis at $D$, as shown in Figure 23. The arc $ADB$, not including the endpoints $A$, $B$, is mapped onto $R$ by projecting $P$ onto $x$ by a line from the center $C$. The mapping is defined by $x = \text{ctn}\,\theta$ if $CD = 1$ and $D$ is the zero point on the $x$ axis. We can see from this construction that $R$ is homeomorphic with the arc $ADB$ (the end points excluded). If we extend the mapping by agreeing that $A(\theta = \pi)$ corresponds to $-\infty$ and $B$ $(\theta = 0)$ corresponds to $+\infty$, we see that the arc, with its endpoints included, is homeomorphic with $R^*$. The arc, a compact set in $R^2$, is then a topological model of $R^*$.

*Example 2.* It is easy to use the diagram in Figure 23 to illustrate a process of compactification of the space $R^2$. Let us imagine the entire diagram to be revolved about the line $CD$. The semicircular $ADB$ then generates a hemispherical surface and the tangent line generates a plane tangent to the hemisphere at $D$. The plane can be taken as $R^2$ (with origin at $D$). By projecting as before from $C$, the plane is in homeomorphic correspondence with the hemispherical surface, *not* including the circular rim generated by the ends of the revolving arc. The hemisphere, *inclusive* of this circular rim, is a compact space, with the relative topology induced by $R^3$. To compactify the plane $R^2$ we adjoin a whole collection of "points at infinity," a distinct one corresponding in the obvious way to each point on the rim of the hemisphere; and then we define the topology of this enlargement of $R^2$ by using the mapping of the compact hemisphere to transfer the open sets on the hemisphere into the open sets of the space which is our compactification of $R^2$.

If $P$ is a point on the rim of the compact hemisphere, we can take, as a typical element of a basis of neighborhoods at $P$, the part of the hemisphere inside a sphere with center $P$ and

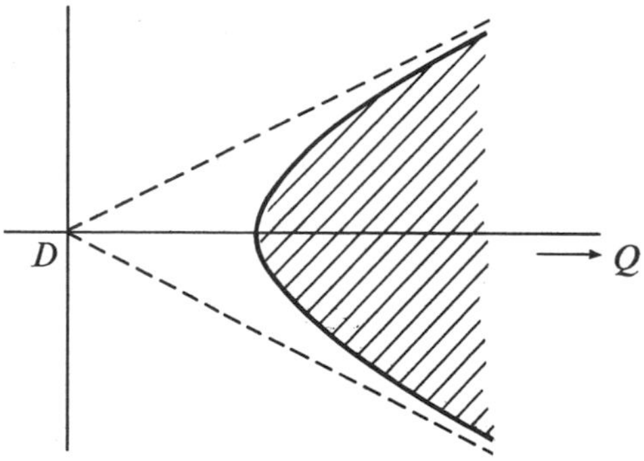


FIGURE 24

radius less than the distance $CP$. If $Q$ is the "point at infinity" which corresponds to $P$, we can think of it as lying at "one end" of a line $L$ through $D$ in the tangent plane. The corresponding member of the basis of neighborhoods at $Q$ consists of all points of the plane lying in the convex region bounded by one arc of a certain hyperbola with axis $L$ and center at $D$, together with all the points at infinity "at the ends of" half-lines through $D$ between the asymptotes of the hyperbola (see Figure 24).

*Example 3.* There is another way of compactifying $R^2$, by the use of stereographic projection. In this case we add just one "point at infinity," and the compactification of $R^2$ is homeomorphic to the complete surface of a sphere in $R^3$. If we think of $R^2$ as the complex plane, this compactification of $R^2$ is what is called "the extended complex plane" in the theory of functions of a complex variable.

The geometric representation in this case is obained by taking a plane tangent to a sphere and projecting from the point $C$ on the sphere diametrically opposite to the point of tangency (see Figure 25). To each point $P$ of the sphere, other than $C$, corresponds a unique point $x$ of the plane. The one additional point "$\infty$" of the extended plane corresponds to $C$. A typical element of a basis of neighborhoods at $\infty$ consists of $\infty$ and all points $x$ outside a circle of arbitrary positive radius with center at $D$ (the origin).

There is still another way of compactifying the plane $R^2$. This is the way which leads to the "projective plane." In this case there is one "point at infinity" on each line through the

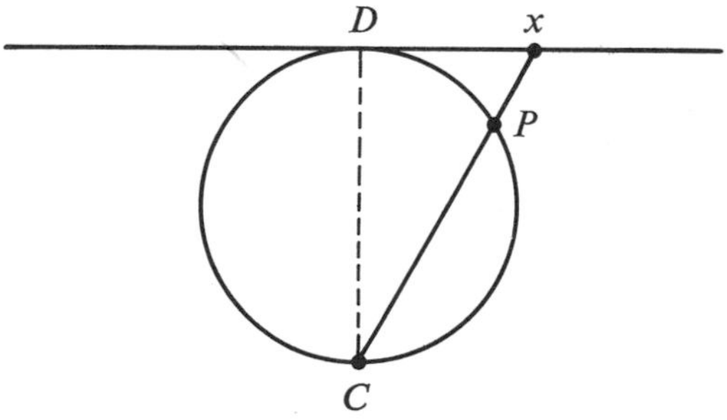


FIGURE 25

origin, instead of two such points, as in Example 2. We shall not describe the process in detail; for reference see Hilbert and Cohn-Vossen [1], pp. 276–283 and Seifert and Threlfall [1], pp. 9–12.

## ONE-POINT COMPACTIFICATION

We shall now describe a process of compactifying a noncompact space by the adjunction of one point. The compactification of the plane $R^2$ in Example 3 is a particular case of the general method.

THEOREM 3–5 I. *Let $X$ be a noncompact topological space. Let $\mathscr{W}$ be the family of all open subsets $W$ of $X$ such that $W^\sim$ is compact. Let $Y$ be a set consisting of the elements of $X$ and one new element $y_0$. Let $\mathscr{S}$ be the family of all subsets $S$ of $Y$ such that $S$ is open in $X$ if $y_0 \notin S$, and $S \cap X \in \mathscr{W}$ if $y_0 \in S$. Then $\mathscr{S}$ is a topology for $Y$, and with this topology $Y$ is a compactification of $X$. If $X$ is a $T_1$ space, so is $Y$.*

*Proof.* Of the proof that $\mathscr{S}$ is a topology for $Y$ we shall give only one part; other parts are left to the reader. Suppose that $\{S_\alpha\}$ is a family of members of $\mathscr{S}$, and let $S = \bigcup_\alpha S_\alpha$. We wish to prove that $S \in \mathscr{S}$. If $y_0 \notin S$, then $y_0$ is not in any of the $S_\alpha$'s. Then each $S_\alpha$ is open in $X$, and hence so is $S$, so that $S \in \mathscr{S}$. If $y_0 \in S$, then $y_0 \in S_\alpha$ for some value of $\alpha$, say $\alpha = \beta$. This implies that $S_\beta \cap X \in \mathscr{W}$, and we wish to prove that $S \cap X \in \mathscr{W}$. Now $S \cap X = \bigcup_\alpha (S_\alpha \cap X)$; from this we conclude that $S \cap X$ is open in $X$, because each $S_\alpha \cap X$ is open in $X$. Now, $X - (S \cap X) = \bigcap_\alpha [X - (S_\alpha \cap X)]$. Each set $X - (S_\alpha \cap X)$ is closed in $X$, and $X - (S_\beta \cap X)$ is compact. It then follows by Theorem 3–2 II that $X - (S \cap X)$ is compact; it therefore belongs to $\mathscr{W}$, and this part of the proof is finished.

It is obvious that the relative topology of $X$ as a subset of $Y$ is just the original topology of $X$.

To prove that $X$ is dense in $Y$ we must show that $y_0$ is an accumulation point of $X$. Now, the fact that $X$ is not compact shows that $\varnothing \notin \mathscr{W}$. If $S$ is a neighborhood of $y_0$, $S \cap X \in \mathscr{W}$, and therefore $S \cap X \neq \varnothing$. This proves that $y_0 \in X'$.

We leave it for the reader to verify that $Y$ is compact. The nature of the family $\mathscr{W}$ is crucial for this.

We also leave it for the reader to verify that $Y$ is a $T_1$ space if $X$ is.

When a space $Y$ is obtained from a space $X$ in the manner described in Theorem 3–5 I, we shall call *$Y$ the one-point compactification of $X$.*

## LOCALLY COMPACT SPACES

With $X$ and $Y$ as in Theorem 3–5 I, the issue, as to whether or not $Y$ is a Hausdorff space when $X$ is a Hausdorff space, is bound up with a property called local compactness. A space is called *locally compact* if every point has a neighborhood whose closure is compact. We can see that the Euclidean space $R^k$ is locally compact, for $\{x : \|x - x_0\| < 1\}$ is a neighborhood of $x_0$, and the closure of this neighborhood is compact, because it is bounded.

There are important examples of spaces which are not locally compact. We shall be more explicit about this in Section 3–13.

THEOREM 3–5 II. *The one-point compactification Y of a noncompact topological space X is a Hausdorff space if and only if X is both locally compact and a Hausdorff space.*

*Proof.* If we suppose that $Y$ is a Hausdorff space, it is evident that the $T_2$-separation axiom holds in $X$. Furthermore, if $x \in X$, there exist disjoint open sets $U$ and $V$ in $Y$ such that $x \in U$ and $y_0 \in V$. Let $W = V \cap X$. Then $W \in \mathscr{W}$, $X - W$ is closed in $X$ and compact, and $X \cap U \subset X - W$. It follows that the closure in $X$ of $X \cap U$ is contained in $X - W$, and is therefore compact, by Theorem 3–2 II. Since $X \cap U$ is a neighborhood of $x$, this proves that $X$ is locally compact.

Conversely, if $X$ is a locally compact Hausdorff space, the space $Y$ satisfies the $T_2$-separation axiom. It is enough to consider the separation of $y_0$ and a point $x \in X$. In the argument which we proceed to give, the signs of closure and complementation are to be understood in relation to $X$ as the basic space. If $x \in U$ and $U$ is an open set in $X$ such that $\bar{U}$ is compact, it follows that $(\bar{U})^{\sim} \in \mathscr{W}$. The set consisting of $y_0$ and $(\bar{U})^{\sim}$ is then an open set in $Y$, and it is disjoint from $U$, which is also an open set in $Y$. Thus we have the required separation of $x$ and $y_0$.

## PROBLEMS

1. Show that the mapping $x = f(t) = \dfrac{t}{1 - t^2}$ maps $(-1, 1)$ homeomorphically onto $R$, and that it can be extended to give a homeomorphic mapping of $[-1, 1]$ onto $R^*$.

2. Use Figure 25 to describe a compactification of $R$ by the addition of a single point $\infty$; the compact enlargement of $R$ is to be homeomorphic to a circular circumference.

3. (a) In the proof of Theorem 3–5 I, give the rest of the proof that $\mathscr{S}$ is a topology for $Y$. (b) Prove that $Y$ is compact. (c) Prove that $Y$ is a $T_1$ space if $X$ is.

## 3–6 Metric spaces

We pointed out in Section 2–1 that $R^k$ is what is called a metric space. The concept of a metric space can be explained in very general terms as follows: If $X$ is any nonempty collection of elements $x, y, \ldots$, and if there exists a function $D$ with domain the set of all ordered pairs $(x, y)$ of elements from $X$, and range in the real number system, such that the following three postulates are satisfied, then $X$ together with this function $D$ is called a metric space. The elements of $X$ are called points. The postulates:

1. $D(x, y) = D(y, x)$.
2. $D(x, z) \leq D(x, y) + D(y, z)$.
3. $D(x, y) = 0$ if and only if $x = y$.

As we know, a function $D$ with these properties can be defined when $X$ is $R^k$. But since many useful theorems can be deduced from the above three postulates, regardless of anything else that may be known about $X$ or about the particular way in which the function $D$ is constructed, it is eminently worthwhile, as experience has shown, to study metric spaces in the abstract, strictly from the postulates. Much of this general study of metric spaces is concerned with the topology for a metric space $X$ which can be defined with the aid of the function $D$. This function is called *the metric*, and the number $D(x, y)$ is called the distance between $x$ and $y$. It was not explicitly assumed that $D(x, y) \geq 0$, but we can prove the truth of this inequality. In fact, if we put $x = z$ in the second postulate, we obtain

$$D(x, x) \leq D(x, y) + D(y, x).$$

From the first and third postulates it then follows that $0 \leq 2D(x, y)$, whence $D(x, y) \geq 0$.

## THE TOPOLOGY OF A METRIC SPACE

If $X$ is a metric space with metric $D$, we define a system of neighborhoods $N_\epsilon(x)$ as follows: If $\epsilon > 0$ and $x$ is in $X$, $N_\epsilon(x)$ consists of all points $y$ in $X$ such that $D(x, y) < \epsilon$. The set $N_\epsilon(x)$ certainly contains $x$; there is no assurance that it contains any other points. Whether it does or not will depend on the particular space $X$, and perhaps on the particular $x$ and $\epsilon$. If we let $\mathscr{N}$ be the family of all the pairs $(N_\epsilon(x), x)$ ($\epsilon$ and $x$ arbitrary), it is easy to see that the construction used in Section 3–4 makes $X$ into a Hausdorff space. For example, to verify postulate 3 of Section 3–4 for this case, suppose $y \in N_\epsilon(x)$. Let $\delta = \epsilon - D(y, x)$. Then $N_\delta(y) \subset N_\epsilon(x)$. For, if $z \in N_\delta(y)$, this means that $D(z, y) < \delta$. But $D(z, x) \leq D(z, y) + D(y, x) < \delta + D(y, x) = \epsilon$, so that $z \in N_\epsilon(x)$. The $T_2$-separation axiom is fulfilled in our present situation, because, if $x \neq y$ and $\epsilon = \frac{1}{2} D(x, y)$, the sets $N_\epsilon(x)$ and $N_\epsilon(y)$ have no elements in common. For, if they did have a common element $z$, we would have

$$D(x, y) \leq D(x, z) + D(z, y) < \epsilon + \epsilon = D(x, y),$$

with the resulting contradiction $D(x, y) < D(x, y)$. We leave it for the reader to verify that postulates 1 and 2 in Section 3–4 are satisfied.

The importance of the postulate 2 of this section is apparent from the foregoing arguments. This postulate is called the "triangularity postulate," or the triangular inequality.

For a fixed positive $\epsilon$ and any $x$, the set $\{y : D(x, y) < \epsilon\}$ is called the open sphere with radius $\epsilon$ and center $x$. It *is* an open set in the metric space. The family of all open spheres with a fixed center $x$ is a basis of neighborhoods at $x$. But we can also get a basis at $x$ by using fewer than all of these neighborhoods. It suffices to take any countable family corresponding to a sequence $\{\epsilon_n\}$ of radii such that $\epsilon_n \to 0$. Hence, *a metric space always satisfies the first axiom of countability* (see Section 3–2). Some, but not all, metric spaces satisfy the second axiom of countability.

It can happen that several metrics are defined for the same set of elements. If $d$ and $D$ are metrics on $X$, and if $d$ and $D$ determine the same topology for $X$, we say that $d$ and $D$ are *equivalent metrics* on $X$. For convenience let us call the set $\{y : D(x, y) < \epsilon\}$ an open $D$ sphere; it is an open set in the topology determined by $D$. Likewise, for $d$ spheres. The topologies determined by $D$ and $d$ are equivalent if and only if, for each point $x$ in $X$ each open $D$ sphere with center $x$ contains an open $d$ sphere with center $x$, and likewise with $d$ and $D$ reversed. A sufficient condition for this to be true is that there exist positive constants $m$, $M$ such that

(1) $$mD(x, y) \leq d(x, y) \leq MD(x, y)$$

for each pair of points $x, y$ in $X$. If this inequality is satisfied we see, for instance, that the open $d$ sphere with center $x$ and radius $m\epsilon$ is contained in the open $D$ sphere with center $x$ and radius $\epsilon$.

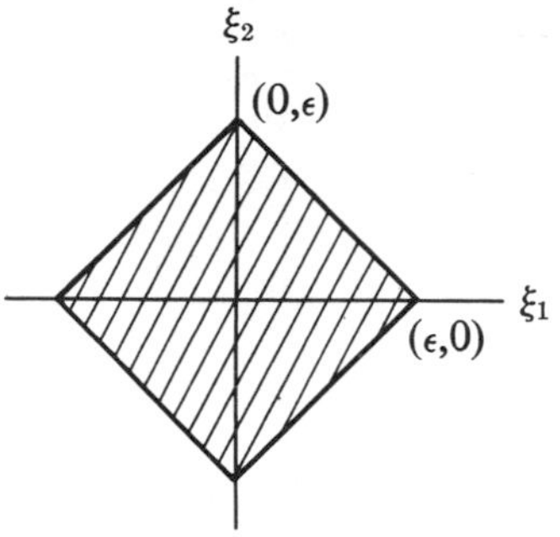


FIGURE 26

*Example 1.* In the space $R^k$ the Euclidean metric is defined by

(2) $$D_2(x, y) = \left[\sum_{i=1}^{k} (\xi_i - \eta_i)^2\right]^{1/2},$$

where $x = (\xi_1, \ldots, \xi_k)$, $y = (\eta_1, \ldots, \eta_k)$. An equivalent metric $D_1$ is defined by

(3) $$D_1(x, y) = \sum_{i=1}^{k} |\xi_i - \eta_i|,$$

and still another equivalent metric $D_\infty$ is defined by

(4) $$D_\infty(x, y) = \max\,[|\xi_1 - \eta_1|, \ldots, |\xi_k - \eta_k|].$$

The various subscripts on $D_1$, $D_2$, $D_\infty$ are used as particular instances of $D_p$. In the problems it is indicated how to obtain a metric $D_p$ for each $p$, $1 \le p \le \infty$. All these metrics yield the same topology for $R^k$.

We leave it for the reader to verify that $D_1$ and $D_\infty$ are metrics. It is easy to see that

(5) $$D_\infty(x, y) \le D_2(x, y) \le \sqrt{k}\,D_\infty(x, y)$$

and

(6) $$D_\infty(x, y) \le D_1(x, y) \le k D_\infty(x, y),$$

and from these inequalities it follows that $D_1$, $D_2$, and $D_\infty$ define the same topology. The $D_1$ sphere in $R^2$ with center (0, 0) and radius $\epsilon$ is shown in Figure 26. The corresponding $D_\infty$ sphere is shown in Figure 27.

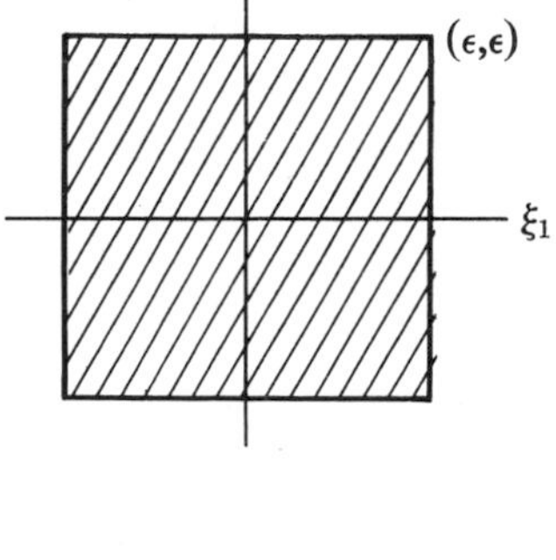


FIGURE 27

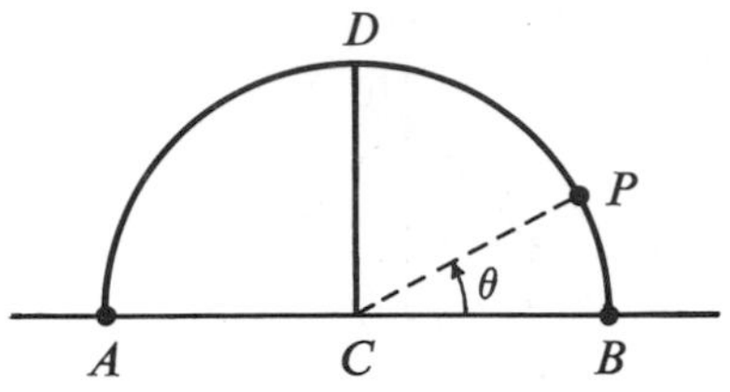


FIGURE 28

*Example 2.* Consider the space of points $P$ on the compact semicircular arc $ADB$ in Figure 28. With the angular coordinate $\theta$ for $P$ as marked ($\theta$ in radians), define the distance between two points $P_1$, $P_2$ on the arc as $D(P_1, P_2) = |\theta_1 - \theta_2|$. The correspondence $P \to \theta$ clearly maps the space in a one-to-one fashion onto $[0, \pi]$. Since $d(\theta_1, \theta_2) = |\theta_1 - \theta_2|$ defines the restriction to $[0, \pi]$ of the usual Euclidean metric in $R$, it is clear that $D$ is a metric on the semicircular arc. If we refer to Figure 23 and the discussion of $R^*$ in Section 3–5, we see that we can define a metric $d$ in $R^*$ as follows:

$$d(x, y) = |\text{ctn}^{-1}x - \text{ctn}^{-1}y|$$

if $x$ and $y$ are real numbers, $d(+\infty, -\infty) = \pi$,

$$d(x, +\infty) = \text{ctn}^{-1}x,\ d(x, -\infty) = \pi - \text{ctn}^{-1}x.$$

Here it is understood that $0 < \text{ctn}^{-1}x < \pi$ for real $x$, and of course we require

$$d(-\infty, +\infty) = d(+\infty, -\infty)$$

and the other symmetries of distances involving $+\infty$ and $-\infty$. The topology determined by $d$ is that discussed in Section 3–5.

## SUBSPACES OF A METRIC SPACE

Any nonempty set $S$ in a metric space $X$ is a metric space if we use the metric of $X$ and restrict it to the subspace. The resulting topology is just the relative topology of $S$.

## METRIZABLE SPACES

A topological space $X$ is said to be *metrizable* if a metric $D$ can be defined on $X$ in such a way that the topology determined by the metric is the same as the original topology of $X$.

One of the principal theorems about metrizability is the following: *A perfectly separable $T_1$ space is metrizable if and only if it is normal.* The "if" part of this theorem is due to P. Urysohn. Any metric space is normal (see Problem 3). However, there exist metric spaces which are not perfectly separable. For more about metrization theorems see Hocking and Young [1], pp. 67–70 and pp. 80–81; also Kelley [1], pp. 124–130 and pp. 184–190.

## BOUNDEDNESS

A nonempty set $S$ in a metric space $X$ is called *bounded* if it is contained in some open sphere. We also consider $\varnothing$ to be a bounded set. When $S$ is bounded and $x_0$ is any point of $X$, $S$ is contained in some open sphere with center $x_0$.

For any nonempty set $S$, bounded or not, we define the *diameter* of $S$, denoted by diam $(S)$, as

(7) $$\text{diam}(S) = \sup \{D(x, y) : x, y \in S\}.$$

It is easy to see that $S$ is bounded if and only if diam $(S) < +\infty$.

The property of boundedness is not invariant under homeomorphisms. For instance, in $R$, the sets $\{x : 0 < x < 1\}$ and $\{x : 0 < x\}$ are homeomorphic, and only one of them is bounded.

## METRIC SPACES OF FUNCTIONS

In analysis we find it very useful to consider various metric spaces whose elements are functions. Here we shall consider just a few examples. Metrics are often defined by the use of integration; we shall see examples of this in later chapters of this book.

*Example 3.* The class of all real-valued continuous functions defined on the compact interval $[a, b]$ is denoted by $C[a, b]$. If $x, y \in C[a, b]$, let

(8) $$D(x, y) = \sup |x(t) - y(t)|,$$

the supremum being taken with respect to all $t$ on $[a, b]$. Because the functions are continuous the supremum is an attained value of $|x(t) - y(t)|$; that is

(9) $$D(x, y) = \max_{a \le t \le b} |x(t - y(t)|.$$

It is easily verified that $D$ is a metric.

Another quite different metric $d$ may be defined on $C[a, b]$ as follows:

(10) $$d(x, y) = \int_a^b |x(t) - y(t)|\, dt.$$

Evidently $d(x, y) \le (b - a)\, D(x, y)$. The two metrics are not equivalent, however. We can see this as follows. Let 0 denote the zero function, and let $S = \{x : D(x, 0) < 1\}$. If $d$ and $D$ were equivalent metrics, $S$ would contain some open $d$ sphere $\{x : d(x, 0) < \epsilon\}$. But this is not the case. For simplicity let us demonstrate this on the assumption that $a = 0$, $b = 1$. For any given $\epsilon$, choose the positive integer $n$ so that $1 < \epsilon(n + 1)$, and let $x_n$ be defined by $x_n(t) = t^n$. Then $D(x_n, 0) = 1$, so $x_n$ is not in $S$. But $d(x_n, 0) = \dfrac{1}{n+1} < \epsilon$. Hence $\{x : d(x, 0) < \epsilon\}$ is not contained in $S$.

*Example 4.* Let $C^1[0, 1]$ be the class of all continuous functions $x : [0, 1] \to R$ having continuous derivative $x'$ on $[0, 1]$, and for two such functions $x, y$ let

(11) $$d(x, y) = \max_{0 \le t \le 1} |x(t) - y(t)| + \max_{0 \le t \le 1} |x'(t) - y'(t)|.$$

Then $C^1[0, 1]$ is a metric space.

We see that $C^1[0, 1]$ is a subset of $C[0, 1]$. Hence there are two metrics defined on $C^1[0, 1]$: by (11) and (9), respectively. They do not define the same topology, however.

## THE ROLE OF SEQUENCES IN METRIC SPACES

If $\{x_n\}$ is a sequence in the metric space $X$, the assertion $x_n \to x$ is equivalent to $D(x_n, x) \to 0$, as is easily verified. Since

$$D(x, y) \le D(x, x_n) + D(x_n, y),$$

we see that $x_n \to x$ and $x_n \to y$ imply $x = y$. (This conclusion is true, more generally, in Hausdorff spaces.)

In metric spaces it is frequently useful to deal with sequences as a technique in discussing such topics as points of accumulation, closure, and compactness. The following propositions are true in any topological space $X$. We leave proofs to the reader.

*If $S \subset X$, if $\{x_n\}$ is a sequence in $S$, and if $x_n \to x$, then $x \in \bar{S}$.*

*If $x_n \to x$ and if $x_n \neq x$ for infinitely many values of $n$, then $x$ is an accumulation point of any set $S$ which contains all the $x_n$'s.*

The propositions in the following theorem are not true for topological spaces in general, not even for Hausdorff spaces. In conjunction with the foregoing propositions they give characterizations, valid in metric spaces, of the closure of $S$ and the derived set of $S$ by means of convergent sequences.

THEOREM 3–6 I. *Let $S$ be a set in a metric space $X$. Then:*
(a) *If $x \in \bar{S}$, there exists a sequence $\{x_n\}$ in $S$ such that $x_n \to x$.*
(b) *If $y \in S'$, there exists a sequence $\{x_n\}$ in $S$ such that $x_1, x_2, \ldots$ are all distinct, $x_n \neq y$, and $x_n \to y$.*

*Proof of* (a). If $x \in \bar{S}$, the open sphere with center $x$ and radius $1/n$ contains some point of $S$, say $x_n$. Then $D(x_n, x) \to 0$, and hence $x_n \to x$.
*Proof of* (b). Exactly the same as the proof of Theorem 2–4 III, except that we now write $D(x_n, y)$ in place of $\|x_n - y\|$.

We remark that (a) holds true in any space which satisfies the first axiom of countability. The argument is like that in the proof of Theorem 3–2 V. If the space is also a $T_1$ space, (b) holds true.
The role of sequences in connection with compactness in metric spaces is discussed in Section 3–7.

## DISTANCES BETWEEN SETS

Let $S$ be any nonempty set in the metric space $X$, and suppose $x \in X$. We define

$$D(x, S) = \inf_{y \in S} D(x, y), \tag{12}$$

and call this the distance between $x$ and $S$. Likewise, if $S_1$ and $S_2$ are nonempty sets, we define the distance $D(S_1, S_2)$ between $S_1$ and $S_2$ as the infimum of the numbers $D(x, y)$ as $x$ and $y$ vary over $S_1$ and $S_2$, respectively. It is easy to see that

$$D(S_1, S_2) = \inf_{x \in S_1} D(x, S_2). \tag{13}$$

We can see that $D(x, S) = 0$ is equivalent to $x \in \bar{S}$.
It is possible to have $D(S_1, S_2) = 0$ even when $S_1$ and $S_2$ are disjoint closed sets. For example, in $R^2$ let

$$S_1 = \{x : \xi_2 \leq 0,\} \qquad S_2 = \{x : \xi_1^2\xi_2 \geq 1\},$$

where $x = (\xi_1, \xi_2)$.
By using the notion of distance from a point to a set it is possible to prove rather easily that a metric space is normal. See Problem 3.

## CONTINUITY

If $X_1$ and $X_2$ are metric spaces with metrics $D_1$ and $D_2$, respectively, the topological definition of continuity is equivalent to the following metric criterion: A function $f: X_1 \to X_2$ is continuous at a point $x_0$ in $X_1$ if and only if to each $\epsilon > 0$ corresponds a $\delta > 0$ such that $D_1(x, x_0) < \delta$ implies $D_2(f(x), f(x_0)) < \epsilon$. An alternative criterion: $f$ is continuous at $x$ if and only if $x_n \to x$ always implies $f(x_n) \to f(x)$. See Problem 8.

## ISOMETRIES

If $X$ and $Y$ are metric spaces with metrics $D$, $d$, and if $f: X \to Y$ is a mapping such that $d[f(x_1), f(x_2)] = D(x_1, x_2)$ for each pair $x_1$, $x_2$ in $X$, we call $f$ an *isometry*, or an *isometric* mapping. Observe that $f(x_1) = f(x_2)$ implies $x_1 = x_2$, so that the inverse $f^{-1}$ exists. An isometry is obviously continuous, and so is the inverse, for it is an isometric mapping of $f(X)$ onto $X$. If $f(X) = Y$ in this case, we say that $X$ and $Y$ are in isometric correspondence.

## UNIFORM CONTINUITY

The concept of uniform continuity is defined exactly as in Section 2–7: If $X_1$ and $X_2$ are metric spaces, the function $f: X_1 \to X_2$ is said to be uniformly continuous on $X_1$ if to each $\epsilon > 0$ corresponds some $\delta > 0$ such that $D_2[f(x_1), f(x_2)] < \epsilon$ whenever $D_1(x_1, x_2) < \delta$. This concept is not generally available to us when $X_1$ and $X_2$ are merely topological spaces. There is nothing in the concept of a topological space, even with strong separation axioms, which permits us to speak of anything comparable to the family of all open spheres of radius $\epsilon$, with arbitrary centers. There is a class of topological spaces, more general than metric spaces, in which notions of uniformity can be defined and usefully developed. These are called *uniform spaces, or spaces with uniform structure* (see Kelley [1], Chapter 6). We shall not consider such spaces in this book. Our principal interest in uniform continuity appears in connection with Theorem 3–7 III (see also Theorem 2–7 V).

## UNIFORM CONVERGENCE

Let $X$ be topological space and let $Y$ be a metric space. Suppose $f: X \to Y$ and $f_n: X \to Y$ ($n = 1, 2, \ldots$) are given. We say that $\{f_n\}$ converges to $f$ *uniformly* on $X$ if to each $\epsilon > 0$ corresponds some positive integer $N$ such that $D(f_n(x), f(x)) < \epsilon$ when $n \geq N$, for each $x$ in $X$. Concerning this concept we have the following important theorem about the transmission of the property of being continuous. It is a generalization of a familiar theorem of advanced calculus.

THEOREM 3–6 II. *Suppose $X$, $Y$, $\{f_n\}$, and $f$ are given as in the preceding paragraph with $\{f_n\}$ converging to $f$ uniformly on $X$. Suppose that each $f_n$ is continuous at the point $x_0$. Then $f$ is continuous at $x_0$.*

*Proof.* Suppose $\epsilon > 0$. Select $N$ so that, for each $x$, $D(f_n(x), f(x)) < \epsilon/3$ if $n \geq N$. Since $f_N$ is continuous at $x_0$, we can choose a neighborhood $U$ of $x_0$ so that $D(f_N(x), f_N(x_0)) < \epsilon/3$ if $x \in U$. Then $x \in U$ implies

$$D(f(x), f(x_0)) \leq D(f(x), f_N(x)) + D(f_N(x), f_N(x_0)) + D(f_N(x_0), f(x_0)) < \frac{\epsilon}{3} + \frac{\epsilon}{3} + \frac{\epsilon}{3} = \epsilon,$$

and therefore $f$ is continuous at $x_0$.

## CONTINUITY OF THE METRIC

If $x, y, x_0$ are any three points of the metric space $X$, we have

$$|D(x, x_0) - D(y, x_0)| \leq D(x, y). \tag{14}$$

More generally, if $x, y, x_0, y_0$ are any four points,

$$|D(x, y) - D(x_0, y_0)| \leq D(x, x_0) + D(y, y_0). \tag{15}$$

To prove (14) observe that

$$D(x, x_0) - D(y, x_0) \leq D(x, y),$$

by the triangular inequality. The same result holds with $x$ and $y$ exchanged, and therefore (14) is true. Next, we have

$$|D(x, y) - D(x_0, y_0)| \leq |D(x, y) - D(x, y_0)| + |D(x, y_0) - D(x_0, y_0)|.$$

We apply (14) to each of the absolute values here on the right, and we obtain (15).

The inequality (14) enables us to show that the mapping $x \to D(x, x_0)$ is continuous on $X$ ($x_0$ fixed). Likewise, (15) shows that the mapping $(x, y) \to D(x, y)$ is a continuous function of the two variables $x, y$. We discuss continuity of functions of several variables in Section 3–11.

## PROBLEMS

1. Prove that a separable metric space is perfectly separable.

2. (a) Let $D$ and $D_1$ be two metrics for the space $X$. Show that these metrics are equivalent if and only if to each pair $\epsilon, y$, where $\epsilon > 0$ and $y \in X$, there corresponds a $\delta > 0$ and an $\eta > 0$ such that

$$\{x : D_1(x, y) < \delta\} \subset \{x : D(x, y) < \epsilon\}$$

and

$$\{x : D(x, y) < \eta\} \subset \{x : D_1(x, y) < \epsilon\}.$$

(b) Show that another way of expressing the equivalence of $D$ and $D_1$ is the following: Whenever $D(x_n, x) \to 0$ then $D_1(x_n, x) \to 0$, and whenever $D_1(x_n, x) \to 0$, then $D(x_n, x) \to 0$.

3. Prove that a metric space is normal. [*Suggestion*. Suppose $A$ and $B$ are disjoint closed sets. For $x \in A$ let $U(x) = \{y : D(y, x) < \frac{1}{2} D(x, B)\}$ and for $x \in B$ let $V(x) = \{y : D(y, x) < \frac{1}{2} D(x, A)\}$. Let $S = \bigcup_{x \in A} U(x)$, $T = \bigcup_{x \in B} V(x)$.]

4. Show that a metric for $R^*$, equivalent to that of Example 2, can be defined by $D(x, y) = |f(x) - f(y)|$, where $f : R^* \to R$ is defined by $f(x) = x(1 + |x|)^{-1}$ if $x$ is real, $f(+\infty) = 1$, and $f(-\infty) = -1$.

5. Prove that the metrics $d$ and $D$ in $C^1[0, 1]$, defined by (11) and (9), respectively, are not equivalent.

6. If $S \neq \varnothing$, show that the mapping $x \to D(x, S)$ is continuous.

7. Let $X$ be a metric space with metric $D$. Define a function $D_1$ by

$$D_1(x, y) = \frac{D(x, y)}{1 + D(x, y)}.$$

Show that $D_1$ is also a metric on $X$, and that it is equivalent to $D$. Observe that $D_1(x, y) < 1$ always. Thus $X$ is bounded when the metric $D_1$ is used, regardless of whether or not it was bounded for the metric $D$. [*Suggestion.* The proof that $D_1$ satisfies the triangularity postulate 2 for a metric can be based on the following lemma: If $a \geq 0$, $b \geq 0$, and $c \geq 0$, and if $a + b \geq c$, then

$$\frac{a}{1+a} + \frac{b}{1+b} \geq \frac{c}{1+c}.$$

Begin by proving this.

8. (a) If $f: X_1 \to X_2$, where $X_1$ and $X_2$ are metric spaces, prove that the $\epsilon$, $\delta$-formulation of continuity at a point $x$ of $X_1$ is equivalent to the definition phrased in topological terms.

(b) Show that still another equivalent formulation is the following one (the *sequential* formulation): $f$ is continuous at $x$ if and only if $x_n \to x$ always implies $f(x_n) \to f(x)$. Are the sequential and topological formulations of continuity equivalent under certain conditions when $X_1$ and $X_2$ are not both metrizable?

9. This problem deals with some inequalities which are useful for the study of certain examples of metric spaces. The important results contained here are presented in such a way that they will be readily available for reference in connection with other parts of the text.

(a) If $A > 0$, $B > 0$, $\alpha > 0$, $\beta > 0$, and $\alpha + \beta = 1$, then

$$A^\alpha B^\beta \leq \alpha A + \beta B.$$

In proving this, note that it is clearly true if $A = B$. Hence one deals with the case $A \neq B$, and by symmetry one can assume $A > B$. Writing $x = A/B$, the problem becomes that of proving that $x^\alpha - 1 \leq \alpha(x - 1)$ if $x > 1$ and $0 < \alpha < 1$. Prove this, using differential calculus.

(b) Hölder's inequality asserts that if $p > 1$, $p' = \dfrac{p}{p-1}$, and $a_1, a_2, \ldots, b_1, b_2, \ldots$ are real or complex numbers, then

$$\sum_i |a_i b_i| \leq \Big(\sum_i |a_i|^p\Big)^{1/p} \Big(\sum_i |b_i|^{p'}\Big)^{1/p'}.$$

Observe that Cauchy's inequality (Lemma 2–1 I) is a special case. The sums are to be over the same range in all three summation signs—either a finite range or $\sum_{i=1}^{\infty}$. In the case of infinite series, it is assumed that the two series on the right are convergent, and it is part of the conclusion that the series on the left is convergent. For the proof it is evidently sufficient to deal with the case of a finite range of summation; the proof for the case of infinite series is then obtained by a standard argument about the boundedness of partial sums.

It is also clear that we may as well assume $a_i \geq 0$, $b_i \geq 0$, since absolute values only are involved. Also, we can assume some $a_i > 0$ and some $b_i > 0$. We give the following suggestions. Let $\alpha = 1/p$, $\beta = 1/p'$,

$$A_j = \frac{a_j^p}{\sum_i a_i^p}, \qquad B_j = \frac{b_j^{p'}}{\sum_i b_i^{p'}}.$$

Apply the result in (a), sum on $j$, and so obtain the desired proof of Hölder's inequality.

(c) Minkowski's inequality asserts that if $p \geq 1$ and the $a_i$'s and $b_i$'s are real or complex numbers, then

$$\Big(\sum_i |a_i + b_i|^p\Big)^{1/p} \leq \Big(\sum_i |a_i|^p\Big)^{1/p} + \Big(\sum_i |b_i|^p\Big)^{1/p}.$$

Observe that (6) in Lemma 2–1 II is a special case of this ($p = 2$). The remarks made in (b) about the ranges of the summations (finite or infinite) apply here. Again it is sufficient to give the proof for the case of finite sums. We note also that validity of the inequality is apparent if $p = 1$. Hence we can assume $p > 1$ for the following proof. The device is to write

$$\begin{aligned} |a_i + b_i|^p &= |a_i + b_i|\,|a_i + b_i|^{p-1} \\ &\leq |a_i|\,|a_i + b_i|^{p-1} + |b_i|\,|a_i + b_i|^{p-1}. \end{aligned}$$

Now apply Hölder's inequality to

$$\sum |a_i|\,|a_i + b_i|^{p-1},$$

and note that $p'(p-1) = p$. After another such application of Hölder's inequality to a sum involving $|b_i|$, one has to consider separately the two cases according as

$$\sum_i |a_i + b_i|^p$$

is or is not 0. Note also that $1 - \dfrac{1}{p'} = \dfrac{1}{p}$. With these suggestions, write out the complete proof.

10. Let $x = (\xi_1, \ldots, \xi_k)$ and $y = (\eta_1, \ldots, \eta_k)$ be points in $R^k$. Suppose $1 \le p$, and define

$$D_p(x, y) = \left(\sum_{i=1}^{k} |\xi_i - \eta_i|^p\right)^{1/p}.$$

Show that $D_p$ is a metric in $R^k$. Investigate the set of points $x$ in $R^2$ such that $D_p(x, 0) = 1$ and the set for which $D_p(x, 0) < 1$. Compare with the diagrams in Figures 26, 27. Note that $D_2$ is the standard metric of $R^k$.

11. (a) Suppose $0 < p < q$ and $0 \le a_i$, $i = 1, \ldots, n$. Then prove that

$$\left(\sum_1^n a_i^q\right)^{1/q} \le \left(\sum_1^n a_i^p\right)^{1/p}.$$

This inequality is clearly valid if $a_1 = \cdots = a_n = 0$, so suppose at least one $a_i$ is positive. Let

$$b_j = \frac{a_j}{\left(\sum_1^n a_i^p\right)^{1/p}}.$$

What is the value of $\sum b_j^p$? Why is $b_j^q \le b_j^p$? With these leading questions, give the required proof.

(b) Referring to the metric $D_p$ for $R^k$ defined in Problem 10, show that $D_\infty(x, y) \le D_p(x, y) \le D_1(x, y)$ if $1 \le p$, where $D_\infty$ is the metric defined in Example 1 of this section (Formula (4)). Hence show that the metrics $D_p$ in $R^k$ for various values of $p$ are all equivalent.

(c) Suppose that $\alpha_1 \ge \cdots \ge \alpha_k \ge 0$. Show that

$$\alpha_1 \le (\alpha_1^p + \cdots + \alpha_k^p)^{1/p} \le k^{1/p}\alpha_1$$

and hence that

$$\lim_{p\to\infty} D_p(x, y) = \max\{|\xi_1 - \eta_1|, \ldots, |\xi_k - \eta_k|\}.$$

This motivates the notation $D_\infty(x, y)$.

12. Denote by $l^p$ the class of all real sequences $x = \{\xi_n\}$ such that $\sum_{n=1}^{\infty} |\xi_n|^p < \infty$, where $p$ is a fixed real number such that $p > 0$. For the case in which $p \ge 1$, show that $l^p$ becomes a metric space with metric $D_p$ if we define

$$D_p(x, y) = \left(\sum_{n=1}^{\infty} |\xi_n - \eta_n|^p\right)^{1/p}.$$

Use Minkowski's inequality (Problem 8(c)).

Observe (and explain) the class inclusion $l^p \subset l^q$ if $1 \le p < q$. We can then consider both metrics $D_p$, $D_q$ in $l^p$. Show that any set in $l^p$ which is open in the topology determined by $D_q$ is also open in the topology determined by $D_p$. The metrics $D_p$ and $D_q$ in $l^p$ are not equivalent, however. This can be seen as follows. For given $n$ consider the point $x_n$ which is the sequence each of whose first $n$ terms is $n^{-1/p}$, the rest of the terms being 0's. Let 0 denote also the element $x = \{\xi_n\}$ of $l^p$ for which each $\xi_n$ is 0. Then $D_p(x_n, 0) = 1$ but $D_q(x_n, 0) \to 0$ as $n \to \infty$. Verify the details and explain why this shows that $D_p$ and $D_q$ are not equivalent metrics.

## 3–7 Compactness in metric spaces

We have discussed compactness in $R^k$ (Section 2–6), in arbitrary topological spaces (Section 3–2), and in Hausdorff spaces (Section 3–3). Now we shall consider the situation for metric spaces. Our first theorem duplicates Theorem 2–6 I, which applied to $R^k$.

THEOREM 3–7 I. *If $S \subset X$, $X$ is a metric space, and $S$ is compact, then $S$ is closed and bounded.*

*Proof that S is bounded.* The argument in the proof of Theorem 2–6 I applies.

*Proof that S is closed.* Here also the earlier argument applies, for it is in fact valid in the case of any Hausdorff space. We can give a different and simpler proof, however, using the metric. Suppose that $S$ is compact but not closed, so that $S' - S$ contains some point $x$. Let $U_n = \left\{y : D(y, x) > \frac{1}{n}\right\}$. Then the family $U_1, U_2, \ldots$ is an open covering of $S$. Hence, since $U_n \subset U_{n+1}$ and $S$ is compact, it follows that $S \subset U_n$ for some value of $n$. But then $V \cap S = \varnothing$ if $V = \left\{y : D(y, x) < \frac{1}{n}\right\}$, in contradiction of the fact that $x \in S'$.

THEOREM 3–7 II. *In order that a set $T$ in a metric space $X$ be compact, it is both necessary and sufficient that $S' \cap T \neq \varnothing$ whenever $S$ is an infinite subset of $T$.*

*Proof.* Just like that of Theorem 2–6 II (a) and (b) (the special case $X = R^k$). We point out that the condition is necessary in an arbitrary topological space (Theorem 3–2 III).

We now give an example to show that the converse of Theorem 3–7 I is false.

*Example 1.* Consider the space $C[0, 1]$ (see Example 3, Section 3–6). Let

$$T = \{x : D(x, 0) \leq 1\}.$$

That is, $x \in T$ means that $|x(t)| \leq 1$ for each $t \in [0, 1]$. This is a closed and bounded set, but it is not compact. To see that $T$ is not compact, let $x_n(t) = t^n$, and let $S$ be the set consisting of $x_1, x_2, \ldots$. Then $S \subset T$. If $T$ were compact there would be some $x \in S' \cap T$, and by Theorem 3–6 I (b) there would be some subsequence of $\{x_n\}$ converging to $x$. Now, convergence in $C[0, 1]$ is convergence which is uniform with respect to $t$ on $[0, 1]$, by the definition of the metric in $C[0, 1]$. But every subsequence of $\{x_n(t)\}$ has limit 0 if $0 \leq t < 1$ and 1 if $t = 1$, and it is easy to see that the convergence is not uniform, because it is not uniform in any neighborhood of $t = 1$. Hence $S' \cap T = \varnothing$ and $T$ is not compact.

### COMPACTNESS AND UNIFORM CONTINUITY

Theorem 2–7 V was stated in the context of mappings defined in Euclidean spaces, but both the theorem and the proof as given in Section 2–7 carry over at once to the metric space situation. We state the result here for reference:

THEOREM 3–7 III. *If $f : X \to Y$ is continuous, where $X$ and $Y$ are metric spaces and $X$ is compact, then $f$ is uniformly continuous on $X$.*

## RELATIVELY COMPACT SETS

A set $T$ in a topological space $X$ is called *relatively compact* (also *conditionally* compact) if the closure $\bar{T}$ is compact. If $X$ is a Hausdorff space, a compact set in $X$ is relatively compact. Here we shall deal with this concept in the context of metric spaces. For applications in analysis, where we often wish to deal with sequences, it is of interest to characterize relatively compact sets by a property described in terms of sequences.

THEOREM 3–7 IV. *A set $T$ in a metric space $X$ is relatively compact if and only if every sequence $\{x_n\}$ whose elements belong to $T$ has a convergent subsequence.*

*Proof.* Suppose $\bar{T}$ is compact and $\{x_n\}$ is a sequence in $T$. Let $E$ be the set $\{x_1, x_2, \ldots\}$ (bear in mind the distinction between the set $E$ and the sequence $\{x_n\}$). If $E$ is a finite set it must contain an element $x$ such that $x_n = x$ for infinitely many values of $n$, and in this way we see that $\{x_n\}$ must contain a convergent subsequence. If $E$ is an infinite set, there must be an accumulation point $x$ of $E$ in $\bar{T}$ (Theorem 3–7 II). We can then get the desired convergent subsequence of $\{x_n\}$ by using Theorem 3–6 I (b).

Now, suppose $T$ has the property that every sequence from $T$ has a convergent subsequence. Let $S$ be any infinite subset of $\bar{T}$. We shall show that $S' \cap \bar{T} \neq \varnothing$, thus proving $T$ relatively compact (again using Theorem 3–7 II). Let $\{y_n\}$ be a sequence of distinct elements of $S$. Since $y_n \in \bar{T}$, there exists $x_n \in T$ such that $D(x_n, y_n) < \frac{1}{n}$, where $D$ is the metric in $X$. By hypothesis $\{x_n\}$ contains a convergent subsequence, which we shall denote by $\{u_n\}$. Let $\{v_n\}$ be the corresponding subsequence of $\{y_n\}$. Then $D(u_n, v_n) \to 0$. Let $x$ be the limit of the sequence $\{u_n\}$. It is also the limit of $\{v_n\}$, as is easily seen. Since the $v_n$'s are all distinct elements of $S$, and since $S \subset \bar{T}$, we see that $x \in S' \cap \bar{T}$. This ends the proof.

## PRECOMPACT SETS

A set $T$ in a metric space $X$ is called *precompact* if for each $\epsilon > 0$ there is a finite set of points in $X$, say $x_1, \ldots, x_n$, such that $T$ is contained in the union of the open spheres $S(x_i; \epsilon)$, $i = 1, \ldots, n$, where

$$S(x_i; \epsilon) = \{x : D(x, x_i) < \epsilon\}.$$

If $A$ is the finite set $\{x_1, \ldots, x_n\}$, the condition $T \subset \bigcup_{i=1}^{n} S(x_i; \epsilon)$ can also be expressed by the requirement that $D(x, A) < \epsilon$ for each $x$ in $T$.

Sets which are precompact have also been described in mathematical literature as *totally bounded* sets. The empty set is clearly precompact.

It is easy to see that if $T$ is nonempty, precompact, and if $\epsilon > 0$, $T$ is contained in the union of a finite number of open spheres *with centers in* $T$, each sphere having radius $\epsilon$.

Sometimes it is convenient to observe the following: *If $T$ is such that to each $\epsilon > 0$ corresponds a finite number of sets $T_1, \ldots, T_n$ such that $T \subset T_1 \cup \cdots \cup T_n$ and each $T_i$ has diameter not exceeding $\epsilon$, then $T$ is precompact.*

THEOREM 3–7 V. *A relatively compact set in a metric space is precompact. Certainly then, a compact set is precompact.*

*Proof*. Suppose $T$ is not precompact. Then, for some $\epsilon > 0$, $T$ is not contained in the union of any finite number of open spheres each with radius $\epsilon$. Choose $x_1$ in $T$; then choose $x_2$ in $T$ so that $D(x_1, x_2) \geq \epsilon$. Then choose $x_3$ in $T$ so that $D(x_1, x_3) \geq \epsilon$ and $D(x_2, x_3) \geq \epsilon$. When $x_1, \ldots, x_n$ have been chosen, there is some point $x_{n+1}$ of $T$ not in the set

$$\bigcup_{i=1}^{n} S(x_i;\epsilon).$$

The infinite set $\{x_1, x_2, \ldots\}$ which is thus obtained has no point of accumulation. (Why not?) Since this set is a subset of $\bar{T}$, $\bar{T}$ is not compact (Theorem 3–7 II). That is, $T$ is not relatively compact. This proves the theorem.

The converse of Theorem 3–7 V is false. Let $X$ be the set of all rational numbers in $R$; $X$ is a metric space with the usual metric of $R$. Let $T = \{x \in X : 0 \leq x \leq 1\}$. Then $T$ is precompact but not relatively compact in the space $X$, as the reader may verify for himself. In Section 3–8 we shall see (Theorem 3–8 II) that the converse of Theorem 3–7 V becomes a valid theorem if we add the proviso that the space $X$ have a property called *completeness*.

### PRECOMPACTNESS AND SEPARABILITY

It is easily proved that a metric space is separable if and only if it is perfectly separable (definitions in Section 3–2). The following theorem is sometimes useful:

THEOREM 3–7 VI. *A metric space X which is precompact is separable.*

*Proof*. For each positive integer $n$ there is some finite set $S_n$ such that $D(x, S_n) < \frac{1}{n}$ for each $x$ in $X$. Let $S = \bigcup_n S_n$. Then $S$ is a countable set. Choose any $x \in X$. If $\epsilon > 0$ and $n$ is chosen so that $\frac{1}{n} \leq \epsilon$, there is some $y_n \in S_n$ such that $D(x, y_n) < \epsilon$. This implies that $x \in \bar{S}$, so that $X = \bar{S}$. Hence $X$ is separable.

### PROBLEMS

1. Prove that a subset $S$ of a metric space is compact if and only if every sequence of points from $S$ contains a subsequence converging to a limit in $S$.

2. Prove: (a) if $S$ is a nonempty compact set, and if $x_0 \notin S$, there is a point $x_1 \in S$ such that $D(x_0, S) = D(x_0, x_1)$.

   (b) If $S_1$ and $S_2$ are nonempty and $S_2$ is compact, $D(S_1, S_2) = 0$ if and only if $\bar{S}_1 \cap S_2 \neq \varnothing$.

   (c) If $S_1$ and $S_2$ are compact sets, there exist points $x_i \in S_i$ $(i = 1, 2)$ such that $D(S_1, S_2) = D(x_1, x_2)$.

3. Prove that a set $T$ in $R^k$ is precompact if and only if it is bounded.

4. Prove that a set in a metric space is bounded if it is precompact.

5. Let $X$ be the space composed of all bounded sequences $x = \{\xi_n\}$, where the $\xi_n$'s are real numbers. If $y = \{\eta_n\}$ is also in $X$, let $D(x, y) = \sup_n |\xi_n - \eta_n|$. Show that $D$ is a metric on $X$. Show that a set $\{x : D(x, y) \leq \epsilon\}$ (where $\epsilon$ and $y$ are fixed and $\epsilon > 0$) is never compact, and hence that $X$ is not locally compact. This space $X$ is often denoted by either $(m)$ or $l^\infty$.

6. Is the union of two relatively compact sets relatively compact? Is the situation different for metric spaces from what it is for more general types of topological spaces?

7. Suppose $X$ and $Y$ are metric spaces. Let $A$ be a relatively compact subset of $X$, and suppose $f : X \to Y$ is continuous. Is $f(A)$ relatively compact? What can be said if we do not require $X$ and $Y$ to be metrizable spaces?

8. Suppose we are given $\varphi : X \to Y$, where $X$ and $Y$ are metric spaces. Let $\mathscr{F}$ be a certain family of subsets of $X$. If $F \in \mathscr{F}$, we regard $F$ as a metric space with the metric inherited from $X$. Let $f$ be the restriction of $\varphi$ to $F$. We pose the problem: Find various choices of $\mathscr{F}$ (independent of $\varphi$) with the property that $\varphi$ is continuous on $X$ provided that $f$ is continuous on $F$ for each choice of $F$ in $\mathscr{F}$. Is it permissible to take for $\mathscr{F}$ the class of all the compact subsets of $X$? What if $\mathscr{F}$ is taken to consist of all the sets $F$, each of which is countable, closed, and has just one point of accumulation?

## 3–8 Completeness and completion

Let $X$ be a metric space, and let $\{x_n\}$ be a sequence of elements in $X$ with the property that $D(x_n, x_m) \to 0$ as $m \to \infty$ and $n \to \infty$. That is, we suppose that to each $\epsilon > 0$ corresponds some positive integer $N$ such that $D(x_n, x_m) < \epsilon$ if $N \leq m$ and $N \leq n$. Under these circumstances the sequence is called *a Cauchy sequence*. Every convergent sequence is a Cauchy sequence. For, if $x_n \to x$ and $\epsilon > 0$, there is some $N$ such that $D(x_n, x) < \epsilon/2$ if $N \leq n$. Then, if $N \leq m$ also,

$$D(x_n, x_m) \leq D(x_n, x) + D(x, x_m) < \epsilon.$$

We know from Theorem 2–4 V that, in the Euclidean space $R^k$, every Cauchy sequence is convergent to a limit in $R^k$. But this is not true in all metric spaces.

*Example 1.* Consider the open interval (0, 1) in $R$ as a metric space $X$ by itself, with the Euclidean metric. The sequence $\{x_n\}$ defined by $x_n = \dfrac{1}{n}$ is a Cauchy sequence in $X$, but it is not convergent in $X$; that is, there is no real number $x$ such that $0 < x < 1$ and $x_n \to x$.

*Example 2.* Consider the space $X$ of all rational real numbers $x$, and regard it as a metric subspace of $R$. Let $\{x_n\}$ be a sequence of rational numbers which converges to an irrational number as limit. Then $\{x_n\}$ is a Cauchy sequence in $X$, but it has no limit in $X$.

When a metric space has the property that every Cauchy sequence in it is convergent to a limit in the space, we call the space *complete*. By this definition, $R^k$ is complete.

It is a fundamental fact about metric spaces that an incomplete metric space $X$ can be enlarged so as to yield a complete space. Moreover, this can be done in a minimal way; no new points are added except as absolutely necessary to obtain a complete space, and the original space is a dense subset of the enlarged space. Actually, the procedure which we follow entails the construction of a complete metric space $Y$ of such a character that there exists an isometric mapping $f : X \to Y$ such that $f(X)$ is dense in $Y$. We can then identify $X$ with $f(X)$. The concept of an isometric mapping was defined in Section 3–6.

THEOREM 3–8 I. *If $X$ is an incomplete metric space, there exists a complete metric space $Y$ such that $X$ is isometric with a subspace of $Y$ which is dense in $Y$.*

*Proof.* We begin by defining two Cauchy sequences $\{x_n\}$ and $\{u_n\}$ in $X$ to be equivalent if $D(x_n, u_n) \to 0$ as $n \to \infty$. Then the collection of all Cauchy sequences in $X$ can be grouped into *equivalence classes*. An equivalence class has certain Cauchy sequences as its members.

Any two members of the same equivalence class are equivalent, whereas no member of one equivalence class is equivalent to a member of a different equivalence class. Let $Y$ be the collection of all equivalence classes.

Let us observe that, if a Cauchy sequence $\{x_n\}$ has a limit $x$ in $X$, then any equivalent Cauchy sequence $\{u_n\}$ has this same limit $x$. This follows at once from the fact that

$$D(u_n, x) \leq D(u_n, x_n) + D(x_n, x).$$

For each $x$ in $X$ there is a unique equivalence class of Cauchy sequences such that $x_n \to x$ for each sequence $\{x_n\}$ from this class. In fact, the sequence $\{x_n\}$ for which $x_n = x$ for all values of $n$ is a Cauchy sequence, and clearly $x_n \to x$. Also, if $\{x_n\}$ and $\{y_n\}$ are any two non-equivalent Cauchy sequences, it is not possible that these sequences are both convergent to the same limit. Accordingly, if we denote by $Y_0$ that subset of $Y$ consisting of those equivalence classes whose Cauchy sequences are convergent in $X$, there is a natural one-to-one correspondence between the elements of $X$ and the elements of $Y_0$: the element of $Y_0$ corresponding to the element $x$ of $X$ is the equivalence class of all those Cauchy sequences which converge to $x$.

We shall now define a metric for $Y$ in such a way that $X$ is isometric with $Y_0$. Let $\{x_n\}$ and $\{y_n\}$ be any two Cauchy sequences. Then $\{D(x_n, y_n)\}$ is a Cauchy sequence of real numbers. For, from (15) in Section 3–6, we see that

$$|D(x_n, y_n) - D(x_m, y_m)| \leq D(x_n, x_m) + D(y_n, y_m),$$

and therefore we can draw the desired conclusion. Since $R$ is a complete space, we know that $\lim_{n\to\infty} D(x_n, y_n)$ exists. Next, we wish to show that $\lim_{n\to\infty} D(x_n, y_n) = \lim_{n\to\infty} D(u_n, v_n)$ if $\{u_n\}$ is a Cauchy sequence equivalent to $\{x_n\}$, and $\{v_n\}$ is likewise equivalent to $\{y_n\}$. This fact follows at once from the inequality

$$|D(x_n, y_n) - D(u_n, v_n)| \leq D(x_n, u_n) + D(y_n, v_n).$$

Now, let $A, B, \ldots$ denote elements of $Y$. Suppose $\{x_n\}$ and $\{y_n\}$ are Cauchy sequences from $A$ and $B$, respectively. Let us define

$$d(A, B) = \lim_{n\to\infty} D(x_n, y_n).$$

In particular, if $x_n \to x$ and $y_n \to y$, we see readily that $d(A, B) = D(x, y)$. It is easy to verify that $d$ is a metric on $Y$, that is, that it satisfies the three axioms occurring in the definition of a metric space. Thus $Y$ is a metric space. From what has been said it is clear that $X$ and $Y_0$ are isometric.

Next, we prove that $Y_0$ is dense in $Y$. Suppose $A \in Y$ and $\epsilon > 0$. We have to find an element $B$ of $Y_0$ such that $d(A, B) < \epsilon$. Suppose $\{x_n\}$ is a Cauchy sequence from $A$. There is a positive integer $N$ such that $D(x_n, x_N) < \epsilon/2$ if $n \geq N$. Let $B$ be the equivalence class containing all the Cauchy sequences which converge to $x_N$. One such sequence is $\{y_n\}$, where $y_n = x_N$ for all $n$. Then

$$d(A, B) = \lim_{n\to\infty} D(x_n, x_N),$$

and this limit is certainly not larger than $\epsilon/2$.

Finally, we have to prove that $Y$ is complete. We suppose that $\{A_n\}$ is a Cauchy sequence in $Y$. Using the fact that $Y_0$ is dense in $Y$, we choose $B_n$ from $Y_0$ so that $d(A_n, B_n) < 1/n$. Let $x_n$ be the element of $X$ which is matched with $B_n$ in the isometric correspondence between

$X$ and $Y_0$. We can prove that $\{B_n\}$ is a Cauchy sequence in $Y$, by using the fact that $\{A_n\}$ is a Cauchy sequence. The isometric correspondence then shows that $\{x_n\}$ is a Cauchy sequence in $X$. Hence there is a unique $A$ in $Y$ which contains $\{x_n\}$. The final step is then to prove that $d(A_n, A) \to 0$ as $n \to \infty$. We leave it to the student to supply the details of these last steps in the proof. One needs the triangular inequality for the metric $d$, and the fact that

$$d(B_n, A) = \lim_{m\to\infty} D(x_n, x_m).$$

In order to regard $Y$ as an enlargement of $X$ we must identify $X$ with $Y_0$. But it is also clear that we can form a space isometric with $Y$ and containing $X$ as a subspace by forming the union of $X$ and $Y - Y_0$ and defining the metric suitably. This minimal complete enlargement of $X$ is called the completion of $X$.

We know that $R$ is a complete metric space. Its completeness as a metric space traces back to the fact that the real numbers form a complete ordered field. There are here two uses of the adjective "complete." Completeness of an ordered field is defined by an order of ideas entirely different from those used in defining completeness of a metric space. However, the procedures used in proving Theorem 3–8 I shed a new light on the relation between the system of rational numbers and the system of real numbers. *With the real numbers already known to us*, we can see that if we regard the rational numbers as a metric space $X$, with metric defined by $D(x_1, x_2) = |x_1 - x_2|$, the completion of $X$ is isometric with the metric space of all real numbers. Thus, if we like, we may think of a real number as an equivalence class of Cauchy sequences of rational numbers. This real number will be "irrational" if and only if the Cauchy sequences which are comprised in it are not convergent to a limit in $X$.

It would be possible to use Cauchy sequences of rational numbers to construct a complete ordered field, without any prior development of the real number system. The starting point would be the fact that the rational numbers form an ordered field, though not a complete one. With $X$ the metric space of rational numbers (and all distances being rational), just as in the proof of Theorem 3–8 I we can introduce the notion of Cauchy sequences and the collection $Y$ of all equivalence classes of Cauchy sequences from $X$. We also have the subset $Y_0$ of those members of $Y$ whose constituent Cauchy sequences are convergent in $X$. But now the main problem is not to define a metric on $Y$; it is to make the necessary definitions to form $Y$ into an ordered field, and then to prove that $Y$ is *complete as an ordered field.* Some of the steps toward this end are indicated in one of the problems.

Now that we have the concept of completeness available to us, we can finish dealing with the relation between precompactness and relative compactness. We have the following qualified converse of Theorem 3–7 V:

THEOREM 3–8 II. *If $X$ is a complete metric space, a precompact set in $X$ is relatively compact.*

*Proof.* Suppose $T$ is a precompact set. By Theorem 3–7 IV it will suffice to show that every sequence in $T$ contains a Cauchy subsequence. Let $\{x_n\}$ be a given sequence in $T$. Now, $T$ is contained in the union of a finite number of open spheres, each of radius 1. At least one of these spheres must contain a subsequence from $\{x_n\}$. Let such a subsequence be denoted by $x_{11}, x_{12}, x_{13}, \ldots$. Next we consider spheres of radius 1/2, and we conclude (from the precompactness of $T$) that some sphere of radius 1/2 must contain a subsequence of the foregoing subsequence. We proceed by induction, obtaining sequences $x_{k1}, x_{k2}, x_{k3}, \ldots$ ($k = 1, 2, \ldots$), each sequence a subsequence of its predecessor, and the $k$th sequence contained in a sphere of radius $1/k$. The diagonal sequence $x_{11}, x_{22}, x_{33}, \ldots$ is then a Cauchy sequence and a subsequence of the original sequence $\{x_n\}$. So we are finished.

**PROBLEMS**

1. Fill in all the details of the proof that $Y$ is complete in the last part of the proof of Theorem 3–8 I.

2. Prove: (a) A Cauchy sequence is convergent if it has a convergent subsequence. (b) A Cauchy sequence is bounded.

3. Prove: (a) A closed set $S$ in a complete metric space is complete as a subspace. (b) If $S$ is a compact set in the metric space $X$, then $S$ is complete as a space, even if $X$ is not.

4. Let $X$ be the metric space of all rational numbers, with $D(x_1, x_2) = |x_1 - x_2|$. Taking the view that the real number system is not known, but is to be constructed from $X$ in the manner indicated in the discussion which precedes Theroem 3–8 II, discuss the considerations which are needed to show that the set $Y$ can be made into a complete ordered field. In particular: (a) If $A$ and $B$ are distinct elements of $Y$, with $\{x_n\} \in A$, $\{y_n\} \in B$, show that for some rational $\epsilon > 0$ either $x_n + \epsilon < y_n$ for all sufficiently large $n$, or that $y_n + \epsilon < x_n$ for all sufficiently large $n$. In the first case write $A < B$, in the second case $B < A$. Verify that this yields a total ordering of $Y$. (b) With notation as in (a), but allowing the possibility $A = B$, define $A + B$ as the equivalence class which contains $\{x_n + y_n\}$. Show that this is an unambiguous definition. Give a suitable definition of $A \cdot B$ and show that $Y$ becomes a field. (c) Discuss the completeness of $Y$ as an ordered field.

5. Let $X$ be a metric space. Let $\mathscr{F}$ be the class of all nonempty closed and bounded subsets of $X$. If $E$ and $F$ are in $\mathscr{F}$, let $\delta(E, F) = \sup_{x\in E} D(x, F)$, and let $d(E, F) = \max [\delta(E, F), \delta(F, E)]$. (a) Prove that $d$ is a metric on $\mathscr{F}$. We call $d(E, F)$ the "Hausdorff distance" between $E$ and $F$. (b) Prove that $\mathscr{F}$ becomes a complete metric space with the metric $d$ if $X$ is complete. In fact, if $\{E_n\}$ is a Cauchy sequence in $\mathscr{F}$, $\{E_n\}$ has as its limit the set $E = \bigcap_n G_n$, where $G_n = \bar{F}_n$ and $F_n = \bigcup_{i\geq n} E_i$. Show also that this set $E$ can be characterized (in this case) as the set of points $x$ in $X$ such that there exists a sequence $\{x_n\}$ with $x_n \to x$ and $x_n \in E_n$, $n = 1, 2, \ldots$. See Kuratowski [1], p. 198 and Dieudonné [1], p. 59. (c) Prove that $\mathscr{F}$ is precompact if $X$ is, and that $\mathscr{F}$ is compact if $X$ is.

## 3–9 Category

If $X$ is a topological space, a set $S$ in $X$ is called *nowhere dense* (in $X$) if its closure has no interior points: $(\bar{S})^o = \varnothing$. It is useful to express this requirement in other ways. We know from (2) in Section 3–1 that $(\bar{A})^\sim = (A^\sim)^o$ for any set $A$ in $X$. Let $A = (\bar{S})^\sim$, so that $A^\sim = \bar{S}$. Then $(\bar{S})^o = (A^\sim)^o = (\bar{A})^\sim$. Thus $(\bar{S})^o = \varnothing$ is equivalent to $(\bar{A})^\sim = \varnothing$, or to $\bar{A} = X$. Note also that $A = (S^\sim)^o$. Thus we see that the conditions

(1) $$(\bar{S})^o = \varnothing,$$

(2) $$(\bar{S})^\sim \text{ is dense in } X,$$

and

$$(S^\sim)^o \text{ is dense in } X$$

are equivalent ways of expressing the fact that $S$ is nowhere dense in $X$. It is also easy to verify the following proposition: *The set $S$ is nowhere dense in $X$ if and only if each nonempty* *open set $U$ in $X$ contains another nonempty open set $V$ such that $S \cap V = \varnothing$.* We leave verification to the reader.

If a set $S$ in $X$ can be expressed as the union of a countable collection of nowhere dense sets, it is described as *a set of the first category*. If $S$ is not of the first category, it is called *a set of the second category*. This terminology was introduced by the French mathematician R. Baire (1874–1932) in 1899. More recently another adjective has been introduced; a set $S$ which is of the first category in $X$ is also called *meager* (French *maigre*) in $X$, while a set of the second category is called *nonmeager* in $X$. This newer terminology appears to have merit because it is more descriptive than Baire's terminology. It is not yet in general use, however.

Our main concern with these notions derives from a famous theorem of Baire, which has many important applications. Before we come to it, we must consider an auxiliary theorem, which is a generalization of the theorems on nests of intervals in Euclidean space (Theorems 1–9 I and 2–4 I).

THEOREM 3–9 I. *Let $X$ be a complete metric space. Let $\{S_n\}$ be a sequence of nonempty closed and bounded sets in $X$ such that $S_{n+1} \subset S_n$ for each $n$. Suppose also that $\operatorname{diam}(S_n) \to 0$ as $n \to \infty$. Then there is a unique point in the intersection of all the $S_n$'s.*

*Proof.* Let $x_n$ be a point in $S_n$. If $m < n$, $x_m$ and $x_n$ are both in $S_m$, and so

$$D(x_n, x_m) \leq \operatorname{diam}(S_m).$$

It follows at once that $\{x_n\}$ is a Cauchy sequence. Since $X$ is complete, the sequence converges to a limit $x$ in $X$. For any fixed $m$, $x_n$ is in $S_m$ when $n \geq m$. From $x_n \to x$ and the fact that $S_m$ is closed we infer that $x \in S_m$. Finally, the intersection of all the $S_n$'s cannot contain two distinct points because of the fact that $\operatorname{diam}(S_n) \to 0$.

Now we come to the theorem of Baire.

THEOREM 3–9 II. *If $X$ is a complete metric space, it is of the second category (as a subset of itself).*

*Proof.* Suppose, to the contrary, that $X$ is the union of $S_1, S_2, \ldots$, where each $S_n$ is nowhere dense. As a matter of convenience in notation let us define

$$B(x_0; r) = \{x : D(x, x_0) \leq r\},$$

where $r > 0$ and $x_0 \in X$ are arbitrary. This set is closed, as a consequence of the continuity of the distance function. We call $B(x_0; r)$ the *closed ball* of radius $r$ and center $x_0$. Evidently $B(x_0; r)$ contains the open sphere $S(x_0; r)$. Now, the earlier discussion of nowhere dense sets makes it clear that if $S$ is a nowhere dense set, any closed ball in $X$ contains another closed ball whose intersection with $S$ is empty. Hence we can obtain by induction a sequence of closed balls $B_n = B_n(x_n; r_n)$ such that $B_n \cap S_n = \varnothing$, $0 < r_n < \frac{1}{n}$, and $B_{n+1} \subset B_n$. Since $\operatorname{diam}(B_n) \leq \frac{2}{n}$, we can apply Theorem 3–9 I to obtain a point $x \in \bigcap_n B_n$. But $X = \bigcup_n S_n$ implies that $x \in S_n$ for some $n$, and this contradicts $B_n \cap S_n = \varnothing$. Thus the proof is completed.

It is clear from facts about countability that the union of a countable number of meager sets is a meager set. In $R^k$ any countable set is meager, because a set consisting of a single point is nowhere dense. In particular, the set of all the rational numbers is meager in $R$. But the set of all the irrational numbers is nonmeager, because the union of the rationals and the irrationals is the complete space $R$.

There do exist uncountable sets which are meager. The Cantor set $S_C[0, 1]$ (Section 2–10) is uncountable and nowhere dense, and hence meager.

Let us now revert to Example 2 in Section 3–4, in which a curious illustration of a $T_3$ space $X$ was given. We can now use the concept of the category (first or second) of a set to assist in proving that $X$ is not a normal space. Let $P$ be the set of all points $(\xi, 0)$ with $\xi$ a rational number, and let $I$ be the set of those points $(\xi, 0)$ for which $\xi$ is irrational. In the peculiar topology of the space $X$ both $P$ and $I$ are closed sets. If we assume that $X$ is normal, there will then exist disjoint open sets $U$, $V$ in $X$ such that $P \subset U$ and $I \subset V$. Accordingly, to each point $x$ in $I$ we can make correspond one of its special neighborhoods, say $N_\epsilon(x)$, such that $N_\epsilon(x) \subset V$. We recall that $N_\epsilon(x)$ consists of $x$ and the points which are inside one or the other of the circles of radii $\epsilon$ with centers at $(\xi, \pm\epsilon)$. Let us denote by $I_n$ the set of those points $x$ in $I$ for which the corresponding $\epsilon$ satisfies the condition $\epsilon \geq \dfrac{1}{n}$. Clearly, $I$ is the union of the sets $I_1, I_2, \ldots$. But since $I$ is a nonmeager set when it is regarded as a subset of the real line, the closure of some one of the sets $I_n$, *in the sense of the sense of the topology of R*, must contain an open interval $(a, b)$. That is, for a certain $n$, the $\epsilon$ of $N_\epsilon(x)$ satisfies $\epsilon \geq (1/n)$ when $x = (\xi, 0)$, $a < \xi < b$, and $\xi$ is irrational. But this immediately implies that the union of all the neighborhoods $N_\epsilon(x)$ of this kind contains all points $(\alpha, \beta)$ for which $a \leq \alpha \leq b$ and $0 < \beta < \epsilon$. (With $(\alpha, \beta)$ given we have simply to choose an irrational $\xi$ such that $a < \xi < b$ and $(\xi - \alpha)^2 < \epsilon^2 - (\epsilon - \beta)^2$.) All of these points $(\alpha, \beta)$ are certainly in $V$. But, since there are points of $P$ on the interval $(a, b)$, we see at once that some of these points $(\alpha, \beta)$ are also in $U$. This contradicts the fact that $U \cap V = \varnothing$. Hence the space $X$ cannot be normal.

## PROBLEMS

1. Verify the truth of the italicized proposition which comes immediately after (3) in the text.
2. (a) Prove that a finite union of nowhere dense sets is nowhere dense.
   (b) Suppose $S$ is nowhere dense in $X$. Prove that $S^\sim$ is dense in $X$.
   (c) Show that $S$ is nowhere dense if $S$ is closed and $S^\sim$ is dense in $X$.
   (d) Show that the boundary $\beta(S)$ is nowhere dense provided that $S$ is either closed or open.
   (e) Suppose that $A$ and $B$ are subsets of $X$, with $A$ open and $A \cap B$ of the first category in $X$. Prove that $\bar{A} \cap B$ is also of the first category.
3. If $S \subset R^k$ is such that $S'$ is a finite set, show that $S$ is nowhere dense in $R^k$.
4. Let $X$ be a space of the second category. Suppose $S = \bigcap_n S_n$, where each $S_n$ is open and dense in $X$. Show that $S$ is of the second category in $X$. What is the category of $S^\sim$?
5. Suppose $A \subset B \subset X$, where $X$ is the basic space. The set $A$ is said to be nowhere dense in $B$ when $B - \bar{A}$ is dense in $B$; that is, $B$ is contained in the closure of $B - \bar{A}$.
   (a) Show that this is equivalent to saying that $A$ is nowhere dense in $B$ *as a space*, using the relative topology of $B$.
   (b) Show, when $A \subset B \subset X$ and $B$ is nowhere dense in $X$, then $A$ is nowhere dense in $X$.
   (c) Show that, when $A \subset B \subset X$ and $A$ is nowhere dense in $B$, it is nowhere dense in $X$.
   (d) Suppose $A \subset B \subset X$. Then, if $B$ is of the first category in $X$, show that $A$ is of the first category in $X$.

(e) Suppose $A \subset B \subset X$. Show that, if $A$ is of the first category in $B$ (as a space with the relative topology), then $A$ is of the first category in $X$. Show also that, if $A$ is of the second category in $X$, then $A$ is of the second category in $B$ and $B$ is of the second category in $X$.

6. Consider the following properties which a topological space $X$ may have:

($\alpha$) If $S_1, S_2, \ldots$ are open sets, each dense in $X$, then $S = \bigcap_n S_n$ is dense in $X$.

($\beta$) If $S$ is a set of the first category in $X$, then $S^\sim$ is dense in $X$.

($\gamma$) Every nonempty open subset of $X$ is of the second category in $X$. (In particular, $X$ itself is then of the second category.) Prove that if $X$ has any one of these three properties, it has all three properties.

7. Let $X$ be a space which satisfies condition ($\gamma$) in Problem 6. Let $X_1$ be a nonempty open subset of $X$. Considering $X_1$ as a space with the relative topology, show that it also satisfies condition ($\gamma$).

8. Prove that a complete metric space has the three properties listed in Problem 6. An argument much like that in the proof of Theorem 3–9 II may be arranged.

9. Any locally compact Hausdorff space, or more generally, any locally compact regular space, has the three properties listed in Problem 6. The first thing to be noted here is that if $U$ is a neighborhood of $x$, then there exists a neighborhood $V$ of $x$ such that $\bar{V} \subset U$ and $\bar{V}$ is compact. It may then be shown that the space has property ($\alpha$). See Kelley [1], p. 146 and p. 200.

10. Let $X$ and $Y$ be metric spaces. Suppose that $f: X \to Y$ and $f_n : X \to Y$ are given ($n = 1, 2, \ldots$), with each $f_n$ continuous and $f_n(x) \to f(x)$ for each $x$. Let $C$ be the set of points $x$ at which $f$ is continuous. Let $U$ be the set of points $x_0$ for which to each $\epsilon > 0$ corresponds an $m$ and a neighborhood $V$ of $x_0$ such that $D[f_n(x), f(x)] < \epsilon$ if $n \geq m$ and $x \in V$. It is a familiar fact that $U \subset C$. Prove that $U^\sim$ and $C^\sim$ are of the first category in $X$. Observe that this implies that $U$ and $C$ are dense in $X$ if $X$ satisfies condition ($\beta$) in Problem 6. This is true, in particular, if $X$ is complete.

[*Suggestion for the proof*. For positive integers $k, m, n$ let $S_{mnk} = \left\{x : D[f_n(x), f_m(x)] > \frac{1}{k}\right\}$, where $D$ is the metric in $Y$. Then let $S_{mk} = \bigcup_{n \geq m} S_{mnk}$, $B = \bigcup_{k=1}^{\infty} \bigcap_{m=1}^{\infty} \bar{S}_{mk}$. Now show (a) that $B^\sim \subset U$, and (b) that $B$ is of the first category in $X$. For (b) use Problem 2(d) and observe that $\bigcap_m S_{mk} = \varnothing$.]

This result, for the case where $Y$ is $R$ and $X$ is an interval in $R$, goes back to Osgood [1], p. 155. For further study see Hahn [1], pp. 220–222, Hausdorff [1], pp. 252–253, Hobson [1], Vol. 2, pp. 109–113 and pp. 123–139, Goffman [1], pp. 108–110.

11. This problem involves the notion of a lower semicontinuous function $f: X \to R$. This is a special case of the same notion for a function $f: X \to R^*$. For relevant information see Section 6–9; nothing more than the definition and Theorem 6–9 II is needed here. For our purpose we may say that a function $f: X \to R$ is l.s.c. (lower semicontinuous) if and only if for each real number $c$ the set $\{x : f(x) > c\}$ is open. Here $X$ can be any topological space. Suppose that $X$ satisfies the conditions ($\alpha$)–($\gamma$) given in Problem 6. Let $\mathcal{G}$ be a family of l.s.c. functions $g : X \to R$ such that $\sup_{g \in \mathcal{G}} g(x) < +\infty$ for each $x$. Let $G$ be the set of points $x$ such that for some neighborhood $V$ of $x$ and some real $M$ it is true that $g(x) \leq M$ when $x \in V$ and $g \in \mathcal{G}$. Then $G$ is an open set dense in $X$.

[*Suggestions for the proof*. Since $G$ is obviously open, the problem is to prove that $G$ is dense in $X$. Let $f(x) = \sup_{g \in \mathcal{G}} g(x)$. Then $f: X \to R$ is l.s.c. Let $F$ be the set of points $x$ such that $f$ is bounded above in some neighborhood of $x$. Since $F \subset G$, it will suffice to prove that $F$ is dense in $X$. Let $X_1$ be any nonempty open set in $X$. Then $X_1$ as a space is of the second category (see Problem 7). But $X_1 = \bigcup_n S_n$, where $S_n = \{x : x \in X_1, f(x) \leq n\}$. It must now be shown that some $S_n$ has a nonvoid interior; the desired conclusion about $F$ will then follow.]

12. Let $X$ be any topological space, $Y$ any metric space. Then, if $f: X \to Y$ is given it can be shown that the set $S$ of points in $X$ at which $f$ is discontinuous is expressible as a countable union of

closed sets (that is, $S$ is an $F_\sigma$ set). This implies, in particular, that it is impossible to have a case in which $S$ is of the second category and $S^\sim$ is dense in $X$. For instance, it is impossible to have a function $f: [0, 1] \to R$ such that $f$ is continuous at $x$ if $x$ is rational and discontinuous at $x$ if $x$ is irrational. [*Suggestion for proof of the assertion about S*. If $U$ is a nonempty open set in $X$, let

$$\varphi(U) = \sup D[f(y), f(z)]$$

as $y$ and $z$ vary in $U$. Then let $\omega(x)$ be the infimum of $\varphi(U)$ as $U$ varies over the class of all neighborhoods of $x$; $\omega$ is a function on $X$ to $R^*$. Prove that $\omega(x) > 0$ if and only if $x \in S$, and prove that $\{x : \omega(x) < c\}$ is open for each $c$ in $R^*$. Let $S_n = \left\{x : \omega(x) \geq \frac{1}{n}\right\}$ and note that $S = \bigcup_n S_n$.]

13. It is possible to use Theorem 3–9 II to prove that there exist continuous functions which are nowhere differentiable. The metric space $C[0, 1]$ (defined in Section 3–6) is complete. Let $S$ be the set of elements $x$ in $C[0, 1]$ such that $\frac{dx(t)}{dt}$ exists for some $t$. It can be proved that $S$ is of the first category, whence $S^\sim$ is of the second category. In particular, $S^\sim$ is not empty. [*Suggestions for the proof*. Let $S_n$ be the class of those $x$ in $C[0, 1]$ such that, for some $s \in [0, 1]$,

$$\left|\frac{x(t) - x(s)}{t - s}\right| \leq n$$

if $t \in [0, 1]$ and $t \neq s$. Evidently $S \subset \bigcup_n S_n$. Now show that $S_n$ is closed. Finally, show that $S_n^\sim$ is dense in $C[0,1]$. This can be done in two stages. Any function $x \in C[0, 1]$ can be uniformly approximated to any desired degree of accuracy by a function $u$ having a continuous derivative. Then we can approximate $u$ by a function $u + v_k$, where $v_k(t) = \frac{1}{k} \sin 2\pi k^2 t$. If $k$ is sufficiently large, $u + v_k$ will be in $S_n^\sim$.]

## 3–10 Zorn's lemma

In this book we do not deal formally with the axiomatics of set theory; our use of the concept of a set is on the level of something taken for granted, just as is our use of the ordinary rules of logic. There are however some places in analysis where it seems indispensable to have precise technical formulations of some principles of set theory. There are several equivalent principles which have been found to be useful and important. One of them is known as *the axiom of choice*. Another is called the principle (or theorem) of *well-ordering*. Still another is a *maximality principle*, which may assume various forms. There are forms due to Hausdorff, Zorn, and Tukey which are in common use, each form having particular advantages for particular purposes. We do not intend to discuss all these different but equivalent principles. We shall rely on a formulation of the maximality principle which is commonly known as *Zorn's lemma*. We may regard this formulation as a basic principle in the theory of sets, for the purposes of this book it is not necessary to think of deducing it from more primitive assumptions. We shall show that the assertion made in the axiom of choice is deducible from Zorn's form of the maximality principle. The student who wishes to orient himself further on the axiom of choice and these other equivalent principles of set theory may consult the references cited at the end of this section.

We must first explain the concept of *a partially ordered set*. Let $P$ be a set of elements, and suppose there is a binary relation defined between certain pairs of elements $a, b$ of $P$, expressed symbolically by $a \prec b$, with the properties:

1. If $a \prec b$ and $b \prec c$, then $a \prec c$.
2. If $a \in P$, then $a \prec a$.
3. If $a \prec b$ and $b \prec a$, then $a = b$.

Then $P$ is said to be partially ordered by the relation.

As an example of a partially ordered set, let $X$ be a set, and let $P$ be a family of subsets $A, B \ldots$ of $X$. For the binary relation use ordinary set inclusion; that is, let $A \prec B$ mean $A \subset B$. Then $P$ is partially ordered.

If $P$ is a partially ordered set such that for every pair $a, b$ in $P$ we have either $a \prec b$ or $b \prec a$, we say that $P$ is *completely ordered* by the relation $\prec$. The adjectives *linearly*, *simply*, and *totally* are sometimes used instead of *completely*. The real line $R$ is completely ordered by the relation $\leq$.

If $Q$ is a subset of the partially ordered set $P$, $Q$ is itself partially ordered by the relation which partially orders $P$. It can happen that $Q$ is completely ordered by this relation.

If $S$ is a subset of the partially ordered set $P$, an element $b$ of $P$ is called *an upper bound* of $S$ if $a \in S$ implies $a \prec b$.

An element $m$ of the partially ordered set $P$ is called *a maximal element* of $P$ if there exists no element $a$ of $P$ such that $a \neq m$ and $m \prec a$.

We can now state our basic maximality principle. (See Zorn [1].)

ZORN'S LEMMA. *Let $P$ be a nonempty partially ordered set with the property that every completely ordered subset of $P$ has an upper bound in $P$. Then $P$ contains at least one maximal element.*

*Example 1.* As one illustration of the use of Zorn's lemma we shall employ it to demonstrate the existence of what is called a *Hamel basis* of the real number system.

A set $S$ of real numbers is called rationally linearly independent if an equality of the form $r_1x_1 + \cdots + r_nx_n = 0$, with $x_1, \ldots, x_n$ a finite subset of $S$ and $r_1, \ldots, r_n$ rational, always implies $r_1 = \cdots = r_n = 0$. If $S$ is a rationally independent set of real numbers such that each real number $x$ can be expressed in the form

$$x = r_1x_1 + \cdots + r_nx_n, \tag{1}$$

with $r_1, \ldots, r_n$ rational and $x_1, \ldots, x_n$ selected from $S$ (with $n$ depending on $x$), we call $S$ a Hamel basis of the real number system. (The point of requiring $S$ to be rationally linearly independent is that the coefficients $r_1, \ldots, r_n$ in (1) are then uniquely determined by $x$.) The naming of the basis is after the German mathematician G. Hamel (1877–1954), who in 1905 published a paper (Hamel [1]) establishing the existence of such a basis of the real number system, and used the basis to discuss the nature of functions $f$ mapping $R$ into $R$ and having the property that $f(x + y) = f(x) + f(y)$ for every real $x$ and $y$.

To establish the existence of a Hamel basis, let $P$ be the class whose members are the rationally linearly independent subsets of $R$, and let $P$ be partially ordered by the relation of set inclusion. Then $P$ satisfies the conditions of Zorn's lemma. First of all, $P$ is not empty because, if $x_1$ is a nonzero real number, $\{x_1\}$ is in $P$. If $Q$ is a completely ordered subset of $P$, let $B$ be the subset of $R$ obtained by forming the union of all the subsets of $R$ comprised in $Q$. Then $B$ is a member of $P$. For, if $x_1, \ldots, x_n$ are elements of $B$, each $x_i$ is a member of some $S_i$, where $S_i \in Q$. Since $Q$ is completely ordered, there is one $S_i$ which includes all the others, and hence contains all the numbers $x_1, \ldots, x_n$. It is then clear that $r_1x_1 + \cdots + r_nx_n = 0$ implies $r_1 = \cdots = r_n = 0$; hence $B$ is a rationally linearly independent set. Now, let $H$ be a maximal element of $P$, whose existence is guaranteed by Zorn's lemma. The maximal character of $H$ as an element of $P$ allows us to prove that $H$ is a Hamel basis. For, if $x \in R$, and if $K$ is the set $H \cup \{x\}$, the fact that $H \subset K$ implies either that $H = K$ (whence $x \in H$) or that $K$ is not a member of $P$. In either case we see readily that $x$ can be expressed as a finite linear combination, with rational coefficients, of elements from $H$.

*Example 2.* For a second illustration of the use of Zorn's lemma we consider the notion of a family of sets with *the finite intersection property*. For brevity we refer to this as "property $F$." Let $X$ be any nonempty set, and let $\mathscr{S}$ be a family of subsets of $X$ (a typical one denoted by $S$) such that $\bigcap_{j=1}^{n} S_i \neq \varnothing$ for every finite collection $S_1, \ldots, S_n$ of members of $\mathscr{S}$. Then we say that $\mathscr{S}$ has property $F$. In Theorem 3–2 IV we saw that the property $F$ has a bearing on the characterization of compact sets in a topological space. For later applications we shall find the following considerations useful.

Let $\mathscr{S}_0$ be a fixed family of subsets of $X$, having the property $F$. Let $\mathscr{E}(X)$ denote the collection of *all* subsets of $X$. Then $\mathscr{S}_0 \subset \mathscr{E}(X)$, the elements of $\mathscr{S}_0$ being members of $\mathscr{E}(X)$. Let $P$ be the collection of all subsets $\mathscr{S}$ of $\mathscr{E}(X)$ such that $\mathscr{S}_0 \subset \mathscr{S}$ and such that $\mathscr{S}$ has property $F$. Let $P$ be partially ordered by set inclusion. Then it is easy to see that $P$ satisfies the conditions of Zorn's lemma. We omit the details of this verification. Hence $P$ contains a maximal element $\mathscr{M}$. That is, $\mathscr{M}$ is a family of subsets of $X$, $\mathscr{M}$ has property $F$, $\mathscr{S}_0 \subset \mathscr{M}$, and $\mathscr{M}$ is not a proper subfamily of any family of subsets of $X$ having property $F$. The existence of this $\mathscr{M}$ will be used in our proof of the theorem of Tychonoff (Theorem 3–11 I).

We come now to the axiom of choice, first stated explicitly in 1908 by Ernst Zermelo (1871–1953). Since we are going to deduce the principle involved from Zorn's lemma, we shall not refer to the principle as an axiom. We shall call it *Zermelo's principle of choice.*

ZERMELO'S PRINCIPLE OF CHOICE. *Let $\mathscr{E}$ be a nonempty family of nonempty subsets of a set $X$. Then there exists a function $f : \mathscr{E} \to X$ such that $f(E) \in E$ for each $E$ in $\mathscr{E}$.*

*Proof* (by Zorn's lemma). Consider the class $P$ of all functions $p : \mathscr{D}(p) \to X$ such that the domain $\mathscr{D}(p)$ of $p$ is a subset of $\mathscr{E}$ and $p(E) \in E$ for each $E$ in $\mathscr{D}(p)$. This is a nonempty class, because $\mathscr{E}$ contains a nonempty set $E$, and if $x \in E$ the function with domain $\{E\}$ and range $\{x\}$ (one-element sets) is a member of $P$. Each element of $P$ is a subset of the product $\mathscr{E} \times X$; we partially-order $P$ by the inclusion relation in $\mathscr{E} \times X$. Thus, if $p_1, p_2$ are in $P$, $p_1 \subset p_2$ is seen to mean that $p_2$ is an extension of $p_1$, that is, that $\mathscr{D}(p_1) \subset \mathscr{D}(p_2)$ and that $p_1(E) = p_2(E)$ if $E \in \mathscr{D}(p_1)$. Now, $P$ satisfies the conditions of Zorn's lemma. For, if $Q$ is a completely ordered subset of $P$, let $q$ be that subset of $\mathscr{E} \times X$ which is the union of all the elements of $Q$, each viewed as a subset of $\mathscr{E} \times X$. From the fact that $Q$ is totally ordered we can easily show that $q$ is a function, that is, that if $(E, x_1)$ and $(E, x_2)$ are in $q$, then $x_1 = x_2$. In fact, we shall have $(E, x_1) \in p_1$ and $(E, x_2) \in p_2$, where $p_1$ and $p_2$ are in $Q$. Thus $p_i(E) = x_i$, $i = 1, 2$. But one of the $p_i$'s is an extension of the other, and so $x_1 = x_2 = q(E)$. We see also that $q(E) \in E$, so that $q \in P$. Obviously $q$ is an upper bound of $Q$.

We can now assert that $P$ contains a maximal element $f$. For this $f$ we must have $\mathscr{D}(f) = \mathscr{E}$. For, suppose $E_0 \in \mathscr{E} - \mathscr{D}(f)$ and $x_0 \in E_0$. If we then define $g$, an extension of $f$, by adding $E_0$ to $\mathscr{D}(f)$ and defining $g(E_0) = x_0$, we contradict the maximality of $f$ in $P$. We have thus completed the proof.

For further reading about the subject matter of this section we refer the interested student to the following sources:

BIRKHOFF [1], pp. 42–44.
BOURBAKI [1a], pp. 32–38, especially pp. 36–37.
BOURBAKI [1c], pp. 37–45.
GRAVES [1], pp. 321–327.
HALMOS [3], pp. 59–69.
KELLEY [1], pp. 31–36.
MCSHANE and BOTTS [1], pp. 29–31 and pp. 251–259.
WILDER [1], p. 132.

## 3–11 Cartesian product topologies

The study of functions of several variables leads naturally to the investigation of topologies for product spaces. Let $X$ and $Y$ be nonempty sets. We have already had occasion to mention the set consisting of all ordered pairs $(x, y)$, where $x$ is an element of $X$ and $y$ is an element of $Y$. This set of pairs is called the Cartesian product $X \times Y$. If $X_1, \ldots, X_n$ are nonempty sets, the Cartesian product $X_1 \times X_2 \times \cdots \times X_n$ is defined in the obvious way as an extension of the case for $n = 2$, namely, as the collection of all ordered sets $(x_1, \ldots, x_n)$ where $x_i \in X_i$, $i = 1, \ldots, n$.

A function $f$ defined on $X_1 \times \cdots \times X_n$ is called a function of $n$ variables; its value at $(x_1, \ldots, x_n)$ is denoted by $f(x_1, \ldots, x_n)$. Such a function may occur also with a domain of definition which is a proper subset of the product space.

*Example 1.* Suppose $X$ is the interval $[0, 4]$ of the real axis and $Y$ is the interval $[0, 2]$ of the real axis. Then $X \times Y$ is the closed rectangular region in $R^2$ consisting of all points $(x, y)$ such that $0 \leq x \leq 4$, $0 \leq y \leq 2$. We might have a function defined on the part of $X \times Y$ for which

$$\frac{(x-2)^2}{4} + (y-1)^2 \leq 1.$$

This domain of definition is not a Cartesian product of the type $A \times B$, where $A \subset X$, $B \subset Y$.

When $X$ and $Y$ are topological spaces, there is a natural way of defining a topology for $X \times Y$. We use the following scheme: suppose $x \in X$ and $y \in Y$. Choose any neighborhood of $x$ in $X$, say $U$, and any neighborhood of $y$ in $Y$, say $V$. Let $N = U \times V$, and let $\mathcal{N}$ be the family of all ordered pairs $\{N, (x, y)\}$ formed in this manner. Then use this family $\mathcal{N}$ to define a topology for $X \times Y$ in the manner indicated in Section 3–4 (with $X \times Y$ now taking the place of the $X$ of Section 3–4). It is easy to show that the Postulates 1–3 in Section 3–4 are satisfied. Moreover, if each of the spaces $X$, $Y$ is a Hausdorff space, so is $X \times Y$. All of this extends naturally to the case of $X_1 \times \cdots \times X_n$, where each $X_i$ is a topological space. The topology thus defined for the product space is called the Cartesian product topology.

*Example 2.* The topology of $R^2$, as defined in Section 2–3, is the same as the topology arrived at by regarding $R^2$ as $R \times R$ and applying the foregoing procedure, using the standard topology for $R$. Verification is left to the student. Likewise, if $k = m + n$, we can regard $R^k$ and its topology as $R^m \times R^n$ with the Cartesian product topology.

The following observation is interesting. Let us define functions $f$, $g$ in this way: $f$ maps $X \times Y$ onto $X$ and is defined by $f(x, y) = x$; $g$ maps $X \times Y$ onto $Y$ and is defined by $g(x, y) = y$. These functions $f$, $g$ are continuous. Moreover, the topology just defined for $X \times Y$ is the minimal topology for the product space with respect to the property of making $f$ and $g$ continuous. That is, any topology for $X \times Y$ with respect to which $f$ and $g$ are continuous certainly contains among its open sets all the sets which are open in the previously defined topology for $X \times Y$. See the last part of Section 3–1.

## PRODUCTS OF METRIC SPACES

If $X_1, \ldots, X_n$ are metric spaces, with distance functions $D_1, \ldots, D_n$, the product space $X = X_1 \times \cdots \times X_n$ can be made into a metric space in a variety of ways, of which we mention three. Let $x = (x_1, \ldots, x_n)$ and $a = (a_1, \ldots, a_n)$ be points of the product space. Then

$$D(x, a) = [\{D_1(x_1, a_1)\}^2 + \cdots + \{D_n(x_n, a_n)\}^2]^{1/2}$$

defines a metric $D$ on $X$. Another metric for $X$, equivalent to the one just described, is defined by

$$D(x, a) = \max_{1 \le i \le n} D_i(x_i, a_i).$$

Still another metric, equivalent to the first two, is

$$D(x, a) = D_1(x_1, a_1) + \cdots + D_n(x_n, a_n).$$

It is not hard to see that when $X$ is made into a metric space by any one of the three metrics just mentioned, the resulting topology is one in which a basis of neighborhoods at $x = (x_1, \ldots, x_n)$ may be taken to consist of all sets of the form $U_1 \times \cdots \times U_n$, where $U_i$ is a neighborhood of $x_i$ in $X_i$.

## CONTINUITY IN PRODUCT SPACES

Let $X = X_1 \times \cdots \times X_n$, where each $X_i$ is a topological space and the product-space topology is defined as has been indicated. Let $Y$ be any topological space. If $f$ is a function with domain $\mathscr{D}$ in $X$ and range $\mathscr{R}$ in $Y$, the condition that $f$ be continuous at a point $a = (a_1, \ldots, a_n)$ in $\mathscr{D}$ can be expressed in this way: to each neighborhood $V$ of $f(a)$ in $Y$ corresponds a set of neighborhoods $U_1, \ldots, U_n$ [$U_1$ a neighborhood of $a_1$ in $X_1, \ldots, U_n$ a neighborhood of $a_n$ in $X_n$], such that $f(x_1, \ldots, x_n) \in V$ if $x \in \mathscr{D} \cap \{U_1 \times \cdots \times U_n\}$.

It should be noted that the requirement that $f$ be continuous as a function of $x = (x_1, \ldots, x_n)$ is not the same as the requirement that $f$ be continuous as a function of each $x_k$ separately. That is (for $n = 2$, for instance), it can happen that $f(x_1, x_2)$ is continuous on $X_1$ as a function of $x_1$ for each fixed value of $x_2$, and $f(x_1, x_2)$ is continuous as a function of $x_2$ for each fixed value of $x_1$, and yet that $f$ is not continuous as a function of $x = (x_1, x_2)$ on $X_1 \times X_2$ (that is, that $f$ fails to be continuous at some points of the product space).

*Example 3.* Take $X_1 = X_2 = R$. Define $f$ by

$$f(0, 0) = 0, \qquad f(x_1, x_2) = \frac{x_1 x_2}{x_1^2 + x_2^2} \quad \text{if} \quad x_1^2 + x_2^2 > 0.$$

Then $f$ is continuous in each variable separately, without exception, but $f$ is discontinuous at (0, 0).

There are certain situations, however, in which one can infer quite a good deal about continuity of $f$ as a function of the pair $(x_1, x_2)$ from the assumption of continuity in each of the variables separately. For instance, suppose that $X_1$ is any complete metric space, that $X_2$ is any topological space satisfying the first axiom of countability, and that $Y$ is a metric space. Then, if $f: X_1 \times X_2 \to Y$ is continuous in each variable separately, the set of points $(x_1, x_2)$ at which $f$ is continuous on $X_1 \times X_2$ is dense in $X_1 \times X_2$. See Problems 2, 3, and 4.

## INFINITE CARTESIAN PRODUCTS

An element $x = (x_1, \ldots, x_n)$ of the finite Cartesian product $X_1 \times \cdots \times X_n$ can be looked upon as a function defined on the set of positive integers $1, 2, \ldots, n$, the value of the function at $k$ being $x_k$. With this point of view in mind we proceed to define an arbitrary Cartesian product, where the number of "factors" may be infinite.

Suppose we have any nonempty family of nonempty sets. As a convenience of notation let us suppose the family comes to us with an indexing variable $\alpha$, where $\alpha$ varies over a set $A$ and to each $\alpha$ corresponds a nonempty set $X_\alpha$. The sets $X_\alpha$ and $X_\beta$ need not be different when $\alpha \neq \beta$. Now consider functions $x$ with domain $A$ such that the value $x(\alpha)$ is in $X_\alpha$. The range of each such function is then a special sort of subset of the union $\bigcup_{\alpha \in A} X_\alpha$. The Cartesian product

$$X = \Pi_{\alpha \in A} X_\alpha$$

is, by definition, the collection of all such functions $x$. On occasion we may write $x_\alpha$ instead of $x(\alpha)$. Also, for reasons of typography, we shall sometimes write $X(\alpha)$ for $X_\alpha$.

*Example 4.* If $A$ is the set of positive integers and $X_\alpha = R$ for each $\alpha \in A$, the Cartesian product is just the collection of all real sequences $\{x_n\}$.

Now suppose that each $X_\alpha$ is a topological space. We shall define a certain topology for the Cartesian product $X$ of all the $X_\alpha$'s; this topology will be referred to as the Cartesian product topology for $X$. To define this Cartesian product topology we shall specify, for each $x$, a certain family $\mathscr{F}_x$ of sets containing $x$, and declare these sets to be a basis of neighborhoods at $x$. The topology is then uniquely determined. Suppose $x$ is fixed. Let $\alpha_1, \ldots, \alpha_n$ be any positive finite number of members of $A$, and let $U_i$ be any neighborhood of $x(\alpha_i)$ in $X(\alpha_i)$. Let $U$ be the set of all $y$ in $X$ such that $y(\alpha_i) \in U_i$, $i = 1, \ldots, n$. No restriction is placed on $y(\alpha)$ if $\alpha$ is not one of the $\alpha_i$'s. Let $\mathscr{F}_x$ be the family of all sets $U$ obtainable in this way. It is easy to see that the set of all pairs $(U, x)$, where $U \in \mathscr{F}_x$ and $x$ varies over $X$, satisfies the postulates at the beginning of Section 3–4, so that there is a uniquely determined topology for $X$ with $\mathscr{F}_x$ as a basis of neighborhoods at $x$. In the special case when the index set $A$ is finite, this Cartesian product topology is the same as the topology for the product space as we defined it earlier in this section. Suppose for instance that $A$ is the finite set $\{1, 2\}$. There are three types of sets $U$ in the basis $\mathscr{F}_x$ at a point $x$, depending on whether the finite set $\{\alpha_1, \ldots, \alpha_n\}$ from $A$ is $\{1\}$, $\{2\}$, or $\{1, 2\}$. The corresponding $U$'s are of the form $U_1 \times X_2$, $X_1 \times U_2$, and $U_1 \times U_2$. The case $U = U_1 \times U_2$ is illustrated schematically in Figure 29.

The function $f_\alpha$ which maps each point $x$ of the product space $X$ onto the value $x(\alpha)$, which is an element of $X_\alpha$, is called the *projection mapping* of $X$ onto $X_\alpha$. It is a continuous function. In fact, the Cartesian product topology is the minimal topology for $X$ with respect to which every $f_\alpha$ is continuous.

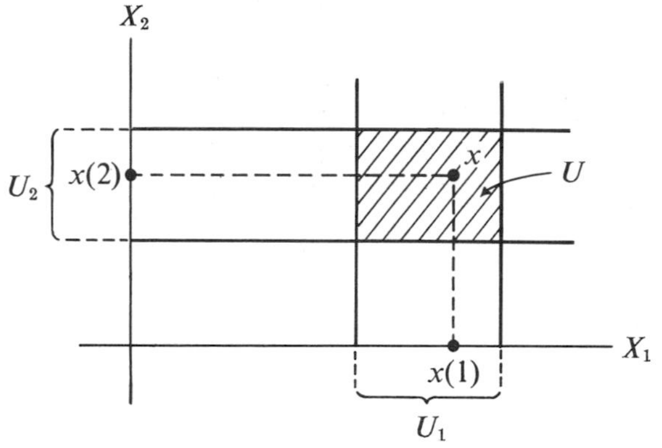


FIGURE 29

It is useful to know that if each $X_\alpha$ is a Hausdorff space, so is the product space $X$. This is simple to prove, and we leave the proof to the reader.

One of the basic theorems about product spaces is the following theorem about compactness. This theorem is due to Tychonoff.

THEOREM 3–11 I. *If each of the spaces $X_\alpha$ is compact, the product space $X = \Pi_{\alpha \in A} X_\alpha$, with the Cartesian product topology, is also compact.*

*Proof.* In the proof we shall make use of the criterion for compactness contained in Theorem 3–2 IV (c). Let $\mathscr{S}_0$ be a family of subsets of $X$, with the finite intersection property $F$. We wish to show that there is a point of $X$ belonging to all the closures $\bar{S}$ of the members of $\mathscr{S}_0$. Let $\mathscr{M}$ be a maximal member of the collection of all families $\mathscr{S}$ of subsets of $X$ such that $\mathscr{S}_0 \subset \mathscr{S}$ and $\mathscr{S}$ has property $F$. (For the existence of $\mathscr{M}$ see Example 2 in Section 3–10.) Clearly, it will suffice to show that $\bigcap_{M \in \mathscr{M}} \bar{M} \neq \varnothing$. If $M \in \mathscr{M}$, let $M_\alpha$ be the projection of $M$ on $X_\alpha$. That is, $M_\alpha = \{x_\alpha : x \in M\}$. We recall the alternative notations $x_\alpha$ and $x(\alpha)$ for the value of $x$ at $\alpha$. If $\alpha$ is given a subscript, the notation $x(\alpha)$ is preferable to $x_\alpha$ for reasons of typography. Likewise, we shall when convenient write $X(\alpha)$ in place of $X_\alpha$ and $M(\alpha)$ in place of $M_\alpha$. For a fixed $\alpha$ the family of all sets $M_\alpha$ ($M$ varying over $\mathscr{M}$) is a family with property $F$. Since $X_\alpha$ is compact, there is a point $u_\alpha$ in $X_\alpha$ which belongs to all the closures $\bar{M}_\alpha$. Now let $u$ be that element of $X$ whose value at $\alpha$ is $u_\alpha$, for each index $\alpha$. We shall prove that $u \in \bar{M}$ for each $M$ in $\mathscr{M}$, and this will finish the proof of the theorem.

Before proceeding directly with the proof, let us make some observations about simple facts which are consequences of the maximality of $\mathscr{M}$. First of all, $\mathscr{M}$ contains the intersection of any finite number of its members. Otherwise we could contradict the maximality of $\mathscr{M}$ by adjoining to $\mathscr{M}$ the intersection in question, for the enlarged family would still have property $F$. For later reference we call this first observation Remark I. Secondly, if $T$ is a subset of $X$ such that the intersection of $T$ with any finite number of members of $\mathscr{M}$ is nonvoid, then $T \in \mathscr{M}$. (Otherwise adjoin $T$ to $\mathscr{M}$ and get a contradiction.) We call this Remark II.

We now turn to the proof that $u \in \bar{M}$ for each $M$ in $\mathscr{M}$. Let $\alpha_1, \ldots, \alpha_n$ be any finite set of the $\alpha$'s, and let $U_i$ be a neighborhood of $u(\alpha_i)$ in $X(\alpha_i)$. Let $U$ be the set of all $x$ such that $x(\alpha_i) \in U_i$, $i = 1, \ldots, n$. This set $U$ is a typical member of the basis of neighborhoods at $u$. We have to show that $U \cap M \neq \varnothing$ for each $M$ in $\mathscr{M}$. By property $F$, it is sufficient to show that $U \in \mathscr{M}$. Now, we can write $U = V_1 \cap \cdots \cap V_n$, where $V_i$ is the set of all $x$ such that $x(\alpha_i) \in U_i$, but $x(\alpha)$ is unrestricted if $\alpha \neq \alpha_i$. By Remark I we can conclude $U \in \mathscr{M}$ if we prove that each of the $V_i$'s is in $\mathscr{M}$.

Since $u_\alpha \in \bar{M}_\alpha$ for each $M$, there is some element $v(\alpha_i)$ of $X(\alpha_i)$ in $U_i \cap M(\alpha_i)$. By the definition of $M(\alpha_i)$ there is some element $v$ in $M$ whose projection on $X(\alpha_i)$ is $v(\alpha_i)$ (of course this $v$ will depend on $i$). Clearly $v \in V_i \cap M$. Thus $V_i \cap M \neq \varnothing$ for $i = 1, \ldots, n$ and for each $M$ in $\mathscr{M}$. By Remark I we see that $V_i$ has a nonvoid intersection with each intersection of a finite number of members of $\mathscr{M}$. Hence, by Remark II, $V_i \in \mathscr{M}$. Now finally, as noted in the preceding paragraph, we can conclude that $U \in \mathscr{M}$, and thus finish the proof.

## PROBLEMS

1. Prove that the Cartesian product of Hausdorff spaces is a Hausdorff space.

2. Let $X$ and $Y$ be topological spaces, and let $Z$ be a metric space. Suppose that $Y$ satisfies the first axiom of countability. Let $f : X \times Y \to Z$ be a function which is continuous in each variable separately. Then it can be proved that to each $y$ in $Y$ corresponds a set $A(y)$ in $X$ with the following properties: (a) $A(y)$ is of the first category in $X$; (b) if $y_0 \in Y$ and $x_0 \in X - A(y_0)$, and if $\epsilon > 0$, there exists a neighborhood $U$ of $x_0$ in $X$ and a neighborhood $V$ of $y_0$ in $Y$ such that $D[f(x, y), f(x, y_0)] < \epsilon$ if $x \in U$ and $y \in V$. [*Suggestions.* Fix $y_0 \in Y$. For $y \in Y$ and $n = 1, 2, \ldots$ define a set $S_n(y)$ in $X$ by

$$S_n(y) = \left\{x : D[f(x, y), f(x, y_0)] > \frac{1}{n}\right\}.$$

Let $\{V_i\}$ be a basis of neighborhoods of $y_0$. Let

$$T_{ni} = \bigcup_{y \in V_i} S_n(y), \qquad B_n = \bigcap_{i=1}^{\infty} T_{ni}.$$

Finally, let

$$A_n = \bigcap_{i=1}^{\infty} \bar{T}_{ni}, \qquad A(y_0) = \bigcup_{n=1}^{\infty} A_n.$$

Observe that $S_n(y)$ is open. (Why?) Show that $B_n = \varnothing$ and hence that

$$A_n \subset \bigcup_i (\bar{T}_{ni} - T_{ni}),$$

from which it follows that $A_n$ and $A(y_0)$ are sets of the first category in $X$.

Next, observe that

$$X - A(y_0) = \bigcap_n \bigcup_i (T_{ni}^{\sim})^o.$$

[The assertion in (b) can now be proved.]

3. Continuing with the situation of Problem 2, prove that $f$ is continuous at $(x_0, y_0)$ if $x_0 \in X - A(y_0)$. In particular, then, the points of $X \times Y$ at which $f$ is continuous form a set dense in $X \times Y$ provided that $X$ is a complete metric space, or, more generally, provided that $X$ satisfies any one of the three conditions ($\alpha$), ($\beta$), ($\gamma$) mentioned in Problem 6, Section 3–9. The result stated here was first proved (for the case in which $X = Y = Z = R$) by R. Baire in his thesis [1]. The method was somewhat different. See also Hobson [1], Vol. 1, pp. 447–449.

4. Continuing with the situation of Problems 2 and 3, assume that $X$ and $Y$ are both complete metric spaces, and prove that the set of points of $X \times Y$ at which $f$ is continuous is a set of the second category, and that the complementary set is of the first category. See Problem 12, Section 3–9.

## DIRECTED FUNCTIONS AND THE MOORE-OSGOOD THEOREM

Problems 5–11 are concerned with relations between double limits and iterated limits. The most important result is given in Problem 8. In a very general form this embraces many of the standard theorems in analysis which assert that, given a certain uniformity condition, the result of two successive limiting processes is the same, regardless of the order of carrying out the processes. First we must give some general definitions.

Let $X$ be a nonempty set, and let $\mathscr{N}$ be a nonempty family of nonempty subsets of $X$ such that if $N_1$ and $N_2$ are in $\mathscr{N}$, there exists a member $N_3$ of $\mathscr{N}$ such that $N_3 \subset N_1 \cap N_2$. Then $\mathscr{N}$ is called a *direction* in $X$. If $f$ is a function with domain $X$ we call the pair $(f, \mathscr{N})$ *a directed function*. Let $Z$ be a Hausdorff space, and suppose the range of $f$ is in $Z$. We say that $(f, \mathscr{N})$ converges to the element $z$ of $Z$, and write $(f, \mathscr{N}) \to z$, if to each neighborhood $W$ of $z$ corresponds some $N$ in $\mathscr{N}$ such that $f(N) \subset W$. This general notion of convergence is dealt with in full detail in the book of McShane and Botts [1].

If $Z$ is a metric space, the directed function $(f, \mathscr{N})$ is said to be of Cauchy type if to each $\epsilon > 0$ corresponds some $N \in \mathscr{N}$ such that $D[f(x_1), f(x_2)] < \epsilon$ when $x_1$ and $x_2$ are in $N$. When $Z$ is complete, a directed function of Cauchy type is convergent to some element $z$ of $Z$ (see Problem 7).

*Some important examples of directions.*

(a) $X$ the positive integers, $\mathscr{N}$ the family of sets $N_m = \{n \in X : m \leq n\}$, where $m \in X$.

(b) $X$ a topological space, $S \subset X$, and $x_0 \in \bar{S}$; $\mathscr{N}$ the family of sets $N = S \cap U$, where $U$ varies over the class of all neighborhoods of $x_0$.

(c) $X_1$ a topological space, $X$ a subset of $X_1$, $x_0$ an accumulation point of $X$; $\mathscr{N}$ the family of sets $X \cap U - \{x_0\}$, where $U$ varies over the class of all neighborhoods of $x_0$.

Now suppose that we have $f : X \times Y \to Z$, and directions $\mathscr{M}$, $\mathscr{N}$ in $X$, $Y$, respectively. We suppose that $Z$ is a metric space. The family $\mathscr{P}$ of all sets $M \times N$, where $M \in \mathscr{M}$ and $N \in \mathscr{N}$, is a direction in $X \times Y$, so that $(f, \mathscr{P})$ is a directed function. For fixed $x$, the function which maps $y$ into $f(x, y)$ is denoted by $f(x, \cdot)$; there is a similar meaning for $f(\cdot, y)$. Thus $(f(x, \cdot), \mathscr{N})$ and $(f(\cdot, y), \mathscr{M})$ are directed functions. There is a concept of uniform convergence: We say that $(f(x, \cdot), \mathscr{N})$ converges to $g(x)$ uniformly on $X$ if to each $\epsilon > 0$ corresponds some $N \in \mathscr{N}$ such that $D[f(x, y), g(x)] < \epsilon$ if $x \in X$ and $y \in N$.

If $(f, \mathscr{P}) \to z_1$, we call $z_1$ the *double limit* of $f(x, y)$ with respect to $\mathscr{M}, \mathscr{N}$. If $(f(x, \cdot), \mathscr{N}) \to g(x)$ for each $x$, and if $(g, \mathscr{M}) \to z_2$, we call $z_2$ the *iterated limit* of $f(x, y)$, first with respect to $\mathscr{N}$ and then with respect to $\mathscr{M}$. There is another iterated limit $z_3$, in case $(f(\cdot, y), \mathscr{M}) \to h(y)$ for each $y$, and $(h, \mathscr{N}) \to z_3$.

5. Suppose that $(f, \mathscr{P}) \to z$ and $(f(x, \cdot), \mathscr{N}) \to g(x)$ for each $x$. Show that $(g, \mathscr{M}) \to z$. In the course of the argument it is necessary to prove that if for some fixed $x$, $N$ and $W_1$ we know that $f(x, y) \in W_1$ when $y \in N$, then $g(x) \in \bar{W}_1$.

6. Suppose that $(f(x, \cdot), \mathscr{N})$ converges to $g(x)$ uniformly on $X$, and that $(g, \mathscr{M}) \to z$. Then $(f, \mathscr{P}) \to z$. Prove this.

7. Suppose $(F, \mathscr{M})$ is a directed function of Cauchy type, the values of $F$ being in the complete metric space $Z$. Using the following suggestions, prove that $(F, \mathscr{M})$ converges to a limit $z$ in $Z$. Choose $M_n \in \mathscr{M}$ so that $D[F(x_1), F(x_2)] < \frac{1}{n}$ if $x_1$ and $x_2$ are in $M_n$. Choose $x_n \in M_n$ and let

$S_n = \left\{z \in Z : D(z, F(x_n)) \le \frac{1}{n}\right\}$. Let $T_n = S_1 \cap \cdots \cap S_n$. Show that $\bigcap_n T_n$ contains a single point $z$, and that $(F, \mathscr{M}) \to z$.

8. Suppose that the metric space $Z$ is complete. Suppose $(f(x, \cdot), \mathscr{N}) \to g(x)$ uniformly on $X$, and suppose $(f(\cdot, y), \mathscr{M}) \to h(y)$ for each $y$. Then $(f, \mathscr{P})$ converges to an element $z$ of $Z$, and we have both

$$(g, \mathscr{M}) \to z \quad \text{and} \quad (h, \mathscr{N}) \to z.$$

That is, the double limit and the two iterated limits all exist, and all three are equal. This is called the Moore-Osgood theorem. E. H. Moore's version goes back to 1900; see Graves [1], p. 100. Osgood's version was for the case of double sequences; see Osgood [2], Vol. 1, p. 619. Prove the theorem by proving that $(f, \mathscr{P})$ is a directed function of Cauchy type (see Problem 7). Then use Problem 5.

9. As examples to illustrate various situations where the double limit and the two iterated limits may not all be equal, or where some of the limits exist while others do not, study the following double sequences $[m, n = 1, 2, \ldots]$.

(i) $f(m, n) = 1$ if $n \ge m$, $f(m, n) = 0$ if $n < m$.

(ii) $f(m, n) = \dfrac{1 - (-1)^n}{m}$.

(iii) $f(m, n) = 0$ if $|m - n|$ is odd, $f(m, n) = \dfrac{1}{\min(m, n)}$ if $|m - n|$ is even.

(iv) $f(m, n) = \dfrac{2mn}{m^2 + n^2}$.

10. Let $u_k(m) = \dfrac{m(m-1)\cdots(m-k+1)}{k!}\left(\dfrac{x}{m}\right)^k$ if $1 \le k \le m$, $u_k(m) = 0$ if $m < k$. Let $f(m, n) = \sum_{k=1}^{n} u_k(m)$. Show that the Moore-Osgood theorem can be applied to deduce that

$$\lim_{m\to\infty}\left[\left(1 + \frac{x}{m}\right)^m - 1\right] = \sum_{k=1}^{\infty} \frac{x^k}{k!}.$$

11. Suppose that $a_{mn} \ge 0$, $m, n = 1, 2, \ldots$. Let $f(m, n) = \sum_{i=1}^{m} \sum_{j=1}^{n} a_{ij}$. Show that if either one of the iterated limits

$$\lim_{m\to\infty}\left[\lim_{n\to\infty} f(m, n)\right], \qquad \lim_{n\to\infty}\left[\lim_{m\to\infty} f(m, n)\right]$$

exists, so does the other, so does the double limit, and all three limits are equal.

## 3–12 Vector spaces

In Section 2–1 we explained how two elements $x, y$ of $R^k$ can be added to yield another element $x + y$, and how an element $x$ can be multiplied by a real number $\alpha$ to yield an element $\alpha x$. We also explained briefly the reasons for saying that $R^k$ can be regarded as a real vector space. Now, we turn to a more detailed consideration of the notion of an abstract vector space.

Let $X$ be a set of elements $x, y, \ldots$ and suppose there is defined a mapping of $X \times X$ into $X$, called the addition function. Let the image of $(x, y)$ be denoted by $x + y$. Suppose also there is defined a mapping of $R \times X$ into $X$, called the scalar multiplication function; the image of $(\alpha, x)$ is to be denoted by $\alpha x$. Concerning $X$ and these two functions the following axioms will be assumed to be satisfied. Here $x$, $y$, $z$ denote elements of $X$; $\alpha$ and $\beta$ denote real numbers.

1. $x + y = y + x$.
2. $x + (y + z) = (x + y) + z$.
3. There is in $X$ a unique element, denoted by 0 and called the zero element of $X$, such that $x + 0 = x$ for each $x$.
4. To each $x$ corresponds a unique element of $X$ denoted by $-x$, such that $x + (-x) = 0$.
5. $\alpha(x + y) = \alpha x + \alpha y$.
6. $(\alpha + \beta)x = \alpha x + \beta x$.
7. $\alpha(\beta x) = (\alpha\beta)x$.
8. $1 \cdot x = x$.
9. $0 \cdot x = 0$.

It follows from the axioms that $-1 \cdot x = -x$. In axiom 9 we use the same symbol for the zero of $R$ and the zero of $X$. We continue this double usage of the symbol 0; it will cause no ambiguity, for we shall be able to recognize the proper meaning of 0 from the context in which it occurs. The set $X$ together with the two mappings, subject to axioms 1–9, is called a *real vector space*, or also a *real linear* space.

## COMPLEX VECTOR SPACES

We can also define a *complex* vector space. The definition is just the same as for a real vector space, except that in the scalar multiplication $\alpha x$ we permit $\alpha$ to be any complex number. For the development of many of the algebraic properties of vector spaces it makes no difference whether the space is real or complex. When we speak of a vector space $X$ without specifying if it is real or complex, it is to be understood that our statements apply equally to real vector spaces and complex vector spaces. In such cases we may refer to "the scalar field associated with $X$"; this reference will be to either the field $R$ or to the field of complex numbers, as the case may be. Elements of the field will be referred to either as "scalars," or as "numbers."

The space analogous to $R^k$, but with elements $x = (\xi_1, \ldots, \xi_k)$, where the $\xi_i$'s are complex numbers, will be denoted by $C^k$. It is a complex vector space. We write $C$ for $C^1$.

As we saw in Section 2–1, $R^k$ is a real vector space. There are numerous examples of real vector spaces which are of interest in analysis. Typically, in such examples, the class $X$ is a class of functions.

*Example 1.* Let $T$ be an arbitrary nonempty set. We consider functions with domain $T$ and range in $R$. If $x$ and $y$ are such functions, let $x + y$ be the function with domain $T$ and range in $R$ defined to have as its value at $t (t \in T)$ the sum $x(t) + y(t)$. We can express this by

$$(x + y)(t) = x(t) + y(t).$$

We say that we obtain $x + y$ by *pointwise addition* of $x$ and $y$. Likewise, if $\alpha \in R$, define $\alpha \cdot x$ (usually written without the dot) by

$$(\alpha x)(t) = \alpha \cdot x(t).$$

Define the zero function 0 as the function whose range contains just the single real number 0. Define $-x = -1 \cdot x$. Then it is clear that the class of all functions with domain $T$ and range in $R$ is a real vector space. We may also obtain examples of real vector spaces by confining attention to certain particular subclasses of the class of all these functions.

A standard notation for the class of all functions with domain $T$ and range in a set $S$ is $S^T$. Hence in this case our vector space is $(R)^T$. If $T$ is the class consisting of the $k$ integers $1, 2, \ldots, k$, we see that $(R)^T$ is precisely the Euclidean space $R^k$ (but without the additional structure furnished in $R^k$ by the definitions of distance and dot-product).

It is clear that we may also form a complex linear space of complex-valued functions defined on $T$.

*Example 2.* Consider the class of functions defined in Example 1, and let $B(T)$ denote the subclass consisting of those functions which are bounded (that is, which have a range which is a bounded set in $R$). If $x$ and $y$ are in $B(T)$, it is easily seen that $x + y$ and $\alpha x$ are in $B(T)$, and that $B(T)$ is a real vector space.

*Example 3.* Let $T$ be a compact topological space, and let $C(T)$ be the class of functions $x$ with domain $T$ and range in $R$ such that $x$ is continuous on $T$. Then $C(T)$, with definitions of $x + y$ and $\alpha x$ as in Example 1, is a real vector space. We may note that the elements of $C(T)$ are bounded functions, as a consequence of the compactness of $T$ (see Theorems 3–2 I and 2–6 I).

In particular, if $T$ is the finite closed interval $[a, b]$ in $R$, where $a < b$, we denote $C(T)$ by $C[a, b]$.

*Example 4.* A number of interesting vector spaces occur as spaces of functions defined on $T$, where $T$ is the class of all positive integers. The functions are then sequences of real numbers. We use the notation $x = \{\xi_n\}$, where $x(n) = \xi_n$. We get various spaces by placing various restrictions on the class of sequences. The space of all convergent sequences $\{\xi_n\}$ is usually denoted by (c). If $0 < p$, the space of all sequences $\{\xi_n\}$ such that

$$\sum_{n=1}^{\infty} |\xi_n|^p < \infty$$

is denoted by $l^p$. The case $p = 2$ is especially interesting and important in analysis. The reasons for this will appear later (see Section 3–14, where it is proved that $l^2$ can serve as a concrete model for any separable Hilbert space). To verify that $l^p$ is actually a vector space, we must be assured that if $x = \{\xi_n\}$ and $y = \{\eta_n\}$ are in $l^p$, then so is the sequence $x + y = \{\xi_n + \eta_n\}$. This matter is taken care of by Minkowski's inequality (Problem 9 (c), Section 3–6) if $p \geq 1$, but a different method must be used when $0 < p < 1$. The following inequality, valid for any $p > 0$, can be used.

$$(1) \qquad |A + B|^p \leq 2^p\{|A|^p + |B|^p\},$$

where $A$ and $B$ are any real or complex numbers. To prove this, observe that

$$\max\{|A|, |B|\} \leq |A| + |B| \leq 2 \max\{|A|, |B|\}.$$

Hence,

$$\begin{aligned} |A + B|^p \leq (|A| + |B|)^p &\leq [2 \max\{|A|, |B|\}]^p \\ &= \max\{2^p |A|^p, 2^p |B|^p\} \\ &\leq 2^p |A|^p + 2^p |B|^p. \end{aligned}$$

It was pointed out in Problem 12, Section 3–6, that $l^p$ can be made into a metric space if $p \geq 1$. But the function $D_p$ which is a metric when $p \geq 1$ is not a metric if $0 < p < 1$, because it fails to satisfy the triangular inequality.

## LINEAR DEPENDENCE

A finite set $x_1, \ldots, x_n$ of elements of the linear space is called *linearly dependent* if there exist scalars $\alpha_1, \ldots, \alpha_n$, not all zero, such that $\alpha_1 x_1 + \cdots + \alpha_n x_n = 0$. A finite set which is not linearly dependent is called *linearly independent*. In that case, a relation $\alpha_1 x_1 + \cdots + \alpha_n x_n = 0$ implies that $\alpha_1 = \cdots = \alpha_n = 0$. An infinite set is called linearly independent if every finite subset of it is linearly independent. Otherwise it is called linearly dependent.

A linearly independent set cannot contain the vector 0.

*Example 5.* In the space $C[0, 1]$ let $x_n$ be defined by $x_n(t) = t^n$, $n = 1, 2, \ldots, 0 \leq t \leq 1$, and let $x_0(t) = 1$ for each $t$. Then the set $\{x_0, x_1, x_2, \ldots\}$ is linearly independent. For, as is well known and easily proved, if $\alpha_0 + \alpha_1 t + \cdots + \alpha_n t^n = 0$ when $0 \leq t \leq 1$, then $\alpha_0 = \cdots = \alpha_n = 0$.

It is not our purpose or intention to develop systematically the algebraic theory of linear spaces. We assume that the student either already knows or can readily learn from other sources the basic facts and theorems which are necessary for the purposes of this book. We shall give definitions and cite facts and theorems as necessary. Sections 1–1 and 1–2 of Chapter 1 of Taylor [2] contain all that is essential for our immediate purpose, in particular for the discussion of dimensionality, to which we shall come presently.

## SUBSPACES

If $X$ is a vector space, a nonempty subset $M$ of $X$ is called a *subspace* of $X$, or a *linear manifold* in $X$, if $x + y$ and $\alpha x$ are in $M$ whenever $x$ and $y$ are in $M$ and $\alpha$ is any scalar. For example, if $X = C[0, 1]$ (real-valued continuous functions), the set $M$ of all polynomials in $t$ with real coefficients is a subspace of $X$. So also is the subset of $M$ consisting of all the polynomials $p$ such that $p(0) = 0$. But the subset of $M$ consisting of all polynomials $p$ for which $p(0) = 1$ is *not* a subspace.

Clearly $X$ is a subspace of itself. The set $\{0\}$ is a subspace of $X$. A *proper* subspace $M$ of $X$ is a subspace $M$ such that $M \neq X$.

Let $S$ be any nonempty subset of $X$, and let $M$ be the set of all finite linear combinations of elements of $S$. That is, $x \in M$ if and only if there exist elements $x_1, \ldots, x_n$ in $S$ and scalars $\alpha_1, \ldots, \alpha_n$ such that $x = \alpha_1 x_1 + \cdots + \alpha_n x_n$. This set $M$ is a subspace of $X$. We say that $M$ is *generated* (or *determined*, or *spanned*) by $S$. We also say that the *linear span* of $S$ is $M$.

The intersection of any number of subspaces is a subspace.

A subspace of a vector space is a vector space.

## DIMENSIONALITY

If $X$ is a linear space, there may be some positive integer $n$ such that $X$ contains a set of $n$ vectors which are linearly independent, while every set of $n + 1$ vectors in $X$ is linearly dependent. In this case we say that $X$ is *finite-dimensional*, of dimension $n$. A vector space with just one element (which must then be 0) is also called finite-dimensional, of dimension 0. If $X$ is not finite dimensional, we call it infinite dimensional.

Finite-dimensional spaces form the natural medium for the algebraic study of finite systems of linear equations involving a finite number of "unknowns." In analysis, where we often consider spaces whose elements are functions, we typically encounter infinite-dimensional spaces. Nevertheless, we frequently find ourselves dealing with finite-dimensional subspaces.

*Example 6.* Let $X$ be the vector space of all functions $x : R \to R$ such that $x$ has derivatives of all orders. Let $M$ be the class of all $x$ such that $\frac{d^2x}{dt^2} = x(t)$ for every $t$. As we know, $M$ consists of the linear combinations of the elements $x_1$, $x_2$, where $x_1(t) = e^t$, $x_2(t) = e^{-t}$. Since $\{x_1, x_2\}$ is a linearly independent set, $M$ is 2-dimensional.

If $X$ is $n$-dimensional, where $n \geq 1$, there exists a linearly independent set $S$ consisting of $n$ elements, and the linear manifold generated by $S$ is $X$ itself. Moreover, any linearly independent set in $X$ whose linear span is $X$ contains exactly $n$ elements. A set of this kind is called a *basis* of (or for) $X$.

We know, for instance, that the $k$ vectors $e_1 = (1, 0, \ldots, 0)$, $e_2 = (0, 1, 0, \ldots, 0)$, $\ldots, e_k = (0, 0, \ldots, 1)$ form a basis of $R^k$, which is $k$-dimensional. There are, of course, infinitely many different sets which form bases for $R^k$. Any two nonzero, noncollinear vectors in $R^2$ form a basis in $R^2$. For example, $u_1 = (1, 1)$ and $u_2 = (1, 2)$ form a basis. We can write

$$(\xi_1, \xi_2) = (2\xi_1 - \xi_2)u_1 + (\xi_2 - \xi_1)u_2.$$

## LINEAR CONFIGURATIONS IN A VECTOR SPACE

The concepts of straight lines, planes, and hyperplanes in $R^k$, as set forth in Section 2–2, can be defined in any real vector space. The discussion of straight lines and line segments follows exactly the same form as in Section 2–2, except that $R^k$ is replaced by an arbitrary real vector space $X$. By a plane through 0 in $X$ we mean a subspace of $X$. By a *hyperplane* through 0 we mean a maximal proper subspace of $X$. That is, $M$ is a hyperplane through 0 if $M$ is a subspace, $M \neq X$, and any subspace $N$ such that $M \subset N$ is either $M$ or $X$. If $X$ is $n$-dimensional, one can show that such a maximal proper subspace is $(n-1)$-dimensional.

By a plane (or hyperplane) $M$ *not through* 0 we mean a set which is obtained by starting with a plane (or hyperplane) $M_0$ through 0 and adding on to each of its elements some fixed vector $x_0$, where $x_0$ does not belong to $M_0$. For instance, the set of all polynomials $p$ such that $p(0) = 1$ is a plane (not through 0) in the space $C[0, 1]$. It is obtained by adding the constant function 1 to the members of the class of all polynomials $p_0$ such that $p_0(0) = 0$.

## 3–13 Normed linear spaces

A *norm* on a vector space $X$ is a real-valued function, whose value at $x$ we usually denote by $\|x\|$, with the properties:

(a) $\|x_1 + x_2\| \leq \|x_1\| + \|x_2\|$,
(b) $\|\alpha x\| = |\alpha| \, \|x\|$,
(c) $\|x\| \geq 0$,
(d) $\|x\| \neq 0$ if $x \neq 0$.

Observe that $\|0\| = 0$ by (b), because $0 \cdot x = 0$. Property (c) is listed to emphasize it, but it is actually a consequence of (a) and (b), so that (a), (b), (d) are the conditions which we have to verify if we are testing a function to see if it is a norm. The deduction of (c) is as follows. We have

$$0 = \|x - x\| \le \|x\| + \|-x\| = 2\|x\|,$$

whence $\|x\| \ge 0$.

With the aid of a norm on $X$ we can define a metric $D$ on $X$, by setting $D(x, y) = \|x - y\|$. We leave it to the reader to verify that $D$ is a metric. When a vector space becomes a metric space (and thus acquires a topology) by using a norm to define the metric in this way, we call it a *normed vector space*, or a *normed linear space*. We call property (a) of the norm the triangular inequality because it leads to the inequality

$$D(x, z) \le D(x, y) + D(y, z),$$

which expresses the fact that the length of one side of a triangle is not greater than the sum of the other two sides.

It is important to know that the addition and scalar multiplication mappings,

$$(x, y) \to x + y \quad \text{and} \quad (\alpha, x) \to \alpha x,$$

are continuous upon their respective domains. The norm is also continuous; in particular, then, $x_n \to x$ implies $\|x_n\| \to \|x\|$.

The simplest example of a normed linear space is $R$, with $\|x\|$ the absolute value of $x$. As we saw in Section 2–1, $R^k$ is a normed linear space (see (1) and (14) in Section 2–1) with norm

(1) $$\|x\| = (\xi_1^2 + \cdots + \xi_k^2)^{1/2}, \; x = (\xi_1, \ldots, \xi_k).$$

We can define other norms on $R^k$. If $p \ge 1$ let

(2) $$\|x\|_p = (|\xi_1|^p + \cdots + |\xi_k|^p)^{1/p}.$$

This is a norm; see Minkowski's inequality, Problem 9 (c), Section 3–6. With this notation the norm in (1) is $\|x\|_2$. The normed linear space which results from putting the norm $\|x\|_p$ on the elements of $R^k$ will be designated by $l^p(k)$. The corresponding metric is denoted by $D_p$. See Problem 11 (b), Section 3–6. When we speak of $R^k$ as a normed linear space, we shall ordinarily have the norm $\|x\|_2$ in mind. It is only with the metric arising from this norm that $R^k$ as a space deserves the adjective "Euclidean."

Here is an example of a deviation from Euclidean geometry in the space $l^1(2)$: The three points $A = (1, 0)$, $B = (0, 1)$, $C = (0, 0)$ form a nondegenerate triangle, but $D_1(A, B) = 2$, $D_1(B, C) = D_1(C, A) = 1$, so that the sum of the lengths of two sides is *equal* to the length of the third side.

## EQUIVALENT NORMS

When two norms for the same space lead to the same topology, they are called *equivalent norms*. From the discussion of equivalent metrics in Section 3–6 it is clear that two norms (denoted, say, by $\|\ \|_1$ and $\|\ \|_2$) for $X$ are equivalent if and only if $\|x_n - x\|_1 \to 0$ implies $\|x_n - x\|_2 \to 0$, and vice-versa.

The various norms $\|\ \|_p$ defined on $R^k$ by (2) are all equivalent. See Problem 11 (b) in Section 3–6.

It may be proved, as a general theorem, that norms $\|\ \|_1$ and $\|\ \|_2$ for $X$ are equivalent if and only if there exist positive constants $m$, $M$ such that

$$m\|x\|_2 \le \|x\|_1 \le M\|x\|_2$$

for each $x$ in $X$. The proof is left as a problem.

In this book we shall often use integrals to define norms on linear spaces.

*Example 1.* If $X = C[a, b]$ (see Example 3, Section 3–12), the mapping $x \to \|x\|_1$ is a norm, where

$$\|x\|_1 = \int_a^b |x(t)|\, dt. \tag{3}$$

The customary norm for $C[a, b]$ is given by

$$\|x\| = \max |x(t)|; \tag{4}$$

the continuity of $x$ on the compact set $[a, b]$ insures that $|x(t)|$ does attain a maximum. As we saw in Example 3, Section 3–6, the norms defined in (3) and (4) do not yield the same topology for $C[a, b]$, and therefore are not equivalent.

We can define many different nonequivalent norms for $C[a, b]$ by using integrals in other ways. For any $p > 0$ let

$$\|x\|_p = \left(\int_a^b |x(t)|^p\, dt\right)^{1/p}. \tag{5}$$

Then the mapping $x \to \|x\|_p$ is a norm on $C[a, b]$ if $p \geq 1$. To see that $\|x\|_p$ satisfies the triangular inequality when $p > 1$ we need the integral form of Minkowski's inequality:

$$\left(\int_a^b |x(t) + y(t)|^p\, dt\right)^{1/p} \leq \left(\int_a^b |x(t)|^p\, dt\right)^{1/p} + \left(\int_a^b |y(t)|^p\, dt\right)^{1/p}. \tag{6}$$

We are dealing here with continuous functions, but Minkowski's inequality is actually valid for a much larger class of functions, with Lebesgue integrals. Minkowski's inequality is proved with the aid of Hölder's inequality for integrals: Suppose $p > 1$ and $p' = \dfrac{p}{p-1}$. Then

$$\int_a^b |x(t)y(t)|\, dt \leq \left(\int_a^b |x(t)|^p\, dt\right)^{1/p} \left(\int_a^b |y(t)|^{p'}\, dt\right)^{1/p'}. \tag{7}$$

Here also the inequality is valid with Lebesgue integrals. However, at this stage we do not presume any knowledge of the Lebesgue theory of integration. A student should be able to prove first (7) and then (6), using simple facts about integrals of continuous functions, and assuming $x$ and $y$ are in $C[a, b]$. The proofs resemble the proofs in (b) and (c) of Problem 9, Section 3–6. For a discussion of the inequalities of Hölder and Minkowski in a more abstract setting, see Problem 5, at the end of this section of the text.

It is possible to show that

$$\|x\|_p \leq \|x\|_q (b - a)^{(q-p)/pq} \quad \text{if} \quad 0 < p < q. \tag{8}$$

Hence, assuming $1 \leq p < q$, we see that if $\{x_n\}$ is a sequence in $C[a, b]$ such that $x_n \to 0$ in the topology defined by the norm $\|x\|_q$, then also $x_n \to 0$ in the topology defined by the norm $\|x\|_p$. In other words, $\|x_n\|_q \to 0$ implies $\|x_n\|_p \to 0$. But the reverse implication is not valid (see Problem 4), and hence the norms $\|x\|_p$ and $\|x\|_q$ are not equivalent.

## FINITE-DIMENSIONAL SPACES

It turns out that a normed linear space $X$ is finite-dimensional if and only if it is locally compact. We shall not give the proof of this. See Taylor [2], Theorems 3.12–D, 3.12–F.

## LINEAR FUNCTIONALS

Let $X$ be a normed linear space. By a *linear functional* on $X$ we mean a mapping $f: X \to R$ or $f: X \to C$, according as $X$ is a real or complex space, such that for every $x, y$ in $X$ and every scalar $\alpha$ we have

$$f(\alpha x) = \alpha f(x), \qquad f(x + y) = f(x) + f(y).$$

Observe that the first condition implies that $f(0) = 0$. Our principal interest will be in linear functionals which are continuous. If $X$ is finite dimensional, it turns out that any linear functional is necessarily continuous, but when $X$ is infinite dimensional this is no longer true. The following theorem reveals a simple characteristic property of linear functionals which are continuous.

THEOREM 3–13 I. *If $f$ is a linear functional on $X$, it is continuous on $X$ if and only if*

(9) $$\sup_{\|x\| \le 1} |f(x)| < \infty.$$

*Proof.* Suppose the supremum in (9) is finite; denote it by $M$. Given $x_0$ and $\epsilon > 0$, we have to show the existence of some $\delta > 0$ such that $|f(x) - f(x_0)| < \epsilon$ if $\|x - x_0\| < \delta$. Any choice of $\delta > 0$ such that $M\delta < \epsilon$ will suffice. In fact, with $\delta$ so chosen, let $0 < \|x - x_0\| < \delta$. Let

$$y = \frac{x - x_0}{\|x - x_0\|}.$$

Then $\|y\| = 1$, and so $|f(y)| \le M$. But

$$f(y) = \frac{1}{\|x - x_0\|}[f(x) - f(x_0)].$$

Therefore

$$|f(x) - f(x_0)| \le M\|x - x_0\| \le M\delta < \epsilon.$$

For the other half of the proof we are to prove the supremum in (9) finite if $f$ is continuous on $X$. It in fact suffices to assume $f$ continuous at the single point $x = 0$. Making this assumption, it follows that there is some $\delta > 0$ such that $|f(x)| < 1$ if $\|x\| \le \delta$. Now, if $0 < \|x\| \le 1$, we see that $\|y\| = \delta$ when $y = \delta x/\|x\|$. Therefore $|f(y)| < 1$. But

$$f(y) = \frac{\delta}{\|x\|} f(x).$$

Therefore $|f(x)| < \dfrac{\|x\|}{\delta}$ if $0 < \|x\| \le 1$, whence certainly

$$\sup_{\|x\| \le 1} |f(x)| \le \frac{1}{\delta}.$$

This completes the proof.

It is customary to denote the supremum in (9) by $\|f\|$ and to call it the *norm* of $f$. One can show that the collection of all continuous linear functionals on $X$ becomes a normed linear space with this norm.

Linear functionals are of interest in a course on analysis because they are very intimately connected with the theory of integration. We are not now ready to develop this connection. However, we can illustrate situations in which integrals as used to define continuous linear functionals.

*Example 2.* Let $g$ be any member of $C[a, b]$. For $x \in C[a, b]$ define

$$f(x) = \int_a^b g(t)x(t)\, dt. \tag{10}$$

Then $f$ is a linear functional on $C[a, b]$. If we let $X = C[a, b]$ and use for $X$ either the norm defined by (4) or any one of the norms defined by (5) with $p \geq 1$, $f$ is continuous on $X$ with respect to the topology determined by the chosen norm. In fact, if we use the norm in (4) (usually called the supremum norm, or maximum norm), we see from (10) that $|f(x)| \leq (b - a)\, \|g\|\, \|x\|$, so that $f$ satisfies the condition of Theorem 3–13 I, with $\|f\| \leq (b - a)\|g\|$. Here $\|g\|$ is the supremum norm of $g$ as an element of $C[a, b]$. If we use the norm $\|x\|_1$ for $X$, we see from (10) that

$$|f(x)| \leq \max_t |g(t)| \int_a^b |x(t)|\, dt \leq \|g\|\, \|x\|_1,$$

so this time $\|f\| \leq \|g\|$, where $\|g\|$ is still the supremum norm of $g$. Finally, if we use the norm $\|x\|_p$ for $X$, with $p > 1$, we see from (7) that

$$|f(x)| \leq \|g\|_{p'}\, \|x\|_p,$$

so that $\|f\| \leq \|g\|_{p'}$.

## BANACH SPACES

A normed linear space may or may not be complete as a metric space. If it *is* complete, it is called a Banach space. The name honors the work of the Polish mathematician Stefan Banach (1892–1945). Banach did much important research on the subject of complete normed linear spaces, and wrote a book [1] which exerted a profound influence.

If $X$ is a normed linear space, a sequence $\{x_n\}$ in $X$ is a Cauchy sequence (see Section 3–8) if and only if $\|x_n - x_m\| \to 0$ as $m \to \infty$ and $n \to \infty$. We recall that $X$ is a complete space if and only if every Cauchy sequence in $X$ is convergent to a limit in $x$. We know (Theorem 2–4 V) that the Euclidean space $R^k$ is complete.

We shall give some examples of complete and incomplete spaces composed of functions.

*Example 3.* The space $C[a, b]$ with the supremum norm (4) is a Banach space. We see this as follows. Suppose $\{x_n\}$ is a Cauchy sequence in $C[a, b]$ with this norm. Since $|x(t)| \leq \|x\|$ for each $t$, we have

$$|x_n(t) - x_m(t)| \leq \|x_n - x_m\|,$$

and therefore $\{x_n(t)\}$ is a Cauchy sequence in $R$, for each choice of $t$. But $R$ is complete; therefore the sequence $\{x_n(t)\}$ converges to a limit in $R$; this limit depends on $t$, and we shall denote it by $x(t)$. In this way a function $x : [a, b] \to R$ is defined. We call it the *pointwise limit* of the sequence $\{x_n\}$. We have to prove, first, that $x \in C[a, b]$, and second, that $\|x_n - x\| \to 0$. Now, if $\epsilon > 0$, the fact that $\{x_n\}$ is a Cauchy sequence in $C[a, b]$ implies that there is some $N$ such that $\|x_n - x_m\| < \epsilon$ if $N \leq m$ and $N \leq n$. Consequently, for such $m$ and $n$, and for each $t$,

$$|x_n(t) - x_m(t)| < \epsilon.$$

In this inequality we now take the limit as $m \to \infty$. As a result we can assert

$$|x_n(t) - x(t)| \leq \epsilon \tag{11}$$

if $N \leq n$. Since $N$ does not depend on $t$, we see that $\{x_n(t)\}$ converges to $x(t)$ *uniformly* on $[a, b]$. Hence, by Theorem 3–6 II, $x$ is continuous on $[a, b]$. The inequality (11) now shows

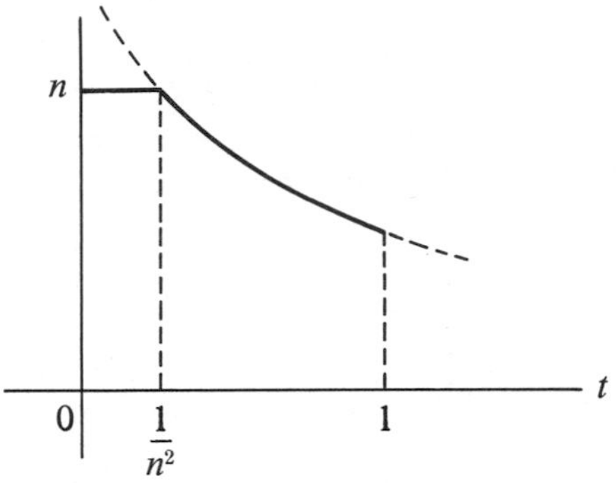


FIGURE 30

that $\|x_n - x\| \leq \epsilon$ if $n \geq N$; that is, $x_n \to x$. This shows that $C[a, b]$ is a complete space when the supremum norm is used. *We emphasize that convergence, in the sense of the supremum norm, is uniform convergence on* $[a, b]$.

*Example 4.* Let $X$ be the class of functions $C[a, b]$, made into a normed linear space with the norm $\|x\|_1$ defined by (3). Then $X$ is not complete. We shall demonstrate this, for simplicity, with $a = 0$, $b = 1$. Let $x_n$ be the element of $C[0, 1]$ defined as follows:

$$x_n(t) = \begin{cases} n & \text{if } 0 \leq t \leq \dfrac{1}{n^2} \\[2ex] \dfrac{1}{\sqrt{t}} & \text{if } \dfrac{1}{n^2} \leq t \leq 1. \end{cases}$$

The graph of $x_n$ is shown in Figure 30. If $m < n$ we readily compute that

$$\|x_n - x_m\|_1 = \frac{1}{m} - \frac{1}{n};$$

therefore $\{x_n\}$ is a Cauchy sequence in $X$. The sequence is not convergent in $X$, however. For, no matter what $x \in X$ is chosen, we can show that $\|x_n - x\|_1$ does not converge to 0. In fact, let $M$ be the larger of the numbers 1, $\max_{0 \leq t \leq 1} |x(t)|$ and suppose $n \geq 2M$. Then if $0 \leq t \leq 1/M^2$, we have

$$|x_n(t) - x(t)| = x_n(t) - x(t) \geq x_n(t) - M,$$

and so

$$\|x_n - x\|_1 \geq \int_0^{1/M^2} [x_n(t) - M]\, dt = \frac{1}{M} - \frac{1}{n} \geq \frac{1}{2M}.$$

Since $M$ is fixed, we see that $\{x_n\}$ does not converge to $x$ in $X$. Thus $X$ is not complete.

As we shall see later (Theorem 5–9 II and the ensuing discussion of $L(\mu)$; also Theorem 6–5 IV) one of the features of the Lebesgue theory of integration is that if the Lebesgue integral

$$\int_a^b |x(t)|\, dt$$

is used to define a norm on a space suitably constructed from the class of all functions defined on $[a, b]$ and integrable in the Lebesgue sense, *then this space is complete.*

## COMPLETION OF A NORMED LINEAR SPACE

In Section 3–8 we discussed the process of completing an incomplete metric space. If $X$ is an incomplete normed linear space, the completion process can be applied to $X$ as a metric space; let $Y$ be the complete metric space obtained from $X$, and let $Y_0$ be the part of $Y$ which is in one-to-one isometric correspondence with $X$, as described in the proof of Theorem 3–8 I. Then we can define addition and multiplication by scalars in $Y$, and we can define a norm on $Y$, in such a way that the norm yields the same metric that we already have on $Y$, $Y$ becomes a Banach space, and $Y_0$ is a subspace of $Y$. Moreover, $X$ and $Y_0$ are isomorphic as linear spaces.

We shall indicate how these things are done, without going into the details. We use the terminology of the proof of Theorem 3–8 I. If $y$ and $v$ are in $Y$, and if $\{x_n\}$, $\{u_n\}$ are Cauchy sequences from $X$ which are in the equivalence classes $y$, $v$ respectively, then $\{x_n + u_n\}$ is a Cauchy sequence, and it turns out to be satisfactory to define $y + v$ as that equivalence class which contains $\{x_n + u_n\}$. We define $\alpha y$ as the equivalence class which contains $\{\alpha x_n\}$, and we define $\|y\| = \lim_{n\to\infty} \|x_n\|$. For a fuller discussion see Section 3–13 in Taylor [2].

If we have an incomplete normed linear space $X$ whose elements are functions on some common domain $\mathscr{D}$, the foregoing process can be applied to $X$, and we obtain a Banach space $Y$. But the elements of $Y$ are not functions defined on $\mathscr{D}$; they are equivalence classes of Cauchy sequences from $X$. Now, it sometimes turns out that we can find an enlargement of the class $X$ of functions on $\mathscr{D}$ in just such a way that this enlarged class is in one-to-one correspondence with $Y$ and the correspondence maps $X$ onto $Y_0$. When this occurs we have a concrete realization of the completion of $X$ by a process of widening the class of functions with which we start. In the next example we give a rather simple illustration of such a completion by enlarging the class of functions.

*Example 5.* Let $X$ consist of all sequences $x = \{\xi_n\}$ in $R$ such that for each $x$ the set of $n$'s for which $\xi_n \neq 0$ is finite. We define a norm on $X$ as follows:

$$\|x\| = \sum_i |\xi_i|. \tag{12}$$

The sum in (12) involves merely a finite number of terms, but this number depends on $x$. The elements of $X$ form a subset of the set $(R)^T$ of all functions on $T$ to $R$, where $T$ is the set of all positive integers. It is clear that $X$ is a subspace of the vector space $(R)^T$ (see Example 1, Section 3–12); hence with (12) $X$ is a normed vector space. However, $X$ is not complete. For, let $x_n$ be the sequence

$$x_n = \left\{1, \frac{1}{2^2}, \ldots, \frac{1}{n^2}, 0, 0, \ldots\right\}.$$

Then, if $m < n$, we have

$$\|x_n - x_m\| = \sum_{i=m+1}^{n} \frac{1}{i^2} \to 0$$

as $m \to \infty$ and $n \to \infty$, so that $\{x_n\}$ is a Cauchy sequence. But this sequence cannot converge to any element $x$ of $X$. For, supposing $x = \{\xi_i\}$ given, choose $N$ a positive integer such that $\xi_i = 0$ if $i > N$, and suppose $n \geq N + 1$. Then

$$x_n - x = \left\{1 - \xi_1, \frac{1}{2^2} - \xi_2, \ldots, \frac{1}{N^2} - \xi_N, \frac{1}{(N+1)^2}, \ldots, \frac{1}{n^2}, 0, 0, \ldots\right\},$$

and hence we see that certainly $\|x_n - x\| \geq \dfrac{1}{(N+1)^2}$. Thus $\{x_n\}$ does not converge to $x$.

If we examine the construction of $Y$ in the proof of Theorem 3–8 I, as it applies to this particular space $X$, it is not difficult to see that each element of $Y$ determines a unique sequence $\{\xi_i\}$ of real numbers by the following process. If $\{x_n\}$ is a Cauchy sequence in $X$, with $x_n = \{\xi_{n1}, \xi_{n2}, \ldots\}$, then $\lim_{n\to\infty} \xi_{ni}$ exists for each $i$, and this limit has the same value if $\{x_n\}$ is replaced by any equivalent Cauchy sequence in $X$. If we write $\xi_i = \lim_{n\to\infty} \xi_{ni}$, it turns out that

$$\sum_{i=1}^{\infty} |\xi_i| < \infty. \tag{13}$$

That is, the sequence $x = \{\xi_i\}$ is a member of the vector space $l^1$ (see Problem 12, Section 3–6 and Example 4, Section 3–12). Conversely, if $x = \{\xi_i\}$ is any element of $l^1$, and if we define $x_n = \{\xi_1, \ldots, \xi_n, 0, 0, \ldots\}$, then $x_n \in X$ and $\{x_n\}$ is Cauchy sequence in $X$.

Now, $l^1$ is a normed linear space with the sum of the series in (13) as the norm of an element $x = \{\xi_n\}$. It is not difficult to prove directly that $l^1$ is complete. But one can also see from the foregoing discussion that $l^1$ is in one-to-one correspondence with the space $Y$ which is constructed as the completion of $X$ by the method of Theorem 3–8 I; moreover, the normed linear space structure of $l^1$ corresponds exactly to the normed linear space structure of $Y$. Thus $l^1$ is a realization of the completion of $X$. We observe that $l^1$ is an enlargement of the class of functions which $X$ constitutes.

At this point we propose the following thought (and question) for consideration: If $X$ is the incomplete space formed by using the norm $\|\ \|_1$ of (3) on the class $C[a, b]$, is it possible to realize the completion of $X$ as a class of functions defined on $[a, b]$? Can one somehow imitate what was done in our discussion of Example 5? We shall say nothing more about this at present.

## BANACH SPACES WITH COUNTABLE BASIS

Let $X$ be a Banach space of infinite dimension, and let $\{x_n\}$ be a sequence of elements of $X$ such that each element $x$ of $X$ can be represented in one and only one way as a series of the form

$$x = \sum_{n=1}^{\infty} \xi_n x_n. \tag{14}$$

That is, to each $x$ corresponds a unique sequence $\{\xi_n\}$ of scalars such that

$$\lim_{n\to\infty} \left\| \sum_{i=1}^{n} \xi_i x_i - x \right\| = 0.$$

Under these conditions we say that the sequence $\{x_n\}$ is a *countable basis* for $X$.

One sees readily that the elements of a countable basis form a linearly independent set.

*Example 6.* Let $X$ be the space $l^1$ of all real sequences $x = \{\xi_n\}$ such that

$$\|x\| = \sum_{n=1}^{\infty} |\xi_n| < \infty.$$

As was remarked in Example 5, $l^1$ is a Banach space. Let $x_1 = (1, 0, 0, \ldots)$, $x_2 = (0, 1, 0, 0, \ldots)$, $x_3 = (0, 0, 1, 0, 0, \ldots)$ and so on. That is, if $x_n = \{\xi_k^{(n)}\}$, $\xi_k^{(n)} = 1$ if $k = n$ and $\xi_k^{(n)} = 0$ if $k \neq n$. It is readily evident that $\{x_n\}$ is a countable basis for $l^1$. In fact,

$$\left\| x - \sum_{i=1}^{n} \xi_i x_i \right\| = \sum_{i=n+1}^{\infty} |\xi_i| \to 0$$

as $n \to \infty$, and it is easy to see that the expression of $x$ in the form (14) is unique.

It can be proved that any Banach space with a countable basis is separable. It is a famous unsolved problem of long standing to determine whether for *every* separable Banach space there exists a countable basis. It can be a matter of rather intricate analysis in particular cases to determine whether a given sequence $\{x_n\}$ in $X$ is in fact a countable basis for $X$.

## PROBLEMS

1. Show that two norms $\| \ \|_1$ and $\| \ \|_2$ on $X$ are equivalent if and only if to each $a > 0$ corresponds a $b > 0$ such that $\{x : \|x\|_2 < b\} \subset \{x : \|x\|_1 < a\}$, with a corresponding situation when the roles of the norms are exchanged. Hence prove that the norms are equivalent if and only if there exist positive constants $m$, $M$ such that $m \|x\|_2 \leq \|x\|_1 \leq M \|x\|_2$ for every $x$.

2. Prove (8), using (7). Let $\alpha = \dfrac{q}{p}$, $\alpha' = \dfrac{\alpha}{\alpha - 1} = \dfrac{q}{q - p}$.

3. If $X$ is a Banach space with a countable basis (in the sense of (14)), prove that $X$ is separable.

4. Suppose $0 < p < q$. For $n \geq 2$ define $x_n \in C[a, b]$ as follows: Let $\alpha_n = n^{-q}$ and let

$$x_n(t) = \begin{cases} 0 & \text{if } 0 \leq t \leq 1 - 2\alpha_n \\ \dfrac{n}{\alpha_n}(t - 1 + 2\alpha_n) & \text{if } 1 - 2\alpha_n \leq t \leq 1 - \alpha_n \\ n & \text{if } 1 - \alpha_n \leq t \leq 1. \end{cases}$$

Show that $\|x_n\|_q > 1$ but $\|x_n\|_p \to 0$.

5. Let $T$ be a nonempty abstract set, and let $X$ be a linear space of functions $x : T \to R$ (or $x : T \to C$). Suppose $X$ is such that if $x, y \in X$, then $xy \in X$, where $xy$ is the function $t \to x(t)y(t)$. Let $X_0$ be a subspace of $X$ and let $\varphi : X_0 \to R$ be a function such that $\varphi$ and $X_0$ satisfy the following conditions:

(1) if $y \in X_0$, $x \in X$, and $0 \leq x(t) \leq y(t)$ for each $t$, then $x \in X_0$;
(2) under the conditions on $x$ and $y$ in (1), $\varphi(x) \leq \varphi(y)$;
(3) if $\alpha \geq 0$, if $x \in X_0$ and $x(t) \geq 0$ for each $t$, then $\varphi(\alpha x) = \alpha\varphi(x)$;
(4) if $x \in X_0$, $0 \leq x(t)$ for each $t$, and $\varphi(x) = 0$, then $x = 0$.

We observe that $\varphi(0) = 0$, as a consequence of (3). Then, using (2), we see that $\varphi(x) \geq 0$ if $x \in X_0$ and $x(t) \geq 0$ for each $t$.

We define the class $\Phi^p$, where $p \geq 1$, as follows:

$$\Phi^p = \{x \in X : |x|^p \in X_0\}.$$

Here $|x|^p$ denotes the function $t \to |x(t)|^p$. Since $X_0$ is a subspace, it follows from property (1) and the inequality $|A + B|^p \leq 2^p[A^p + B^p]$ (see (1) in Example 4, Section 3–12) that $x, y \in \Phi^p$ imply $x + y \in \Phi^p$. Hence it is clear that $\Phi^p$ is a subspace of $X$.

Now show that Hölder's inequality holds in the following form: If $p > 1$, if $p' = \dfrac{p}{p - 1}$, if $x \in \Phi^p$ and $y \in \Phi^{p'}$, then $x, y \in \Phi^1$, and

$$\varphi(|xy|) \leq \varphi(|x|^p)^{1/p}\varphi(|y|^{p'})^{1/p'}.$$

The proof can be made by imitating the proof of Hölder's equality for sums (Problem 9(b), Section 3–6).

Next, prove Minkowski's inequality in the following form: If $p \geq 1$ and if $x, y \in \Phi^p$, then

$$\varphi(|x + y|^p)^{1/p} \leq \varphi(|x|^p)^{1/p} + \varphi(|y|^p)^{1/p}.$$

Note that, as a consequence of this, the mapping $x \to \varphi(|x|^p)^{1/p}$ is a norm on $\Phi^p$.

By choosing $X$, $X_0$, and $\varphi$ in various ways we can get a great number of different normed linear spaces as particular realizations of $\Phi^p$.

6. To see how to construct a countable basis for $C[0, 1]$, start from the following observation: Suppose $x \in C[0, 1]$. Choose $n$ points $P_0, P_1, \ldots, P_{n-1}$ in order along the graph of $x$, with $P_0$ and $P_{n-1}$ at the points corresponding to $t = 0$ and $t = 1$, respectively. Join these points successively by line segments, thus forming the graph of a certain function $y$ belonging to $C[0, 1]$. Then $\|y - x\|$ is small if $n$ is large and the differences $t_i - t_{i-1}$ are small (where $P_i$ corresponds to $t_i$). The idea now is to arrange for a countable basis by choosing $x_1, x_2, \ldots$ and $\xi_1, \xi_2, \ldots$ so that

$$s_n = \xi_1 x_1 + \cdots + \xi_n x_n$$

approximates $x$ in the manner described if $n \geq 2$. Show that this is possible, according to the following scheme. Let $t_{ij} = i/2^j$, $i = 0, 1, \ldots, 2^j$, $j = 0, 1, \ldots$. Let $x_{ij}(t)$ be 0 except when $i/2^j \leq t \leq (i + 1)/2^j$, and on this special interval let the graph of $x_{ij}$ rise linearly from 0 at $t = i/2^j$ to 1 at $t = (2i + 1)/2^{j+1}$ and then fall back linearly to 0 at $t = (i + 1)/2^j$. Now let $x_1(t) = t$, $x_2(t) = 1 - t$, $x_3 = x_{00}$, $x_4 = x_{01}$, $x_5 = x_{11}$, $x_6 = x_{02}$, and so on. Show that the coefficients are to be given by $\xi_1 = x(1)$, $\xi_2 = x(0)$, and

$$\xi_n = x(t_n) - s_{n-1}(t_n) \qquad \text{if} \quad n > 2,$$

where $t_n$ is the point at which $x_n(t) = 1$ if $n > 2$.

## 3–14 Hilbert spaces

Among normed linear spaces there are certain ones in which the norm is associated in a certain way with a function of two variables, called an *inner product*. Such spaces can occur with either the real numbers or the complex numbers as scalars.

If $X$ is a complex vector space, a mapping $f: X \times X \to C$ is called an inner product in $X$ if the following conditions are satisfied:

1. $f(x_1 + x_2, x_3) = f(x_1, x_3) + f(x_2, x_3)$,
2. $f(x_2, x_1) = \overline{f(x_1, x_2)}$ (the bar denoting complex conjugate),
3. $f(\alpha x_1, x_2) = \alpha f(x_1, x_2)$,
4. $f(x, x) \geq 0$ and $f(x, x) \neq 0$ if $x \neq 0$. (Observe that $f(x, x)$ must be real, by the second condition.)

If $X$ is a real vector space, a mapping $f: X \times X \to R$ is called an inner product in $X$ if Conditions 1–4 are satisfied. The bar for the complex conjugate can be omitted in Condition 2 when $X$ is a real space. To simplify the exposition we shall treat the cases of real $X$ and complex $X$ together, writing bars where they are needed for the complex case. They can be ignored in the real case, since $\bar{\alpha} = \alpha$ if the imaginary part of $\alpha$ is 0.

In dealing with just one inner product in a given space $X$ we shall customarily write $\langle x_1, x_2 \rangle$ instead of $f(x_1, x_2)$. On occasion the notation $x_1 \cdot x_2$ (dot-product) is suggestive. In fact, the dot-product of ordinary classical vector algebra is an inner product.

The all-important fact about an inner product is that it can be used to define a norm. If we define

$$\|x\| = \sqrt{\langle x, x \rangle}, \tag{1}$$

the mapping $x \to \|x\|$ is a norm on $X$. The truth of this is not at once apparent. As a first step in the proof we prove that

$$(2) \qquad |\langle x, y\rangle|^2 \le \langle x, x\rangle\langle y, y\rangle$$

for arbitrary $x$ and $y$. This inequality is actually a generalization of the Cauchy inequality of Lemma 2–1 I. It is obvious that (2) is true if $\langle x, y\rangle = 0$. To prove (2) when $\langle x, y\rangle \ne 0$ we consider $t$ real, $\alpha$ real or complex, and note that, by properties 1–4,

$$\begin{aligned} 0 &\le \langle tx + \alpha y, tx + \alpha y\rangle \\ &= t^2\langle x, x\rangle + t\bar{\alpha}\langle x, y\rangle + \alpha t\langle y, x\rangle + \alpha\bar{\alpha}\langle y, y\rangle. \end{aligned}$$

Now let $\alpha = \dfrac{\langle x, y\rangle}{|\langle x, y\rangle|}$. Then we obtain

$$t^2\langle x, x\rangle + 2t\,|\langle x, y\rangle| + \langle y, y\rangle \ge 0.$$

But, when an inequality of the form $At^2 + 2Bt + C \ge 0$, with real coefficients $A$, $B$, $C$, is valid for all values of $t$, we necessarily have $B^2 - AC \le 0$. For the present case this yields the inequality (2).

The result in (2) is variously known as the Cauchy-Schwarz inequality, the Schwarz inequality, or the Cauchy-Schwarz-Bunyakovsky inequality.

Now, to prove that (1) defines a norm, the only serious step is the proof that the triangular equality is satisfied. We note that, for any real or complex number $A$,

$$|A + \bar{A}| \le 2\,|A|.$$

Now, for any $x$, $y$,

$$\begin{aligned} \|x + y\|^2 &= \langle x + y, x + y\rangle \\ &= \langle x, x\rangle + \langle y, x\rangle + \langle x, y\rangle + \langle y, y\rangle \\ &= \|x\|^2 + \langle x, y\rangle + \overline{\langle x, y\rangle} + \|y\|^2. \end{aligned}$$

Therefore,

$$\|x + y\|^2 \le \|x\|^2 + 2\,|\langle x, y\rangle| + \|y\|^2.$$

Using (2), we have

$$\|x + y\|^2 \le \|x\|^2 + 2\,\|x\|\,\|y\| + \|y\|^2 = (\|x\| + \|y\|)^2,$$

which implies the triangular inequality.

When a normed linear space $X$ has a norm which comes from an inner product as in (1), we call $X$ an *inner-product space*. If it is complete we call it a *Hilbert space*.

A finite-dimensional normed linear space is necessarily complete. Hence a finite-dimensional inner-product space is a Hilbert space. We omit the proof. See Section 3–12 in Taylor [2].

An incomplete inner-product space is sometimes called a *pre-Hilbert space*, because an incomplete inner-product space can be completed to form a Hilbert space. The process of completing a normed linear space $X$ has been described briefly in Section 3–13. The definition of the inner product in $X$ can be extended so as to make it an inner product in the completion of $X$, which is then a Hilbert space.

It is useful to notice the fact that $\langle x, y\rangle$ depends continuously on $x$ and $y$. The continuity in just one of the variables at a time is evident from (2), for we have $|\langle x - x_0, y\rangle| \leq \|x - x_0\| \, \|y\|$. More generally, it can be shown that

$$|\langle x, y\rangle - \langle x_0, y_0\rangle| \leq \|x_0\| \, \|y - y_0\| + \|x - x_0\| \, \|y_0\| + \|x - x_0\| \, \|y - y_0\|.$$

See Problem 1.

*Example 1.* The simplest infinite-dimensional Hilbert space is the space $l^2$ of all sequences (real or complex) $x = \{\xi_n\}$ such that $\sum_n |\xi_n|^2 < \infty$. The inner product is defined by

(3) $$\langle x, y\rangle = \sum_{n=1}^{\infty} \xi_n \bar{\eta}_n,$$

where $y = \{\eta_n\}$. The norm is then

(4) $$\|x\| = \left(\sum_{n=1}^{\infty} |\xi_n|^2\right)^{1/2} = \sqrt{\langle x, x\rangle}.$$

The fact that the series in (3) is convergent (in fact, absolutely convergent) follows from Cauchy's inequality (Lemma 2–1 I), for

$$\sum_{i=1}^{n} |\xi_i \bar{\eta}_i| \leq \left(\sum_{i=1}^{n} |\xi_i|^2\right)^{1/2} \left(\sum_{i=1}^{n} |\bar{\eta}_i|^2\right)^{1/2} \leq \|x\| \, \|y\|.$$

We get a real or complex Hilbert space according as we consider the sequences $\{\xi_n\}$ to be sequences in $R$ or $C$. We use the notation $l^2$ for both cases, specifying which case we have in mind by an explicit statement when necessary.

David Hilbert (1862–1943), beginning in 1906, introduced and used the space $l^2$ in his research work on integral equations. The concept of an abstract space, defined axiomatically but with the essential properties suggested by $l^2$ as a concrete model, came later.

*Example 2.* It is clear from Section 2–1 (see especially (11)–(13)) that $R^k$ is a real Hilbert space of finite dimension. The complex vector space $C^k$ (defined early in Section 3–12) becomes a complex Hilbert space in an obvious way. If $x = (\xi_1, \ldots, \xi_k)$ and $y = (\eta_1, \ldots, \eta_k)$ are ordered sets ($k$-tuples) of complex numbers, we define

$$\langle x, y\rangle = \sum_{i=1}^{k} \xi_i \bar{\eta}_i.$$

We pause here to remark that a complex vector space $X$ can also be regarded as a real vector space, simply by considering the situation which results when we use $R$ instead of $C$ as the field of scalars. This change in point of view changes the concepts of linear dependence and of dimensionality. Suppose, for instance, that $x \in X$ and $x \neq 0$, where $X$ is a complex vector space. Then $ix \in X$ also, and, when we regard $X$ as a complex space, the set consisting of $x$ and $ix$ is a linearly dependent set. But if we look upon $X$ as a real space, the set consisting of $x$ and $ix$ is a linearly independent set. In fact, if $\alpha$ and $\beta$ are real numbers such that $\alpha x + \beta(ix) = 0$, then $(\alpha + i\beta)x = 0$, and so $\alpha + i\beta = 0$, because $x \neq 0$. But then $\alpha = \beta = 0$. As a consequence, if $X$ has the finite dimension $k$ as a complex space, it has dimension $2k$ as a real space. The case $X = C^k$ is an example.

Finite-dimensional Hilbert spaces are of such particular interest that we sometimes use special designations for them. A finite-dimensional real Hilbert space is called a Euclidean space. (We shall presently have more to say about the justification of this.) A finite-dimensional complex Hilbert space is sometimes called a *unitary* space; it is also called a *complex Euclidean space.*

Sometimes the name Hilbert space is used with the specific requirement that the space be infinite-dimensional. In the early literature on abstract Hilbert spaces it was usually assumed as part of the definition that the spaces were separable. This is no longer customary.

## ORTHOGONALITY

If $X$ is an inner-product space, we can define the concept of orthogonality in $X$. Two vectors $x, y$ are said to be *orthogonal* if $\langle x, y\rangle = 0$. If $S$ is a set of vectors in $X$, a vector $y$ is said to be orthogonal to $S$ if $\langle x, y\rangle = 0$ for each $x$ in $S$.

A set $S$ of vectors such that $\|x\| = 1$ if $x \in S$ and $\langle x, y\rangle = 0$ if $x$ and $y$ are distinct elements of $S$ is called an *orthonormal* set.

An orthonormal set $S$ in $X$ is called *complete* if there exists no orthonormal set in $X$ of which $S$ is a proper subset. For instance, the set in $R^k$ consisting of $e_1, \ldots, e_k$ (see Example 1, Section 2–1) is a complete orthonormal set. By use of Zorn's lemma (Section 3–10) we can show that in any inner-product space having a nonzero element there is a complete orthonormal set. Moreover, if $S$ is an orthonormal set, there is a complete orthonormal set which contains $S$. (We let $P$ be the class of all orthonormal sets which contain $S$; $P$ is partially ordered by set-inclusion.)

If $X$ is a separable inner-product space, it may be proved without using Zorn's lemma that there exists a complete orthonormal set in $X$. The proof uses a recursive process. See Problem 4.

We do not wish to take the space in this book which would be necessary for a full discussion of orthonormal sets. We confine ourselves to a description of all the essential facts needed for exposition and use in this book. We shall also sketch some of the key proofs. For full details see pp. 106–122 in Taylor [2].

Before proceeding further with the general discussion of orthonormal sets we shall consider another example of an inner-product space and some very important examples of orthonormal sets.

Among the most interesting and useful inner-product spaces, for the purposes of analysis, are spaces of functions with the inner product defined by an integral.

*Example 3.* Let $X$ be the real vector space $C[a, b]$, and define

$$\langle x, y\rangle = \int_a^b x(t)y(t)\,dt. \tag{5}$$

This gives us a pre-Hilbert space. The norm is the norm $\|x\|_2$ defined in Example 1, Section 3–13. The fact that $X$ is not complete can be demonstrated by a suitable modification of the scheme used in Example 4, Section 3–13.

We get a complex inner-product space if we use for $X$ the class of complex-valued continuous functions on $[a, b]$, and define

$$\langle x, y\rangle = \int_a^b x(t)\overline{y(t)}\,dt. \tag{6}$$

More generally, we can choose a fixed continuous function $w$ with positive values, and define

$$\langle x, y\rangle = \int_a^b w(t)x(t)\overline{y(t)}\,dt. \tag{7}$$

An important illustration of orthogonality in a space of functions is provided by the following situation. Let $C[0, 2\pi]$ be made into a real inner-product space with inner product as in (5). Let

(8)
$$\begin{cases} x_0(t) = \dfrac{1}{\sqrt{2\pi}} \\ x_n(t) = \dfrac{1}{\sqrt{\pi}} \cos nt, \qquad y_n(t) = \dfrac{1}{\sqrt{\pi}} \sin nt, \qquad n = 1, 2, \ldots \end{cases}$$

Direct calculation of the integrals shows that the set consisting of $x_0, x_1, x_2, \ldots$ and $y_1, y_2, \ldots$ is an orthonormal set. It is in fact a complete orthonormal set. The proof of this is indicated in Problem 7. If we consider the *complex-valued* continuous functions on $[0, 2\pi]$ and use the inner product as in (6) (with $a = 0$, $b = 2\pi$), a convenient complete orthonormal set is furnished by all the elements $u_n$, $n = 0, \pm 1, \pm 2, \ldots$, where

$$u_n(t) = \frac{1}{\sqrt{2\pi}} e^{int}.$$

The study of Fourier series is intimately connected with the theory of inner-product spaces, as the preceding remarks will suggest to anyone who has even a preliminary acquaintance with the subject of Fourier series. If $x$ is an element of $C[0, 2\pi]$, its Fourier series (quite apart from the question of whether or not the series converges) is

$$\frac{a_0}{2} + \sum_{n=1}^{\infty} (a_n \cos nt + b_n \sin nt),$$

where

$$a_n = \frac{1}{\pi} \int_0^{2\pi} x(s) \cos ns \, ds, \; b_n = \frac{1}{\pi} \int_0^{2\pi} x(s) \sin ns \, ds.$$

In the notation of (8) this Fourier series can be written as

(9)
$$\alpha_0 x_0(t) + \sum_{n=1}^{\infty} [\alpha_n x_n(t) + \beta_n y_n(t)],$$

where

(10)
$$\begin{cases} \alpha_n = \langle x, x_n \rangle, & n = 0, 1, 2, \ldots \\ \beta_n = \langle x, y_n \rangle, & n = 1, 2, \ldots . \end{cases}$$

This naturally suggests that one consider the series

(11)
$$\alpha_0 x_0 + \sum_{n=1}^{\infty} [\alpha_n x_n + \beta_n y_n]$$

as a series of elements of the pre-Hilbert space; one may ask whether the series converges to the element $x$ which appears in the formulas in (10), where convergence is in the sense of the norm. That is, we ask if it is true that

(12)
$$\lim_{n \to \infty} \left\| x - \alpha_0 x_0 - \sum_{k=1}^{n} [\alpha_k x_k + \beta_k y_k] \right\| = 0,$$

where the norm is determined by the inner product (5). This is of course a different question from the query as to whether the series in (9) converges *pointwise* to $x(t)$, as a series of real numbers. For, if $f$ and $f_1, f_2, \ldots$ are continuous functions, it can well happen that

$$\lim_{n\to\infty} \int_a^b |f_n(t) - f(t)|^2 \, dt = 0$$

and yet that, for many values of $t$, the sequence $\{f_n(t)\}$ fails to converge to $f(t)$ (see Problem 5).

It turns out that (12) is indeed true for each element $x$ of $C[0, 2\pi]$. But the most revealing study of this matter is to be made, not by staying with the pre-Hilbert space which we have formed from $C[0, 2\pi]$, but by transferring attention to a Hilbert space which is a completion of the pre-Hilbert space. This Hilbert space is designated by $L^2[0, 2\pi]$; it is constructed with the aid of the Lebesgue theory of integration. Hence we cannot go into details about it at this point. See Section 5–8.

## ORTHONORMAL SETS IN A HILBERT SPACE

An elementary but important fact about orthonormal sets is given in the following theorem.

THEOREM 3–14 I. *Let $S$ be a countable (finite or infinite) orthonormal set in an inner-product space $X$, and let $u_1, u_2, \ldots$ be an enumeration of the elements of $S$, in any order. Then*

$$\sum_k |\langle x, u_k\rangle|^2 \leq \|x\|^2 \tag{13}$$

*for each $x \in X$.*

*Proof.* It is enough to prove (13) for sums with a finite number of terms. Let $\xi_k = \langle x, u_k\rangle$. We observe that

$$0 \leq \left\| x - \sum_{k=1}^n \xi_k u_k \right\|^2 = \left\langle x - \sum_{j=1}^n \xi_j u_j, \; x - \sum_{k=1}^n \xi_k u_k \right\rangle.$$

When we work out in detail the value of the inner product here, using the orthonormality of the set $\{u_1, \ldots, u_n\}$ and the definition of the $\xi_j$'s, we obtain the result

$$0 \leq \|x\|^2 - \sum_{k=1}^n |\xi_k|^2;$$

this is exactly (13) for the case of $n$ terms.

The inequality (13) is called *Bessel's inequality*.

Concerning finite orthonormal sets we have the following:

THEOREM 3–14 II. (a) *A finite orthonormal set $u_1, \ldots, u_n$ in an inner-product space is a basis for the subspace which it generates.* (b) *An inner-product space of finite positive dimension contains a basis which is an orthonormal set.* (c) *A complete orthonormal set in an inner-product space of finite dimension is a basis for the space.*

*Proof of* (a). If $M$ is the subspace generated by $u_1, \ldots, u_n$, every element of $M$ can be written in the form $x = \xi_1 u_1 + \cdots + \xi_n u_n$. From this we see that

$$\langle x, u_i\rangle = \sum_{k=1}^n \xi_k \langle u_k, u_i\rangle = \xi_i, \qquad i = 1, \ldots, n.$$

If $x = 0$, it follows that $\xi_1 = \cdots = \xi_n = 0$. Thus, the set $\{u_1, \ldots, u_n\}$ is linearly independent. Hence it is a basis of $M$.

*Proof of* (c). Let the space be $X$, with dimension $n$, and let $S$ be a complete orthonormal set in $X$. The set $S$ cannot have more than $n$ elements, as a consequence of (a), for $X$ cannot have a subspace whose dimension exceeds $n$. It will suffice to show that $S$ has exactly $n$ elements. Suppose $S$ has $m$ elements $u_1, \ldots, u_m$, where $m < n$. Let $M$ be the subspace generated by $u_1, \ldots, u_m$. Then $M \neq X$, and there exists some element $x \in X - M$. Let

$$y = x - \sum_{k=1}^{m} \xi_k u_k, \qquad \xi_k = \langle x, u_k \rangle.$$

We readily calculate that $\langle y, u_i \rangle = 0$, $i = 1, \ldots, m$. But then we conclude that $y = 0$, because if $y$ were not 0 the set $\dfrac{y}{\|y\|}, u_1, \ldots, u_m$ would be an orthonormal set, in contradiction to the completeness (maximality) of $S$. But $y = 0$ implies that $x \in M$, contrary to assumption.

*Proof of* (b). This follows from (c), because, as we know, every inner-product space contains a complete orthonormal set. Our proof of this fact for the general case was made by appeal to Zorn's lemma. For a space of finite dimension there is a constructive procedure for obtaining a complete orthonormal set. See Problem 4.

In dealing with infinite orthonormal sets we shall consider only the case of a complete inner-product space. It is completeness of the space which makes things work out nicely. For convenience of exposition we deal principally with the case of a separable Hilbert space. The effect of this is to insure that any orthonormal set in the space is at most countably infinite. We omit the proof of this. See Problem 3. The next few theorems enables us to show that, if $X$ is any separable Hilbert space, of infinite dimension, we can use the space $l^2$ of Example 1 to "introduce coordinates" in $X$, in the sense that each point of $X$ is identified by a unique point of $l^2$, and the Hilbert space structure of $X$ is exactly mirrored in the Hilbert space structure of $l^2$. This is true either with $X$ and $l^2$ both real spaces, or both complex spaces.

THEOREM 3–14 III. *Let $X$ be any Hilbert space (separable or not), and let $\{u_n\}$ be an orthonormal set in $X$. Then a series of the form $\sum_1^\infty \xi_n u_n$ is convergent in $X$ if and only if the numerical series $\sum_1^\infty |\xi_n|^2$ is convergent.*

*Proof.* Let us write $x_n = \sum_{k=1}^{n} \xi_k u_k$. If we assume $m < n$ and compute

$$\|x_n - x_m\|^2 = \langle x_n - x_m, x_n - x_m \rangle,$$

using the properties of the inner product and the orthonormality relations, we find that

$$\|x_n - x_m\|^2 = \sum_{k=m+1}^{n} |\xi_k|^2.$$

Thus we see that $\{x_n\}$ is a Cauchy sequence if and only if $\sum_1^\infty |\xi_n|^2$ is convergent. Since $X$ is a complete space, this gives us what was asserted.

Suppose now that $X$ and $\{u_n\}$ are as in Theorem 3–14 III, and let $\sum_1^\infty \xi_n u_n$ be a convergent series. Let $y$ be the element of $X$ defined by the series. Using the continuity of the inner product, we see that

$$\langle y, u_i\rangle = \sum_{n=1}^{\infty} \xi_n \langle u_n, u_i\rangle = \xi_i.$$

Here is one way of obtaining such a convergent series: Choose any $x$ in $X$ and let $\xi_n = \langle x, u_n\rangle$. Then $\sum_1^\infty |\xi_n|^2 < \infty$, by Theorem 3–14 I. Hence the series $\sum_1^\infty \xi_n u_n$ converges. It may be shown easily that this series converges *unconditionally*. That is, every series obtained by a rearrangement of the order of the terms in the given series is convergent and has the same sum. (If $y$ and $z$ represent the sums of the given series and a rearrangement of it, a computation of the inner product shows that $\|y - z\|^2 = 0$.) Hence, the sum of the series depends only on $x$ and the *set* consisting of $u_1, u_2, \ldots$, and not on the particular way in which the elements of the set are indexed. In what follows we denote by $M$ the closure of the linear manifold in $X$ generated by the orthonormal set $\{u_n\}$. Then, if $x \in X$, we write

$$x_M = \sum_1^\infty \langle x, u_n\rangle u_n. \tag{14}$$

It follows from a remark in a previous paragraph that $\langle x_M, u_n\rangle = \langle x, u_n\rangle$, or $\langle x - x_M, u_n\rangle = 0$ for each $n$.

We now consider characteristic consequences of the assumption that $\{u_n\}$ is a *complete orthonormal* set.

THEOREM 3–14 IV. *Let $\{u_n\}$ be an orthonormal set in the Hilbert space $X$. Each one of the following conditions is necessary and sufficient for the orthonormal set to be complete.*

(i) $x = \sum_1^\infty \langle x, u_n\rangle u_n$ *for each $x$ in $X$.*

(ii) $M = X$, *where $M$ is the closure of the linear manifold generated by $\{u_n\}$.*

(iii) $\|x\|^2 = \sum_1^\infty |\langle x, u_n\rangle|^2$ *for each $x$ in $X$.*

*Proof.* Let the condition that $\{u_n\}$ be a complete orthonormal set be denoted by (o). Establishment of the following implications will achieve the proof of the theorem:

$$(o) \to (i) \to (ii) \to (o)$$
$$(iii) \to (o) \quad \text{and} \quad (i) \to (iii).$$

*Proof that* (o) → (i). If (i) is false, $x - x_M \neq 0$ for some $x$ ($x_M$ defined by (14)). But then we can enlarge the orthonormal set by adjoining the element $(x - x_M)/\|x - x_M\|$, for we saw following (14) that $\langle x - x_M, u_n\rangle = 0$ for each $n$. This contradicts (o).

*Proof that* (i) → (ii). This is obvious, for (i) implies that $x \in M$ for each $x$.

*Proof that* (ii) → (o). If the orthonormal set were not complete, we could enlarge it by adding some element $x$ with $\|x\| = 1$ and $\langle x, u_n\rangle = 0$ for each $n$. It follows that $\langle x, y\rangle = 0$ if $y$ is a finite linear combination of the $u_n$'s, and hence also if $y$ is a limit of such linear combinations (that is, an element of $M$), by the continuity of the inner product. But then $\|x\|^2 = \langle x, x\rangle = 0$, because $x \in M$, by (ii). We now have a contradiction.

*Proof that* (iii) → (o). This is evident, for (iii) implies that any element orthogonal to all the $u_n$'s is 0.
*Proof that* (i) → (iii). This follows by direct computation of $\|x\|^2 = \langle x, x\rangle$, using (i) and the continuity of the inner product.

The formula in (iii) is called *Parseval's identity.*

There is a generalization of Theorem 3–14 IV for the case of uncountable orthonormal sets (which can occur only in nonseparable Hilbert spaces). The essential thing which makes such a generalization possible is the fact that, if $S$ is any orthonormal set and $x$ is a fixed element of the Hilbert space, the set $\{u \in S : \langle x, u\rangle \neq 0\}$ is a countable set. This in turn is a consequence of Bessel's inequality (13) in Theorem 3–14 I.

If $X$ is a pre-Hilbert space and $Y$ is its completion, an orthonormal set in $X$ may be complete (maximal) in $X$ and yet not complete in $Y$ (see Theorem 3.2–J and the comment at the bottom of page 114 in Taylor [2]). Yet it may well happen that *some* orthonormal set in $X$, which is complete in $X$, is also complete in $Y$. See Problem 8. This occurs in the case of the standard orthonormal set composed of the trigonometric functions (8) in $C[0, 2\pi]$. The completeness of this set in $C[0, 2\pi]$ is dealt with in Problem 7. To show that it is also complete in $L^2[0, 2\pi]$, which is a "concrete" representation of the completion of $C[0, 2\pi]$, the method of Problem 8 can be applied, with $Ty = x$ meaning that

$$x(t) = \int_0^t y(s)\, ds,$$

and $\varphi(x) = x(0)$, We omit the details, since we are not at present assuming a knowledge of the Lebesgue theory of integration.

Next we shall show that the space $l^2$ is a concrete model for an arbitrary separable Hilbert space $X$. Given $X$, we know that it must contain a countably infinite complete orthonormal set $\{u_n\}$. If $x \in X$ and $\xi_n = \langle x, u_n\rangle$, we know that $\sum_1^\infty |\xi_n|^2 < \infty$ and $x = \sum_1^\infty \xi_n u_n$. The mapping $x \to \{\xi_n\}$ now gives us a one-to-one mapping of $X$ onto all of $l^2$, in such a way that every feature of the Hilbert space structure in $X$ corresponds to the same feature of the structure in $l^2$. In particular, for instance, (iii) in Theorem 3–14 IV shows that $\|x\|$ is equal to the norm of $\{\xi_n\}$ in $l^2$. We say that $X$ and $l^2$ are in isometric and isomorphic correspondence. We can think of $l^2$ as a concrete model of $X$. We can also think of $(\xi_1, \xi_2, \ldots)$ as coordinates of $x$.

Exactly the same kind of considerations show us that a real Hilbert space of finite dimension $k \geq 1$ can be mapped isometrically and isomorphically on $R^k$, while for a complex Hilbert space of dimension $k$ the space $C^k$ will serve as a concrete model. In $R^k$ or $C^k$ we of course use the norm

$$\|(\xi_1, \ldots, \xi_k)\| = (|\xi_1|^2 + \cdots + |\xi_k|^2)^{1/2}.$$

It is from this point of view that we can say that any $n$-dimensional subspace of $R^k$ can be regarded as a "copy" of $R^n$. See the remarks made about this in Section 2–2.

## CONTINUOUS LINEAR FUNCTIONALS

If $y$ is a fixed element of the Hilbert space $X$, and if we define $f(x) = \langle x, y\rangle$, then $f$ is evidently a linear functional. It is continuous, also, and it is easy to see that $\|f\| = \|y\|$. For,

$|f(x)| \leq \|x\| \, \|y\|$, whence $\|f\| \leq \|y\|$. (For discussion of the norm of a linear functional, see Theorem 3–13 I and the remark following the proof.) If $y \neq 0$, $f\left(\frac{y}{\|y\|}\right) = \|y\|$, so $\|y\| \leq \|f\|$ in this case, whence $\|y\| = \|f\|$. This result is also valid, obviously, if $y = 0$.

The following theorem shows that the foregoing example actually typifies the general situation with linear functionals in Hilbert space.

THEOREM 3–14 V. *Let $X$ be any Hilbert space, and let $f$ be an arbitrary continuous linear functional on $X$. Then there exists a unique element $y$ in $X$ such that $f(x) = \langle x, y\rangle$ for each $x$. Moreover, $\|f\| = \|y\|$.*

*Proof.* There cannot be more than one such $y$, for if $\langle x, y_1\rangle = \langle x, y_2\rangle$ for every $x$, we put $x = y_1 - y_2$ and obtain $\|y_1 - y_2\|^2 = 0$. Now let

$$P_0 = \{x : f(x) = 0\}, \qquad P = \{x : f(x) = \|f\|^2\}.$$

If $\|f\| = 0$, we can take $y = 0$ in the theorem. Hence we assume $\|f\| \neq 0$. Let

$$d = \inf\{\|x\| : x \in P\}.$$

We shall prove that there exists $y \in P$ such that $\|y\| = d$. Suppose $x_n \in P$, $\|x_n\| \to d$. Then $\frac{1}{2}(x_n + x_m) \in P$, so $\|x_n + x_m\| \geq 2d$. Because of the fact that $\langle u, u\rangle = \|u\|^2$ for elements $u \in X$, it is easy to verify that

$$\|u + v\|^2 + \|u - v\|^2 = 2(\|u\|^2 + \|v\|^2). \tag{15}$$

We apply this with $u = x_n$, $v = x_m$. Then

$$\|x_n - x_m\|^2 = 2(\|x_n\|^2 + \|x_m\|^2) - \|x_n + x_m\|^2$$
$$\leq 2(\|x_n\|^2 + \|x_m\|^2) - 4d^2.$$

As $m \to \infty$ and $n \to \infty$ we see from this that $\|x_n - x_m\| \to 0$. Therefore there is some $y \in X$ such that $x_n \to y$. Also, $\|x_n\| \to \|y\|$, so $\|y\| = d$. The set $P$ is closed, because $f$ is continuous. Therefore $y \in P$.

Next, we show that $d = \|f\|$. From $f(y) = \|f\|^2$ we conclude $\|f\|^2 \leq \|f\| \, \|y\|$ so $\|f\| \leq \|y\|$. By the definition of $\|f\|$ there exists a sequence $\{u_n\}$ with $\|u_n\| = 1$ and $|f(u_n)| \to \|f\|$. We can assume $f(u_n) \neq 0$. Let $v_n = \frac{\|f\|^2}{f(u_n)} u_n$. Then $v_n \in P$. Also, $\|v_n\| = \frac{\|f\|^2}{|f(u_n)|} \to \|f\|$. It follows that $d \leq \|f\|$. Since $d = \|y\|$, we now conclude that $\|y\| = \|f\|$.

Next, we prove that $x \in P_0$ implies $\langle x, y\rangle = 0$. This is evident if $x = 0$, so we assume $x \neq 0$. Let

$$y_1 = \frac{\langle y, x\rangle}{\|x\|^2} x, \qquad y_2 = y - y_1.$$

We are assuming $f(x) = 0$. Hence, $f(y_1) = 0$, whence $f(y_2) = f(y) = \|f\|^2$; that is, $y_2 \in P$. Therefore $\|y_2\| \geq d = \|y\|$. A simple calculation shows that $\langle y_1, y_2\rangle = 0$, and therefore, calculating $\|y\|^2 = \langle y_1 + y_2, y_1 + y_2\rangle$, we find that

$$\|y\|^2 = \|y_1\|^2 + \|y_2\|^2 \geq \|y_2\|^2.$$

The fact that $\|y_2\| \geq \|y\|$ now implies that $\|y\| = \|y_2\|$ and that $\|y_1\| = 0$. This in turn implies $\langle y, x\rangle = \langle x, y\rangle = 0$ (see the definition of $y_1$).

We are now at the final step of the proof. For any given $x$, let

$$x_1 = x - \frac{f(x)}{f(y)}\, y.$$

Then $f(x_1) = 0$, and therefore $\langle x_1, y \rangle = 0$. But

$$\langle x_1, y \rangle = \langle x, y \rangle - \frac{f(x)}{f(y)} \|y\|^2 = \langle x, y \rangle - f(x),$$

because $f(y) = \|f\|^2 = \|y\|^2$. Thus we have $f(x) = \langle x, y \rangle$. This ends the proof.

## PROBLEMS

1. Prove that $\langle x, y \rangle$ is a continuous function of $(x, y)$, as indicated in the discussion which precedes Example 1.

2. Let $x$ and $y$ be nonzero elements of a real inner-product space $X$, and let $M$ be the subspace generated by $x$. Show that $x$ and $y$ are orthogonal if and only if the distance from $y$ to $M$ is $\|y\|$.

3. Prove that in a separable inner-product space an orthonormal set $S$ is countable (perhaps finite). [*Suggestion.* Consider the size of $\|x - y\|$ if $x, y$ are distinct elements of $S$.]

4. Let $x_1, x_2, \ldots$ be a finite or countably infinite set of linearly independent elements in the inner-product space $X$. Define $y_1, y_2, \ldots$ and $u_1, u_2, \ldots$ recursively as follows:

$$y_1 = x_1, \qquad u_n = \frac{y_n}{\|y_n\|},$$

$$y_{n+1} = x_{n+1} - \sum_{i=1}^{n} \langle x_{n+1}, u_i \rangle u_i.$$

Show that the $u_n$'s form an orthonormal set and that the linear manifold generated by $u_1, \ldots, u_n$ is the same as that generated by $x_1, \ldots, x_n$.

The process of obtaining the $u_n$'s from the $x_n$'s is called the Gram-Schmidt orthogonalization process, in honor of J. P. Gram (1850–1916) and Erhard Schmidt (1876–1959).

Prove, with the aid of the Gram-Schmidt process, that a separable and infinite-dimensional Hilbert space contains a countably infinite complete orthonormal set.

5. Construct a sequence of continuous functions $\{f_n\}, f_n : [0, 1] \to R$ such that $\int_0^1 |f_n(t)|\, dt \to 0$ and yet $\lim_{n\to\infty} f_n(t) = 0$ is false for each $t$ in a set of points dense on $[0, 1]$. The functions may even be constructed so that $\int_0^1 |f_n(t)|^p\, dt \to 0$ for each $p \geq 1$. One possible procedure is suggested by the diagrams in Figure 31.

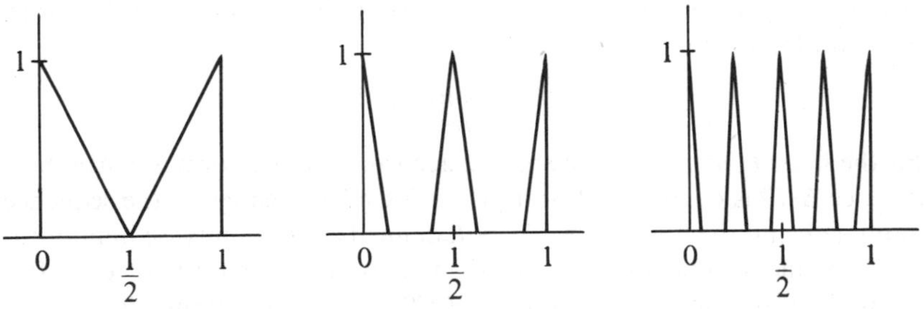


FIGURE 31

6. Let $X$ be a Hilbert space, and let $f$ be a scalar-valued function defined on $X \times X$ such that (a) $f(x, y)$ is linear in $x$, (b) $\overline{f(x, y)}$ is linear in $y$, (c) $f$ is continuous as a function of $(x, y)$. This condition is equivalent to the requirement that the supremum of $\dfrac{|f(x, y)|}{\|x\| \, \|y\|}$ be finite as $x$ and $y$ vary over all nonzero values. The supremum is denoted by $\|f\|$. Show that there exists a function $T : X \to X$ such that $T$ is linear and continuous, with $f(x, y) = \langle x, Ty\rangle$ for each $x$ and $y$, and $\sup_{x \neq 0} \dfrac{\|Tx\|}{\|x\|} = \|f\|$. Use Theorem 3–14 V. This result is used in the proof of Theorem 8–6 II.

7. Consider $C[0, 2\pi]$ as a pre-Hilbert space as in Example 3. Show that the set

$$x_0, x_1, y_1, x_2, y_2, \ldots$$

given in (8) is a complete orthonormal set in $C[0, 2\pi]$, by using the following suggestions and filling in all the details of the argument. It suffices to show that, if $\langle x, x_n\rangle = 0$ when $n = 0, 1, 2, \ldots$ and $\langle x, y_n\rangle = 0$ when $n = 1, 2, \ldots$, then $x = 0$. If this conclusion $x = 0$ were not true, we could, by the continuity of $x$, assume that $x(t_0) \neq 0$ at some point $t_0$ such that $0 < t_0 < 2\pi$. It may be assumed that $x(t_0) > 0$. Let $S_n(t) = (1 + \cos(t - t_0) - \cos\delta)^n$, where $\delta$ is chosen so that $0 < \delta < \pi/2$ and $0 < t_0 - \delta$, $t_0 + \delta < 2\pi$. A further restriction on $\delta$ is to be announced later. Let $E$ be the interval $[t_0 - \delta, t_0 + \delta]$, and let $F$ be the rest of the interval $[0, 2\pi]$. It will be seen that $S_n(t) \geq 1$ if $t \in E$ and $|S_n(t)| \leq 1$ if $t \in F$. Moreover, for some $h > 1$ it is true that $S_n(t) \geq h^n$ if $t \in E_0$, where $E_0$ is the interval $[t_0 - \delta/2, t_0 + \delta/2]$. Now, consider the integral

$$\int_0^{2\pi} x(t) S_n(t)\, dt,$$

and express it as the integral over $E$ plus the integral over $F$. The integral has the value 0 for every $n$; why? On the other hand, by making $\delta$ sufficiently small, with due consideration of the continuity of $x$ at $t_0$, it is possible to arrange matters so that the integral tends to $+\infty$ as $n \to \infty$. From this contradiction we infer that $x = 0$.

8. Let $Y$ be an inner-product space, and let $X$ be a subspace of $Y$ (as, for instance, when $X$ is a pre-Hilbert space and $Y$ is its completion). Let $\{u_n\}$ ($n = 1, 2, \ldots$) be a complete orthonormal set in $X$. The following circumstances permit the deduction that the set $\{u_n\}$ is also complete in $Y$. Assume that there exists a mapping $T : Y \to X$ such that $Ty = 0$ implies $y = 0$. Assume there is a linear functional $\varphi$ on $X$ such that $\varphi(u_1) \neq 0$ and $\varphi(Ty) = 0$ for every $y$. Finally, assume that for every $y$ and every $n > 1$, $\langle Ty, u_n\rangle$ is some finite linear combination of $\langle y, u_1\rangle, \langle y, u_2\rangle, \ldots$. The problem now is to show that $y = 0$ if $\langle y, u_n\rangle = 0$ for each $n$. The main obstacle is in showing that $\langle Ty, u_1\rangle = 0$. As a start, consider $\langle Ty - \langle Ty, u_1\rangle, u_n\rangle$.

## 3–15 Spaces of continuous functions

If $T$ is any nonempty set, the class $B(T)$ of all bounded functions $x : T \to R$ is a normed linear space with the norm

$$\|x\| = \sup_{t \in T} |x(t)|. \tag{1}$$

We call this the *supremum norm*. Convergence according to the norm is convergence uniform on $T$. The space $B(T)$ is complete . For if $\{x_n\}$ is a Cauchy sequence, the sequence of norms $\{\|x_n\|\}$ is bounded, and the function $x : T \to R$ defined as the pointwise limit of the sequence $\{x_n\}$, will be a bounded function. One can then show easily that $\|x_n - x\| \to 0$.

If $T$ is a topological space, let us denote by $C(T)$ the class of all functions $x : T \to R$ such that $x$ is bounded and continuous on $T$. (If $T$ is compact, the boundedness is a consequence of the continuity. In general, however, we must explicitly assume that the functions are bounded. Some authors use $C(T)$ to denote the class of all continuous functions $x : T \to R$, without the boundedness condition.) It is clear that $C(T)$ is a subspace of $B(T)$. We shall always use the supremum norm for $C(T)$ unless explicit mention is made of some other norm. It is an important fact that $C(T)$ is a closed subspace of $B(T)$, and is therefore a Banach space in its own right. The proof that $C(T)$ is closed in $B(T)$ depends on Theorem 3–6 II and is much like the argument in Example 3, Section 3–13.

## DINI'S THEOREM

Theorem 3–6 II states that, for functions mapping a topological space into a metric space, the limit of a uniformly convergent sequence of continuous functions is a continuous function. If we attempt to examine more closely the connection between the uniform convergence of the sequence and the continuity of the limit function, we find that although we cannot simply dispense with uniform convergence, it does not always accompany the situation when the limit function is continuous.

*Example 1.* In $C[0, 1]$ let $x_n(t) = t^n$. The sequence $\{x_n\}$ converges pointwise on $[0, 1]$, but not uniformly, to a limit function which is discontinuous at $t = 1$.

*Example 2.* In $C[0, 1]$ let $x_n(t) = n^2te^{-nt}$. The sequence $\{x_n\}$ converges pointwise on $[0, 1]$, but not uniformly, to a continuous limit function (the zero function).

There is, however, an interesting and useful theorem showing a situation in which, if the limit function is continuous, the convergence is necessarily uniform.

THEOREM 3–15 I. *Let $X$ be a compact topological space. Suppose $f$ and $f_1, f_2, \ldots$ are continuous functions mapping $X$ into $R$. Suppose $f_n(x) \le f_{n+1}(x)$ for each $n$ and each $x$, and suppose $f_n(x) \to f(x)$ for each $x$. Then the convergence is uniform on $X$.*

*Proof.* For a given $\epsilon > 0$ and for each given $x$ choose $N$ (depending on $x$) so that $f(x) - f_n(x) < \epsilon/3$ if $n \ge N$. Choose a neighborhood $V$ of $x$ so that $f(y) - f(x) < \epsilon/3$ if $y \in V$, and also so that $f_N(x) - f_N(y) < \epsilon/3$ if $y \in V$. Note that this choice of $V$ is possible because $f$ and $f_N$ are continuous at $x$, by hypothesis. Then $y \in V$ implies

$$f(y) - f_N(y) = f(y) - f(x) + f(x) - f_N(x) + f_N(x) - f_N(y) < \epsilon.$$

As $x$ varies over $X$, the family of all the $V$'s covers $X$. Since $X$ is compact it follows that a finite set of the $x$'s can be chosen so that the corresponding finite set of $V$'s covers $X$. Denote these $x$'s and the corresponding $V$'s by $x_1, \ldots x_k$, $V_1, \ldots, V_k$. Let $N_i$ be the value of $N$ corresponding to $x_i$, and let $M = \max(N_1, \ldots, N_k)$. Now, suppose $x \in X$ and $n \ge M$. We have $x \in V_i$ for some $i$, and $N_i \le M$. Therefore

$$0 \le f(x) - f_n(x) \le f(x) - f_M(x) \le f(x) - f_{N_i}(x) < \epsilon.$$

This proves the theorem.

Theorem 3–15 I is called Dini's theorem because Ulisse Dini (1845–1918) presented the original version of it in his book on the theory of functions of a real variable, published in Pisa in 1878.

We make some observations about possible generalizations of the theorem. In the first place, we did not make the fullest possible use of the continuity assumptions. We could invoke the concept of semicontinuity, which is discussed elsewhere in this text (in Sections 6–9 and 9–7). For the conclusion of Theorem 3–15 I the assumptions on continuity can be replaced by the following assumptions: Each $f_n$ is lower semicontinuous, and $f$ is upper semicontinuous. The proof is exactly as before.

## RELATIVELY COMPACT SETS IN $C(T)$

Let $T$ be a topological space. Then $C(T)$ is a complete metric space, and a set $S$ in $C(T)$ is relatively compact if and only if it is precompact (Theorems 3–7 V and 3–8 II). Also, $S$ is relatively compact if and only if every sequence $\{x_n\}$ in $S$ contains a convergent subsequence.

It turns out that the investigation of relative compactness in $C(T)$ is closely connected with the concept of *equicontinuity*. For the definition of this concept let $X$ be a topological space, let $Y$ be a metric space, and let $\mathscr{F}$ be a family of functions $f: X \to Y$. If $x_0 \in X$, we say that $\mathscr{F}$ is *equicontinuous* at $x_0$ if to each $\epsilon > 0$ corresponds a neighborhood $U$ of $x_0$ such that $D(f(x), f(x_0)) < \epsilon$ if $f \in \mathscr{F}$ and $x \in U$. Clearly, each $f$ is continuous at $x_0$; the essential feature, however, is that one $U$ will serve for every $f$.

If $X$ and $Y$ are both metric spaces, and if $\mathscr{F}$ is a family of functions $f: X \to Y$, we say that $\mathscr{F}$ is *uniformly* equicontinuous on $X$ if to each $\epsilon > 0$ corresponds a $\delta > 0$ such that $D(f(x_1), f(x_2)) < \epsilon$ if $f \in \mathscr{F}$ and $D(x_1, x_2) < \delta$. We use the same symbol $D$ for the metrics in $X$ and $Y$. If $\mathscr{F}$ is uniformly equicontinuous on $X$ it is, evidently, equicontinuous at each point of $X$. The mere statement that $\mathscr{F}$ is equicontinuous at each point of $X$ could be expressed as follows: To each $\epsilon > 0$ and to each $x_0 \in X$ corresponds a $\delta > 0$ such that $D(f(x), f(x_0)) < \epsilon$ if $f \in \mathscr{F}$ and $D(x, x_0) < \delta$. This does not imply uniform equicontinuity of $\mathscr{F}$ unless some further assumption is made. However, *when $X$ is a compact metric space and $F$ is equicontinuous at each point of $X$, then $\mathscr{F}$ is uniformly equicontinuous on $X$.* Theorem 3–7 III is the special case of this which occurs when $\mathscr{F}$ consists of a single function. The proof can be adapted at once to the case of the more general proposition.

THEOREM 3–15 II. *Let $T$ be a topological space. Let $S$ be a relatively compact set in $C(T)$. Then $S$ is a bounded set in $C(T)$, and $S$ is equicontinuous at each point of $T$.*

*Proof.* We know by Theorem 3–7 V that $S$ is precompact. Suppose $\epsilon > 0$. Then there exist elements $x_1, \ldots, x_n$ in $S$ such that to each $x$ in $S$ corresponds an $i$ such that $\|x - x_i\| < \epsilon/3$. Let $M = \max(\|x_1\|, \ldots, \|x_n\|)$. We see that

$$|x(t) - x_i(t)| \leq \|x - x_i\| < \frac{\epsilon}{3}$$

for each $t$ in $T$. Therefore

$$|x(t)| \leq |x_i(t)| + \frac{\epsilon}{3} \leq \|x_i\| + \frac{\epsilon}{3} \leq M + \frac{\epsilon}{3},$$

and so $\|x\| \leq M + \epsilon/3$ if $x \in S$. Thus $S$ is bounded. Suppose $t_0 \in T$. To show that $S$ is equicontinuous at $t_0$, observe that we can choose a neighborhood $V$ of $t_0$ so that

$$|x_j(t) - x_j(t_0)| < \frac{\epsilon}{3}$$

if $t \in V$ and $j = 1, 2, \ldots, n$. Thus, with $t \in V$, $x \in S$, and $i$ chosen so that $\|x - x_i\| < \epsilon/3$, we have

$$|x(t) - x(t_0)| \leq |x(t) - x_i(t)| + |x_i(t) - x_i(t_0)| + |x_i(t_0) - x(t_0)| < \epsilon.$$

This ends the proof.

The proof that $S$ is bounded if it is relatively compact in $C(T)$ could have been made more directly. In fact, a relatively compact set in any metric space is bounded. This is easily proved with the aid of Theorem 3–7 IV.

When $T$ is a compact metric space we have a converse of the preceding theorem.

THEOREM 3–15 III. *Suppose $T$ is a compact metric space and let $S$ be a bounded subset of $C(T)$ which is equicontinuous at each point of $T$. Then $S$ is relatively compact in $C(T)$.*

*Proof.* Since $T$ is compact, it is precompact. For each positive integer $k$ let $V_k$ be a finite set in $T$ such that each point of $T$ is at a distance less than $1/k$ from some point of $V_k$. Let $t_1, t_2, \ldots$ be an enumeration of the countable set which is the union of all the $V_k$'s. We shall use Theorem 3–7 IV to show that $S$ is relatively compact. Let $\{x_n\}$ be a sequence in $S$. Then, because $S$ is bounded in $C(T)$, $\{x_n(t_1)\}$ is bounded in $R$; hence it has a convergent subsequence, which we denote by $x_{11}(t_1), x_{12}(t_1), x_{13}(t_1), \ldots$. Likewise, considering $\{x_{1n}(t_2)\}$, we obtain a convergent subsequence $\{x_{2n}(t_2)\}$. The sequence $\{x_{2n}(t_1)\}$ is also convergent, because it is a subsequence of $\{x_{1n}(t_1)\}$. Proceeding in this way, we obtain sequences $\{x_{1n}\}$, $\{x_{2n}\}$, $\{x_{3n}\}, \ldots$, each a subsequence of its predecessor and of $\{x_n\}$, such that $\lim_{n\to\infty} x_{kn}(t_i)$ exists if $1 \leq i \leq k$. Let $y_n = x_{nn}$. Then $\{y_n\}$ is a subsequence of $\{x_n\}$ and $\lim_{n\to\infty} y_n(t_i)$ exists if $i = 1, 2, \ldots$. We shall show that $\{y_n\}$ is a Cauchy sequence in $C(T)$. Because $C(T)$ is complete, this will finish the proof that $S$ is relatively compact.

Suppose $\epsilon > 0$. Now, $S$ is uniformly equicontinuous on $T$ (because $T$ is compact). Hence we can choose an integer $k$ so that $|y_n(t') - y_n(t)| < \epsilon/3$ for every $n$ if $D(t', t) < 1/k$. Choose $N$ in such a way that $|y_n(t_i) - y_m(t_i)| < \epsilon/3$ when $m \geq N$ and $n \geq N$, for each of the finite set of indices $i$ such that $t_i \in V_k$. Now, if $t \in T$, we know that $D(t, t_i) < 1/k$ for some $t_i \in V_k$. Therefore, if $m \geq N$ and $n \geq N$, we have

$$\begin{aligned}|y_n(t) - y_m(t)| \leq |y_n(t) - y_n(t_i)| &+ |y_n(t_i) - y_m(t_i)| \\ &+ |y_m(t_i) - y_m(t)| < \epsilon.\end{aligned}$$

In other words, $\|y_n - y_m\| < \epsilon$ if $m \geq N$ and $n \geq N$. This completes the proof.

For real functions of a real variable the concept of equicontinuity at a point goes back to the Italian mathematicians Giulio Ascoli (1843–1896) and Césare Arzelà (1847–1912), in the early 1880's. Theorem 3–15 III has important applications in various branches of analysis, and in its classical formulation is usually referred to as the theorem of Ascoli, or sometimes as the theorem of Arzelà-Ascoli. Ascoli's paper of 1883–84 may be said to contain an early form of Theorem 3–15 III, while Arzelà's paper of 1889 contains an early form of Theorem 3–15 II. For further historical notes on the evolution of the concept of equicontinuity and its relation to compactness in $C(T)$, see Dunford-Schwartz [1], page 382.

## THE SPACE $C(T; X)$

Let $T$ and $X$ be a topological space and a metric space, respectively. Let $C(T; X)$ be the class of all functions $f: T \to X$ such that $f$ is bounded and continuous on $T$. We make $C(T; X)$ into a metric space by defining

$$d(f_1, f_2) = \sup_{t \in T} D[f_1(t), f_2(t)].$$

Here $D$ is the metric in $X$ and $d$ is the metric defined in $C(T; X)$. It is clear that $d(f_n, f) \to 0$ means that $D[f_n(t), f(t)] \to 0$ uniformly on $T$. If $X$ is complete, so is $C(T; X)$.

We can now discuss the question of when a subset of $C(T; X)$ is relatively compact. There is an easy generalization of Theorem 3–15 II.

THEOREM 3–15 IV. *Suppose $S$ is a relatively compact subset of $C(T; X)$, where $T$ is any topological space and $X$ is any metric space. For each $t$ let*

$$S(t) = \{f(t) : f \in S\}.$$

*Then $S(t)$ is precompact in $X$. The set $S$ is bounded in $C(T; X)$. Also, $S$ is equicontinuous at each point of $T$.*

*Proof.* Theorem 3–7 V implies that $S$ is precompact. Suppose $\epsilon > 0$. Then there exists in $S$ a finite set $f_1, \ldots, f_n$ such that to each $f$ in $S$ corresponds some $i$ such that $d(f, f_i) < \epsilon/3$. This implies that $D[f(t), f_i(t)] < \epsilon/3$ for each $t$, and from this we can conclude that $S(t)$ is precompact. The fact that $S$ is bounded is a direct consequence of the fact that it is relatively compact. See the remark following the end of the proof of Theorem 3–15 II.

Suppose now that $t_0$ is given in $T$. Choose a neighborhood $V$ of $t$ so that $t \in V$ implies $D[f_i(t), f_i(t_0)] < \epsilon/3$ if $i = 1, 2, \ldots, n$. If $f \in S$ and $i$ is chosen so that $d(f, f_i) < \epsilon/3$, we see that $t \in V$ implies

$$D[f(t), f(t_0)] \leq D[f(t), f_i(t)] + D[f_i(t), f_i(t_0)] + D[f_i(t_0), f(t_0)] < \epsilon.$$

Therefore $S$ is equicontinuous at $t_0$.

Let $\mathscr{R}(S)$ be the union of all the sets $S(t)$, as $t$ varies over $T$. This is the same as the union of all the ranges $f(T)$, as $f$ varies over $S$. It is easy to see that the set $\mathscr{R}(S)$ is bounded in $X$ if and only if $S$ is bounded in $C(T; X)$. If $X = R$, $\mathscr{R}(S)$ is precompact if and only if it is bounded. In the situation of Theorem 3–15 IV we do not conclude that $\mathscr{R}(S)$ is precompact, but only that each $S(t)$ is precompact. However, if $T$ is a compact metric space, we can prove that $\mathscr{R}(S)$ is precompact. For, in this case, each of the functions $f_1, \ldots, f_n$ is uniformly continuous on $T$, so that there exists a $\delta > 0$ such that $D(t', t) < \delta$ implies $D[f_i(t'), f_i(t)] < \epsilon/2$ for $i = 1, \ldots, n$. Now choose points $t_1, \ldots, t_k$ in $T$ so that to each $t$ corresponds some one of these points, say $t_j$, such that $D(t, t_j) < \delta$. With $f$ and $f_i$ related as in the proof of Theorem 3–15 IV we then have $D[f(t), f_i(t_j)] < \epsilon/3 + \epsilon/2$. Hence $\mathscr{R}(S)$ is precompact.

We shall now present a generalization of Theorem 3–15 III, with an entirely different method of proof.

THEOREM 3–15 V. *Let $T$ be a compact topological space. Let $X$ be a complete metric space. Suppose $S \subset C(T; X)$, and for each $t$ in $T$ let $S(t) = \{f(t) : f \in S\}$. Suppose $S$ is equicontinuous at each point of $T$ and let $S(t)$ be relatively compact in $X$, for each $t$. Then $S$ is relatively compact in $C(T; X)$.*

*Proof.* Since $C(T; X)$ is complete, it suffices to show that $S$ is precompact (Theorem 3–8 II). Suppose $\epsilon > 0$. Corresponding to each $t$ choose a neighborhood $V(t)$ so that $D[f(t'), f(t)] < \epsilon/4$ if $t' \in V(t)$ and $f \in S$. Here we use the equicontinuity of $S$. Choose a finite set $t_1, \ldots, t_n$ in $T$ so that $T$ is the union of the sets $V(t_1), \ldots, V(t_n)$. Here we use the compactness of $T$. Consider $W = \bigcup_{i=1}^{n} S(t_i)$. It is a relatively compact set in $X$, since each of the sets $S(t_1), \ldots, S(t_n)$ has this property. We may therefore choose points $x_1, \ldots, x_k$ in $W$ so that to each $x$ in $W$ corresponds some $j$ for which $D(x, x_j) < \epsilon/4$. Let $\mathscr{J}$ be the collection of all ordered $n$-tuples

$$J = (j_1, \ldots, j_n),$$

where each $j_i$ comes from the set $\{1, 2, \ldots, k\}$. Evidently $\mathscr{J}$ is a finite set. Corresponding to $J$, let

$$S_J = \left\{f \in S : D[f(t_i), x_{j_i}] < \frac{\epsilon}{4}, i = 1, \ldots, n\right\}.$$

It is clear that each $f$ in $S$ belongs to some $S_J$. Some $S_J$'s may be empty, of course. We shall show that the diameter of each nonempty $S_J$ does not exceed $\epsilon$. Then, since $S$ is contained in the union of a finite number of the $S_J$'s, it will follow that $S$ is precompact.

For a given $J$ suppose $f$ and $g$ are in $S_J$. If $t \in T$, $t$ belongs to $V(t_i)$ for some $i$, and we have $D[f(t), f(t_i)] < \epsilon/4$, $D[g(t), g(t_i)] < \epsilon/4$. By the definition of $S_J$ we have $D[f(t_i), x_{j_i}] < \epsilon/4$, and a similar inequality with $f$ replaced by $g$. Then $D[f(t_i), g(t_i)] \leq D[f(t_i), x_{j_i}] + D[x_{j_i}, g(t_i)] < \epsilon/2$. Using the triangular inequality in an obvious way, we see that $D[f(t), g(t)] < \epsilon$. Thus $d(f, g) \leq \epsilon$, so that diam $(S_J) \leq \epsilon$. This ends the proof.

## IMPORTANT EXAMPLES OF EQUICONTINUOUS FAMILIES

*Example 3.* Let $(s, t) \to k(s, t)$ be a continuous mapping of $[0, 1] \times [0, 1]$ into $R$. Define a mapping $F : C[0, 1] \to C[0, 1]$ as follows:

$$F(x) = y, \qquad \text{where } y(s) = \int_0^1 k(s, t)x(t)\, dt.$$

Then, if $S$ is any bounded set in $C[0, 1]$, the image set $F(S)$ is bounded in $C[0, 1]$ and uniformly equicontinuous on $[0, 1]$. Therefore $F(S)$ is relatively compact in $C[0, 1]$.

*Proof.* Suppose $\|x\| \leq M$ for each $x$ in $S$, and let $K$ be the maximum value of $k(s, t)$. Then evidently $\|y\| \leq KM$ for each $y$ in $F(S)$. Also,

$$y(s_1) - y(s_2) = \int_0^1 [k(s_1, t) - k(s_2, t)]x(t)\, dt.$$

From the fact that $k$ is uniformly continuous on its domain of definition it is then easy to see that $F(S)$ is uniformly equicontinuous on $[0, 1]$.

The property of $F$ expressed in Example 3 is the basis for one important method in the theory of linear integral equations—a method due to F. Riesz. (The mapping $F$ is an instance of what is called a *completely continuous* operator, or, in another terminology, a *compact* operator. See A. E. Taylor [2], pp. 274–285.)

For an understanding of the next example the reader must be familiar with the rudiments of the classical theory of analytic functions of a complex variable. If he knows nothing of this theory he may simply pass over this example.

*Example 4.* Let $D$ be an open set in the complex plane $C$. Let $\mathscr{F}$ be a family of functions $f : D \to C$, each $f$ being analytic in $D$ (that is, differentiable at each point of $D$). Suppose that to each compact subset $T$ of $D$ there corresponds a positive constant $M_T$ such that $|f(z)| \leq M_T$ for each $z$ in $T$ and each $f$ in $\mathscr{F}$. Then $\mathscr{F}$ is equicontinuous at each point of $D$.

*Proof.* The argument depends on the use of Cauchy's integral formula. If $z_0 \in D$, we can choose a circle $\Gamma$ with center $z_0$ such that all points on and inside $\Gamma$ are in $D$. Let $2r$ be the radius of such a $\Gamma$. Now suppose $f \in \mathscr{F}$ and let $z$ be any point such that $|z - z_0| \leq r$. We have

$$f(z) = \frac{1}{2\pi i} \int_\Gamma \frac{f(t)}{t - z}\, dt,$$

and a similar formula for $f(z_0)$, whence

$$f(z) - f(z_0) = \frac{1}{2\pi i} \int_\Gamma \frac{z - z_0}{(t - z)(t - z_0)} f(t)\, dt.$$

From this it is easily seen that

$$|f(z) - f(z_0)| \leq \frac{M_\Gamma\, |z - z_0|}{r}.$$

It is then clear that $\mathscr{F}$ is equicontinuous at $z_0$. The proof may be modified to show directly that $\mathscr{F}$ is uniformly equicontinuous on any compact subset of $D$.

If $\mathscr{F}$ is a family of functions of the sort described in Example 4, Theorem 3–15 V makes clear that, if $\{f_n\}$ is a sequence from $\mathscr{F}$ and $T$ is a compact subset of $D$, there is a subsequence of $\{f_n\}$ which converges uniformly on $T$. This situation can be exploited in important ways in the theory of analytic functions.

## THE STONE-WEIERSTRASS THEOREM

The classical theorem of Karl Weierstrass (1815–1897) asserts that if $x : [a, b] \to R$ is continuous, then to each $\epsilon > 0$ corresponds a polynomial $p$ with real coefficients such that $|x(t) - p(t)| < \epsilon$ when $a \leq t \leq b$. This proposition can be restated as follows: *Let $P$ be the class of all polynomials in one variable, with real coefficients. Then, if we regard $P$ as a subset of the real Banach space $C[a, b]$ (provided with the supremum norm), $P$ is dense in $C[a, b]$.* What is meant by "regarding $P$ as a subset of $C[a, b]$" is, of course, that although each element of $P$ is in fact a continuous funtion on $R$, we restrict attention to $[a, b]$ and thus get an element of $C[a, b]$.

There are many proofs of the Weierstrass theorem, by a great variety of methods. In 1937 M. H. Stone published an immense generalization of the Weierstrass theorem. Stone's result not only yields a great insight into the reasons for the validity of the Weierstrass theorem; it also encompasses a great deal more when one reckons all its particularizations.

Let $T$ be a compact topological space, and consider the real Banach space $C(T)$ with the supremum norm. Stone's generalization of the Weierstrass theorem is concerned with the question of when certain subsets of $C(T)$ are dense in $C(T)$. Before dealing with Stone's theorem we must prepare the way with some discussion of particular aspects of $C(T)$. Now, $C(T)$ is not only a Banach space, but also an *algebra* and a *lattice*. It is an algebra because we can define a multiplication of two elements of $C(T)$ to yield another element of $C(T)$, in such a way that $C(T)$ becomes a ring as well as a vector space, and all the appropriate rules governing the three mappings

$$(\alpha, x) \to \alpha x, \qquad (x, y) \to x + y, \qquad (x, y) \to xy$$

are satisfied. The definition of $xy$ is that of pointwise multiplication:

$$(xy)(t) = x(t)\, y(t).$$

It may be noted that the product $xy$ depends continuously on the pair $(x, y)$. This is easily proved with the aid of the inequality

$$\|xy\| \leq \|x\| \, \|y\|,$$

which holds for all $x$ and $y$ in $C(T)$.

A subset $A$ of $C(T)$ is called a *subalgebra* of $C(T)$ if it is a subspace of $C(T)$ as a vector space and if $xy \in A$ whenever $x \in A$ and $y \in A$. We note, for instance, that the class $P$ of polynomial functions with real coefficients is a subalgebra of $C[a, b]$.

If $A$ is a subalgebra of $C(T)$, its closure $\bar{A}$ (in the topology of $C(T)$) is also a subalgebra. This is easily proved by continuity arguments. For instance, if $x, y \in \bar{A}$, there exist sequences $\{x_n\}$, $\{y_n\}$ in $A$ such that $x_n \to x$ and $y_n \to y$. But then $x_n y_n \to xy$, by continuity. Hence, $xy \in \bar{A}$.

We can define a partial ordering of $C(T)$ by the relation $\leq$, where $x \leq y$ means that $x(t) \leq y(t)$ for each $t$. If $x$ and $y$ are in $C(T)$, there is a unique element of $C(T)$, denoted by $x \vee y$, such that $x \leq x \vee y$, $y \leq x \vee y$, and such that furthermore, if $z \in C(T)$ and $x \leq z, y \leq z$, then $x \vee y \leq z$. In other words, $x \vee y$ is the least upper bound in the sense of the partial ordering, of the set $\{x, y\}$. The element $x \vee y$ is obtained from $x, y$ as follows:

(1) $$(x \vee y)(t) = \max \{x(t), y(t)\}.$$

We leave it for the reader to verify that the function $x \vee y$ is indeed a member of $C(T)$. In a similar manner we can see that the set $\{x, y\}$ has a unique greatest lower bound in $C(T)$; we denote it by $x \wedge y$. It is given by

(2) $$(x \wedge y)(t) = \min \{x(t), y(t)\}.$$

The statement that $C(T)$ is a lattice is then in accordance with the general terminology: a lattice is a partially ordered set in which every set of two elements has both a least upper bound and a greatest lower bound (which are necessarily unique).

A subset $S$ of $C(T)$ is called a sublattice of $C(T)$ if $x \vee y$ and $x \wedge y$ are both in $S$ whenever $x$ and $y$ are both in $S$. A subalgebra of $C(T)$ is not necessarily a sublattice. For instance, let $x$ and $y$ be the polynomial functions $x(t) = t$, $y(t) = -t$. Then $(x \vee y)(t) = |t|$, so that $x \vee y$ is not a polynomial function. Thus the subalgebra of the polynomial functions is not a sublattice.

If $x \in C(T)$, denote by $|x|$ the element of $C(T)$ defined by $|x|(t) = |x(t)|$. We see that $|x| = x \vee (-x)$. Furthermore, we see that

(3) $$\begin{cases} x \vee y = \frac{1}{2}(x + y) + \frac{1}{2}|x - y|, \\ x \wedge y = \frac{1}{2}(x + y) - \frac{1}{2}|x - y|. \end{cases}$$

These relations are consequences of the relations

$$\max(\alpha, \beta) = \frac{\alpha + \beta}{2} + \frac{|\alpha - \beta|}{2},$$

$$\min(\alpha, \beta) = \frac{\alpha + \beta}{2} - \frac{|\alpha - \beta|}{2},$$

which are valid for all real numbers $\alpha$, $\beta$. From the foregoing observations we see that a subspace (linear manifold) $M$ in $C(T)$ is a sublattice if and only if $|x| \in M$ when $x \in M$.

We can of course form $(x \vee y) \vee z$ and $x \vee (y \vee z)$; they turn out to be the same, so that we can write $x \vee y \vee z$ without ambiguity. Likewise for $x_1 \vee x_2 \vee \cdots \vee x_n$ and $x_1 \wedge x_2 \wedge \cdots \wedge x_n$.

Another idea which enters in Stone's theorem is that of a subset of $C(T)$ which separates points of $T$. If $S \subset C(T)$, we say that $S$ *separates points of* $T$ if to each pair of distinct points $t_1, t_2$ in $T$ there corresponds an $x \in S$ such that $x(t_1) \neq x(t_2)$.

We can now state Stone's generalization of the Weierstrass theorem.

THEOREM 3–15 VI. *Suppose $T$ is a compact topological space. Let $A$ be a subalgebra of the real algebra $C(T)$ such that* (1) *$A$ contains all the real constant functions defined on $T$, and* (2) *$A$ separates points of $T$. Then $A$ is dense in $C(T)$.*

Before beginning the proof we observe that $A$ will contain all the constant functions if it contains any one nonzero constant function.

The proof of Theorem 3–15 VI will be made in several steps.

*Step 1. The closure $\bar{A}$ is a sublattice of $C(T)$.*

*Proof.* Since we know that $\bar{A}$ is a subalgebra, a remark made earlier shows that it will suffice to prove that $|x| \in \bar{A}$ if $x \in \bar{A}$. We can assume $x \neq 0$. We observe that, if $\alpha$ and $\beta$ are real, with $|\alpha| \leq \beta$ and $\beta > 0$, then

$$|\alpha| = \beta\sqrt{1 - \left(1 - \frac{\alpha^2}{\beta^2}\right)}. \tag{4}$$

Also, we know that the binomial expansion

$$\sqrt{1-t} = 1 - \frac{1}{2}t - \sum_{n=1}^{\infty} \frac{1 \cdot 3 \cdots (2n-1)}{2 \cdot 4 \cdots 2n} \frac{t^{n+1}}{2n+2} \tag{5}$$

is valid if $-1 \leq t \leq 1$, and that the series

$$\sum_{n=1}^{\infty} \frac{1 \cdot 3 \cdots (2n-1)}{2 \cdot 4 \cdots 2n} \frac{1}{2n+2} \tag{6}$$

is convergent. (For notes on (5) and (6) see Problem 1.) Using (4) and (5) and assuming $x \in \bar{A}$, $x \neq 0$, we write

$$\tag{7} \begin{aligned} |x(t)| &= \|x\| \left\{1 - \left[1 - \left(\frac{x(t)}{\|x\|}\right)^2\right]\right\}^{1/2}, \\ |x(t)| &= \|x\| \left\{1 - \frac{1}{2}\left[1 - \left(\frac{x(t)}{\|x\|}\right)^2\right] - \sum_{n=1}^{\infty} \frac{1 \cdot 3 \cdots (2n-1)}{2 \cdot 4 \cdots 2n} \frac{1}{2n+2} [y(t)]^{n+1}\right\}, \end{aligned}$$

where $y(t) = 1 - \left(\dfrac{x(t)}{\|x\|}\right)^2$. Because of the convergence of the series (6), the series (7) converges uniformly on [0, 1] (note that $0 \leq y(t) \leq 1$). Because $\bar{A}$ is an algebra, we see from the uniform convergence in (7) that $|x|$ is the limit in $C(T)$ of a sequence whose terms belong to $\bar{A}$; therefore $|x| \in \bar{A}$. This finishes Step 1.

*Step 2. If $x \in C(T)$ and if $t_1, t_2$ are points of $T$, there exists $y \in A$ such that $y(t_i) = x(t_i)$, $i = 1, 2$.*

*Proof.* If $t_1 = t_2$ we can take $y$ to be the constant function defined by $y(t) = x(t_1)$. If $t_1 \neq t_2$ there exists a $z$ in $A$ such that $z(t_1) \neq z(t_2)$. Then the linear equations

$$\alpha z(t_1) + \beta = x(t_1)$$
$$\alpha z(t_2) + \beta = x(t_2)$$

can be solved for $\alpha$ and $\beta$, and we may define the required $y$ by $y(t) = \alpha z(t) + \beta$.

In what follows we shall need to exhibit the dependence of $y$ on $t_1$ and $t_2$. Rather than to use $t_1$ and $t_2$ as subscripts, which would cause difficulty in printing, we denote the function by $y(t_1, t_2; \cdot)$; then its value at $t$ is $y(t_1, t_2; t)$.

*Step 3.* We now come to the final stages of the proof of Theorem 3–15 VI. Suppose $x \in C(T)$ and $\epsilon > 0$. If $s, t$ are points of $T$, let $y(s, t; \cdot)$ be a chosen element of $A$ such that $y(s, t; s) = x(s)$ and $y(s, t; t) = x(t)$. We see that there is a neighborhood of $s$, say $U(s)$, such that $y(s, t; u) > x(u) - \epsilon$ if $u \in U(s)$. Choose $s_1, \ldots, s_m$ so that the union of $U(s_1), \ldots, U(s_m)$ is $T$. Here we use the compactness of $T$. Now let

$$z(t; \cdot) = y(s_1, t; \cdot) \vee \cdots \vee y(s_m, t; \cdot).$$

We see that

$$z(t; u) > x(u) - \epsilon \quad \text{if} \quad u \in T. \tag{8}$$

Also, $z(t; \cdot) \in \bar{A}$, by Step 1. Observe that $z(t; t) = x(t)$. There is therefore a neighborhood of $t$, say $V(t)$, such that $z(t; u) < x(u) + \epsilon$ if $u \in V(t)$. Select $t_1, \ldots, t_n$ so that the union of $V(t_1), \ldots, V(t_n)$ is $T$, and let

$$w = z(t_1; \cdot) \wedge \cdots \wedge z(t_n; \cdot).$$

Then $w(u) < x(u) + \epsilon$ for each in $T$. We also have $w(u) > x(u) - \epsilon$, because of (8). From these results we see that $\|x - w\| \leq \epsilon$. Since $w \in \bar{A}$ and $\bar{A}$ is closed, we have thus proved that $\bar{A} = C(T)$.

In 1948 Stone published in the Mathematics Magazine an expository article on the subject of his 1937 generalization of the Weierstrass theorem. This expository paper has now been republished as one of the essays in the Mathematical Association of America series, Studies in Mathematics; see Stone [1], [3].

As an immediate corollary of Theorem 3–15 VI we have the classical Weierstrass theorem. We state it in a somewhat generalized form.

THEOREM 3–15 VII. *Let $T$ be a compact set in $R^k$, let $x : T \to R$ be continuous, and suppose $\epsilon > 0$. Then there exists a polynomial $p$ in the $k$ real variables $t_1, \ldots, t_k$, with real coefficents, such that*

$$|x(t_1, \ldots, t_k) - p(t_1, \ldots, t_k)| < \epsilon$$

*for each point $(t_1, \ldots, t_k)$ in $T$.*

*Proof.* The class $P$ of polynomials fulfills the conditions placed on $A$ in Theorem 3–15 VI. If $a$ and $b$ are distinct points of $T$, and if $y_i(t_1, \ldots, t_k) = t_i$, one of the $y_i$'s has distinct values at $a$ and $b$.

It should be pointed out that some of the other methods of proving the Weierstrass theorem have special merits and advantages for particular situations. For example, some of the proofs show more explicitly how to obtain the polynomial which approximates the continuous function. Other proofs show how to approximate $x$ by $p$, and at the same time to approximate a certain number of derivatives of $x$ (when they exist) by derivatives of $p$. For references see Graves [1], pp. 123–125.

It is of considerable interest to have a theorem of the nature of Theorem 3–15 VI for the case in which the continuous functions are allowed to have complex values. For this we now let $C(T)$ denote all the continuous functions $x : T \to C$. Now $C(T)$ is a complex Banach space, and also an algebra. The concept of a subset which separates points of $T$ still makes sense. We also have a new feature. If $x \in C(T)$, there is the conjugate function $\bar{x}$, defined by $\bar{x}(t) = \overline{x(t)}$; it is a fact that $\bar{x} \in C(T)$ also. A subalgebra of $C(T)$ may contain $x$ but not $\bar{x}$, however. (An example may be constructed by using polynomials in one complex variable.)

THEOREM 3–15 VIII. *Suppose $T$ is a compact topological space. Let $A$ be a subalgebra of the complex algebra $C(T)$ such that (1) $A$ contains all the complex constant functions, (2) $A$ separates points of $T$, (3) if $x \in A$ then $\bar{x} \in A$. Then $A$ is dense in $C(T)$.*

*Proof.* We now denote by $C_r(T)$ the class of all real-valued continuous functions on $T$. Let $A_r = A \cap C_r(T)$. Then $A_r$ is a real subalgebra of $C_r(T)$, and it contains all the real constant functions on $T$. Suppose $x = x_1 + ix_2$, where $x_1, x_2 \in C_r(T)$. Then $x_1 = \frac{1}{2}(x + \bar{x})$, $x_2 = \dfrac{1}{2i}(x - \bar{x})$. Hence $x \in A$ implies $x_1, x_2 \in A_r$. We can see from this that $A_r$ separates points of $T$, because $x(t) \neq x(s)$ implies that $x_j(t) \neq x_j(s)$ for either $j = 1$ or $j = 2$. Therefore $A_r$ is dense in $C_r(T)$. From this we can see immediately that $A$ is dense in $C(T)$.

As a corollary of Theorem 3–15 VIII we get a theorem about approximation by trigonometric polynomials. By a complex trigonometric polynomial in the real variable $\theta$ we mean a finite linear combination of the functions $e^{in\theta} (n = 0, \pm 1, \pm 2, \ldots)$. By a real trigonometric polynomial we mean a finite linear combination, with real coefficients, of the functions $\cos n\theta$, $\sin n\theta$ $(n = 0, 1, 2, \ldots)$.

THEOREM 3–15 IX. *If $f : R \to C$ is continuous and admits the period $2\pi$, and if $\epsilon > 0$, there is a complex trigonometric polynomial $p$ such that $|f(\theta) - p(\theta)| < \epsilon$ for all values of $\theta$. The same assertion remains true if we replace $f : R \to C$ by $f : R \to R$ and replace the word "complex" by the word "real" in describing $p$.*

*Proof.* Since the real part of a complex trigonometric polynomial is a real trigonometric polynomial, we see that the second assertion is an easy consequence of the first. Hence, we shall merely prove the first assertion.

We take $T$ to be the set $[t : |t| = 1]$ in $C$. We can parametrize $T$ by setting $t = e^{i\theta}$, where $\theta$ is real, and in this way we get a correspondence between the elements of the complex algebra $C(T)$ and the set of all continuous complex functions on $R$, of period $2\pi$, by setting $x(e^{i\theta}) = f(\theta)$, where $x \in C(T)$. Now let $A$ be the subalgebra of $C(T)$ generated by the two functions $u$, $v$, where $u(t) = t$, $v(t) = 1/t$ (with $t$ restricted to $T$). Observe that $\bar{u} = v$, $\bar{v} = u$. Clearly $A$ satisfies the conditions of Theorem 3–15 VIII. Since the functions of $\theta$ corresponding to the elements of $A$ are the complex trigonometric polynomials, the statement to be proved is true, for it says precisely that $\bar{A} = C(T)$ in this case.

## PROBLEMS

1. Prove that the series (6) is convergent by showing that

$$\left[\frac{1 \cdot 3 \cdots (2n-1)}{2 \cdot 4 \cdots (2n)}\right]^2 < \frac{1}{2n+1} \quad \text{if} \quad n \geq 1.$$

For a general discussion of the validity of binomial expansions, including (5) in particular, see Section 17.5 (including the exercises) in Taylor [1].

2. Suppose $f : [a, b] \to R$ is continuous, and that

$$\int_a^b f(x)x^n\, dx = 0 \qquad n = 0, 1, 2, \ldots$$

Show that $f = 0$. It is assumed that $a, b \in R$ and $a < b$. [*Suggestion.* Suppose $f \neq 0$. Let $g(x) = \max\,[0, f(x)]$. Then $fg \in C[a, b]$ and $\int_a^b f(x)g(x)\, dx > 0$. (Why?) There exists a polynomial $P(x)$ such that

$$\int_a^b f(x)[g(x) - P(x)]\, dx < \int_a^b f(x)g(x)\, dx.$$

Why is this true? Now deduce a contradiction.]

3. Let $X$ be a Cartesian product $\prod_\alpha X_\alpha$, where each $X_\alpha$ is a compact Hausdorff space. Let $P$ be the class of functions $f : X \to R$ of the following type: there is some finite set of $\alpha$'s, say $\alpha_1, \ldots, \alpha_n$, and a corresponding set of functions $f_1, \ldots, f_n$, where $f_i \in C(X_{\alpha_i})$, such that $f(x) = f_1(x(\alpha_1))f_2(x(\alpha_2)) \cdots f_n(x(\alpha_n))$ for each $x$. Let $Y$ be the linear manifold in $C(X)$ generated by $P$. Then $Y$ is dense in $C(X)$. Prove this.

4. Let $T$ be a compact metric space. Use Theorem 3–15 VI to prove that the space $C(T)$ is separable. [*Suggestion.* Let $\{G_n\}$ be a countable basis of neighborhoods for $T$, such that $T - G_n \neq \varnothing$ for each $n$. Define $g_n : T \to R$ by $g_n(t) = D(t, T - G_n)$, and consider the subalgebra $A$ of $C(T)$ generated by the $g_n$'s.]

5. Is the space $C(R)$ separable?

6. Let $K : R \to R$ be a function such that

$$\int_{-\infty}^{\infty} |K(t)|\, dt < \infty \quad \text{and} \quad \int_{-\infty}^{\infty} K(t)\, dt = 1.$$

For present purposes the integrals may be considered to be improper Riemann integrals, but they may also be Lebesgue integrals. If $f \in C(R)$, define $f_n$ by

$$f_n(x) = \int_{-\infty}^{\infty} f\left(x + \frac{t}{n}\right) K(t)\, dt = n\int_{-\infty}^{\infty} f(u)\, K[n(u - x)]\, du.$$

Show that $f_n(x) \to f(x)$ uniformly on each compact subset of $R$. An example of $K$ is furnished by $K(t) = \frac{1}{\pi}\left(\frac{\sin t}{t}\right)^2$ (the Féjer kernel).

7. Let $A$ be a nonempty closed subset of the metric space $T$. Let $\varphi : A \to R$ be continuous. Then there exists a continuous function $f : T \to R$ such that $f(a) = \varphi(a)$ if $a \in R$, such that $\sup_{t \in T} f(t) = \sup_{a \in A} \varphi(a)$ (not necessarily finite), and such that the corresponding relation holds true with infima in place of suprema. Hence, in particular, $f \in C(T)$ if $\varphi \in C(A)$.

The proof of this is indicated in stages, with details of the problem left to the reader. For a different approach see McShane and Botts [1], p. 96.

(a) Assume at first that $\varphi$ is bounded and that $\inf_{a \in A} \varphi(a) > 0$. In this case $f$ can be obtained as follows: Let $f(t) = \varphi(t)$ if $t \in A$, and let $f(t) = g(t)/D(t, A)$ if $t \in T - A$, where

$$g(t) = \inf_{a \in A}\, [\varphi(a)D(t, a)], \qquad t \in T - A.$$

The main difficulty here is in proving that $f$ is continuous at points on the boundary of $A$.

(b) If $\varphi$ is bounded but part (a) does not apply, a simple device enables us to reduce the problem back to (a).

(c) Before attempting the proof when $\varphi$ is not bounded, it is convenient to prove the following supplementary proposition: Suppose the range of $\varphi$ is contained in the open interval $(-1, 1)$. Then there exists an extension $f$ of $\varphi$ as asserted in the main proposition, with the additional property that the range of $f$ is also contained in $(-1, 1)$. [*Suggestion.* Let $f_1$ be an extension of $\varphi$ as guaranteed by (a) and (b). If $\alpha$ and $\beta$ are the infimum and supremum, respectively, of the values of $\varphi$, then the range of $f_1$ is contained in the closed interval $[\alpha, \beta]$. A suitable $f$ can be found by modifying $f_1$ at points of $T - A$. The idea is to make $f$ continuous everywhere and such that $\alpha < f(t) < \beta$ if $t \in T - A$. The functions with values $\alpha + \epsilon h(t)$, $\beta - \epsilon h(t)$ will be useful, where $\epsilon$ is a small positive number and $h(t) = \min \{1, D(t, A)\}$.

(d) Now suppose that $\varphi : A \to R$ is continuous, but not bounded. Use the mapping $t \to \dfrac{t}{1 + |t|} = s$ and its inverse $s \to \dfrac{s}{1 - |s|} = t$, which establish a homeomorphism between $R$ and $(-1, 1)$, to convert the problem back to the case considered in (c).

8. As a corollary of the result in Problem 7, prove the following: Let $A$, $B$ be disjoint nonempty closed sets in the metric space $T$. Then there exists $f \in C(T)$, with the range of $f$ in $[0, 1]$ and $f(t) = 1$ if $t \in A$, $f(t) = 0$ if $t \in B$. This is a special case of "Urysohn's lemma"; in the general form of the lemma, $T$ is any normal topological space.

## SUGGESTED READING FOR CHAPTER 3

In reference to Sections 3–0 to 3–11:

BOURBAKI [2], Chapters 1, 2, 9, 10.
DIEUDONNÉ [1], Chapter 3.
DUNFORD and SCHWARTZ [1], Chapter 1B.
GOFFMAN [1], Chapters 4, 5, 7, 8.
GRAVES [1], Chapter 14.
HAHN [1], Chapters 2, 3.
HALL and SPENCER [1], Chapters 3, 4.
HAUSDORFF [1], Chapter 6.
HOCKING and YOUNG [1], Chapters 1, 2.
KELLEY [1], parts of all chapters.
KURATOWSKI [1], Chapters 1, 2, 3.
MCSHANE [3].
MCSHANE and BOTTS [1], Chapters 2, 3.
MUNROE [1], Chapter 1.
NATANSON [1], Vol. 2, Chapter 14.
TAYLOR [2], Chapter 2.

In reference to Sections 3–12 to 3–15:

BANACH [1], Chapters 2, 3, 4, 5.
BECKENBACH and BELLMAN [1], parts of Chapter 1.
BERBERIAN [1], Chapters 1, 2, parts of Chapters 3, 4, 5.
DAY [1], Chapters 1, 2, 4, 5.
DIEUDONNÉ [1], Chapters 5, 6, 7.
HALMOS [2], Chapters 1, 3, 4.
HARDY, LITTLEWOOD, and PÓLYA [1], Chapters 1, 2.
STONE [1], [3].
TAYLOR [2], parts of Chapters 1, 3.

CHAPTER FOUR

# The Theory of Measure

## 4–0 Introduction

The theory of measure began to develop in a period when the attention of mathematicians was being drawn to the importance of examining very general sorts of point-sets in Euclidean space. It was necessary to seek, for arbitrary point-sets on the real line, something which specialized to *length* when the point-set was an interval; likewise, for point-sets in the plane, it was desired to assign a "measure" to the set in such a way that the measure was *area* in the special case of rectangular domains. The connection between measure of planar sets and integrals of real functions of one real variable appears already with a certain degree of generality in the conception of the integral of a positive continuous function as a measure of the area between the axis of abscissas and the graph of the function (the area limited laterally by two ordinate lines). The classical theory of measure and integration, developed along the lines laid out by Lebesgue, stayed mainly in the realms of sets in Euclidean space and real functions defined in Euclidean space. But generalizations and abstractions have appeared as part of the theory from a rather early stage; today, in this part of analysis as in algebra, abstract axiomatic method appears to be the necessary and reasonable way of developing the theory of measure so that its essential structure can be perceived and so that its applicability can, from the beginning, be relieved of the limitation to Euclidean space.

In this chapter we present the theory of measure in a general setting, giving the definitions and the theorems in forms which have very broad applicability. For the student whose primary need is to learn enough measure theory to use it in the study of integration, and who wants to understand all of this mainly or wholly in the context of classical Lebesgue measure in Euclidean spaces, the appropriate thing is to study the present chapter merely through Section 4–8, and then go to Chapter 5.

In a purely logical sense the basic theory in Chapter 5 depends merely on Section 4–1 through Section 4–4. That is, a measure function on a $\sigma$-ring of sets, no matter how obtained, provides us the means for constructing a theory of summable functions and their integrals. But it is somehow comforting to have a specific and concrete example of the abstract theory of measure and integration. The classical and very important example is that which stems from Lebesgue measure in Euclidean space. We follow Caratheodory's method of basing the theory of Lebesgue measure on a general procedure of passing from an outer measure to a measure. This general procedure is discussed in Section 4–7. The specific aspects of Lebesgue outer measure and Lebesgue measure in $R^k$ are discussed in Section 4–5, Section 4–6, and Section 4–8.

There are outer measures and measures more general than those of the classical Lebesgue theory in $R^k$. Some of these generalizations are discussed in Sections 4–9, 4–10.

A wholly different approach to the theory of integration is discussed in Chapter 6. In this alternative approach measure theory is consequent to, instead of antecedent to, integration theory.

## 4–1 Algebraic operations in $R^*$

In this chapter we shall be dealing with functions whose ranges lie in the extended real number system $R^*$. This system was defined in Section 1–7. We recall that $R^*$ is composed of the elements of $R$ and the two elements $-\infty$, $+\infty$, and that $R^*$ is totally ordered by the relation $<$. In Example 1, Section 3–5, we showed how to define a topology for $R^*$ in such a way that $R^*$ is a compact space with $R$ as a dense set in $R^*$. We can regard the topology of $R^*$ as coming from a metric. Two equivalent metrices for $R^*$ are indicated in Section 3–6 (Example 2 and Problem 4). The second of these two metrics is the one most frequently used. It is defined by

$$D(x, y) = |f(x) - f(y)|, \qquad x, y \in R^*, \tag{1}$$

where

$$\begin{cases} f(x) = \dfrac{x}{1 + |x|} & \text{if } x \in R \\ f(+\infty) = 1, & f(-\infty) = -1. \end{cases} \tag{2}$$

If we are dealing with a function $f: X \to R^*$, where $X$ is a set of some kind, we sometimes use inequalities to indicate that particular values of $f$ are in $R$ (that is, not $\pm\infty$). Thus, $f(x) < +\infty$ indicates that $f(x) \neq +\infty$, and $-\infty < f(x) < +\infty$ indicates that $f(x) \in R$.

We can extend the definition of absolute value so that $x \to |x|$ is a function on $R^*$ to $R^*$. We simply add the definitions $|+\infty| = +\infty$, $|-\infty| = +\infty$. Then, if we have $f: X \to R^*$, $|f(x)| < +\infty$ indicates that $f(x) \in R$. An element of $R^*$ which is in $R$ is called "finite".

### ADDITION AND SUBTRACTION IN $R^*$

To extend the definitions already in force in $R$ we make the following definitions:

$$a + (+\infty) = (+\infty) + a = +\infty \quad \text{if } a \in R, \tag{3}$$

$$a + (-\infty) = (-\infty) + a = -\infty \quad \text{if } a \in R, \tag{4}$$

$$(+\infty) + (+\infty) = +\infty, \tag{5}$$

$$(-\infty) + (-\infty) = -\infty, \tag{6}$$

$$(+\infty) + (-\infty) = (-\infty) + (+\infty) = 0. \tag{7}$$

Addition in $R^*$ is commutative. *It is not always associative, however*. The reason for non-associativity lies with the definition (7), for it is always true that $(a + b) + c = a + (b + c)$ in $R^*$ if no addition of $+\infty$ and $-\infty$ occurs. But note that $[(-\infty) + (+\infty)] + (+\infty) = +\infty$, $(-\infty) + [(+\infty) + (+\infty)] = 0$. On this account, and for other reasons, some authors prefer not to make the definition (7), leaving $a + b$ undefined if $a = +\infty, b = -\infty$, or vice versa. For certain purposes in the theory of integration it is nevertheless convenient to have the definition (7), and we shall retain it.

For elements in $R^*$ we define $a - b = a + (-b)$, where $-(+\infty) = -\infty, -(-\infty) = +\infty$. Then $a + (-a) = 0$, but it is not true in general that the equation $x + b = a$ has the unique solution $x = a - b$. For instance, there is no solution of $x + (+\infty) = -\infty$ or $x + (-\infty) = 3$, and any $x$ except $-\infty$ satisfies $x + (+\infty) = +\infty$. Thus $R^*$ is by no means a group with respect to addition.

The inequality $|a + b| \leq |a| + |b|$ remains true in $R^*$. It is also true that

(8) $$|a - c| \leq |a - b| + |b - c|,$$

even though it can happen that $a - c \neq (a - b) + (b - c)$. (Try $a = +\infty$, $b = -\infty$, $c = 0$, for example.)

## MULTIPLICATION AND DIVISION IN $R^*$

We make the following definitions:

(9) $$a(+\infty) = (+\infty)a = +\infty \quad \text{if} \quad 0 < a \leq +\infty,$$

(10) $$a(-\infty) = (-\infty)a = -\infty \quad \text{if} \quad 0 < a \leq +\infty,$$

(11) $$a(+\infty) = (+\infty)a = -\infty \quad \text{if} \quad -\infty \leq a < 0,$$

(12) $$a(-\infty) = (-\infty)a = +\infty \quad \text{if} \quad -\infty \leq a < 0.$$

(13) $$0(\pm\infty) = (\pm\infty)0 = 0.$$

Multiplication is commutative and associative, and $ab = 0$ implies $a = 0$ or $b = 0$. Some authors refrain from making the definition (13), but it is useful in the theory of integration.

The only extensions we make of the definition of division are the following:

(14) $$\frac{a}{\pm\infty} = 0 \quad \text{if} \quad a \in R,$$

(15) $$\frac{\pm\infty}{a} = \left(\frac{1}{a}\right)(\pm\infty) \quad \text{if} \quad 0 < |a| < +\infty.$$

We leave $a/b$ undefined if $b = 0$ or if $|a| = |b| = +\infty$.

The relation $|ab| = |a|\,|b|$ is always true in $R^*$.

## CONTINUITY OF ADDITION AND MULTIPLICATION

The function $(x, y) \to x + y$ is continuous except at $(+\infty, -\infty)$ and $(-\infty, +\infty)$, but discontinuous at these two points. Likewise, the function $(x, y) \to xy$ is continuous except at $(0, \pm\infty)$ and $(\pm\infty, 0)$.

## SUMS AND INFINITE SERIES IN $R^*$

Let $\{a_n\}$ be a sequence in $R^*$ such that either, for every $n$, $a_n \neq -\infty$, or, for every $n$, $a_n \neq +\infty$. In forming sums with the $a_n$'s we have associativity of addition in this case, and so

$$s_n = a_1 + \cdots + a_n$$

is a well defined element of $R^*$. It is finite if and only if each of the terms $a_1, \ldots, a_n$ is finite. If the sequence $\{s_n\}$ has a limit in the topological space $R^*$, we denote this limit by

$$\sum_{i=1}^{\infty} a_i$$

The case in which $0 \leq a_n$ for each $n$ is particularly important in practice. In this case $s_n \leq s_{n+1}$, and the sequence $\{s_n\}$ certainly has a limit in $R^*$. The limit is $+\infty$ if either some $a_i$ is $+\infty$ or each $a_i$ is finite but $s_n \to +\infty$. The limit is finite if and only if each $a_i$ is finite and $\{s_n\}$ is bounded as a sequence in $R$. We can write

$$\sum_{i=1}^{\infty} a_i < +\infty \tag{16}$$

in this case. This inequality then expresses the fact that the series in (16) is convergent in the usual sense of the word for infinite series of real numbers.

### PROBLEMS

1. Consider associativity of addition in $R^*$ by examining the 27 cases in which each of $a, b, c$, can be $+\infty$, $-\infty$, or in $R$. If definition (7) is rejected, there are only 15 cases left to consider, and addition is associative in these cases. It is also associative in some but not all of the other 12 cases. For instance, $[(+\infty) + x] + (-\infty) = (+\infty) + [x + (-\infty)] = 0$ if $x \in R$, but $[3 + (-\infty)] + (+\infty) = 0$, while $3 + [-\infty + (+\infty)] = 3$.
2. Discuss the continuity of addition and multiplication in $R^*$. Give examples to illustrate the discontinuities at the exceptional points mentioned in the text.
3. Suppose $a, b, c$ are in $R^*$ and that $a \leq b$. Show that $a + c \leq b + c$.
4. Show that $a < b$ is equivalent to $0 < b - a$ and that $a \leq b$ is equivalent to $0 \leq b - a$.
5. Show that $(a - b) + b = a$ and $(a + b) - b = a$ if $b$ is finite.

## 4–2 Rings and σ-Rings

Throughout this section $X$ denotes an arbitrary nonempty class with elements $x, y, \ldots$. We consider sets $E, F, \ldots$ which are subsets of $X$.

### RINGS OF SETS

A nonempty class **S** of subsets of $X$ is called a *ring* if $E \cup F$ and $E - F$ belong to **S** whenever $E$ and $F$ do. Since $E - E = \varnothing$, we see that $\varnothing \in$ **S**. If **S** is a ring and $E, F \in$ **S**, then $E \cap F \in$ **S** also, for if $G = E \cup F$, we have

$$E \cap F = G - \{(E - F) \cup (F - E)\}. \tag{1}$$

Observe that (1) can be written $E \cap F = G - (E \,\Delta F)$. See Figure 1 in Section 1–2.

*Example 1.* The class **S** of all subsets of $X$ is a ring.

*Example 2.* Let $\mathscr{F}$ be a nonempty family of subsets of $X$. Let **S** be the class of all sets $E$, each of which is a subset of some finite union $F_1 \cup \cdots \cup F_n$, where each $F_i$ is in $\mathscr{F}$. Then **S** is a ring.

The following observation indicates a useful way of representing certain unions of sets as unions of other sets which are disjoint. Suppose that certain sets $E_1, E_2, \ldots$ are given. The

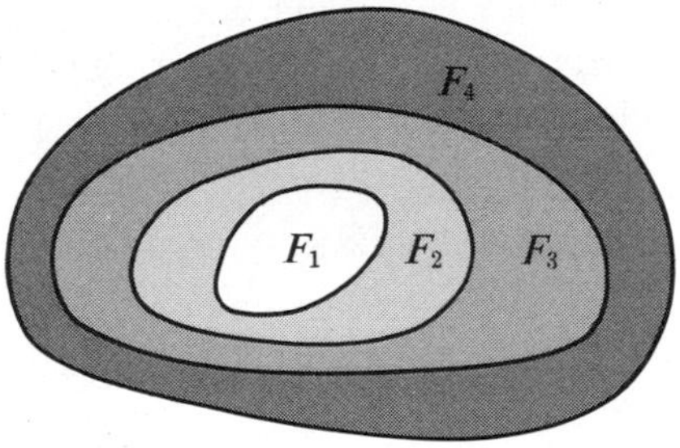


FIGURE 32

number may be finite or countably infinite. Define sets $F_1, F_2, \ldots$ recursively as follows:

(2)
$$\begin{cases} F_1 = E_1 \\ F_{k+1} = E_{k+1} - (E_1 \cup \cdots \cup E_k) \qquad \text{if} \quad k \geq 1. \end{cases}$$

Then $F_n \subset E_n$ for each $n$, and

(3)
$$\bigcup_{k=1}^{n} F_k = \bigcup_{k=1}^{n} E_k.$$

If we write $G_n = E_1 \cup \cdots \cup E_n$, then $G_1 = E_1$, $F_{k+1} = G_{k+1} - G_k$ if $k \geq 1$, and (3) can be written

$$\bigcup_{k=1}^{n} F_k = G_n.$$

The situation is shown schematically in Figure 32, where $G_n$ is represented as being composed of a "core" ($G_1 = F_1 = E_1$) and a number of disjoint "layers" $F_2, \ldots, F_n$.

We observe that if the $E_i$'s belong to a ring $\mathbf{S}$, then so do the $F_i$'s and $G_i$'s.

## σ-RINGS

A ring $\mathbf{S}$ such that $\bigcup_n E_n \in \mathbf{S}$ whenever $E_n \in \mathbf{S}$ for each $n$ ($n = 1, 2, \ldots$) is called a σ-ring.

*Example 3.* The class of all bounded subsets of the Euclidean space $R^k$ is a ring but not a σ-ring.

*Example 4.* Let $\mathbf{S}$ be the class of all countable subsets of $R$. Then $\mathbf{S}$ is a σ-ring.

A σ-ring contains the intersection of any countable collection of its members. This is true because, if $E = \bigcup_n E_n$, we have

(4)
$$\bigcap_n E_n = E - \bigcup_n (E - E_n).$$

## RINGS GENERATED BY A CLASS OF SETS

Let $\mathscr{E}$ be a nonempty collection of subsets of $X$. There certainly exists a ring which contains all the members of $\mathscr{E}$, namely, the ring of all subsets of $X$. If we consider all rings $\mathbf{S}$ (composed of subsets of $X$) such that $\mathscr{E} \subset \mathbf{S}$, we see that the collection of sets which is the intersection of all such rings $\mathbf{S}$ is itself a ring which contains all the members of $\mathscr{E}$. We call it *the ring generated* by $\mathscr{E}$. Similarly, we can define the $\sigma$-ring generated by $\mathscr{E}$; it is the intersection of all the $\sigma$-rings which contain $\mathscr{E}$. For convenience we shall denote by $\sigma(\mathscr{E})$ the $\sigma$-ring generated by $\mathscr{E}$.

*Example 5.* Let $X$ be an infinite set and let $\mathscr{E}$ be the family of all sets consisting of exactly one point. Then $\sigma(\mathscr{E})$ will certainly include every countable subset of $X$. Hence, since the class of all countable subsets of $X$ is a $\sigma$-ring, it must coincide with $\sigma(\mathscr{E})$.

## ALGEBRAS

In the definition of a ring it is not required that the entire set $X$ be a member of the ring. A ring $\mathbf{S}$ of subsets of $X$ is called an *algebra* if $X \in \mathbf{S}$. If intersection is considered as a kind of multiplication in the ring $\mathbf{S}$ ($E \cap F$ the "product" of $E$ and $F$), then $X$ plays the role of a unit element, because $E \cap X = E$ for every $E$. When $X$ is in the ring $\mathbf{S}$, the complement of each element of $\mathbf{S}$ belongs to $\mathbf{S}$, because $E^{\sim} = X - E$.

It is easy to see that a nonempty family of subsets of $X$ is an algebra if and only if $E \cup F$ and $E^{\sim}$ are in $\mathbf{S}$ whenever $E$ and $F$ are in $\mathbf{S}$. See Problem 2.

An algebra which is a $\sigma$-ring is called a $\sigma$-algebra.

*Example 6.* Let $X$ be the set of all positive integers, and let $\mathbf{S}$ be the class of subsets $E$ of $X$ such that one of the sets $E$, $E^{\sim}$ is finite. Then $\mathbf{S}$ is an algebra, but not a $\sigma$-algebra.

The $\sigma$-ring of Example 4 is not an algebra, because $X$ $(=R)$ is not countable.

*Example 7.* Here is an interesting case of a ring which is neither an algebra nor a $\sigma$-ring: Let $X = R$ and let $\mathscr{A}$ be the family of subsets of $R$ of the form $\{x : a \leq x < b\}$, where $a, b \in R$ and $a < b$. We denote this set by $[a, b)$. We call such a set a finite interval which is left-closed and right-open. Let $\mathbf{S}$ consist of $\varnothing$ and the collection of all finite unions of members of $\mathscr{A}$. It is evident that $\mathbf{S}$ contains the union of any two of its members. We leave it to the reader to show that $\mathbf{S}$ contains the difference of any two of its members. One may begin by considering $A - B$ when $A, B \in \mathscr{A}$.

In some later consideration of this example we shall find it useful to take note of the following fact: If $A, B \in \mathscr{A}$ and $A \cap B \neq \varnothing$, then $A \cup B \in \mathscr{A}$. As a consequence, each member of $\mathbf{S}$ except $\varnothing$ can be expressed as a finite union of disjoint members of $\mathscr{A}$.

## THE BOREL SETS IN $R^k$

Let $X = R^k$ be the basic set, and let $\mathbf{S}$ be the $\sigma$-ring generated by the family of all the compact sets in $X$. The elements of $\mathbf{S}$ are called *Borel sets*. It is not difficult to see that $X \in \mathbf{S}$, so that $\mathbf{S}$ is a $\sigma$-algebra. It is also not difficult to see that $\mathbf{S}$ is the same as the $\sigma$-ring generated by the open sets in $R^k$. We leave this to the reader.

The Borel sets play an important role in the theory of Lebesgue measure, as we shall see later on in this chapter.

The notion of a Borel set is used in other spaces besides $R^k$. Many authors define the Borel sets as the members of the $\sigma$-algebra generated by the closed sets. Halmos ([1], p. 219), however, defines the Borel sets of a locally compact Hausdorff space as the members of the $\sigma$-ring generated by the compact sets. These definitions are equivalent when applied to $R^k$.

## MONOTONE FAMILIES

A nonempty family $\mathbf{M}$ of sets is said to be *monotone* if $E_n \in \mathbf{M}$ and $E_n \subset E_{n+1}$ for $n = 1, 2, \ldots$ imply $\bigcup_n E_n \in \mathbf{M}$ and if $E_n \in \mathbf{M}$ and $E_{n+1} \subset E_n$ for $n = 1, 2, \ldots$ imply $\bigcap_n E_n \in \mathbf{M}$. Later on in the text we shall have use for the concept of the monotone family generated by a given class of sets. The class of all subsets of $X$ is a monotone family, and the intersection of any collection of monotone families is a monotone family. Hence, given a nonempty family $\mathscr{E}$ of subsets of $X$, we may define the monotone family generated by $\mathscr{E}$ to be the intersection of all monotone families which contain $\mathscr{E}$.

The following theorem is needed in connection with Theorem 7–5 III.

THEOREM 4–2 I. *Let $\mathscr{E}$ be a ring. Then the monotone family generated by $\mathscr{E}$ is the same as the σ-ring generated by $\mathscr{E}$.*

*Proof.* A σ-ring is certainly a monotone family. Hence the σ-ring $\sigma(\mathscr{E})$ generated by $\mathscr{E}$ contains the monotone family $\mathbf{M}$ generated by $\mathscr{E}$. If we can prove that $\mathbf{M}$ is a σ-ring, it will follow that $\sigma(\mathscr{E}) \subset \mathbf{M}$ and hence that $\mathbf{M} = \sigma(\mathscr{E})$. The tricky part of the proof lies in showing that $\mathbf{M}$ is a ring. Once that is known, we can easily show that $\mathbf{M}$ is a σ-ring. For if $E_n \in \mathbf{M}$ and $\mathbf{M}$ is a ring, let $F_n = \bigcup_{i=1}^{n} E_i$. Then $F_n \subset F_{n+1}$, so that $\bigcup_n F_n \in \mathbf{M}$. But then $\bigcup_n E_n \in \mathbf{M}$, for $\bigcup_n E_n = \bigcup_n F_n$.

Now, for any subset $B$ of $X$ let $\mathbf{M}(B)$ be the class of all subsets $A$ of $X$ such that $A - B$, $B - A$, and $A \cup B$ are in $\mathbf{M}$. If $\mathbf{M}(B)$ is not empty it is a monotone family; we leave verification of this as an exercise for the reader. Now suppose that $A$ and $B$ are in the ring $\mathscr{E}$. Then $A - B$, $B - A$ and $A \cup B$ are in $\mathscr{E}$, and hence in $\mathbf{M}$, so that $A \in \mathbf{M}(B)$. Therefore $\mathscr{E} \subset \mathbf{M}(B)$, whence $\mathbf{M} \subset \mathbf{M}(B)$. Now suppose that $A \in \mathbf{M}$ and $B \in \mathscr{E}$. Then $A \in \mathbf{M}(B)$. By the symmetry of the original definition of $\mathbf{M}(B)$ we now see that we also have $B \in \mathbf{M}(A)$, and thus that $\mathscr{E} \subset \mathbf{M}(A)$ and $\mathbf{M} \subset \mathbf{M}(A)$ for each $A$ in $\mathbf{M}$. From this and the definition of $\mathbf{M}(A)$ we conclude that $\mathbf{M}$ is a ring. The proof of the theorem is thereby completed.

For the proof in Step 6 of Theorem 7–5 III we shall also need the following proposition.

THEOREM 4–2 II. *Let $\mathscr{E}$ be a nonempty collection of subsets of $X$. Let $F_0$ be a fixed subset of $X$, and let $\mathscr{E}_0$ be the collection of all sets $E \cap F_0$, where $E \in \mathscr{E}$. Then $\sigma(\mathscr{E}_0)$ is composed of all sets $A \cap F_0$, where $A \in \sigma(\mathscr{E})$.*

*Proof.* Let $\mathbf{S} = \{A \cap F_0 : A \in \sigma(\mathscr{E})\}$. Clearly $\mathscr{E}_0 \subset \mathbf{S}$. Since it is easily seen that $\mathbf{S}$ is a σ-ring, we see that $\sigma(\mathscr{E}_0) \subset \mathbf{S}$. Hence, in particular, every element of $\sigma(\mathscr{E}_0)$ is contained in $F_0$.

It remains to prove that $\mathbf{S} \subset \sigma(\mathscr{E}_0)$. For this purpose let $\mathbf{T}$ be the class of all sets of the form $B \cup (A - F_0)$, where $B \in \sigma(\mathscr{E}_0)$ and $A \in \sigma(\mathscr{E})$. We shall show that $\mathbf{T}$ is a σ-ring. Once this has been done the rest will be easy. In what follows let $B_1, B_2, \ldots$ and $A_1, A_2, \ldots$ denote elements of $\sigma(\mathscr{E}_0)$ and $\sigma(\mathscr{E})$, respectively. Now

$$\bigcup_n [B_n \cup (A_n - F_0)] = \left[\bigcup_n B_n\right] \cup \left[\left(\bigcup_n A_n\right) - F_0\right],$$

and so **T** is closed under countable unions. A straightforward calculation shows that

$$[B_1 \cup (A_1 - F_0)] - [B_2 \cup (A_2 - F_0)]$$
$$= (B_1 - B_2 - A_2) \cup [(B_1 - B_2) \cap F_0] \cup [A_1 \cap A_2^{\sim} \cap B_2^{\sim} \cap F_0^{\sim}].$$

This expression can be simplified. Since elements of $\sigma(\mathscr{E}_0)$ are contained in $F_0$, we can write

$$(B_1 - B_2 - A_2) \cup [(B_1 - B_2) \cap F_0] = B_1 - B_2.$$

Moreover, $B_2 \subset F_0$, whence $B_2^{\sim} \cap F_0^{\sim} = F_0^{\sim}$, and so

$$A_1 \cap A_2^{\sim} \cap B_2^{\sim} \cap F_0^{\sim} = (A_1 - A_2) - F_0.$$

Therefore,

$$[B_1 \cup (A_1 - F_0)] - [B_2 \cup (A_2 - F_0)] = (B_1 - B_2) \cup [(A_1 - A_2) - F_0],$$

and this finishes the proof that **T** is a $\sigma$-ring.

If $E \in \mathscr{E}$, then $E \in \sigma(\mathscr{E})$ and $E \cap F_0 \in \sigma(\mathscr{E}_0)$, so that $E = (E \cap F_0) \cup (E - F_0) \in \mathbf{T}$. Therefore $\mathscr{E} \subset \mathbf{T}$, whence $\sigma(\mathscr{E}) \subset \mathbf{T}$, and so **S** is contained in the set of elements of the form $C \cap F_0$, where $C \in T$. But, for a typical element of **T** we have

$$[B \cup (A - F_0)] \cap F_0 = B \cap F_0 = B.$$

Thus, the set of elements of the form $C \cap F_0$, where $C \in \mathbf{T}$, is precisely $\sigma(\mathscr{E}_0)$. Therefore $\mathbf{S} \subset \sigma(\mathscr{E}_0)$.

### PROBLEMS

1. In connection with Example, 7 prove that $A, B \in \mathscr{A}$ implies $A - B \in \mathbf{S}$.

2. Express $E - F$ in terms of $E$ and $F$, using only unions and complements. Hence show that **S** is an algebra if $\mathbf{S} \neq \varnothing$ and if $E, F \in \mathbf{S}$ implies $E \cup F \in \mathbf{S}$ and $E^{\sim} \in \mathbf{S}$.

3. Prove that in $R^k$ the $\sigma$-ring generated by all the open sets is the same as the $\sigma$-ring of all Borel sets. Use the fact that for the topology of $R^k$ there is a countable basis of neighborhoods, each of which is an open box, as defined in Section 2–3.

4. Prove that in any topological space $X$ the $\sigma$-ring generated by the open sets is the same as the $\sigma$-ring generated by the closed sets.

5. Show that, if $X$ is a topological space, the collection of all sets of the first category in $X$ is a $\sigma$-ring.

6. Let $X$ be a Hausdorff space in which each open set is a countable union of compact sets. Is $R^k$ a space of this kind? Show that in $X$ the $\sigma$-ring generated by the open sets is the same as the $\sigma$-ring generated by the compact sets.

7. Let $X$ be a locally compact Hausdorff space. Let $\mathscr{E}$ be the class of compact sets $E$ in $X$, let $\mathscr{U}$ be the class of open sets $U$ which belong to $\sigma(\mathscr{E})$, and let $\mathscr{B}$ be the class of open sets $B$ such that $\bar{B}$ is compact. Show that $\sigma(\mathscr{E}) = \sigma(\mathscr{U}) = \sigma(\mathscr{B})$. [*Suggestion.* Show that $\sigma(\mathscr{U}) \subset \sigma(\mathscr{E}) \subset \sigma(\mathscr{B}) \subset \sigma(\mathscr{U})$. The local compactness enables an element $E$ of $\mathscr{E}$ to be expressed in the form $B - (B - E)$. Any open set $A$ can be expressed as $\bar{A} - \beta(A)$.]

8. In the preceding problem, show that $X \in \sigma(\mathscr{E})$ if and only if $X$ is a countable union of compact sets. More generally, show that if $A \in \sigma(\mathscr{E})$ then $A$ is contained in a countable union of compact sets. [*Suggestion.* Observe that the class of all subsets of arbitrary countable unions of compact sets is a $\sigma$-ring.]

9. In the case of an arbitrary nonempty family $\mathscr{E}$ of subsets of $X$, show that each element of $\sigma(\mathscr{E})$ is contained in a countable union of members of $\mathscr{E}$.

10. Verify the assertion, made in the proof of Theorem 4–2 I, that $\mathbf{M}(B)$ is a monotone family if it is not empty.

## 4-3 Additive set functions

We consider functions $\varphi : \mathbf{S} \to R^*$, where $\mathbf{S}$ is a nonempty class of subsets of a nonempty class $X$. Such a function is called *additive* if the range of $\varphi$ does not contain both $-\infty$ and $+\infty$ and if

$$\varphi(E_1 \cup E_2) = \varphi(E_1) + \varphi(E_2) \tag{1}$$

whenever $E_1$ and $E_2$ are members of $\mathbf{S}$ such that $E_1 \cup E_2 \in \mathbf{S}$ and $E_1 \cap E_2 = \varnothing$.

We shall be interested mainly in the case when $\mathbf{S}$ is a ring. In this case we can prove by induction that the additive function $\varphi$ is *finitely additive* in the following sense: If $E_1, \ldots, E_n$ are disjoint members of $\mathbf{S}$, then

$$\varphi\left(\bigcup_{i=1}^{n} E_i\right) = \sum_{i=1}^{n} \varphi(E_i). \tag{2}$$

The sum on the right in (2) is unambiguously defined because of the restriction that the range of $\varphi$ does not contain both $-\infty$ and $+\infty$ (see the discussion in Section 4–1).

If $\varphi$ is an additive function on the ring $\mathbf{S}$, it can be proved that $\varphi(\varnothing) = 0$, provided that $\varphi(E)$ is finite for at least one $E$. For $E \cup \varnothing = E$, whence $\varphi(E) + \varphi(\varnothing) = \varphi(E)$. The fact that $\varphi(E)$ is finite implies that $\varphi(\varnothing)$ is finite, and then we can deduce that $\varphi(\varnothing) = 0$.

If $\varphi$ is additive on the ring $\mathbf{S}$, if $E, F \in \mathbf{S}$, with $F \subset E$ and $\varphi(F)$ finite, we can prove that

$$\varphi(E - F) = \varphi(E) - \varphi(F). \tag{3}$$

We say that this is the *subtractive* property of $\varphi$. To prove (3) we write $E = (E - F) \cup F$, apply (1), and make use of the fact that $\varphi(F)$ is finite.

A function $\varphi : \mathbf{S} \to R^*$ is called *monotone* if $\varphi(E) \leq \varphi(F)$ when $E, F \in \mathbf{S}$ and $E \subset F$. If $\mathbf{S}$ is a ring and if $\varphi$ is additive and has nonnegative values, it is monotone. For, given $E, F$ as indicated, we can write $F = E \cup (F - E)$, $\varphi(F) = \varphi(E) + \varphi(F - E)$. Since $\varphi(F - E) \geq 0$, it follows that $\varphi(F) \geq \varphi(E)$.

*Example 1.* Let $\mathscr{A}$ be the class of finite, left-closed and right-open intervals $[a, b)$ in $R$. If $E = [a, b)$, let $\varphi(E) = b - a$. Then $\varphi$ is additive, but $\mathscr{A}$ is not a ring.

*Example 2.* Let $\mathbf{S}$ consist of $\varnothing$ and the class of all finite unions of elements of $\mathscr{A}$, where $\mathscr{A}$ is defined in Example 1. Then $\mathbf{S}$ is a ring (see Example 7, Section 4–2), and it can be shown that if $E \in \mathbf{S}$ is represented as a finite union of disjoint elements of $\mathscr{A}$, say $E = \bigcup_{i=1}^{n} A_i$, with the length of $A_i$ represented by $|A_i|$, then $\sum_{i=1}^{n} |A_i|$ depends only on $E$ and not on the particular representation of $E$. Hence we may define

$$\varphi(E) = \sum_{i=1}^{n} |A_i| . \tag{4}$$

This function $\varphi$ is additive on $\mathbf{S}$.

It can be proved that $\varphi$ is countably additive in the sense defined in the following paragraph. But this fact will emerge later as a particular consequence of the theory of Lebesgue measure, so we shall not stop over it now.

## COUNTABLE ADDITIVITY

Let **S** be a nonempty class of sets and let the range of $\varphi : \mathbf{S} \to R^*$ contain at most one of the values $-\infty$, $+\infty$. We call $\varphi$ *countably additive* if, whenever $E_1, E_2, \ldots$ and $\bigcup_n E_n$ are in **S** and the $E_n$'s are disjoint, then $\lim_{n\to\infty} \sum_{i=1}^{n} \varphi(E_i)$ exists in $R^*$, and

$$\varphi\left(\bigcup_n E_n\right) = \sum_{n=1}^{\infty} \varphi(E_n). \tag{5}$$

If **S** is a ring and $\varphi(\varnothing) = 0$, we may take all but a finite number of the $E_n$'s to be $\varnothing$, and in this way see that under these conditions $\varphi$ is also finitely additive.

## MEASURES

We shall mainly be interested in cases when $\varphi(E) \geq 0$ for every $E \in \mathbf{S}$. If **S** is a ring and if $\varphi : \mathbf{S} \to R^*$ is countably additive, has nonnegative values, and if $\varphi(\varnothing) = 0$, we call $\varphi$ a *measure* on $S$. The value $\varphi(E)$ is called the measure of $E$ (for this particular measure). In most of the work on measure theory in this book, the measures will be defined on $\sigma$-rings. In the classical theory of Lebesgue measure and some of its important generalizations, we study measures on $\sigma$-rings of sets in $R^k$, and one of the important features of the theory is that the $\sigma$-rings always contain all the Borel sets.

*Example 3.* Let $X$ be $R$, and let **S** be the $\sigma$-algebra of all subsets of $R$. Define $\varphi : \mathbf{S} \to R$ as follows: $\varphi(E) = 1$ if $0 \in E$, $\varphi(E) = 0$ if $0 \notin E$. Then $\varphi$ is a measure on **S**. We could modify this example by taking **S** to be the class of all subsets of an arbitrary nonempty set $X$, choosing a fixed element $x_0$ of $X$, and defining $\varphi(E)$ to be 1 or 0 according as $x_0 \in E$ or $x_0 \notin E$.

*Example 4.* Let $X$ be the class of positive integers, and let **S** be the class of all subsets of $X$. If $E \in \mathbf{S}$, define $\varphi(E) = n$ if $E$ is a finite set with $n$ elements, and $\varphi(E) = +\infty$ if $E$ is an infinite set. Then $\varphi$ is a measure.

*Example 5.* Let $X$ and **S** be as in Example 4, but define $\varphi : S \to R^*$ as follows: $\varphi(\varnothing) = 0$, $\varphi(E) = +\infty$ if $E$ is an infinite set, and

$$\varphi(E) = \sum_{n \in E} \frac{1}{n^2}$$

if $E$ is a nonempty finite set. Then $\varphi$ is additive, but it is not a measure, because it is not countably additive.

*Example 6.* Let $X$ be an infinite set, **S** the class of all subsets of $X$, and $\{x_n\}$ a sequence of distinct elements of $X$. Let $\{a_n\}$ be a sequence of positive real numbers. Define $\psi_n(E) = 1$ if $x_n \in E$, $\psi_n(E) = 0$ if $x_n \notin E$. Then define $\varphi : \mathbf{S} \to R^*$ by

$$\varphi(E) = \sum_{n=1}^{\infty} a_n \psi_n(E).$$

The function $\varphi$ is a measure. The situation in Example 4 is a special case, with $x_n = n$, $a_n = 1$.

*Example 7.* Let $X$ be any nonempty set, $\mathbf{S}$ the ring of all finite subsets of $X$, and let $f: X \to R^*$ be a function whose range does not contain $-\infty$. Define $\varphi(\varnothing) = 0$, and if $E$ is the finite set with distinct elements $x_1, \ldots, x_n$, define

$$\varphi(E) = f(x_1) + \cdots + f(x_n).$$

Then $\varphi$ is additive. If $X$ is an infinite set, $\mathbf{S}$ is not a $\sigma$-ring, but $\varphi$ is countably additive.

## FINITE AND $\sigma$-FINITE MEASURES

Let $\varphi$ be a measure on a ring $\mathbf{S}$. If $\varphi(E)$ is finite for each $E$ in $\mathbf{S}$, we say that $\varphi$ is *a finite measure*.

In the theory of Lebesgue measure in $R^k$ we shall find that we have to deal with some measures which are not finite. In these cases, however, it turns out that $\varphi(E)$ is finite when $E$ is compact, and since any set in $R^k$ is contained in some countable union of compact sets, these measures all have a property called $\sigma$-finiteness which can be defined without reference to compactness or other topological notions. A measure $\varphi$ on a ring $\mathbf{S}$ is called *$\sigma$-finite* if each $E$ in $\mathbf{S}$ is contained in some countable union:

$$E \subset \bigcup_n E_n,$$

where $E_n \in \mathbf{S}$ and $\varphi(E_n)$ is finite. Since $E \cap E_n \in \mathbf{S}$ and $\varphi(E \cap E_n)$ is also finite (because $\varphi$ is monotone), we see from the fact that

$$E = \bigcup_n (E \cap E_n)$$

that $\varphi$ is $\sigma$-finite if and only if each element of $\mathbf{S}$ is expressible as a countable union of members of $\mathbf{S}$, each having finite measure. We can even arrange to express $E$ in the form

$$E = \bigcup_n F_n$$

where $F_n \in \mathbf{S}$, $\varphi(F_n)$ is finite, and the $F_n$'s are disjoint. We simply use the scheme explained in connection with (2) and Figure 32 in Section 4–2.

## COMPLETE MEASURES

In a number of important instances (including the classical theory of Lebesgue measure) it turns out that we encounter measures $\varphi$ such that $\varphi(E) = 0$ for certain nonempty sets $E$. Now, the ring $\mathbf{S}$ on which $\varphi$ is defined does not always contain all subsets of the basic set $X$, and it can happen that a set $E$ in $\mathbf{S}$, for which $\varphi(E) = 0$, contains certain subsets $F$ which do not belong to $\mathbf{S}$. If this phenomenon does not occur, the consequences are of sufficient interest to justify a name for this property of the measure. We say that $\varphi$ is a *complete* measure if $F \in \mathbf{S}$ whenever $E \in \mathbf{S}$, $\varphi(E) = 0$, and $F \subset E$. If $\varphi$ is not complete, it is possible to enlarge $\mathbf{S}$ and extend the definition of $\varphi$ so as to obtain a complete measure (see Section 4–11).

## PROBLEMS

1. Let $X$ be an uncountable set, and let $\mathbf{S}$ be the class of all subsets of $X$. Define $\varphi : S \to R^*$ by setting $\varphi(E) = +\infty$ if $E$ is uncountable, and $\varphi(E) = 0$ otherwise. Is $\varphi$ a measure?

2. Let $X$ be a countable set, and let $\mathbf{S}$ be the class of all subsets of $X$. Suppose that $\varphi : \mathbf{S} \to R$ is countably additive. Find a representation of $\varphi(E)$ for arbitrary $E$ by making use of the values which $\varphi$ assumes for one-element sets. Prove that $\varphi$ is a bounded function.

3. (a) In Example 2, prove that (4) defines $\varphi$ unambiguously and that $\varphi$ is additive.
(b) Prove that $\varphi$ is countably additive. (See Halmos [1], pp. 32–36.)

## 4–4 Some properties of measures

Throughout this section let $\mathbf{S}$ be a ring of sets and let $\varphi : \mathbf{S} \to R^*$ be a measure. We shall state and prove several easy and useful theorems for which we shall frequently find applications.

THEOREM 4–4 I. *Suppose $E$ and $E_1, E_2, \ldots$ are elements of $\mathbf{S}$ such that $E \subset \bigcup_n E_n$. Then*

$$\varphi(E) \leq \sum_n \varphi(E_n).$$

*Proof.* Let $F_n = E \cap E_n$, $G_1 = F_1$,

$$G_n = F_n - (F_1 \cup \cdots \cup F_{n-1}) \qquad \text{if } n \geq 2.$$

Then $G_n \subset F_n \subset E_n$, so that $\varphi(G_n) \leq \varphi(E_n)$. Also,

$$E = E \cap \bigcup_n E_n = \bigcup_n F_n = \bigcup_n G_n.$$

Here we use the device described in connection with (2), Section 4–2. Since $\varphi$ is countably additive, we have

$$\varphi(E) = \sum_n \varphi(G_n) \leq \sum_n \varphi(E_n).$$

THEOREM 4–4 II. *Let $\{E_n\}$ be a disjoint countable collection of elements of $\mathbf{S}$, and let $E$ be any member of $\mathbf{S}$ such that $\bigcup_n E_n \subset E$. Then*

$$\sum_n \varphi(E_n) \leq \varphi(E).$$

*Proof.* We see at once that it suffices to give the proof for the case that the number of $E_n$'s is finite, for the conclusion in this case implies the conclusion for the countably infinite case. But, in the finite case, $\bigcup_n E_n$ belongs to $\mathbf{S}$, and the additivity of $\varphi$ implies that

$$\sum_n \varphi(E_n) = \varphi\left(\bigcup_n E_n\right).$$

Then, since $\varphi$ is monotone, we infer

$$\varphi\left(\bigcup_n E_n\right) \leq \varphi(E),$$

and the desired conclusion follows.

THEOREM 4–4 III. *Let $\{E_n\}$ be a sequence of members of $\mathbf{S}$ such that $E_n \subset E_{n+1}$ and $\bigcup_n E_n \in \mathbf{S}$. Then*

$$\varphi\left(\bigcup_n E_n\right) = \lim_{n\to\infty} \varphi(E_n).$$

*Proof.* Let $F_1 = E_1$, $F_{n+1} = E_{n+1} - E_n$. Then the $F_n$'s are disjoint and $\bigcup_n F_n = \bigcup_n E_n$. Hence

$$\varphi\left(\bigcup_n E_n\right) = \sum_n \varphi(F_n) = \lim_{n\to\infty} \sum_{k=1}^{n} \varphi(F_k).$$

But

$$\sum_{k=1}^{n} \varphi(F_k) = \varphi\left(\bigcup_{k=1}^{n} F_k\right) = \varphi\left(\bigcup_{k=1}^{n} E_k\right) = \varphi(E_n).$$

Thus the proof is completed.

THEOREM 4–4 IV. *Let $\{E_n\}$ be a sequence of members of* **S** *such that $E_{n+1} \subset E_n$ and $\bigcap_n E_n \in$* **S**. *Suppose also that $\varphi(E_n) < +\infty$ for some $n$. Then*

$$\varphi\left(\bigcap_n E_n\right) = \lim_{n\to\infty} \varphi(E_n).$$

*Proof.* Since $\bigcap_n E_n$ is unchanged (in this situation) by the omission of $E_1, \ldots, E_k$, for any $k$, we may as well suppose that $\varphi(E_n)$ is finite for every $n$. Since $\varphi$ is monotone, it follows that $\varphi\left(\bigcap_n E_n\right) < +\infty$. Let $F_n = E_1 - E_n$, $E = \bigcap_n E_n$. Then $F_n \subset F_{n+1}$ and $E_1 - E = \bigcup_n F_n$. Hence, by Theorem 4–4 III,

$$\varphi(E_1 - E) = \lim_{n\to\infty} \varphi(E_1 - E_n).$$

But $E_1 = E \cup (E_1 - E)$, so $\varphi(E_1) = \varphi(E) + \varphi(E_1 - E)$; since all the values of $\varphi$ here are finite, $\varphi(E_1 - E) = \varphi(E_1) - \varphi(E)$. In the same way, $\varphi(E_1 - E_n) = \varphi(E_1) - \varphi(E_n)$. Thus we have proved that

$$\varphi(E_1) - \varphi(E) = \lim_{n\to\infty} \{\varphi(E_1) - \varphi(E_n)\}.$$

This implies

$$\varphi(E) = \lim_{n\to\infty} \varphi(E_n).$$

We observe that the hypothesis that some $\varphi(E_n)$ is finite is essential in the foregoing theorem. For, if we take $X$, **S**, and $\varphi$ as in Example 4 of Section 4–3, and define $E_n = \{x : x \geq n\}$, then $\varphi(E_n) = +\infty$ for each $n$, but $\varphi\left(\bigcap_n E_n\right) = 0$.

**PROBLEM**

Let $\varphi$ be a measure on a $\sigma$-ring **S**. If $E_1, E_2, \ldots$ are in **S**, let $E_* = \liminf_{n\to\infty} E_n$, $E^* = \limsup_{n\to\infty} E_n$ (see (5) and (6) in Section 1–2). Prove that $\varphi(E_*) \leq \liminf_{n\to\infty} \varphi(E_n)$, and that $\varphi(E^*) \geq \limsup_{n\to\infty} \varphi(E_n)$ if $\varphi\left(\bigcup_{k\geq n} E_k\right) < +\infty$ for some $n$.

## 4–5 Preliminary remarks about Lebesgue measure

When mathematicians began seriously to study problems of analysis without restricting themselves to continuous functions, they were eventually led to make penetrating investigations of sets of points on the real line $R$. Many topics contributed to this trend, notably the study of the representation of functions by Fourier series and the study of integration.

Riemann's theory of integration, for bounded functions $f: [a, b] \to R$, where $[a, b]$ is a compact interval, proved to be too confining. The inadequacies of the Riemann integral as an analytical tool were revealed in various ways, and many attempts were made to broaden the class of functions which could be brought under a satisfactory theory of integration.

The decisive advance was made by Lebesgue in the first years of the 20th century (Lebesgue [1]). His study of integration was based on improvement and generalization of the work of Borel on the theory of measure. Borel had already in 1898 (Borel [1]) presented a theory of measure for the class of sets now known as Borel sets.

The aim of the classical theory of Lebesgue measure, for the real line $R$, is to find a very inclusive ring **S** of subsets of $R$ and a measure $\mu$ on **S**, of such a nature that **S** will contain every finite interval and that the measure of such an interval will be its length. In fact the classical Lebesgue theory arrives at a $\sigma$-ring, the members of which are called "the sets of $R$ which are measurable in the Lebesgue sense" (briefly, the $L$-measurable sets of $R$), and this $\sigma$-ring contains all open sets, including $R$ itself. Hence it also includes all closed sets. Since the $\sigma$-ring generated by the open sets is the family of Borel sets (see Section 4–2), every Borel set is $L$-measurable. But there are some $L$-measurable sets which are not Borel sets. Since every compact interval is contained in some finite interval $[a, b]$, the measure of the compact set is finite, not exceeding $b - a$.

It turns out that a set consisting of a single point has $L$-measure 0. Since the measure is countably additive, any countable set has measure 0. There are even some uncountable sets which are $L$-measurable and have measure 0. It also turns out that there are some sets in $R$ which are not $L$-measurable.

The classical method of developing the theory of Lebesgue measure proceeds in the following way: First, with the aid of the simple concept of the length of an interval, we construct a function called an *outer measure*. This function, which we shall denote by $\mu^*$, has for its domain the class of *all* subsets of $R$, and its range lies in $R^*$. It has the property that $\mu^*(E)$ is the length of $E$ if $E$ is an interval. The values of $\mu^*$ are nonnegative, $\mu^*$ is monotone, and $\mu^*$ has a property like additivity, somewhat restricted: $\mu^*(E_1 \cup E_2) = \mu^*(E_1) + \mu^*(E_2)$ if the sets $E_1$, $E_2$ are a positive distance apart. But $\mu^*$ is not countably additive, and hence it is not a measure. The attempt is then made to diminish the domain of $\mu^*$ in such a way that $\mu^*$ actually becomes a measure on the reduced domain. This successful attempt leads to the $\sigma$-ring of the $L$-measurable sets; if $E$ is $L$-measurable, $\mu^*(E)$ is called the Lebesgue measure of $E$.

There are two parts to this procedure for developing the Lebesgue theory of measure. One part is the construction of the outer measure, that is, the definition of $\mu^*$. The other part is the process of "thinning out" the sets for which we have the outer measure defined. We have to discard just enough sets to make the outer measure a countably additive function on the sets which remain.

The first part of the procedure is not greatly increased in difficulty if we modify it so as to make it applicable to multi-dimensional Euclidean space instead of to the real line. Hence we shall in Section 4–6 discuss the Lebesgue outer measure of sets in $R^k$, $k \geq 1$. The second part of the procedure has been found to be very general in character. It does not depend in any essential way on the special properties of the space $R^k$, and it depends only in a very limited way on the properties of the outer measure function. Hence, when we present this part of the development of the Lebesgue theory, we shall cast it in its general form (Section 4–7). We shall then be able to use this general theory for the passage from outer measures to measures in situations which are quite different from the classical situation of Lebesgue's outer measure in $R^k$. Other outer measures in $R$ are discussed in Section 4–10, using some general methodology from Section 4–9 concerning ways of defining outer measures in abstract spaces.

In Section 4–8 is given the detailed study of the nature of the $L$-measurable sets in $R^k$.

The essential difference in scope between Lebesgue's theory and that of Borel lies in the fact that the measure of Lebesgue is complete, in the sense defined in Section 4–3. The general theory of passing from an incomplete measure to its completion is given in Section 4–11.

## 4–6 Lebesgue outer measure in $R^k$

As usual we use $x = (\xi_1, \ldots, \xi_k)$ as a symbol for a variable point in $R^k$. By definition, an *open interval* $I$ in $R^k$ is determined by $k$ pairs of real numbers $(\alpha_i, \beta_i)$ $(i = 1, \ldots, k)$, where $\alpha_i < \beta_i$; the interval $I$ so determined consists of all $x$ such that $\alpha_i < \xi_i < \beta_i$, $i = 1, \ldots, k$. Thus, an open interval is just the same as an *open box*, as defined in Section 2–3. The numbers $\beta_1 - \alpha_1, \ldots, \beta_k - \alpha_k$ are called the *lengths of the edges* of $I$. We define the number

$$|I| = (\beta_1 - \alpha_1) \cdots (\beta_k - \alpha_k)$$

to be the *content* of $I$. Thus, if $k = 1$, content is length, if $k = 2$, content is area, and so on.

For later use we note the following: By the *center* of the above interval $I$ we mean the point with coordinates $\xi_i = \frac{1}{2}(\alpha_i + \beta_i)$, $i = 1, \ldots, k$. By an interval *concentric* with $I$ we mean an interval having the same center as $I$. If $J$ is an interval concentric with $I$, but having its various edges of lengths $\lambda$ times the lengths of the corresponding edges of $I$ (where $\lambda > 0$), then $|J| = \lambda^k |I|$.

If $E$ is any point-set in $R^k$, and if $\{I_n\}$ is a countable collection of open intervals such that $E \subset \bigcup_n I_n$, we shall for convenience refer to $\{I_n\}$ as a *Lebesgue covering* of $E$. There are many such Lebesgue coverings for a given set $E$. We now define the *Lebesgue outer measure* of $E$, denoted by $\mu^*(E)$, as follows: Corresponding to the Lebesgue covering $\{I_n\}$ consider the sum $\sum_n |I_n|$, which is an element of the extended real number system $R^*$. Consider *all* such sums, *corresponding to all possible Lebesgue coverings of E*. The greatest lower bound of all these sums is $\mu^*(E)$:

$$\mu^*(E) = \text{glb}\left\{\sum_n |I_n| : \{I_n\} \text{ a Lebesgue covering of } E\right\}.$$

It is evident that $\mu^*(E) \geq 0$. Also, $\mu^*(E) < +\infty$ if and only if $\sum_n |I_n| < +\infty$ for at least one Lebesgue covering of $E$. A single open interval $I$ is a Lebesgue covering of itself; hence

$$\mu^*(I) \leq |I|. \tag{1}$$

We shall presently see that $\mu^*(I) = |I|$. If $E$ is a set consisting of a single point, $\mu^*(E) = 0$, for it is clear that we can enclose $E$ in an open interval $I$ with $|I|$ as small as we please. Likewise, for the empty set $\varnothing$ we have $\mu^*(\varnothing) = 0$.

We shall now develop the main properties of the outer measure $\mu^*$ in a series of propositions.

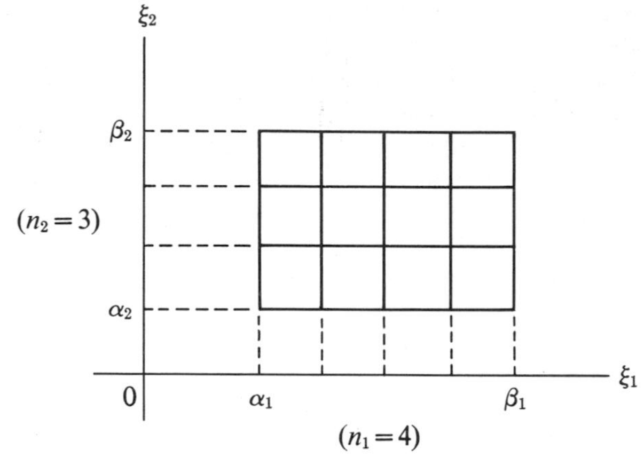


FIGURE 33

LEMMA 4–6 I. *Suppose $I$ is an open interval, and let $\bar{I}$ be its closure. Suppose $\epsilon > 0$ and $\delta > 0$. Then there exists a finite Lebesgue covering of $\bar{I}$, say by intervals $I_1, \ldots, I_N$, such that*

$$|I_1| + \cdots + |I_N| < |I| + \epsilon$$

*and such that each edge of each $I_j$ has length less than $\delta$.*

*Proof.* Let $I$ be determined by the pairs $(\alpha_1, \beta_1), \ldots, (\alpha_k, \beta_k)$. Let the open interval $(\alpha_i, \beta_i)$ of the real line be divided into $n_i$ equal parts, where $n_i$ is chosen so that $\dfrac{\beta_i - \alpha_i}{n_i} < \dfrac{\delta}{2}$. Let $N = n_1 n_2 \cdots n_k$. By using one of the subintervals of $(\alpha_1, \beta_1)$ in place of $(\alpha_1, \beta_1)$, one of the subintervals of $(\alpha_2, \beta_2)$ in place of $(\alpha_2, \beta_2)$, and so on, we determine a new open interval in $R^k$, contained in $I$ and having each of its edges of length less than $\delta/2$. Altogether we get in this way $N$ new intervals $J_1, \ldots, J_N$. The situation for $k = 2$ is shown in Figure 33. It is easy to verify that

$$|I| = |J_1| + \cdots + |J_N|.$$

Now, choose $\lambda$, $1 < \lambda < 2$, and let $I_j$ be an open interval concentric with $J_j$ and having each of its edges $\lambda$ times as long as the corresponding edge of $J_j$. The edge-lengths for $I_j$ are all less than $\delta$. Then $|I_j| = \lambda^k |J_j|$, and so

$$|I_1| + \cdots + |I_N| = \lambda^k |I|.$$

Since $\lambda > 1$, it is clear that $\{I_1, \ldots, I_N\}$ is a Lebesgue covering of $\bar{I}$. Finally, by choosing $\lambda$ sufficiently close to 1, we can be certain that $\lambda^k |I| < |I| + \epsilon$. This completes the proof.

LEMMA 4–6 II. *Let $I$ be any open interval, and suppose that $\{I_n\}$ $(n = 1, \ldots, N)$ is any finite Lebesgue covering of the closure $\bar{I}$. Then*

$$\sum_n |I_n| \geq |I|.$$

*Proof.* Let the intervals determining $I$ and $I_n$ be $(\alpha_1, \beta_1), \ldots, (\alpha_k, \beta_k)$ and $(\alpha_{1n}, \beta_{1n}), \ldots, (\alpha_{kn}, \beta_{kn})$. If we consider all of the hyperplanes $\xi_1 = \alpha_1$, $\xi_1 = \beta_1$, $\xi_1 = \alpha_{1n}$, $\xi_1 = \beta_{1n}$ $(n = 1, \ldots, N)$, $\xi_2 = \alpha_2$, $\xi_2 = \beta_2$, $\xi_2 = \alpha_{2n}$, $\xi_2 = \beta_{2n}$, and so on, we see that they divide

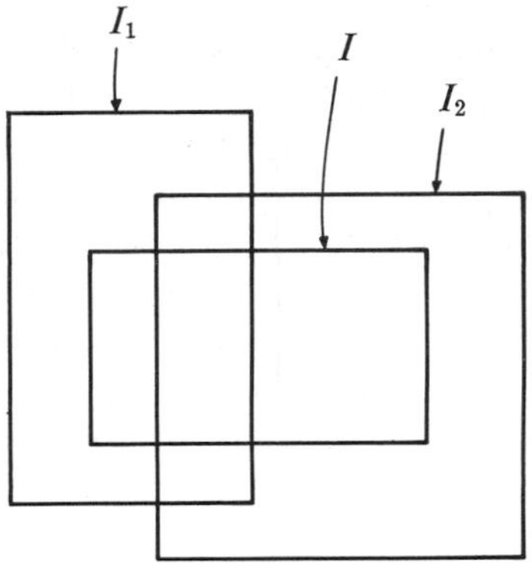


FIGURE 34

each of the $N + 1$ intervals $I, I_1, \ldots, I_N$ into a finite number of open intervals:

$$I \quad \text{divided into } J_1, \ldots, J_p,$$

$$I_n \quad \text{divided into } J_{n1}, \ldots, J_{np(n)}.$$

The phrase "divided into" is not entirely precise, since $I$ is not exactly the union of $J_1, \ldots, J_p$. The open intervals $J_1, \ldots, J_p$ are disjoint, each is contained in $I$, and the union of their closures is the closure of $I$. The situation for $k = 2$ and $N = 2$ is shown in Figure 34 and Figure 35; these figures reveal the essential features of what is going on. Thus, in Figure 35, $I_1$ is divided into 12 parts ($p(1) = 12$), $I_2$ is divided into 12 parts ($p(2) = 12$), and $I$ is divided into 3 parts ($p = 3$).

In the general case

(2) $$|I| = |J_1| + \cdots + |J_p|,$$

(3) $$|I_n| = |J_{n1}| + \cdots + |J_{np(n)}|.$$

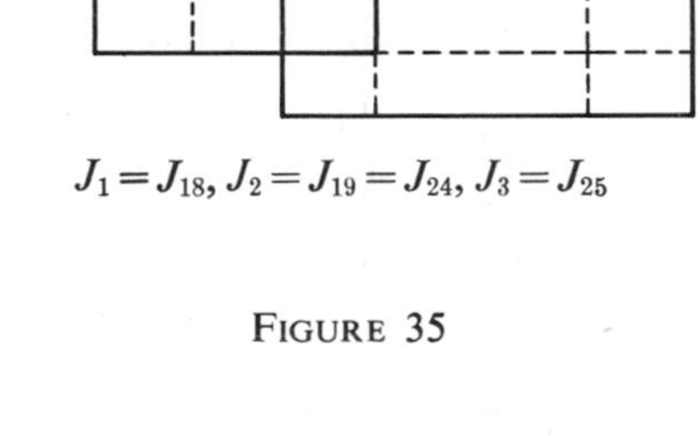


$J_1 = J_{18}, J_2 = J_{19} = J_{24}, J_3 = J_{25}$

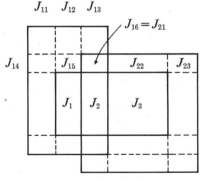

FIGURE 35

Now, the collection of all the open intervals into which $I$ and $I_1, \ldots, I_N$ are thus divided has the property that, given any two of these intervals with different symbolic designation (for example, $J_1$ and $J_{n1}$), the intervals are either identical or they have no points at all in common. Then, since $I_1, \ldots, I_N$ cover $I$, $J_1$ must be the same as $J_{nq}$ for some $n$ and some $q$, say $n_1$ and $q_1$. If we take all the intervals $J_i$ which occur in the list $J_{n_1 1}, \ldots, J_{n_1 p(n_1)}$, the sum of the contents of these $J_i$'s will not exceed $|I_{n_1}|$, because of (3). Next, consider the $J_i$'s *not* taken in the foregoing procedure, and pick the one with smallest index. It will be the same as $J_{nq}$ for some $n$ and $q$, say $n = n_2 \neq n_1$ and $q = q_2$. We then consider all the $J_i$'s which are in the list $J_{n_2 1}, \ldots, J_{n_2 p(n_2)}$ but not in the list $J_{n_1 1}, \ldots, J_{n_1 p(n_1)}$. The sum of the contents of these $J_i$'s will not exceed $|I_{n_2}|$. Proceeding in this way we shall exhaust all the $J_i$'s after a certain number of steps, say $r$ steps, where $r \leq N$. Then

$$|I| = \sum_{n=1}^{p} |J_n| \leq \sum_{j=1}^{r} |I_{n_j}| \leq \sum_{n=1}^{N} |I_n| \,.$$

Thus we have proved the required inequality.

Next we consider the outer measure of the closure of an open interval.

THEOREM 4–6 III. *Let $I$ be an open interval, and $\bar{I}$ its closure. Then $\mu^*(\bar{I}) = |I|$.*

*Proof.* If $\{I_n\}$ is any Lebesgue covering of $\bar{I}$, there exists a finite number of the $I_n$'s, which we redesignate as $J_1, \ldots, J_N$, such that these cover $\bar{I}$. This is true because $\bar{I}$ is compact (the Borel theorem). Then, in view of Lemma 4–6 II,

$$|I| \leq \sum_{i=1}^{N} |J_i| \leq \sum_{n} |I_n| \,,$$

and therefore $|I| \leq \mu^*(\bar{I})$. To prove the reverse of this inequality, observe that we can construct an open interval $K$ concentric with $I$ so that $\bar{I} \subset K$ and $|K|$ exceeds $|I|$ by as little as we please. Thus, if $\epsilon > 0$ and $|K| < |I| + \epsilon$, we conclude that $\mu^*(\bar{I}) \leq |K| < |I| + \epsilon$; therefore, since $\epsilon$ is arbitrary, we have $\mu^*(\bar{I}) \leq |I|$. This completes the proof.

We can now show that the outer measure of an open interval is the same as its content.

THEOREM 4–6 IV. *If $I$ is an open interval, $\mu^*(I) = |I|$.*

*Proof.* It was remarked earlier (see (1)) that, obviously, $\mu^*(I) \leq |I|$. Hence we have only to prove $|I| \leq \mu^*(I)$. Let $J$ be an open interval concentric with $I$ and with edges $\lambda$ times as long as the corresponding edges of $I$, where $0 < \lambda < 1$. Then $\bar{J} \subset I$. From this it follows that any Lebesgue covering of $I$ is also a Lebesgue covering of $\bar{J}$, and therefore $\mu^*(\bar{J}) \leq \mu^*(I)$. But, by Theorem 4–6 III, $\mu^*(\bar{J}) = |J| = \lambda^k |I|$, and so $\lambda^k |I| \leq \mu^*(I)$. We now make $\lambda \to 1$, and the result is $|I| \leq \mu^*(I)$.

Next we establish two general properties of outer measure.

THEOREM 4–6 V. *If $E_1 \subset E_2$, then $\mu^*(E_1) \leq \mu^*(E_2)$.*

This follows from the fact that the class of Lebesgue coverings of $E_2$ is a subclass of the class of Lebesgue coverings of $E_1$.

THEOREM 4–6 VI. *If $\{E_n\}$ is any countable collection of sets in $R^k$, the outer measure $\mu^*$ satisfies the inequality*

$$\mu^*\left(\bigcup_n E_n\right) \leq \sum_n \mu^*(E_n).$$

*Proof.* We can assume $\sum_n \mu^*(E_n) < +\infty$, since otherwise the assertion is obviously correct. Suppose $\epsilon > 0$. From the definition of $\mu^*(E_n)$ it follows that there exists a Lebesgue covering of $E_n$, say $\{I_{n1}, I_{n2}, \ldots\}$, such that

$$\sum_i |I_{ni}| < \mu^*(E_n) + \frac{\epsilon}{2^n}.$$

The entire collection $\{I_{ni}\}$, with $n$ and $i$ varying, is a Lebesgue covering of $\bigcup_n E_n$. Since

$$\sum_n \sum_i |I_{ni}| < \sum_n \left[\mu^*(E_n) + \frac{\epsilon}{2^n}\right] \leq \sum_n \mu^*(E_n) + \epsilon,$$

it is clear that

$$\mu^*\left(\bigcup_n E_n\right) < \sum_n \mu^*(E_n) + \epsilon.$$

Since $\epsilon$ was arbitrary, the conclusion of the theorem follows.

We consider one more very important proposition about Lebesgue outer measure. It concerns the matter of the outer measure of the union of two disjoint sets. If $E_1$ and $E_2$ are the two sets, we might expect that $\mu^*(E_1 \cup E_2)$ would be the sum of $\mu^*(E_1)$ and $\mu^*(E_2)$. This, however, is not always true. (In fact, the existence of a set which is not $L$-measurable implies the existence of two disjoint sets $E_1$, $E_2$ such that $\mu^*(E_1 \cup E_2) < \mu^*(E_1) + \mu^*(E_2)$.) Nevertheless, we can prove that the foregoing expectation is justified if the two sets $E_1$, $E_2$ are a positive distance apart, that is, if $D(E_1, E_2) > 0$, where

$$D(E_1, E_2) = \text{glb}\,\{\|x_1 - x_2\| : x_1 \in E_1, x_2 \in E_2\}.$$

THEOREM 4–6 VII. *If $E_1$ and $E_2$ are nonempty sets in $R^k$, with $D(E_1, E_2) > 0$, then*

$$\mu^*(E_1 \cup E_2) = \mu^*(E_1) + \mu^*(E_2).$$

For the proof of this theorem we need the following lemma.

LEMMA 4–6 VIII. *For any set $E$ in $R^k$ and any $\delta > 0$, let*

$$M_\delta(E) = \text{glb} \sum_n |I_n|,$$

*where the greatest lower bound is taken over the class of all Lebesgue coverings $\{I_n\}$ of $E$ such that each $I_n$ has each of its edges of length less than $\delta$. Then $M_\delta(E) = \mu^*(E)$.*

*Proof.* It is obvious that $\mu^*(E) \leq M_\delta(E)$. Hence it suffices to prove that $M_\delta(E) \leq \mu^*(E)$, and, clearly, we may suppose that $\mu^*(E) < +\infty$. If $\epsilon > 0$, there exists a Lebesgue covering $\{J_n\}$ of $E$ such that

$$\sum_n |J_n| < \mu^*(E) + \frac{\epsilon}{2}.$$

Then, by Lemma 4–6 I, there exists a finite Lebesgue covering of $\bar{J}_n$, by open intervals which we designate by $I_{nj}$ ($j = 1, \ldots, N(n)$), such that each $I_{nj}$ has its edges of lengths less than $\delta$ and such that

$$\sum_{j=1}^{N(n)} |I_{nj}| < |J_n| + \frac{\epsilon}{2^{n+1}} .$$

The combined family $\{I_{nj}\}$, $j = 1, \ldots, N(n)$, $n = 1, 2, \ldots$ is a Lebesgue covering of $E$, and

$$\sum_{j,n} |I_{nj}| < \sum_n |J_n| + \sum_n \frac{\epsilon}{2^{n+1}} < \mu^*(E) + \epsilon.$$

Since each edge of each $I_{nj}$ is of length less than $\delta$, this shows that $M_\delta(E) \leq \mu^*(E) + \epsilon$. But $\epsilon$ was arbitrary, and so $M_\delta(E) \leq \mu^*(E)$. This finishes the proof of the lemma.

*Proof of Theorem* 4–6 VII. In view of Theorem 4–6 VI we need only prove $\mu^*(E_1) + \mu^*(E_2) \leq \mu^*(E_1 \cup E_2)$. Let $\delta = D(E_1, E_2)$ and suppose $\epsilon > 0$. On the strength of Lemma 4–6 VIII we can assert the existence of a Lebesgue covering $\{I_n\}$ of $E_1 \cup E_2$ such that

$$\sum_n |I_n| < \mu^*(E_1 \cup E_2) + \epsilon \tag{4}$$

and such that each $I_n$ has its edges of lengths less than $\delta/\sqrt{k}$. We can safely assume that each $I_n$ contains at least one point of $E_1 \cup E_2$. If two points $x, y$ are in the same $I_n$, their distance apart is less than $\delta$, because of the limitation on the lengths of the edges of $I_n$. Therefore it cannot happen that $x \in E_1$ and $y \in E_2$. We can therefore separate the family of intervals $\{I_n\}$ into two families $\{J_n\}$ and $\{K_n\}$, where $\{J_n\}$ is the family of those $I_j$'s which contain points of $E_1$, and $\{K_n\}$ is the family of those $I_j$'s which contain points of $E_2$. Then, it is clear, $\{J_n\}$ is a Lebesgue covering of $E_1$, so that $\sum_n |J_n| \geq \mu^*(E_1)$, and $\{K_n\}$ is a Lebesgue covering of $E_2$, so that $\sum_n |K_n| \geq \mu^*(E_2)$. Then, since,

$$\sum_n |I_n| = \sum_n |J_n| + \sum_n |K_n| ,$$

we see from (4) that

$$\mu^*(E_1) + \mu^*(E_2) < \mu^*(E_1 \cup E_2) + \epsilon.$$

Since $\epsilon$ was arbitrary, this achieves what is needed for the demonstration of the theorem.

## 4–7 The measure induced by an outer measure

For the purposes of this section we consider an arbitrary nonempty class $X$, and a function $\mu^*$ whose domain is the family of all subsets of $X$ and whose range lies in $R^*$. We shall suppose that $\mu^*$ satisfies the following conditions:

(a) $\mu^*(\varnothing) = 0$,
(b) $\mu^*(E) \geq 0$ for each $E \subset X$,
(c) if $E_1 \subset E_2$, then $\mu^*(E_1) \leq \mu^*(E_2)$,
(d) if $\{E_n\}$ is any countable collection of subsets of $X$, then

$$\mu^*\left(\bigcup_n E_n\right) \leq \sum_n \mu^*(E_n).$$

Under these conditions we shall call $\mu^*$ an outer measure on $X$. (We may also say that $\mu^*$ is an outer measure on the $\sigma$-ring consisting of all subsets of $X$.) If $X$ is a metric space and if $\mu^*$ is an outer measure on $X$ which satisfies the following additional condition:

(e) $\mu^*(E_1 \cup E_2) = \mu^*(E_1) + \mu^*(E_2)$

whenever $E_1$ and $E_2$ are nonempty sets which are a positive distance apart, then we shall call $\mu^*$ *a metric outer measure* on $X$.

From the results of Section 4–6 we see that the Lebesgue outer measure on $R^k$ is a metric outer measure in the sense of our present definition.

We can exhibit other examples of outer measures.

*Example 1.* Choose any fixed element $x_0$ in $X$ and define $\mu^*(E) = 1$ if $x_0 \in E$, $\mu^*(E) = 0$ if $x_0 \notin E$. This satisfies conditions (a)–(d) inclusive. Furthermore, if $E_1$ and $E_2$ are disjoint sets, then $\mu^*(E_1 \cup E_2) = \mu^*(E_1) + \mu^*(E_2)$. Hence, $\mu^*$ is a metric outer measure if $X$ is a metric space.

*Example 2.* Let $\mu^*$ be Lebesgue outer measure in $R^k$ and let $A$ be any fixed nonempty proper subset of $R^k$. For $E \subset R^k$ define $m^*(E)$ by $m^*(E) = \mu^*(E \cap A)$. Then $m^*$ is a metric outer measure on $R^k$.

*Example 3.* Let $X$ be the class of positive integers. If $E \subset X$, define $\mu^*(E) = +\infty$ if $E$ is an infinite set and $\mu^*(E) =$ the number of elements in $E$ if $E$ is a finite set. Then $\mu^*$ is an outer measure on $X$. Actually, if **S** is the $\sigma$-ring of all subsets of $X$, $\mu^*$ is a measure on **S**.

There is an extension of the concept of an outer measure, in which the domain of the outer measure is not necessarily the class of all subsets of $X$, but can be any $\sigma$-ring of a certain special type. For an instance of this see Problem 8.

We shall now turn to the general theory of obtaining a measure from an outer measure. Let $\mu^*$ be an outer measure on $X$. Nothing about a metric is assumed at this stage. The problem of restricting the domain of $\mu^*$ in such a way as to get a measure is solved on the basis of the following definition:

A set $E$ in $X$ is called $\mu^*$-measurable if

$$\mu^*(T) = \mu^*(T \cap E) + \mu^*(T \cap E^\sim) \tag{1}$$

for every subset $T$ of $X$. In (1) we refer to $T$ as the "test set."

The utility of this definition was discovered by C. Caratheodory (1873–1950). For a theory of measure in which $\mu^*(E)$ is to be the measure of $E$ when $E$ is restricted to a suitable ring, (1) must necessarily hold when $T$ is in this ring, because $T \cap E$ and $T \cap E^\sim$ are disjoint and their union is $T$. In Lebesgue's original definition of measurability in $R$, a special condition of the form (1) turned out to be sufficient as a criterion for measurability. Lebesgue considered sets lying on a fixed compact interval $I$ in $R$. For such sets he defined outer measure as in Section 4–6. Then he called a set $E \subset I$ measurable if $\mu^*(I - E) = \mu^*(I) - \mu^*(E)$. This is a special case of (1), with $T = I$. The justifiability of (1) as a general definition is of course dependent on the fact that the definition leads to the development of a satisfactory theory.

Since $(T \cap E) \cup (T \cap E^\sim) = T$, it follows by property (d) of $\mu^*$ that

$$\mu^*(T) \leq \mu^*(T \cap E) + \mu^*(T \cap E^\sim).$$

Hence, $E$ is $\mu^*$-measurable if and only if the following inequality

$$\mu^*(T) \geq \mu^*(T \cap E) + \mu^*(T \cap E^\sim) \tag{2}$$

is satisfied for every subset $T$ of $X$. Since the inequality is obviously true if $\mu^*(T) = +\infty$, it suffices to establish (2) for every $T$ such that $\mu^*(T) < +\infty$.

THEOREM 4–7 I. *A set $E$ is $\mu^*$-measurable if and only if its complement $E^\sim$ is $\mu^*$-measurable.*

The proof is obvious, because $(E^\sim)^\sim = E$.

THEOREM 4–7 II. *The empty set $\varnothing$ and the whole space $X$ are $\mu^*$-measurable.*

*Proof.* These assertions are correct as a consequence of the fact that $\mu^*(\varnothing) = 0$.

THEOREM 4–7 III. *If $E_1$ and $E_2$ are $\mu^*$-measurable, so are $E_1 \cup E_2$, $E_1 \cap E_2$, and $E_1 - E_2$.*

*Proof.* Let $T$ be any subset of $X$. We are assuming that

$$\mu^*(T) = \mu^*(T \cap E_1) + \mu^*(T \cap E_1^\sim). \tag{3}$$

Using $T \cap E_1^\sim$ as the test set, we can write

$$\mu^*(T \cap E_1^\sim) = \mu^*(T \cap E_1^\sim \cap E_2) + \mu^*(T \cap E_1^\sim \cap E_2^\sim), \tag{4}$$

because $E_2$ is $\mu^*$-measurable. In the first term on the right in (3) we can write $T \cap E_1 = T \cap (E_1 \cup E_2) \cap E_1$. In the first term on the right in (4) we can write $T \cap E_1^\sim \cap E_2 = T \cap (E_1 \cup E_2) \cap E_1^\sim$. Therefore

$$\mu^*(T) = \mu^*[T \cap (E_1 \cup E_2) \cap E_1] + \mu^*[T \cap (E_1 \cup E_2) \cap E_1^\sim] + \mu^*(T \cap E_1^\sim \cap E_2^\sim). \tag{5}$$

The sum of the first two terms on the right in (5) is equal to $\mu^*[T \cap (E_1 \cup E_2)]$, as we see by using $T \cap (E_1 \cup E_2)$ as the test set in expressing the $\mu^*$-measurability of $E_1$. Hence, since $E_1^\sim \cap E_2^\sim = (E_1 \cup E_2)^\sim$, we can rewrite (5) in the form

$$\mu^*(T) = \mu^*[T \cap (E_1 \cup E_2)] + \mu^*[T \cap (E_1 \cup E_2)^\sim].$$

Therefore $E_1 \cup E_2$ is $\mu^*$-measurable.

To prove that $E_1 \cap E_2$ is $\mu^*$-measurable, we observe that $E_1 \cap E_2 = (E_1^\sim \cup E_2^\sim)^\sim$ and use Theorem 4–7 I, along with what has just been proved. Then $E_1 - E_2$ is also $\mu^*$-measurable, because $E_1 - E_2 = E_1 \cap E_2^\sim$.

We proceed next to the examination of countable unions of $\mu^*$-measurable sets.

THEOREM 4–7 IV. *If $\{E_n\}$ is a disjoint countable family of $\mu^*$-measurable sets, and if $E = \bigcup_n E_n$, then $E$ is $\mu^*$-measurable. Moreover, if $T \subset X$, we have*

$$\mu^*(T \cap E) = \sum_n \mu^*(T \cap E_n). \tag{6}$$

*Proof.* With $T \cap (E_1 \cup E_2)$ as the test set, and using the fact that $E_2$ is $\mu^*$-measurable, we can write

$$\begin{aligned}\mu^*[T \cap (E_1 \cup E_2)] &= \mu^*[T \cap (E_1 \cup E_2) \cap E_2] + \mu^*[T \cap (E_1 \cup E_2) \cap E_2^\sim]\\ &= \mu^*(T \cap E_2) + \mu^*(T \cap E_1).\end{aligned}$$

By this method of argument and mathematical induction, we can prove that if $F_n = E_1 \cup \cdots \cup E_n$, then

$$\mu^*(T \cap F_n) = \sum_{j=1}^{n} \mu^*(T \cap E_j).$$

Now, by Theorem 4–7 III and induction, $F_n$ is $\mu^*$-measurable. Therefore

$$\begin{aligned} \mu^*(T) &= \mu^*(T \cap F_n) + \mu^*(T \cap F_n^{\sim}) \\ &= \sum_{j=1}^{n} \mu^*(T \cap E_j) + \mu^*(T \cap F_n^{\sim}). \end{aligned}$$

From now on in the proof we can assume that $\{E_n\}$ is an infinite (rather than a finite) family; the finite case of the theorem is fully proved by what has been shown. We observe that $T \cap F_n^{\sim} \supset T \cap E^{\sim}$. Therefore, in view of property (c) of an outer measure, we conclude that

$$\mu^*(T) \geq \sum_{j=1}^{n} \mu^*(T \cap E_j) + \mu^*(T \cap E^{\sim}).$$

We can now replace $n$ by $\infty$ in the summation symbol on the right of the last inequality, thus obtaining

$$\mu^*(T) \geq \sum_{j=1}^{\infty} \mu^*(T \cap E_j) + \mu^*(T \cap E^{\sim}). \tag{7}$$

But then, by property (d) of an outer measure, since

$$\bigcup_j (T \cap E_j) = T \cap E,$$

we have

$$\sum_{j=1}^{\infty} \mu^*(T \cap E_j) \geq \mu^*(T \cap E).$$

Combining this with inequality (7) and noting that

$$\mu^*(T \cap E) + \mu^*(T \cap E^{\sim}) \geq \mu^*(T), \tag{8}$$

we see that the inequalities (7) and (8) are in fact both equalities. One conclusion is that $E$ is $\mu^*$-measurable. Since $T$ is arbitrary, we can replace $T$ by $T \cap E$ in (7) (with the equality holding); the result is that

$$\mu^*(T \cap E) = \sum_{j=1}^{\infty} \mu^*(T \cap E_j).$$

This completes the proof of the theorem.

THEOREM 4–7 V. *The collection* **S** *of all $\mu^*$-measurable subsets of $X$ is a $\sigma$-ring and $\mu^*$ is a measure on* **S**.

*Proof.* We know that **S** is a ring (Theorem 4–7 III). To see that it is a $\sigma$-ring, suppose $E_1, E_2, \ldots,$ are in **S**, and let $F_1 = E_1$, $F_n = E_n - (E_1 \cup \cdots \cup E_{n-1})$ if $n \geq 2$. Then $\{F_n\}$ is a disjoint family of $\mu^*$-measurable sets, and $\bigcup_{n=1}^{\infty} F_n = \bigcup_{n=1}^{\infty} E_n$; Theorem 4–7 IV now shows that **S** is a $\sigma$-ring. The fact that $\mu^*$ is countably additive on **S** follows by taking $T = E$ in the context of (6). Hence, $\mu^*$ is a measure on **S**.

When we say that $\mu^*$ is a measure on **S**, what we mean, of course, is that the restriction of $\mu^*$ to **S** is a measure on **S**. It is a customary notation to drop the asterisk and denote the measure by $\mu$. This measure, whose definition is

$$\mu(E) = \mu^*(E) \qquad \text{if} \quad E \in \mathbf{S},$$

is called *the measure induced by* $\mu^*$.

There is one more important theorem—a very simple one—at this very general level.

THEOREM 4–7 VI. *Every set $E$ for which $\mu^*(E) = 0$ is $\mu^*$-measurable. As a consequence, if $F \subset E$ and $\mu^*(E) = 0$, then $F$ is $\mu^*$-measurable. In other words, the measure induced by $\mu^*$ is complete.*

*Proof.* By property (c) of the outer measure, $\mu^*(T \cap E) \leq \mu^*(E)$ and $\mu^*(T \cap E^\sim) \leq \mu^*(T)$. If $\mu^*(E) = 0$, we conclude that $\mu^*(T \cap E) = 0$, and so

$$\mu^*(T \cap E) + \mu^*(T \cap E^\sim) \leq \mu^*(T).$$

As we remarked earlier (see (2)), this establishes that $E$ is $\mu^*$-measurable. The last assertion of the theorem follows from the first part, because $\mu^*(F) = 0$ under the stated circumstances.

The theory of measure has a certain status quite independent of the sort of considerations which enter analysis through topology or in ways related to topology. Nevertheless, when we encounter mathematical structures where topology and the theory of measure are both present, we may expect to find interrelations between topological matters and measure-theoretic matters. This expectation is borne out in the case of the measure induced by a metric outer measure in a metric space. The fact that the outer measure has the special property (e) (mentioned near the beginning of the present section) enables us to prove that every open set in the metric space is measurable with respect to the given metric outer measure.

THEOREM 4–7 VII. *Let $X$ be a metric space, and let $\mu^*$ be a metric outer measure on $X$. Then every open subset of $X$ is $\mu^*$-measurable.*

*Proof.* Let $E$ be any open set in $X$. In order to show that $E$ is $\mu^*$-measurable, it suffices to show that, if $T$ is any set for which $\mu^*(T) < +\infty$, then

$$\mu^*(T \cap E) + \mu^*(T \cap E^\sim) \leq \mu^*(T). \tag{9}$$

This was remarked immediately before the statement of Theorem 4–7 I.

We may assume that $E \neq \varnothing$ and $E \neq X$, for otherwise the desired result is assured by Theorem 4–7 II. For each positive integer $n$ let $E_n$ be the set of all points $x$ in $X$ such that the distance of $x$ from $E^\sim$ exceeds $1/n$:

$$E_n = \left\{x : D(x, E^\sim) > \frac{1}{n}\right\}.$$

Then the sets $E_n$ and $E^\sim$ are a positive distance apart, and hence so are $T \cap E_n$ and $T \cap E^\sim$ (provided they are nonempty). Consequently, since $\mu^*$ is a metric outer measure,

$$\mu^*(T \cap E_n) + \mu^*(T \cap E^\sim) = \mu^*[(T \cap E_n) \cup (T \cap E^\sim)].$$

But, obviously, $E_n \subset E$, and hence

$$(T \cap E_n) \cup (T \cap E^{\sim}) \subset (T \cap E) \cup (T \cap E^{\sim}) = T,$$

so that

$$\mu^*(T \cap E_n) + \mu^*(T \cap E^{\sim}) \leq \mu^*(T). \tag{10}$$

If we can now prove that $\mu^*(T \cap E_n) \to \mu^*(T \cap E)$ as $n \to \infty$, (10) will imply (9) and it will follow that $E$ is $\mu^*$-measurable. Thus, we turn our attention to proving that $\mu^*(T \cap E_n) \to \mu^*(T \cap E)$.

The fact that $E$ is open insures that $E \subset \bigcup_{n=1}^{\infty} E_n$. (Each point of $E$ is in $E_n$ if $n$ is sufficiently large.) But $E_n \subset E$, and so $E = \bigcup_{n=1}^{\infty} E_n$. Now, $E_n \subset E_{n+1}$, because $\frac{1}{n+1} < \frac{1}{n}$. Let $W_1 = E_1$, $W_n = E_n - E_{n-1}$ if $n \geq 2$. The sets $W_1, W_2, \ldots$ are disjoint, and $E = \bigcup_{n=1}^{\infty} W_n$. Also,

$$T \cap E = (T \cap E_n) \cup \bigcup_{k=n+1}^{\infty} (T \cap W_k),$$

whence

$$\mu^*(T \cap E) \leq \mu^*(T \cap E_n) + \sum_{k=n+1}^{\infty} \mu^*(T \cap W_k). \tag{11}$$

At this point we do not yet know whether $\sum_{k=n+1}^{\infty} \mu^*(T \cap W_k)$ is finite. But, if we can establish the fact that the series $\sum_{k=1}^{\infty} \mu^*(T \cap W_k)$ is convergent, it will follow that

$$\lim_{n \to \infty} \sum_{k=n+1}^{\infty} \mu^*(T \cap W_k) = 0.$$

From (11) it will then follow that $\mu^*(T \cap E_n) \to \mu^*(T \cap E)$, for it is of course true that $\mu^*(T \cap E_n) \leq \mu^*(T \cap E)$ (because $E_n \subset E$).

The proof that $\sum_{k=1}^{\infty} \mu^*(T \cap W_k)$ is convergent is accomplished in a rather clever way. We shall show that, for any positive integer $n$

$$\mu^*(T \cap W_1) + \mu^*(T \cap W_3) + \cdots + \mu^*(T \cap W_{2n+1}) \leq \mu^*(T), \tag{12}$$

and also

$$\mu^*(T \cap W_2) + \mu^*(T \cap W_4) + \cdots + \mu^*(T \cap W_{2n}) \leq \mu^*(T). \tag{13}$$

Hence certainly, for any $n$,

$$\sum_{k=1}^{n} \mu^*(T \cap W_k) \leq 2\mu^*(T).$$

Since $\mu^*(T) < +\infty$, by assumption, this argument will assure the convergence of the series in question. We therefore address our attention to proving the correctness of (12) and (13).

Now, if $k > 1$, $x \in W_k$ means that

$$\frac{1}{k} < D(x, E^{\sim}) \leq \frac{1}{k-1}.$$

Suppose $x \in W_k$, $y \in W_{k+p}$ (where $p \geq 2$), and $z \in E^{\sim}$. Then

$$D(x, y) \geq D(x, z) - D(z, y) > \frac{1}{k} - D(z, y). \tag{14}$$

Now, $D(y, E^{\sim}) \leq \dfrac{1}{k+p-1}$. Therefore, if $\epsilon > 0$, we can choose $z$ in (14) so that $D(z, y) < \dfrac{1}{k+p-1} + \epsilon$. Since $\epsilon$ is arbitrary, the result is that

$$D(W_k, W_{k+p}) \geq \frac{1}{k} - \frac{1}{k+p-1} > 0.$$

It follows that any two different sets in the collection

$$T \cap W_1, T \cap W_3, \ldots, T \cap W_{2n+1}$$

are a positive distance apart. Then, using induction and the property (e) of the metric outer measure $\mu^*$, we see that

$$\sum_{k=0}^{n} \mu^*(T \cap W_{2k+1}) = \mu^*\left[\bigcup_{k=0}^{n} (T \cap W_{2k+1})\right],$$

and hence

$$\sum_{k=0}^{n} \mu^*(T \cap W_{2k+1}) \leq \mu^*(T).$$

This establishes (12). The same kind of argument can be used to prove the validity of (13). This concludes the proof of Theorem 4–7 VII.

## PROBLEMS

1. Let $\mu^*$ be a metric outer measure on the metric space $X$. Let $E_1$, $E_2$, $U$ be sets such that $U$ is open, $E_1 \subset U$, $E_2 \subset U^{\sim}$. Show that $\mu^*(E_1 \cup E_2) = \mu^*(E_1) + \mu^*(E_2)$.

2. If $A$ is $\mu^*$-measurable and $B$ is arbitrary, except that $\mu^*(B) < +\infty$, show that $\mu^*(A \cup B) = \mu^*(A) + \mu^*(B) - \mu^*(A \cap B)$.

3. Suppose $\mu^*(X) < +\infty$, and suppose that to each $T \subset X$ corresponds an $S \subset X$ such that $T \subset S$, $S$ is $\mu^*$-measurable, and $\mu^*(T) = \mu^*(S)$. Then, in order that a set $E$ be $\mu^*$-measurable, it is sufficient that $\mu^*(X) = \mu^*(E) + \mu^*(E^{\sim})$. Prove this. [*Hint.* Use $E$ and $E^{\sim}$ as test sets in expressing the measurability of the $S$ which corresponds to an arbitrary test set $T$.]

4. Suppose the outer measure $\mu^*$ is such that, for each subset $E$ of $X$, $\mu^*(E)$ is the greatest lower bound of $\mu^*(A)$ as $A$ varies over the class of sets which are $\mu^*$-measurable and such that $E \subset A$. Prove that to each set $E$ corresponds some $\mu^*$-measurable set $F$ such that $E \subset F$ and $\mu^*(E) = \mu^*(F)$. (Consider a suitable intersection of sets.)

5. The *symmetric difference* of the sets $A$, $B$, denoted by $A \Delta B$, was defined in (4), Section 1–2. Prove that

$$|\mu^*(A) - \mu^*(B)| \leq \mu^*(A \Delta B)$$

if $\mu^*(A)$ and $\mu^*(B)$ are finite.

6. Suppose $\mu^*(X) < \infty$, and suppose the outer measure has the property that a set $E$ is $\mu^*$-measurable if $\mu^*(E) + \mu^*(E^{\sim}) = \mu^*(X)$ (see Problem 3). Show that a set $E$ is $\mu^*$-measurable if to each $\epsilon > 0$ corresponds a $\mu^*$-measurable set $F$ such that $\mu^*(E \Delta F) < \epsilon$. [*Hint.* See Problem 5.]

7. If $\{\mu_n\}$ is a sequence of outer measures on $X$, and if $\{a_n\}$ is a sequence of positive numbers, prove that the function $\mu$ defined for each subset $E$ of $X$ by

$$\mu(E) = \sum_{1}^{\infty} a_n \mu_n(E)$$

is an outer measure on $X$.

8. Let **S** be a ring of subsets of $X$, and let $\varphi$ be a measure on **S**. Let $H(\mathbf{S})$ be the family of those subsets $E$ of $X$ such that $E$ is contained in some countable union of members of **S**. Obviously any subset of a member of $H(\mathbf{S})$ is a member of $H(\mathbf{S})$. (On this account $H(\mathbf{S})$ is called a *hereditary* family.) Show that $H(\mathbf{S})$ is a $\sigma$-ring. It is called the hereditary $\sigma$-ring generated by **S**.

Define a function $\mu^* : H(\mathbf{S}) \to R^*$ as follows: $\mu^*(E)$ is the greatest lower bound of the sums $\sum_n \varphi(E_n)$ obtained by considering all countable unions $\bigcup_n E_n$ of members of **S** such that $E \subset \bigcup_n E_n$. Show that $\mu^*(E) = \varphi(E)$ if $E \in \mathbf{S}$, and that $\mu^*$ is an outer measure on $H(\mathbf{S})$ (that is, that $\mu^*$ satisfies conditions (a)–(d) listed at the beginning of Section 4–7, where now, instead of arbitrary subsets of $X$, we consider only members of $H(\mathbf{S})$).

## 4–8 Lebesgue measure in $R^k$

In basic outline the theory of Lebesgue measure in $R^k$ is obtained by applying the general theory in Section 4–7 with $X = R^k$, taking $\mu^*$ to be the outer measure on $R^k$ defined in Section 4–6. However, there are certain further developments of the theory which are possible because of the special nature of the space $R^k$ and the particular manner of defining the outer measure $\mu^*$. In this section we shall discuss some of these developments.

In this section all sets, unless otherwise specified, will be subsets of $R^k$. If the set $E$ is $\mu^*$-measurable, where $\mu^*$ is Lebesgue outer measure, we shall say simply that $E$ is measurable. When $E$ is measurable we write $\mu(E) = \mu^*(E)$. We know (Theorems 4–7 V, VI, VII) that the measurable sets form a $\sigma$-ring which contains all open sets and all sets $E$ such that $\mu^*(E) = 0$. Clearly, $\mu(R^k) = \infty$.

### BOREL SETS

By definition, the members of the $\sigma$-ring generated by the compact sets in $R^k$ are called *Borel sets*. It is easily proved that this $\sigma$-ring is the same as the $\sigma$-ring generated by the open sets in $R^k$ (see Problem 6, Section 4–2). We see, therefore, that the $\sigma$-ring of measurable sets contains every Borel set. There are some measurable sets which are not Borel sets, however. This will be shown later.

### THE REGULARITY OF LEBESGUE OUTER MEASURE

For each set $E$ we have

$$\mu^*(E) = \inf \{\mu(U) : U \text{ open}, E \subset U\}; \tag{1}$$

this is seen as follows. Certainly $\mu^*(E) \leq \mu(U)$ for each $U$ of the class considered. If $\{I_n\}$ is a Lebesgue covering of $E$, $U = \bigcup_n I_n$ is an open set which contains $E$, and $\mu(U) \leq \sum_n |I_n|$, because $\mu(I_n) = |I_n|$. Thus (1) is true, on account of the way $\mu^*(E)$ is defined.

We also have, obviously, as a consequence of (1),

$$\mu^*(E) = \inf \{\mu(F) : E \subset F, F \text{ measurable}\}. \tag{2}$$

In a general study of outer measures and the measures induced by them the property in (2) is sometimes used as the characterization of those outer measures which are, by definition, called *regular*.

## MEASURABLE COVERS

We say that $H$ is a *measurable cover* of $E$ if $E \subset H$, $H$ is measurable, and every measurable subset of $H - E$ has measure 0.

THEOREM 4–8 I. (a) *Every set $E$ in $R^k$ has a measurable cover $H$ which is a Borel set such that $\mu(H) = \mu^*(E)$.* (b) *If $H_1$ and $H_2$ are measurable covers of $E$, then $\mu(H_1 \Delta H_2) = 0$ and $\mu(H_1) = \mu(H_2) = \mu^*(E)$.*

*Proof of* (a). Suppose at first that $\mu^*(E) < \infty$. Using (1) we choose an open set $U_n$ so that $E \subset U_n$ and $\mu(U_n) < \mu^*(E) + \frac{1}{n}$. Then let $H = \bigcap_n U_n$; $H$ is a Borel set. Now, $E \subset H$ and $\mu^*(E) \leq \mu(H) \leq \mu(U_n) < \mu^*(E) + \frac{1}{n}$ for all $n$; necessarily then $\mu^*(E) = \mu(H)$. If we suppose $F$ is a measurable set such that $F \subset H - E$, we see that $E \subset H - F$ and $\mu(H) = \mu^*(E) \leq \mu(H - F) = \mu(H) - \mu(F)$, whence $\mu(F) = 0$. Thus $H$ is a measurable cover of $E$.

Now, suppose that $\mu^*(E) = +\infty$. Express $E$ in the form $E = \bigcup_n E_n$, where $\mu^*(E_n) < +\infty$ for each $n$. This is possible, as the reader can easily see for himself. Select a Borel set $H_n$ which is a measurable cover for $E_n$ as in the first part of the proof. Let $H = \bigcup_n H_n$; $H$ is a Borel set. Then $E \subset H$ and $\mu^*(E) \leq \mu(H)$, whence $\mu(H) = +\infty = \mu^*(E)$. To see that $H$ is a measurable cover of $E$, suppose $F$ is a measurable subset of $H - E$. Let $F_n = F \cap H_n$. Then $F_n \subset H_n - E \subset H_n - E_n$, and so $\mu(F_n) = 0$. But $F = \bigcup_n F_n$, and so $\mu(F) \leq \sum_n \mu(F_n)$, whence $\mu(F) = 0$. This finishes the proof of (a).

*Proof of* (b). Let $H_1$, $H_2$ be measurable covers of $E$. Then $H_1 - H_2 \subset H_1 - E$, and so $\mu(H_1 - H_2) = 0$. Likewise, $\mu(H_2 - H_1) = 0$, and so $\mu(H_1 \Delta H_2) = 0$. We can write $H_1 = (H_1 \cap H_2) \cup (H_1 - H_2)$. Then, by what we have just seen, $\mu(H_1) = \mu(H_1 \cap H_2)$. By symmetry $\mu(H_1) = \mu(H_2)$. The common value must be $\mu^*(E)$, by part (a).

## DEFINITION OF INNER MEASURE

For use in the next theorem we need the concept of *inner measure*, which is defined as follows: For each set $E$ in $R^k$ the inner measure $\mu_*(E)$ is defined as

$$\mu_*(E) = \sup \{\mu(F) : F \subset E, F \text{ is measurable}\}. \tag{3}$$

Observe the form of this definition in comparison with (2). Since $F \subset E$ implies $\mu(F) \leq \mu^*(E)$, we see that

$$\mu_*(E) \leq \mu^*(E). \tag{4}$$

We have $\mu_*(\varnothing) = 0$, $\mu_*(R^k) = +\infty$. A study of the properties of inner measure will be made after the next theorem.

## MEASURABLE KERNELS

We say that $K$ is a *measurable kernel* of $E$ if $K \subset E$, $K$ is measurable, and if every measurable subset of $E - K$ has measure 0.

THEOREM 4–8 II. (a) *Every set $E$ in $R^k$ has a measurable kernel $K$ which is a Borel set.* (b) *If $K_1$ and $K_2$ are measurable kernels of $E$, $\mu(K_1 \Delta K_2) = 0$ and $\mu(K_1) = \mu(K_2) = \mu_*(E)$.*

*Proof of* (a). We use Theorem 4–8 I. Let $H$ and $M$ be Borel sets which are measurable covers of $E$ and $H - E$ respectively. Since $H - E \subset M$ we see that $H - M \subset E$. Let $K = H - M$. If $F$ is a measurable subset of $E - K$, we prove that $F \subset M - (H - E)$, whence $\mu(F) = 0$, by the nature of $M$. In fact,

$$E - K = E \cap (H \cap M^{\sim})^{\sim} = E \cap (H^{\sim} \cup M) = E \cap M,$$

and

$$M - (H - E) = M \cap (H \cap E^{\sim})^{\sim} = M \cap (H^{\sim} \cup E) = (M \cap H^{\sim}) \cup (M \cap E),$$

and it is then clear that $E - K \subset M - (H - E)$. This finishes the proof of (a).

*Proof of* (b). If $K$ is any measurable kernel of $E$, we have $\mu(K) \leq \mu_*(E)$ by the definition of $\mu_*(E)$. Suppose $\mu(K) < \mu_*(E)$. Then there exists a measurable set $F$ for which $F \subset E$ and $\mu(K) < \mu(F)$. Now, $F - K \subset E - K$, and so $\mu(F - K) = 0$. But, since $F = (F \cap K) \cup (F - K)$, we then have

$$\mu(F) = \mu(F \cap K) + \mu(F - K) = \mu(F \cap K) \leq \mu(K) < \mu(F),$$

a contradiction. Therefore $\mu(K) = \mu_*(E)$.

If $K_1$ and $K_2$ are measurable kernels of $E$, it is clear that $K_2 - K_1 \subset E - K_1$ and $K_1 - K_2 \subset E - K_2$, so that both $K_2 - K_1$ and $K_1 - K_2$ have measure 0. But then $\mu(K_1 \Delta K_2) = 0$.

## PROPERTIES OF INNER MEASURE

THEOREM 4–8 III. *If $\{E_n\}$ is a disjoint sequence of sets in $R^k$, and if $E = \bigcup_n E_n$, then*

$$\mu_*(E) \geq \sum_n \mu_*(E_n).$$

*Proof.* Let $K_n$ be a measurable kernel of $E_n$. Then the $K_n$'s are disjoint, and

$$\sum_n \mu_*(E_n) = \sum_n \mu(K_n) = \mu\left(\bigcup_n K_n\right) \leq \mu_*(E),$$

because $\bigcup_n K_n \subset E$.

THEOREM 4–8 IV. (a) *If $E$ is a measurable set in $R^k$, $\mu^*(E) = \mu_*(E) = \mu(E)$.* (b) *If $E$ is a set in $R^k$ such that $\mu^*(E) = \mu_*(E) < +\infty$, then $E$ is measurable.*

*Proof.* Part (a) is immediately evident, because when $E$ is measurable we have, from (3) and (4), $\mu(E) \leq \mu_*(E) \leq \mu^*(E) = \mu(E)$. To prove (b), choose for $E$ a measurable cover $H$ and a measurable kernel $K$. Since $\mu(K) = \mu_*(E)$ is finite, we have $\mu(H - K) = \mu(H) - \mu(K) = \mu^*(E) - \mu_*(E) = 0$. Let $T$ be any test set. We first show that

$$\mu^*(T \cap H) \leq \mu^*(T \cap K). \tag{5}$$

For this we write $H = K \cup (H - K)$, $T \cap H = (T \cap K) \cup [T \cap (H - K)]$, whence

$$\mu^*(T \cap H) \leq \mu^*(T \cap K) + \mu^*[T \cap (H - K)].$$

But $\mu^*[T \cap (H - K)] \leq \mu(H - K) = 0$, and so (5) is proved. Now, since $E \subset H$ and $E^\sim \subset K^\sim$, we have

$$\mu^*(T \cap E) + \mu^*(T \cap E^\sim) \leq \mu^*(T \cap H) + \mu^*(T \cap K^\sim)$$
$$\leq \mu^*(T \cap K) + \mu^*(T \cap K^\sim) = \mu^*(T).$$

Here we have used (5) and the fact that $K$ is measurable. But the inequality we have attained suffices to show that $E$ is measurable (see (2) in Section 4–7); thus the proof is complete.

## APPROXIMATION OF MEASURABLE SETS

When $E$ is a measurable set in $R^k$, it is useful to know the existence of sets with particularly simple properties which approximate $E$ in certain ways. We shall discuss some properties of this sort.

THEOREM 4–8 V. *A set $E$ in $R^k$ is measurable if and only if to each $\epsilon > 0$ corresponds a pair of sets $F$, $G$ such that $F \subset E \subset G$, $F$ is closed, $G$ is open, and $\mu(G - F) < \epsilon$.*

*Proof.* The demonstration of the "if" assertion is easy. Taking $\epsilon_n = \frac{1}{n}$, let the corresponding pair of sets be $F_n$, $G_n$, with $\mu(G_n - F_n) < \frac{1}{n}$. Let $F = \bigcup_n F_n$, $G = \bigcap_n G_n$. Observe that $G - F \subset G_n - F_n$, $\mu(G - F) \leq \mu(G_n - F_n) < \frac{1}{n}$, so that $\mu(G - F) = 0$. Then $E - F$ is measurable, because $E - F \subset G - F$ (Theorem 4–7 VI). But $E = F \cup (E - F)$, and therefore $E$ is measurable.

We now assume that $E$ is measurable, and to begin with we prove the "only if" assertion under the added assumption that $E$ is a bounded set. Suppose $\epsilon > 0$. We are going to use property (1). Choose an open set $G$ so that $E \subset G$ and $\mu(G) < \mu(E) + \frac{\epsilon}{2}$. Choose a compact set $S$ so that $E \subset S$, and then choose an open set $V$ so that $S - E \subset V$ and $\mu(V) < \mu(S - E) + \frac{\epsilon}{2}$. Let $F = S - V$. Then $F$ is closed and $F \subset E$. We have

$$\mu(F) = \mu(S) - \mu(S \cap V) \geq \mu(S) - \mu(V)$$
$$> \mu(S) - \mu(S - E) - \frac{\epsilon}{2} = \mu(E) - \frac{\epsilon}{2}.$$

Then $\mu(G - F) = \mu(G) - \mu(F) < \epsilon$. This finishes the proof for the case in which $E$ is bounded.

Now, let $E$ be measurable but unbounded. Let $S_n = \{x : \|x\| \leq n\}$, $E_1 = E \cap S_1$, $E_n = E \cap (S_n - S_{n-1})$ if $n \geq 2$. Then $E = \bigcup_n E_n$; each $E_n$ is bounded and measurable. Using what has already been established, let $F_n$, $G_n$ be a pair of sets such that $F_n \subset E_n \subset G_n$, $F_n$ is closed, $G_n$ is open, and $\mu(G_n - F_n) < \frac{\epsilon}{2^n}$. Let $F = \bigcup_n F_n$, $G = \bigcup_n G_n$. Then $G - F \subset \bigcup_n (G_n - F_n)$, and so $\mu(G - F) < \sum_n \frac{\epsilon}{2^n} = \epsilon$. We see that $G$ is open and that $F \subset E \subset G$, so all that remains is to prove that $F$ is closed. Suppose $\{x_i\}$ is a convergent sequence (say $x_i \to x$) with $x_i \in F$ for each $i$. Then $\{x_i\}$ is bounded, and so is contained in $S_N$ for a certain $N$. Now $F_n \subset S_n - S_N$ if $n > N$. Therefore $x_i \in \bigcup_{n=1}^{N} F_n$ for each $i$. But then the limit $x$ is in $\bigcup_{n=1}^{N} F_n$, for this last set is closed. Therefore $F$ is closed. This finishes the proof.

There is interest in showing that a measurable set of finite measure is, in a certain sense, nearly equal to the union of a finite number of open intervals. We have the following theorem.

THEOREM 4–8 VI. *If $E$ is a measurable set of finite measure in $R^k$, and if $\epsilon > 0$, there is a set $G$ of the form $G = \bigcup_{n=1}^{N} I_n$, where $I_1, \ldots, I_N$ are open intervals, such that $\mu(E \,\Delta\, G) < \epsilon$.*

*Proof.* Let us assume at first that $E$ is bounded. Let $X$ be an open interval such that $E \subset X$. There exist Lebesgue coverings $\{I_n\}$ and $\{J_n\}$, of $E$ and $X - E$ respectively, such that

$$\sum_n |I_n| < \mu(E) + \frac{\epsilon}{3}, \qquad \sum_n |J_n| < \mu(X - E) + \frac{\epsilon}{3},$$

and such that each $I_n$ and $J_n$ is contained in $X$. Choose $N$ so that $\sum_{n>N} |I_n| < \frac{\epsilon}{3}$, and define sets $G$, $H$, $K$ as follows

$$G = \bigcup_{n=1}^{N} I_n, \qquad H = \bigcup_{n>N} I_n, \qquad K = G \cap \bigcup_n J_n.$$

Observe that $E - G \subset H$ and $G - E \subset K$, so that $E \,\Delta\, G \subset H \cup K$ and $\mu(E \,\Delta\, G) \leq \mu(H) + \mu(K)$. We know that $\mu(H) \leq \sum_{n>N} |I_n| < \epsilon/3$. Hence it suffices to prove that $\mu(K) < 2\epsilon/3$. Since $K = \bigcup_n (G \cap J_n)$, we seek an estimate of $\sum_n \mu(G \cap J_n)$. Now, we can see that $X = \left[\bigcup_n I_n\right]^n \cup \left[\bigcup_n (J_n - G)\right]$, whence $\mu(X) \leq \sum_n |I_n| + \sum_n \mu(J_n - G)$. We also have

$$\sum_n |I_n| + \sum_n |J_n| < \mu(E) + \mu(X - E) + \frac{2\epsilon}{3} = \mu(X) + \frac{2\epsilon}{3},$$

whence

$$\sum_n |I_n| + \sum_n |J_n| < \sum_n |I_n| + \sum_n \mu(J_n - G) + \frac{2\epsilon}{3}$$

and therefore, since $J_n = (J_n - G) \cup (J_n \cap G)$,

$$\mu(K) \leq \sum_n \mu(G \cap J_n) = \sum_n \mu(J_n) - \sum_n \mu(J_n - G) < \frac{2\epsilon}{3}.$$

This finishes the proof for the case in which $E$ is bounded.

For the general case, let $S_n = \{x : \|x\| \leq n\}$, $T_1 = S_1$, $T_n = S_n - S_{n-1}$ if $n \geq 2$. Let $E_n = E \cap S_n$. Then $E = \bigcup_{i=1}^{\infty} (E \cap T_i)$, $E - E_n = \bigcup_{i=n+1}^{\infty} (E \cap T_i)$. Because $\mu(E) < +\infty$, we have

$$\mu(E - E_n) = \sum_{i=n+1}^{\infty} \mu(E \cap T_i) \to 0$$

as $n \to \infty$. But $E \,\Delta\, E_n = E - E_n$, and so $\mu(E \,\Delta\, E_n) \to 0$. Using what has already been proved, let $G_n$ be a finite union of open intervals such that $\mu(E_n \Delta G_n) < 1/n$. Now, the following inequality is true:

$$\mu(E \Delta G_n) \leq \mu(E \Delta E_n) + \mu(E_n \Delta G_n).$$

(We refer ahead to (6) for this.) We see, therefore, that $\mu(E \Delta G_n) \to 0$. If $\epsilon > 0$, we shall have $\mu(E \Delta G_n) < \epsilon$ for a suitable value of $n$, and then $G_n$ will serve our purpose. This completes the proof.

### A METRIC SPACE FORMED FROM MEASURABLE SETS

Consider the collection $\mathscr{M}$ of all measurable sets in $R^k$ which have finite measure. If $A$ and $B$ are in $\mathscr{M}$ and if $\mu(A \Delta B) = 0$, we shall write $A \sim B$. This relation $\sim$ is an equivalence relation in $\mathscr{M}$. (The transitivity of the relation follows from the inequality

$$\mu(A \Delta C) \leq \mu(A \Delta B) + \mu(B \Delta C), \tag{6}$$

which is easily proved. See Problem 7(d), Section 1–2.) Denote by $[A]$ the equivalence class in $\mathscr{M}$ which contains $A$; we may call $A$ a *representative* of $[A]$. If $A \sim E$ and $B \sim F$, then $\mu(A \Delta B) = \mu(E \Delta F)$. We can see this as follows. In the first place, for any two sets $A_1$, $A_2$ in $\mathscr{M}$,

$$|\mu(A_1) - \mu(A_2)| \leq \mu(A_1 \Delta A_2). \tag{7}$$

We leave the proof of (7) to the reader. Furthermore, the operation $\Delta$ is commutative and associative (see Problem 7, Section 1–2), and therefore $(A \Delta B) \Delta (E \Delta F) = (A \Delta E) \Delta (B \Delta F)$. From this, using (6) and (7), we can see that

$$|\mu(A \Delta B) - \mu(E \Delta F)| \leq \mu(A \Delta E) + \mu(B \Delta F), \tag{8}$$

whence $\mu(A \Delta B) = \mu(E \Delta F)$ if $A \sim E$ and $B \sim F$.

Let us now denote by $\mathscr{M}_\mu$ the set of all equivalence classes formed in $\mathscr{M}$ by the relation $\sim$. We define a function $D : \mathscr{M}_\mu \times \mathscr{M}_\mu \to R$ as follows:

$$D([A], [B]) = \mu(A \Delta B). \tag{9}$$

This is a bona fide definition, for we have seen that the value of $D([A], [B])$ does not depend on the representatives which are chosen for $[A]$ and $[B]$. It is quickly evident that $D$ is a metric on $\mathscr{M}_\mu$.

Theorem 4–8 VI can be given an interpretation in the metric space $\mathscr{M}_\mu$. It asserts that, if $\mathscr{N}$ is the set of elements in $\mathscr{M}_\mu$ such that each member of $\mathscr{N}$ has a representative which is a finite union of open intervals, then $\mathscr{N}$ is dense in $\mathscr{M}_\mu$.

It is an interesting fact that the space $\mathscr{M}_\mu$ is complete. Indications of how to prove this are given in connection with Problem 13.

Theorem 4–8 I shows that every element of $\mathscr{M}_\mu$ has a representative which is a Borel set.

### LINEAR TRANSFORMATIONS AND OUTER MEASURE

For simplicity we first consider the effect of linear transformations in $R$. If $a$ and $b$ are real numbers and $a \neq 0$, the mapping $T$ defined by $T(x) = ax + b$ is a homeomorphic mapping of $R$ onto $R$.

THEOREM 4–8 VII. *If $a \neq 0$, the mapping $T$ defined on $R$ by $T(x) = ax + b$ has the following properties: $\mu^*[T(E)] = |a|\mu^*(E)$ for each set $E$ in $R$: $T(E)$ is measurable if and only if $E$ is measurable.*

*Proof.* Let us define $T_0, T_1, T_2$ as follows:

$$T_0(x) = \frac{a}{|a|}x, \qquad T_1(x) = |a|\, x, \qquad T_2(x) = x + b.$$

Then, evidently, $T(x) = T_2T_1T_0x$, where $T_ix$ means $T_i(x)$. The reader will easily see how to justify the claims that $\mu^*[T_0(E)] = \mu^*(E)$ and $\mu^*[T_2(E)] = \mu^*(E)$, so we shall use these results and omit the proofs. We now see that for the first assertion of the theorem it suffices to prove that $\mu^*[T_1(E)] = a\mu^*(E)$ on the assumption that $a > 0$. Let $\{I_n\}$ be a Lebesgue covering of $E$, and let $I_n = (\alpha_n, \beta_n)$. Let $J_n = (a\alpha_n, a\beta_n)$. Then $\{J_n\}$ is a Lebesgue covering of $T_1(E)$, and $\sum_n |J_n| = a\sum_n |I_n|$, so that $\mu^*[T_1(E)] \leq a\sum_n |I_n|$, from which it follows that $\mu^*[T_1(E)] \leq a\mu^*(E)$. In a similar way we can show that $a\mu^*(E) \leq \mu^*[T_1(E)]$. Therefore $\mu^*(T_1(E)] = a\mu^*(E)$.

Now consider the matter of showing that $T(E)$ is measurable, assuming that $E$ is measurable. We wish to show that

$$\mu^*(B) = \mu^*[B \cap T(E)] + \mu^*[B \cap T(E)^\sim] \tag{10}$$

for every set $B$, Let $A = T^{-1}(B)$, so that $T(A) = B$. Because $E$ is measurable we know that

$$\mu^*(A) = \mu^*(A \cap E) + \mu^*(A \cap E^\sim).$$

Therefore, by what has been proved, we know that if we multiply this last equation through by $|a|$, we can write it in the form

$$\mu^*[T(A)] = \mu^*[T(A \cap E)] + \mu^*[T(A \cap E^\sim)].$$

But $T(A \cap E) = T(A) \cap T(E)$ and $T(A \cap E^\sim) = T(A) \cap T(E^\sim) = T(A) \cap T(E)^\sim$. Therefore we have (10), as required.

Finally, we wish to show that $E$ is measurable if $T(E)$ is measurable. This follows from what has been proved, as applied to $T^{-1}$, for $E = T^{-1}[T(E)]$ and $T^{-1}$ is of the same type as $T\left(\text{in fact, } T^{-1}x = \frac{1}{a}x - \frac{b}{a}\right)$. The proof of Theorem 4–8 VII is now complete.

For an analogue of Theorem 4–8 VII in $R^k$ when $k \geq 2$ we should discuss mappings of the form $x \to Tx + x_0$, where $x_0$ is a fixed vector in $R^k$ and $T$ is a nonsingular homogeneous linear mapping of $R^k$ onto $R^k$. Such a $T$ is defined in the following way by a square matrix: $T(\xi_1, \ldots, \xi_k) = (\eta_1, \ldots, \eta_k)$, where

$$\eta_i = \sum_{j=1}^{k} t_{ij}\xi_j, \qquad i = 1, \ldots, k. \tag{11}$$

To make $T$ nonsingular we require $det(T) \neq 0$, where $det(T)$ denotes the determinant of the matrix.

Since it is evident that a translation mapping $(x \to x + x_0)$ leaves outer measures unchanged and carries measurable sets into measurable sets, we confine our attention to the homogeneous linear mappings.

THEOREM 4–8 VIII. *If $T$ is a linear mapping* (11) *with* $det(T) \neq 0$, *then* (a) $\mu^*[T(E)] = |det(T)|\ \mu^*(E)$ *for each set* $E$ *in* $R^k$, *and* (b) *the set* $T(E)$ *is measurable if and only if* $E$ *is measurable.*

We shall confine ourselves to a sketch of the proof, presenting the plan, but not the details of the argument. To begin with, it is an algebraic fact that $T$ can be expressed as a composition, or succession, of a finite number of simpler linear mappings, say $Tx = T_1T_2 \cdots T_nx$, where each $T_i$ is of one of three basic types. The three types are:

$U$: A mapping which carries a certain $\xi_i$ into $\alpha\xi_i$, where $\alpha \neq 0$, and carries $\xi_j$ into $\xi_j$ if $j \neq i$.

$V$: A mapping which, for a certain pair $i, j$, with $i \neq j$, carries $\xi_i$ into either $\xi_i + \xi_j$ or $\xi_i - \xi_j$, and carries $\xi_l$ into $\xi_l$ if $l \neq i$.

$W$: A mapping which, for a certain pair $i, j$, carries $\xi_i$ into $\xi_j$, $\xi_j$ into $\xi_i$, and $\xi_l$ into $\xi_l$ if $l$ is neither $i$ nor $j$.

It is also an algebraic fact that $\det(T_1 \cdots T_n) = \det(T_1) \cdot \det(T_2) \cdots (\det T_n)$. For the proof of (a) it then suffices to consider separately the cases in which $T$ is one of the three basic types. Once (a) is proved, (b) is proved just as in the proof of Theorem 4–8 VII. We can deal with a $U$-type mapping with the aid of the method used in the proof of Theorem 4–8 VII. The $W$-type can be handled in an obvious manner. For the $V$-type we observe that if $T$ is of $V$-type, so is $T^{-1}$. Therefore it suffices to prove that for a $T$ of $V$-type we always have

$$\mu^*[T(E)] \leq \mu^*(E), \tag{12}$$

because the reverse of this inequality can then be obtained by applying the first result to $T^{-1}T(E)$. Finally, it is not hard to prove (12) once it has been proved in the special case in which $E$ is an open interval. With this sketch we end our discussion of Theorem 4–8 VIII.

## NONMEASURABLE SETS

We shall prove the existence in $R^k$ of sets which are not measurable. The proof makes essential use of the axiom of choice (see Section 3–10) and of the invariance of measurable sets and their measure under the action of translations. The argument depends on some lemmas.

LEMMA 4–8 IX. *Suppose* $0 < \delta < 1$, *and let* $E$ *be a measurable set in* $R^k$ *such that* $\mu(E) > 0$. *Then there exists an open interval* $I$ *such that* $\mu(E \cap I) > \delta\mu(I)$.

*Proof.* Suppose at first that $\mu(E) < +\infty$. Choose a Lebesgue covering $\{I_n\}$ of $E$ such that $\delta \sum_n |I_n| < \mu(E)$. Let $U = \bigcup_n I_n$. Then $E = E \cap U = \bigcup_n (E \cap I_n)$, and so

$$\delta \sum_n |I_n| < \mu(E \cap U) \leq \sum_n \mu(E \cap I_n).$$

Consequently, there is some $n$ such that $\delta|I_n| < \mu(E \cap I_n)$; this $I_n$ can be our $I$. If $\mu(E) = +\infty$, there must be some open interval $J$ such that $0 < \mu(E \cap J) < +\infty$. Hence there is an open interval $K$ such that $\delta\mu(K) < \mu(E \cap J \cap K)$. But then, if $I = J \cap K$, we have

$$\delta\mu(I) \leq \delta\mu(K) < \mu(E \cap I),$$

and the proof is complete.

For a given set $E$ the set $\{x - y : x, y \in E\}$ is called the *difference set* of $E$; we denote it by $E_d$. If $E$ contains an interior point $x_0$, then $x_0 + y \in E$ if $\|y\|$ is sufficiently small, and so, since $x_0 + y - x_0 = y$, we see that in this case $E_d$ contains a neighborhood of 0. The next lemma deals with this matter without assuming that $E$ has an interior point.

LEMMA 4–8 X. *If $E$ is a measurable set in $R^k$, and if $\mu(E) > 0$, the set $E_d$ contains a neighborhood of* 0.

*Proof.* Choose $\lambda$ so that $1 - 2^{-(k+1)} < \lambda < 1$. Using the preceding lemma, choose an open interval $I$ so that $\lambda\mu(I) < \mu(E \cap I)$. Let $\delta$ be the minimum of the lengths of the edges of $I$, and let $J$ be the interval $\{x : |\xi_i| < \delta/2, i = 1, \ldots, k\}$. We shall prove that $J \subset E_d$, thus proving the lemma. It is sufficient to show that for each choice of $x$ in $J$ the sets $E \cap I$ and $(E \cap I) + x$ have a point in common. (Here we use the notation $F + x$ for the set $\{u + x : u \in F\}$.) For, if $u$ and $v$ are in $E \cap I$ and $u = v + x$, we see that $x = u - v$, so that $x \in E_d$. Let $x$ be a fixed element of $J$. Now, by the way in which $\delta$ was chosen, $I + x$ contains the center of $I$, and therefore $\mu[I \cap (I + x)] > 2^{-k}\mu(I)$. As a consequence,

$$\begin{aligned}\mu[I \cup (I + x)] &= \mu(I) + \mu(I + x) - \mu[I \cap (I + x)]\\ &< 2\mu(I) - 2^{-k}\mu(I),\end{aligned}$$

so that

$$\mu[I \cup (I + x)] < 2\lambda\mu(I). \tag{13}$$

Next, let $A = E \cap I$, $B = (E \cap I) + x$. We observe that $\mu(A) = \mu(B) > \lambda\mu(I)$. Therefore, if $A$ and $B$ were disjoint, we would have $\mu(A \cup B) > 2\lambda\mu(I)$. On the other hand, if $y \in A \cup B$, we can write either $y = u$ or $y = v + x$, where $u$ or $v$ is in $E \cap I$. Thus, certainly $A \cup B \subset I \cup (I + x)$, whence $\mu(A \cup B) < 2\lambda\mu(I)$, by (13). It follows that $A$ and $B$ are not disjoint, and the proof is complete.

Now, let $M$ be a set in $R^k$ constructed as follows: Let $z$ be an irrational number and let $M$ be the set of all points in $R^k$ of the form $a + zb$, where $a = (\alpha_1, \ldots, \alpha_k)$, $b = (\beta_1, \ldots, \beta_k)$, and the $\alpha$'s and $\beta$'s are chosen arbitrarily from the set of all integers. This set has the following properties, which are all that are essential for our present purposes: (a) $M$ is a countable set; (b) $M$ is dense in $R^k$; (c) $M$ contains $x + y$ and $x - y$ if it contains $x$ and $y$. Obviously $M$ contains 0. The only nonobvious property here is (b); for the discussion of it see Problem 12 (a).

If $x, y \in R^k$, let us write $x \sim y$ if $x - y \in M$. This relation $\sim$ is an equivalence relation in $R^k$. Using the axiom of choice, we see that there exists a set $S$ which consists of exactly one point from each equivalence class. We shall prove that $\mu_*(S) = 0$. This will imply (Theorem 4–8 IV) that $\mu(S) = 0$ if $S$ is measurable. Let $E$ be any measurable subset of $S$ and suppose $\mu(E) > 0$. Then (Lemma 4–8 X) $E_d$ contains a neighborhood of 0. Therefore $E_d \cap M$ contains a point $x \neq 0$, because $M$ is dense in $R^k$. But then $x = u - v$, where $u$ and $v$ are in $E$. Consequently, we have both $u \sim v$ and $u \neq v$, which contradicts the nature of $S$. Thus we see that every measurable subset of $S$ has measure 0, whence $\mu_*(S) = 0$.

Consider now the sets $S + x$, where $x$ varies over $M$. If $x_1, x_2, \ldots$ is an enumeration of $M$, we see that $R^k = \bigcup_n (S + x_n)$. Therefore, if $S$ were measurable, we would have $0 = \mu(S) = \mu(S + x_n)$ for each $n$, and hence we would arrive at the contradiction

$$+\infty = \mu(R^k) \leq \sum_n \mu(S + x_n) = 0.$$

Consequently, $S$ is not measurable.

It can be shown (see Problem 12(f)) that any measurable set of positive measure contains a nonmeasurable set. For other results on the existence of nonmeasurable sets fulfilling certain supplementary conditions see Problems 10, 11(c).

## SOME EXAMPLES

*Example 1.* Since a set consisting of a single point has measure 0, it follows that any countable set has measure 0. This is true, in particular, of the set of points $x = (\xi_1, \ldots, \xi_k)$ for which the coordinates $\xi_1, \ldots, \xi_k$ are all rational. Observe that this set is dense in $R^k$.

*Example 2.* The Cantor ternary set $S_C[0, 1]$ is an uncountably infinite set of measure 0 in $R$. This set was defined in Section 2–10, and it was proved to be uncountably infinite. The Cantor set is measurable, for it is defined as $[0, 1] - \bigcup_{n=1}^{\infty} E_n$, where the $E_n$'s are disjoint open sets. Then the measure of $S_C[0, 1]$ is $1 - \sum_{n=1}^{\infty} \mu(E_n)$. But we see from Section 2–10 that

$$\mu(E_n) = 2^{n-1}\left(\frac{1}{3}\right)^n, \qquad \sum_{n=1}^{\infty} \mu(E_n) = 1,$$

and so the measure of $S_C[0, 1]$ is 0.

The Cantor set is nowhere dense in [0, 1], for it is closed and it contains no open interval.

It is easy to construct a nowhere dense set on [0, 1] such that its measure is nearly 1.

*Example 3.* Suppose $0 < \epsilon < 1$. Let $\{r_n\}$ be an enumeration of the rational numbers in the open interval (0, 1). Let $I_n$ be the open interval with center $r_n$ and length $2\delta_n$, where $\delta_n = \epsilon \cdot 2^{-n}$. Let $S = [0, 1] - \bigcup_n I_n$. Then $S$ is closed, nowhere dense, and $\mu(S) \geq 1 - \epsilon$.

It is also possible, with $0 < \epsilon < 1$, to construct a perfect and nowhere dense set $S$ on [0, 1] such that $\mu(S) \geq 1 - \epsilon$. See Problem 11(a).

## MEASURABLE SETS WHICH ARE NOT BOREL SETS

It is possible to use a cardinality argument to show that there must be $L$-measurable sets in $R$ which are not Borel sets. We shall indicate the nature of the argument without giving all the details on which it depends.

For general orientation on the subject of transfinite numbers we refer the reader to the following sources: Graves [1], pp. 308–334; Hahn [1], pp. 20–45; Sierpinski [1].

The Cantor set $S_C[0, 1]$ has the same cardinality as that of the set of all real numbers, namely $2^{\aleph_0} = \mathbf{c}$, where $\aleph_0$ is the cardinal of the set of positive integers. This can be seen from the ternary representation of the elements of $S_C[0, 1]$. Now, if $X$ is a nonempty set of cardinality $\mathbf{m}$, the cardinal number of the class of all subsets of $X$ is $2^{\mathbf{m}}$. It is a theorem that $\mathbf{m} < 2^{\mathbf{m}}$ (Graves [1], p. 310; Hahn [1], p. 42). It can be shown that the cardinality of the class of all Borel sets in $R$ is $\mathbf{c}$, the same as that of the Cantor set. The argument depends on the proposition that if $\mathscr{E}$ is a class of sets and the cardinality of $\mathscr{E}$ is $\leq \mathbf{c}$, then the cardinality of the $\sigma$-ring generated by $\mathscr{E}$ is also $\leq \mathbf{c}$. (See Halmos [1], p. 26.) Now let $Y$ be the class of all subsets of $S_C[0, 1]$. We know that every member of $Y$ is L-measurable, with measure 0, because $S_C[0, 1]$ has measure 0. But the cardinal of $Y$ is $2^c$, which is greater than the cardinal of the class of all Borel sets. Hence some members of $Y$ are not Borel sets.

For a different proof that not all measurable sets are Borel sets see Problem 11.

## PROBLEMS

1. If $\{E_n\}$ is a disjoint sequence of measurable sets in $R^k$, and if $E = \bigcup_n E_n$, then $\mu_*(T \cap E) = \sum_n \mu_*(T \cap E_n)$ for every set $T$ in $R^k$.

2. (a) If $E$ and $F$ are sets in $R^k$, show that $\mu_*(E \cup F) \leq \mu_*(E) + \mu^*(F)$. [*Hint.* Consider a measurable cover of $F$ and a measurable kernel of $E \cup F$.] (b) Show that $\mu_*(E) + \mu^*(F) \leq \mu^*(E \cup F)$ if $E$ and $F$ are disjoint.

3. (a) If $E \subset R^k$, $T \subset R^k$, and $T$ is measurable, show that $\mu_*(T \cap E) + \mu^*(T \cap E^{\sim}) = \mu(T)$. Use the preceding problem. (b) Suppose that $T$ is a measurable set of finite measure, that $E \subset T$ and $\mu^*(E) + \mu^*(T - E) = \mu^*(T)$. Prove that $E$ is measurable.

4. If $E$ is a measurable set in $R^k$, there exist sets $A$, $B$ such that $A \subset E \subset B$ and $\mu(B - A) = 0$, (and hence $\mu(A) = \mu(E) = \mu(B)$) with $A$ an $F_\sigma$ set and $B$ a $G_\delta$ set. For the definitions of these terms see Section 2–3.

5. Show that, if $E$ is a measurable set in $R^k$, $\mu(E) = \sup\{\mu(F) : F \subset E, F \text{ compact}\}$. [*Hint.* Consider separately the cases $\mu(E) = +\infty$, $\mu(E) < +\infty$.]

6. Prove (7). Prove also that $\mu(A \,\Delta\, C) \leq \mu(A) + \mu(C)$. Can this be obtained as a special case of (6)?

7. Use (3) and Theorem 4–8 VII to prove that, in the context of Theorem 4–8 VII, $\mu_*[T(E)] = |a|\, \mu_*(E)$ for every $E$.

8. Prove that if $E_n \subset E_{n+1}$ and $E = \bigcup_n E_n$, then $\mu^*(E_n) \to \mu^*(E)$. [*Hint.* Let $H_n$ be a measurable cover of $E_n$ and let $B_n = \bigcap_{i \geq n} H_i$. Show that $\mu(B_n) = \mu^*(E_n)$ and that $\mu^*(E) \leq \lim_{n\to\infty} \mu(B_n)$.]

9. Let **S** be the $\sigma$-ring of Borel sets in $R^k$, Let $\mathcal{T}$ be the family of all homeomorphic mappings of $R^k$ onto itself. Show that, for each $T \in \mathcal{T}$, $T(E)$ is a Borel set if and only if $E$ is a Borel set. [*Suggestion.* Show that the set $\{T(E) : E \in \mathbf{S}\}$ is a $\sigma$-ring which contains **S**, and then show that it coincides with **S**.]

10. Prove, without using the construction in the text, that any open interval $I$ contains a non-measurable set. [*Suggestion.* Denote by $P$ the set of points $x = (\xi_1, \ldots, \xi_k)$ in $R^k$ such that each $\xi_i$ is rational. Define $x \sim y$ to mean $x - y \in P$. Show that the equivalence classes into which $R^k$ is divided by the relation $\sim$ are precisely the sets of the form $P + x$, $x \in R^k$. Why is $(P + x) \cap I \neq \varnothing$ for each $x$? Let $T$ be a set which consists of exactly one point from each of the distinct sets $(P + x) \cap I$. Show that if $p, q$ are distinct points in $P$, $(T + p) \cap (T + q) = \varnothing$. Let $\{p_n\}$ be a bounded sequence of distinct points of $P$. Show that $\bigcup_n (T + p_n)$ is contained in a finite interval, and that $\mu(T)$ would be 0 if $T$ were measurable. Then draw the conclusion that $T$ is not measurable.]

11. (a) The Cantor set $S_C[0, 1]$, described in Section 2–10, is defined as $[0, 1] - \bigcup_{n=1}^{\infty} E_n$, where $E_n$ is the union of disjoint open intervals $E_{ni}$, $i = 1, 2, \ldots, 2^{n-1}$, and each $E_{ni}$ has length $3^{-n}$. Each of the intervals $E_{ni}$ is situated in the middle of one of the $n$ disjoint closed intervals which compose $[0, 1] - \bigcup_{i=1}^{n-1} E_i$. For any $k \geq 3$ this construction process may be imitated, yielding a set $S_k = [0, 1] - \bigcup_{n=1}^{\infty} F_n$, where $F_n$ is the union of disjoint open intervals $F_{ni}$, $i = 1, 2, \ldots, 2^{n-1}$, each of length $k^{-n}$. We assume that $F_{ni}$ is to the left of $F_{nj}$ if $i < j$. Show that $S_k$ is perfect (that is, $S_k = S_k'$), nowhere dense, and that $\mu(S_k) = \dfrac{k-3}{k-2}$. If $k = 3$ we get the Cantor set.

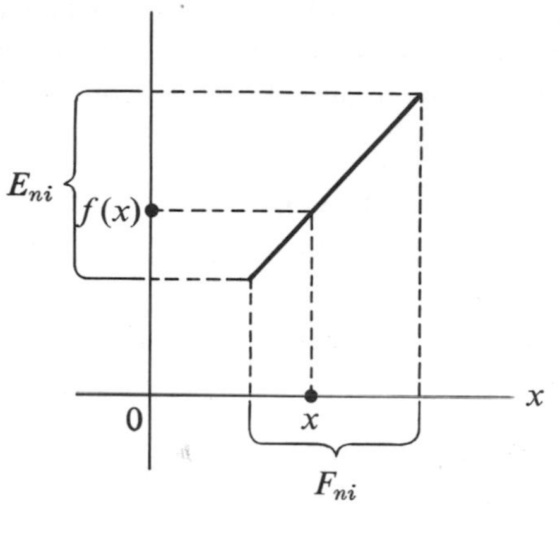


FIGURE 36

(b) Define a function $f : [0, 1] \to R$ as follows. Select a fixed $k > 3$ and use the notations of (a). Define $f$ on $F_{ni}$ so that $f(F_{ni}) = E_{ni}$, with $f(x)$ increasing linearly as $x$ increases (see Figure 36). This defines $f$ on the set $F = \bigcup_n F_n$, which is dense on [0, 1]. The image set $f(F)$ is $E = \bigcup_n E_n$, which is dense on [0, 1]. Show that the definition of $f$ can be extended (in a unique way) to all of [0, 1] so as to make $f$ continuous, increasing, and one-to-one, with $f(S_k) = S_C[0, 1]$.

(c) Let $T$ be a nonmeasurable set contained in (0, 1) (see Problem 10). Explain why $T \cap S_k$ is nonmeasurable for some $k > 3$.

(d) If $f$ is the function in (b), show that $f^{-1}(B)$ is measurable if $B$ is a Borel set on [0, 1]. [*Hint.* Let $\mathbf{S} = \{A \subset [0, 1] : f^{-1}(A)$ is measurable$\}$. Show that $\mathbf{S}$ is a $\sigma$-ring which contains all the Borel sets on [0, 1].]

(e) Referring to (c), choose $k$ so that $T \cap S_k$ is nonmeasurable. Show that $f(T \cap S_k)$ is a measurable set which is not a Borel set.

12. (a) In the construction of the nonmeasurable set $S$ in the text (after the proof of Lemma 4–8 X), use is made of the fact that the set $M$ is dense in $R^k$. To prove this, it is obviously sufficient to show that, when $z$ is irrational, the set of all numbers of the form $m + nz$, where $m$ and $n$ are integers, is dense in $R$. To prove this, observe that for each $n$ the interval $[-nz, 1 - nz)$ (closed at left, open at right) contains exactly one integer, say $p_n$. Then the points $x_n = p_n + nz$ are all in [0, 1), and hence there must be positive differences $|x_n - x_m|$ which are as small as we please. How does the desired result now follow? Where is the irrationality of $z$ used?

(b) Show that the numbers of the form $m + nz$ ($z$ irrational), where $m$ and $n$ are integers and $m$ is even, are dense in $R$, and that the same is true if we require, instead, that $m$ be odd.

(c) Define $M_e$ as the subset of $R^k$ consisting of points $a + zb$, where $a = (\alpha_1, \ldots, \alpha_k)$, $b = (\beta_1, \ldots, \beta_k)$, the $\alpha$'s and $\beta$'s are integers, and $\alpha_1$ is even. Define $M_o$ in the same way, except that $\alpha_1$ is to be odd. Show that $M_e$ and $M_o$ are dense in $R^k$.

(d) Define a set $T$ in $R^k$ as follows: $T = \{x + y : x \in S, y \in M_e\}$, where $S$ is the nonmeasurable set defined in the text. Show that $T^\sim = \{x + y : x \in S, y \in M_o\}$. Use the fact that the set $M_o$ (see (c)) is dense in $R^k$ to prove that $\mu_*(T) = \mu_*(T^\sim) = 0$.

(e) Show that the set $T$ in (d) is such that $\mu_*(T \cap E) = 0$ and $\mu^*(T \cap E) = \mu(E)$ for every measurable set $E$. (Use Problem 3.) What do you conclude about the measurability of $T$?

(f) Show that any measurable set of positive measure (and hence any set of positive outer measure) contains a nonmeasurable set.

13. Prove that the metric space $\mathscr{M}_\mu$ defined in the text (see (9)) is complete. [*Suggestion.* Let $\{E_n\}$ be a sequence in $\mathscr{M}$ such that $\{[E_n]\}$ is a Cauchy sequence in $\mathscr{M}_\mu$. It may be shown that there is a

subsequence $\{G_n\}$ of $\{E_n\}$ such that, if $H = \limsup_{n\to\infty} G_n$ (as defined in Section 1–2), then $H \in \mathcal{M}$ and $\mu(H \,\Delta\, G_n) \to 0$, whence also $\mu(H \,\Delta\, E_n) \to 0$. Moreover, if $G = \liminf_{n\to\infty} G_n$, then $\mu(G \,\Delta\, H) = 0$. To begin with, it may be shown that, if $E = \liminf_{n\to\infty} E_n$ and $F = \limsup_{n\to\infty} E_n$, then $\mu(E - E_n) \to 0$ and $\mu(E_n - F) \to 0$. Next, explain how it is possible to choose a subsequence $\{G_n\}$ of $\{E_n\}$ so that $\mu(G_n \,\Delta\, G_m) < 2^{-m}$ if $m < n$. Then show that $\mu(H - G_n) \to 0$ and $\mu(G_n - G) \to 0$, whence $\mu(H \,\Delta\, G_n) \to 0$, $\mu(G \,\Delta\, G_n) \to 0$, and $\mu(G \,\Delta\, H) = 0$.]

## 4–9 A general method of constructing outer measures

In this section we shall present a general procedure for constructing outer measure functions. The construction of Lebesgue outer measure in $R^k$ is a special case of the application of the general method.

Let $X$ be a nonempty set. Let $\mathcal{G}$ be a family of subsets of $X$ with the following properties:

(a) $\varnothing \in \mathcal{G}$;

(b) If $E \subset X$, then $E$ is contained in some countable union of members of $\mathcal{G}$.

We say that $\mathcal{G}$ is *a sequential covering class* for $X$. If $E \subset \bigcup_n G_n$, where $G_n \in \mathcal{G}$, we call $\{G_n\}$ a *$\mathcal{G}$-covering* of $E$.

Now suppose that we have a function $\lambda : \mathcal{G} \to R^*$ such that $\lambda(\varnothing) = 0$ and $\lambda(G) \geq 0$ for each $G$. For $E \subset X$ let us define

$$\mu^*(E) = \inf \sum_n \lambda(G_n), \tag{1}$$

where the infimum is taken as $\{G_n\}$ varies over all possible $\mathcal{G}$-coverings of $E$.

If $X = R^k$, if $\mathcal{G}$ is the class consisting of $\varnothing$ and all open intervals in $R^k$, and if we define $\lambda(G) =$ the content of $G$ when $G$ is an open interval, we see that $\mu^*$ is exactly the Lebesgue outer measure function.

THEOREM 4–9 I. *Let $\mathcal{G}$ be a sequential covering class for $X$. Then the function $\mu^*$ defined in* (1) *is an outer measure on $X$.*

*Proof,* We refer to conditions (a)–(d) in Section 4–7. Conditions (a) and (b) are obviously satisfied by $\mu^*$ in the present situation. The proofs that conditions (c) and (d) are satisfied are exactly like the corresponding proofs in the case of the construction of Lebesgue outer measure in $R^k$ (Theorems 4–6 V, VI).

In the case of Lebesgue outer measure, with $\lambda(G) = |G|$ (the content of the open interval $G$), we know that $\mu^*(G) = \lambda(G)$. In the present general theory we always have $\mu^*(G) \leq \lambda(G)$, but it may happen that $\mu^*(G) < \lambda(G)$ for certain $G$'s.

*Example 1.* Let $X$ be an infinite class; let $\mathcal{G}$ consist of $\varnothing$, $X$, and the finite subsets of $X$. Suppose $\lambda(\varnothing) = 0$, $\lambda(X) = +\infty$, and $\lambda(G) = n - 1$ if $G$ is a finite class with $n$ elements, $n \geq 1$. Then $\mu^*(E) = 0$ if $E$ is any nonempty countable set, while $\mu^*(E) = +\infty$ if $E$ is an uncountable set. We leave the details to the reader. It turns out in this case that every subset of $X$ is $\mu^*$-measurable.

The next example shows that the members of $\mathcal{G}$ are not necessarily $\mu^*$-measurable.

*Example 2.* Let $X$ be the class of positive integers. Let $\mathcal{G}$ consist of $\varnothing$ and the sets having exactly two members, with $\lambda(\varnothing) = 0$, $\lambda(G) = 2$ if $G \in \mathcal{G}$ and $G \neq \varnothing$. Then it is easy to see that $\mu^*(E) = n$ if $E$ has exactly $n$ elements and $n$ is a positive even integer, while $\mu^*(E) = n + 1$ if $E$ has exactly $n$ elements and $n$ is an odd positive integer. Of course, $\mu^*(E) = +\infty$ if $E$ is an infinite set. In this case $E$ is not $\mu^*$-measurable if $E$ has $2n + 1$ elements ($n \geq 0$). For example, if $E = \{1, 2, 3\}$ and $T = \{1, 2, 3, 4, 5, 6\}$, we have $\mu^*(T) = 6$, but

$$\mu^*(E \cap T) + \mu^*(E^\sim \cap T) = 4 + 4 \neq \mu^*(T).$$

In the next theorem we describe a situation in which the members of $\mathcal{G}$ are $\mu^*$-measurable and $\lambda(G) = \mu^*(G)$ for each $G \in \mathcal{G}$.

THEOREM 4–9 II. *Suppose that $\mathcal{G}$ is a ring of sets in $X$, and a sequential covering class for $X$, and that the function $\lambda$, in addition to having the properties already mentioned, is such that* (a) *$\lambda$ is finitely additive, and* (b) *$\lambda(G) \leq \sum_n \lambda(G_n)$ whenever $G, G_1, G_2, \ldots$ are in $\mathcal{G}$ and $G \subset \bigcup_n G_n$. (In particular, $\lambda$ may be any measure function defined on the ring $\mathcal{G}$.) Then $\mu^*(G) = \lambda(G)$ for each $G$, and each $G$ is $\mu^*$-measurable.*

*Proof.* We have already noted that $\mu^*(G) \leq \lambda(G)$. The reverse inequality follows from property (b) of $\lambda$. Thus $\lambda(G) = \mu^*(G)$. To see that elements of $\mathcal{G}$ are $\mu^*$-measurable, suppose $G \in \mathcal{G}$, $T \subset X$. Let $\{G_n\}$ be any $\mathcal{G}$-covering of $T$. Since $\mathcal{G}$ is a ring, $\{G_n \cap G\}$ is a $\mathcal{G}$-covering of $T \cap G$, and $\{G_n \cap G^\sim\}$ is a $\mathcal{G}$-covering of $T \cap G^\sim$. Thus

$$\mu^*(T \cap G) \leq \sum_n \lambda(G_n \cap G),$$

$$\mu^*(T \cap G^\sim) \leq \sum_n \lambda(G_n \cap G^\sim).$$

But, since $\lambda$ is additive, we have

$$\lambda(G_n \cap G) + \lambda(G_n \cap G^\sim) = \lambda(G_n).$$

Therefore

$$\mu^*(T \cap G) + \mu^*(T \cap G^\sim) \leq \sum_n \lambda(G_n).$$

In view of the arbitrary character of $\{G_n\}$ we see that

$$\mu^*(T \cap G) + \mu^*(T \cap G^\sim) \leq \mu^*(T).$$

This proves that $G$ is $\mu^*$-measurable, for the reverse inequality is certainly true.

We can reach the same conclusions as in Theorem 4–9 II with a somewhat different hypothesis about the natures of $\mathcal{G}$ and $\lambda$. For this we introduce the concept of a semiring.

A class $\mathcal{G}$ of subsets of $X$ is called a *semiring* if $\varnothing \in \mathcal{G}$, if $G_1 \cap G_2 \in \mathcal{G}$ when $G_1$ and $G_2$ are in $\mathcal{G}$, and if, when $G_1, G_2 \in \mathcal{G}$ and $G_1 \subset G_2$, the set $G_2 - G_1$ is expressible as a countable union of disjoint members of $\mathcal{G}$.

*Example 3.* Let $X = R$, and let $\mathcal{G}$ consist of $\varnothing$ and all finite, left-closed, right-open intervals $[a, b)$, where $a < b$. Then $\mathcal{G}$ is a semiring.

THEOREM 4–9 III. *Let $\mathcal{G}$ be a semiring in $X$, and suppose also that $\mathcal{G}$ is a sequential covering class for $X$. Let $\lambda : \mathcal{G} \to R^*$ be a nonnegative and countably additive function on $\mathcal{G}$, such that $\lambda(\varnothing) = 0$. Then, if $\mu^*$ is the outer measure on $X$ defined by* (1), *each member of $\mathcal{G}$ is $\mu^*$-measurable, and $\mu^*(G) = \lambda(G)$ if $G \in \mathcal{G}$.*

*Proof.* We first show that $\lambda$ is monotone. If $G_1, G_2 \in \mathscr{G}$ and $G_1 \subset G_2$, we can write $G_2 - G_1 = \bigcup_n F_n$, where $F_1, F_2, \ldots$ are disjoint members of $\mathscr{G}$. Then, by the countable additivity,

$$\lambda(G_2) = \lambda(G_1) + \sum_n \lambda(F_n).$$

Since $\lambda(F_n) \geq 0$, it follows that $\lambda(G_2) \geq \lambda(G_1)$.

Next, it is possible to show that if $G \in \mathscr{G}$ and $\{G_n\}$ is a $\mathscr{G}$-covering of $G$, then $\lambda(G) \leq \sum_n \lambda(G_n)$. See Problem 1 (c). From this we conclude, as in the proof of Theorem 4–9 II, that $\mu^*(G) = \lambda(G)$.

To show that elements of $\mathscr{G}$ are $\mu^*$-measurable, suppose $G \in \mathscr{G}$, $T \subset X$, and let $\{G_n\}$ be a $\mathscr{G}$-covering of $T$. Then $\{G_n \cap G\}$ is a $\mathscr{G}$-covering of $T \cap G$. By hypothesis we can express $G_n \cap G^\sim = G_n - G$ in the form $G_n - G = \bigcup_j F_{nj}$, where $F_{n1}, F_{n2}, \ldots$ is a disjoint sequence from $\mathscr{G}$. Then $\bigcup_{n,j} F_{nj}$ is a $\mathscr{G}$-covering of $T \cap G^\sim$. We now know that

$$\mu^*(T \cap G) + \mu^*(T \cap G^\sim) \leq \sum_n \lambda(G_n \cap G) + \sum_{n,j} \lambda(F_{nj}). \tag{2}$$

But $G_n = (G_n \cap G) \cup \bigcup_j F_{nj}$, and the countable additivity of $\lambda$ implies that

$$\lambda(G_n) = \lambda(G_n \cap G) + \sum_j \lambda(F_{nj});$$

therefore we see from (2) that

$$\mu^*(T \cap G) + \mu^*(T \cap G^\sim) \leq \sum_n \lambda(G_n).$$

This enables us to conclude that $G$ is $\mu^*$-measurable, just as in the proof of Theorem 4–9 II.

One interesting application of Theorem 4–9 III can be made by taking $X$ and $\mathscr{G}$ as indicated in Example 3, and defining $\lambda$ by $\lambda(\varnothing) = 0$, $\lambda(G) = b - a$ if $G = [a, b)$. It is necessary to show that this $\lambda$ is countably additive on $\mathscr{G}$. This is not difficult. See Problem 2 (b).

## A METRIC OUTER MEASURE

We now consider the general situation of Theorem 4–9 I when $X$ is a metric space. Under certain conditions we can be sure that the outer measure $\mu^*$ defined by (1) is a metric outer measure.

THEOREM 4–9 IV. *Let $X$ be a metric space. Let $\mathscr{G}$ be a sequential covering class for $X$, and let $\lambda : \mathscr{G} \to R^*$ be nonnegative, with $\lambda(\varnothing) = 0$. Let $\mathscr{G}_n$ consist of $\varnothing$ and those members of $\mathscr{G}$ whose diameters do not exceed $1/n$. We assume that each $\mathscr{G}_n$ is a sequential covering class for $X$. Let $\mu_n^*$ be the outer measure derived from $\mathscr{G}_n$ and $\lambda$ as $\mu^*$ is derived from $\mathscr{G}$ and $\lambda$. Finally, suppose that $\mu_n^*(G) \leq \lambda(G)$ if $G \in \mathscr{G}$, for each $n$. Then $\mu^*$ is a metric outer measure.*

*Proof.* First we prove that $\mu_n^* = \mu^*$. It is evident that $\mu^*(E) \leq \mu_n^*(E)$ if $E \subset X$, so we wish to prove that $\mu_n^*(E) \leq \mu^*(E)$. Evidently we may assume $\mu^*(E) < +\infty$. Suppose $\epsilon > 0$. Choose a $\mathscr{G}$-covering $\{G_i\}$ of $E$ such that $\sum_i \lambda(G_i) < \mu^*(E) + \epsilon/2$. Our hypothesis assures us that there exists a $\mathscr{G}_n$-covering $G_{i1}, G_{i2}, \ldots$ of $G_i$ such that $\sum_j \lambda(G_{ij}) < \lambda(G_i) + \epsilon/2^{i+1}$.

The double sequence $\{G_{ij}\}$ is then a $\mathscr{G}_n$-covering of $E$, and

$$\sum_{i,j} \lambda(G_{ij}) < \sum_i \left[\lambda(G_i) + \frac{\epsilon}{2^{i+1}}\right] < \mu^*(E) + \epsilon.$$

Therefore, since $\epsilon$ is arbitrary, $\mu_n^*(E) \leq \mu^*(E)$.

Now, suppose $E_1$ and $E_2$ are nonempty subsets of $X$ a positive distance $D(E_1, E_2)$ apart. Choose $n$ so that $1/n < D(E_1, E_2)$. Let $\{G_i\}$ be a $\mathscr{G}_n$-covering of $E_1 \cup E_2$. By the definition of $\mathscr{G}_n$, no $G_i$ can contain a point of $E_1$ and also a point of $E_2$. Therefore we can divide the sets $G_1, G_2, \ldots$ into two classes, one class forming a $\mathscr{G}_n$-covering of $E_1$, the other a $\mathscr{G}_n$-covering of $E_2$. In this way we see that

$$\mu_n^*(E_1) + \mu_n^*(E_2) \leq \sum_i \lambda(G_i),$$

and hence that $\mu_n^*(E_1) + \mu_n^*(E_2) \leq \mu_n^*(E_1 \cup E_2)$. Since the reverse inequality is also true, and since $\mu_n^* = \mu^*$, we see that $\mu^*$ is a metric outer measure.

The reader should compare this theorem and its proof with Theorem 4–6 VII, Lemma 4–6 VIII, and their proofs.

**PROBLEMS**

1. Assume the conditions placed on $\mathscr{G}$ and $\lambda$ in Theorem 4–9 III.

(a) Show by induction that if $G_1, G_2, \ldots$ are in $\mathscr{G}$, then for $n \geq 2$ $G_n - (G_1 \cup \cdots \cup G_{n-1})$ is expressible as a countable disjoint union of members of $\mathscr{G}$.

(b) If $G, G_1, G_2, \ldots$ are in $\mathscr{G}$, if $G_1, G_2, \ldots$ are disjoint and $\bigcup_n G_n \subset G$, show that $\sum_n \lambda(G_n) \leq \lambda(G)$.

(c) If $G, G_1, G_2, \ldots$ are in $\mathscr{G}$ and $G \subset \bigcup_n G_n$, show that $\lambda(G) \leq \sum_n \lambda(G_n)$. Begin as in the proof of Theorem 4–4 I.

2. (a) Let $\mathscr{G}$ be a semiring and also a sequential covering class for $X$. Suppose $\lambda : \mathscr{G} \to R^*$ has the properties (1) $\lambda(\varnothing) = 0$, (2) $\lambda(G) \geq 0$ for each $G$, (3) if $G$ and $G_1, G_2, \ldots$ are in $\mathscr{G}$ and $G \subset \bigcup_n G_n$, then $\lambda(G) \leq \sum_n \lambda(G_n)$, (4) if $G_1, \ldots, G_n$ are disjoint members of $\mathscr{G}$, if $G \in \mathscr{G}$ and $G \supset \bigcup_{i=1}^n G_i$, then $\lambda(G) \geq \sum_{i=1}^n \lambda(G_i)$. Prove that $\lambda$ is countably additive on $\mathscr{G}$.

(b) With $X$ and $\mathscr{G}$ as in Example 3, let $\lambda(\varnothing) = 0$, $\lambda(G) = b - a$ if $G = [a, b)$. Prove that $\lambda$ is countably additive on $\mathscr{G}$ by using (a). [*Suggestion.* To show that $\lambda$ satisfies condition (3), choose a suitable closed subinterval of $G$ and note Lemma 4–6 II.]

## 4–10 Outer measures in $R$ from monotone functions

In this section we shall examine in some detail a generalization of Lebesgue measure in $R$. First we must discuss a few things about monotone real functions.

Suppose that $D$ is a connected subset of $R$ consisting of more than one point. If $D$ is bounded, it is a finite interval; one or both endpoints of the interval may fail to be in $D$. If $D$ is unbounded, but not all of $R$, there is but one endpoint of $D$; it may belong to $D$, or it may not. Let $v : D \to R$ be a function such that $v(x_1) \leq v(x_2)$ if $x_1$ and $x_2$ are points of $D$ such that $x_1 < x_2$. Then we say $v$ is *a nondecreasing function.* For such a function, $v(x)$ approaches a finite limit as $x$ approaches a point $t$ of $D$ from one side. We denote by $v(t+)$ the limit of $v(x)$ as $x$ approaches $t$ from the right; the limit from the left is denoted by $v(t-)$. It may be, of course, that $x \leq t$ for each $x$ in $D$. In this case $v(t+)$ is undefined. If there are points $x$ in $D$ with $t < x$, $v(t+)$ is the greatest lower bound of the values $v(x)$ for such $x$. Observe that $v(t) \leq v(t+)$. It may happen that $v(t) < v(t+)$. Similar remarks apply to $v(t-)$.

If $v(t) = v(t+)$, we say that $v$ is continuous from the right at $t$; $v$ is continuous from the left at $t$ if $v(t-) = v(t)$. The condition for continuity of $v$ at an interior point of $D$ is that $v(t-) = v(t+)$ (this common value is then necessarily $v(t)$). At an endpoint of $D$, $v$ is continuous if the available one of $v(t+)$, $v(t-)$ coincides with $v(t)$.

It is an important fact that, if $S$ is the set of points at which $v$ is discontinuous, then $S$ is a countable set. Since $D$ has at most two endpoints, it suffices to show that the set of interior points of $D$ in $S$ is countable. If $t$ is such a point, we associate with it the open interval $(v(t-), v(t+))$. If $t_1$ and $t_2$ are two such points, with $t_1 < t_2$, the associated open intervals are disjoint, because $t_1 < t_2$ implies $v(t_1+) \leq v(t_2-)$. But a collection of disjoint nonempty open intervals is certainly countable (for example, because each interval contains a rational point of $R$). This finishes the argument that $S$ is countable.

## METHOD 1: $v$ CONTINUOUS FROM THE RIGHT

We shall use a special case of the method of Section 4–9 to construct an outer measure in $R$. Let $\mathscr{G}$ be the class of subsets of $R$ consisting of $\varnothing$ and all sets $G$ of the form $\{x : a < x \leq b\}$, where $a$, $b$ are in $R$ and $a < b$. For convenience we shall write $G = (a, b]$. It is easy to see that if $G_1$, $G_2$ are two members of $\mathscr{G}$, then $G_1 \cap G_2 \in \mathscr{G}$; also, if $G_1 \subset G_2$, then $G_2 - G_1$ is either in $\mathscr{G}$ or is the union of two disjoint members of $\mathscr{G}$. Hence $\mathscr{G}$ satisfies the conditions imposed on $\mathscr{G}$ in Theorem 4–9 III.

Now let $v : R \to R$ be a nondecreasing function which is continuous from the right at each point. If $G = (a, b]$, let $\lambda(G) = v(b) - v(a)$; also let $\lambda(\varnothing) = 0$. It can be shown that $\lambda$ is countably additive on $\mathscr{G}$ (see Problem 1(d)). Hence, using (1) in Section 4–9, we can define an outer measure $\mu^*$ on $R$, and the conclusions of Theorem 4–9 III are applicable. We shall say that $\mu^*$ is generated by $v$ by Method I.

THEOREM 4–10 I. *Let $\mu^*$ be the outer measure on $R$ generated by the right-continuous nondecreasing function $v$ in the manner heretofore described (Method I). Then $\mu^*$ is a metric outer measure, so that all Borel sets are $\mu^*$-measurable. If $G = (a, b]$, $\mu^*(G) = v(b) - v(a)$. If $E$ is a bounded set, $\mu^*(E)$ is finite. If $F$ is a set consisting of a single point $c$, $\mu^*(F) = v(c) - v(c-)$.*

*Proof.* The assertion about $G$ comes from Theorem 4–9 III. If $E$ is bounded, it is included in some $G$, and hence $\mu^*(E) \leq \mu^*(G) < +\infty$. Proof of the assertion about $F$ is left as a problem.

To see that $\mu^*$ is a metric outer measure we proceed to show that Theorem 4–9 IV is applicable. We use the notation $\mathscr{G}_n$ as in that theorem. It is obvious that $\mathscr{G}_n$ is a sequential covering class for $R$. Suppose $G = (a, b]$ and $\epsilon > 0$. We wish to produce a $\mathscr{G}_n$-covering $\{G_i\}$ of $G$ such that $\sum_i \lambda(G_i) < \lambda(G) + \epsilon$, for this will show that $\mu_n^*(G) \leq \lambda(G)$. Let the interval $[a, b]$ be divided into $m$ equal parts by points $x_0, x_1, \ldots, x_m$, $a = x_0 < x_1 < \cdots < x_m = b$, with $m$ chosen so that $\dfrac{b-a}{m} < \dfrac{1}{2n}$. Since $v$ is continuous from the right we can choose $\delta$, with $0 < \delta \leq \dfrac{1}{2n}$, so that $0 \leq t - x_i \leq \delta$ implies

$$0 \leq v(t) - v(x_i) < \frac{\epsilon}{m}, \qquad i = 1, \ldots, m.$$

Now let $G_i = (x_{i-1}, t_k]$, where $t_i = x_i + \delta$. Then diam $(G_i) < 1/n$, $G \subset \bigcup_i G_i$, and

$$\sum_i \lambda(G_i) = \sum_i [v(t_i) - v(x_i)] + v(b) - v(a) < \lambda(G) + \epsilon.$$

This finishes the proof that Theorem 4–9 IV is applicable. Since $\mu^*$ is a metric outer measure, all open sets are $\mu^*$-measurable. But then, since the $\mu^*$-measurable sets form a $\sigma$-ring, all Borel sets are $\mu^*$-measurable.

The outer measure $\mu^*$ thus generated by $v$ determines a class of $\mu^*$-measurable sets and a measure on this class. This measure is variously called a Lebesgue-Stieltjes measure, a Lebesgue-Radon measure, and a Radon measure. The intervention of the name of Stieltjes here is somewhat curious. The measure in question is a generalization of Lebesgue measure, for it is exactly the classical Lebesgue measure in $R$ if $v(x) = x$ for all $x$. This and other similar generalizations of Lebesgue measure were introduced by J. Radon (1887–1956) (See Radon [1]). However, T. J. Stieltjes (1856–1894) had in 1894 introduced a generalization of the Riemann integral. If $f \in C[a, b]$ and $v : [a, b] \to R$ is nondecreasing, the Stieltjes integral of $f$ with respect to $v$, denoted by $\int_a^b f(x)\, dv(x)$, is defined by the same procedure used in defining the Riemann integral $\int_a^b f(x)\, dx$, except that the length of a subinterval $[\alpha, \beta]$ of $[a, b]$ is replaced by $v(\beta) - v(\alpha)$ in forming the approximating sums. (See Section 9–5.) The existence of this concept of an integral provided a motivation for the generalization of Lebesgue measure, and it turned out that, just as the Riemann integral of a continuous $f$ has the same value as the Lebesgue integral of $f$, so the Stieltjes integral of a continuous $f$ with respect to $v$ has the same value as the integral of $f$ with respect to a suitable measure of the type considered by Radon. We omit details at this point, but see Section 9–5, especially Problem 8.

## ADDITIVE INTERVAL FUNCTIONS

The function $\lambda$ introduced in connection with Theorem 4–10 I is countably additive on a class of intervals. This property of $\lambda$ depends essentially on the assumption that the function $v$ is continuous from the right.

We shall now show how to construct a metric outer measure in $R$ with the aid of an interval function which is merely assumed to be finitely additive. For this purpose we introduce the following notation and definitions.

Let $\mathscr{I}$ be the class consisting of $\varnothing$ and all closed intervals $I = [a, b]$ (where $a < b$). Let $I^o$ denote the interior of $I$. Two intervals $I_1, I_2$ are called *nonoverlapping* if $I_1 \cap I_2^o = I_1^o \cap I_2 = \varnothing$. Let $\alpha : \mathscr{I} \to R$ be a function with nonnegative values such that $\alpha(\varnothing) = 0$ and $\alpha(I_1 \cup I_2) = \alpha(I_1) + \alpha(I_2)$ if $I_1$ and $I_2$ are nonoverlapping intervals from $\mathscr{I}$ such that $I_1 \cup I_2 \in \mathscr{I}$. Then we shall call $\alpha$ a nonnegative additive interval function. If $v : R \to R$ is any nondecreasing function, and if we define $\alpha(\varnothing) = 0$, $\alpha([a, b]) = v(b) - v(a)$, we obtain a function $\alpha$ of the type just described. All nonnegative additive interval functions arise in this way. For, if $\alpha$ is given, and if we define

$$v(x) = \begin{cases} \alpha([0, x]), & x > 0, \\ 0, & x = 0 \\ -\alpha([x, 0]), & x < 0, \end{cases}$$

we can see that $v$ is nondecreasing and that $\alpha([a, b]) = v(b) - v(a)$.

## METHOD II: ARBITRARY $v$

Suppose now that we have $\alpha : \mathscr{I} \to R$ coming from an arbitrary nondecreasing function $v$ in the manner described. Let $\mathscr{G}$ be the class consisting of $\varnothing$ and all nonempty open intervals (the interiors of intervals from $\mathscr{I}$), and define $\lambda(I^\circ) = \alpha(I)$ if $I \in \mathscr{I}$, $\lambda(\varnothing) = 0$. Then we can use $\lambda$ and $\mathscr{G}$ to define an outer measure $\mu^*$ by (1) in Section 4–9. That is, if $E \subset R$,

$$\mu^*(E) = \inf \sum_n \alpha(I_n), \tag{1}$$

where the infimum is taken over all sequences $\{I_n\}$ from $\mathscr{I}$ such that $E \subset \bigcup_n I_n^o$.

We observe that we are covering $E$ with a union of open intervals. Hence the situation here is not the same as it was earlier in this section, where we used coverings by *half-open* intervals of the type $(a, b]$. Here we say that $\mu^*$ is generated by $v$ by Method II.

THEOREM 4–10 II. *The outer measure $\mu^*$ defined on R by (1), with $\mathscr{I}$ and $\alpha$ as specified, is a metric outer measure, so that all Borel sets are $\mu^*$-measurable. For a closed interval $E = [a, b]$ we have $\mu^*(E) = v(b+) - v(a-)$. For a set F consisting of a single point c we have $\mu^*(F) = v(c+) - v(c-)$.*

*Proof.* First we demonstrate the following auxiliary proposition: Given $I \in \mathscr{I}$ and $\epsilon > 0$, $\delta > 0$, there exists a finite number of elements of $\mathscr{I}$, say $J_1, \ldots, J_n$, such that $I^o \subset \bigcup_i J_j^o$, the length of each $J_i$ is less than $\delta$, and $\sum_i \alpha(J_i) < \alpha(I) + \epsilon$. Let $S$ be the countable set of discontinuities of the nondecreasing function $v$. We can choose points $x_0, x_1, \ldots, x_n$ with $a = x_0 < x_1 < \cdots < x_n = b$ in such a way that $x_i - x_{i-1} < \delta$ for each $i$ and $x_1, \ldots, x_{n-1}$ are not in $S$. Let $I_i = [x_{i-1}, x_i]$, $i = 1, \ldots, n$. Then $\alpha(I) = \alpha(I_1) + \cdots + \alpha(I_n)$, and $\alpha(I_i) = v(x_i) - v(x_{i-1})$. Now let $s_1 = x_0$, and choose $s_{i+1} < x_i$ $(i = 1, \ldots, n - 1)$ in such a way that $v(s_{i+1}) > v(x_i) - \epsilon/2n$. Let $t_n = x_n$, and choose $t_i > x_i (i = 1, \ldots, n - 1)$ in such a way that $v(t_i) < v(x_i) + \epsilon/2n$. We also insist that $s_i$ and $t_i$ be chosen in such a way that $t_i - s_i < \delta$. Let $J_i = [s_i, t_i]$. This choice of $J_1, \ldots, J_n$ meets the requirements of our proposition.

Next we assert that for any $E$ the infimum in (1) is not changed if we choose any $\delta > 0$ and consider only sequences $\{I_n\}$ from $\mathscr{I}$ such that $E \subset \bigcup_n I_n^0$ and the length of each $I_n$ is less than $\delta$. The proof is like that of Lemma 4–6 VIII, with our auxiliary proposition taking the place of Lemma 4–6 I.

The proof that $\mu^*$ is a metric outer measure is now like the proof of Theorem 4–6 VII.

We now know (see Theorem 4–7 VII and the early part of Section 4–8) that all Borel sets are $\mu^*$-measurable. If $F$ is the set consisting of a single point $c$, we see that $F \subset [c - \epsilon, c + \epsilon]$ when $\epsilon > 0$. Hence $\mu^*(F) \leq v(c + \epsilon) - v(c - \epsilon)$. Letting $\epsilon \to 0$, we see that $\mu^*(F) \leq v(c+) - v(c-)$. On the other hand, if $a < c < b$, $v(a) \leq v(c-)$, $v(c+) \leq v(b)$, so $v(c+) - v(c-) \leq v(b) - v(a)$. From this it is clear that if $F \subset \bigcup_n I_n^o$, where $I_n \in \mathscr{I}$, we certainly have $v(c+) - v(c-) \leq \sum_n \alpha(I_n)$, whence $v(c+) - v(c-) \leq \mu^*(F)$. Thus $\mu^*(F)$ has the value asserted.

To compute $\mu^*(E)$, where $E = [a, b]$, we proceed as follows: Since $E \subset [a - \epsilon, b + \epsilon]$ if $\epsilon > 0$, we certainly have $\mu^*(E) \leq v(b + \epsilon) - v(a - \epsilon)$, and therefore $\mu^*(E) \leq v(b+) - v(a-)$. Next we show that $v(b) - v(a) \leq \mu^*(E)$. Suppose that $E \subset \bigcup_n I_n^o$, where $I_n \in \mathscr{I}$.

By the Borel theorem we may suppose the number of $I_n$'s is finite. But then $\alpha(E) \leq \sum_n \alpha(I_n)$. (This comes from Problem 1 (b), for if $G = (a, b]$, $\lambda(G)$ in the problem is $v(b) - v(a) = \alpha(E)$. No continuity conditions on $v$ are needed.) Thus we see that $\alpha(E) \leq \mu^*(E)$. We now know that

$$v(b) - v(a) \leq \mu^*(E) \leq v(b+) - v(a-).$$

This implies that $\mu^*(E) = v(b) - v(a)$ if $a$ and $b$ are points of continuity of $v$. We can choose an interval $[\alpha, \beta]$ with $a < \alpha < \beta < b$ in such a way that $v$ is continuous at $\alpha$ and $\beta$, with $\alpha$ and $\beta$ as close as we please to $a$ and $b$, respectively. Now, $[\alpha, \beta] \cup \{a\} \cup \{b\} \subset E$. Therefore, since all these sets are measurable,

$$\mu^*([\alpha, \beta]) + \mu^*(\{a\}) + \mu^*(\{b\}) \leq \mu^*(E).$$

Evaluating the terms on the left, we have

$$v(\beta) - v(\alpha) + v(a+) - v(a-) + v(b+) - v(b-) \leq \mu^*(E).$$

By choosing a sequence of $\beta$'s converging to $b$ and a sequence of $\alpha$'s converging to $a$ we obtain the result $v(b+) - v(a-) \leq \mu^*(E)$, and so finally $\mu^*(E) = v(b+) - v(a-)$. This completes the proof of Theorem 4–10 II.

## COMPARISON OF METHODS I AND II

We shall show that if $v$ is nondecreasing and continuous from the right, the outer measures $\mu_1^*$ and $\mu_2^*$ generated by $v$, using Methods I and II respectively, are the same. Given any set $E$ and any sequence $\{I_n\}$ from $\mathscr{I}$ such that $E \subset \bigcup_n I_n^o$, suppose $I_n = [a_n, b_n]$ and let $G_n = (a_n, b_n]$. Then $E \subset \bigcup_n G_n$, and hence, by Method I, $\mu_1^*(E) \leq \sum_n \lambda(G_n)$. But

$$\sum_n \lambda(G_n) = \sum_n [v(b_n) - v(a_n)] = \sum_n \alpha(I_n).$$

Therefore $\mu_1^*(E) \leq \mu_2^*(E)$.

Next we wish to prove that $\mu_2^*(E) \leq \mu_1^*(E)$, and for this we may assume $\mu_1^*(E) < +\infty$. If $\epsilon > 0$, choose $\{G_n\}$ with $G_n = (a_n, b_n]$ so that $E \subset \bigcup_n G_n$ and $\sum_n \lambda(G_n) < \mu_1^*(E) + \epsilon/2$. Using the fact that $v$ is continuous from the right at $b_n$, choose $\beta_n > b_n$ so that $v(\beta_n) < v(b_n) + \epsilon/2^{n+1}$. Let $I_n = [a_n, \beta_n]$. Then $G_n \subset I_n^o$, so that

$$\mu_2^*(E) \leq \sum_n \alpha(I_n) < \sum_n \left[\lambda_n(G) + \frac{\epsilon}{2^{n+1}}\right] < \mu_1^*(E) + \epsilon.$$

It follows that $\mu_2^*(E) \leq \mu_1^*(E)$ and so that $\mu_2^* = \mu_1^*$.

If $v$ is not continuous from the right, we can use Method II, but not Method I. However, we can associate with $v$ in a simple way a function which is continuous from the right. With $v$ given, define $\bar{v}$ by

(2) $$\bar{v}(x) = v(x+).$$

Then $\bar{v}(x) = v(x)$ at every point $x$ where $v$ is continuous. We see readily that $\bar{v}$ is nondecreasing. Since the set of points of discontinuity is countable, it is easy to see that

(3) $$\bar{v}(x+) = v(x+), \qquad \bar{v}(x-) = v(x-).$$

Hence $\bar{v}$ is continuous from the right. Let $\bar{\mu}^*$ be the outer measure generated by $\bar{v}$; as we have seen, we get the same results by Methods I and II.

We shall show that $\mu^* = \bar{\mu}^*$, where $\mu^*$ is obtained from $v$ by Method II. We begin by finding the measure of an open interval. From Theorem 4–10 II we see that, if $E = (a, b)$,

$$\mu^*(E) = v(b+) - v(a-) - [v(a+) - v(a-)] - [v(b+) - v(b-)],$$

or

$$\mu^*(E) = v(b-) - v(a+). \tag{4}$$

By (3) we see that $\bar{\mu}^*(E) = \mu^*(E)$ when $E$ is an open interval.

Next we show that for any $E$,

$$\mu^*(E) = \inf \mu^*(U), \tag{5}$$

where the infimum is taken as $U$ varies over all open sets $U$ such that $E \subset U$. If $I$ is a closed interval $[a, b]$, we observe that $\mu^*(I^o) = v(b-) - v(a+) \leq v(b) - v(a) = \alpha(I)$. Now suppose that $\epsilon > 0$. Choose a sequence $\{I_n\}$ of closed intervals such that $E \subset \bigcup_n I_n^o$ and $\sum_n \alpha(I_n) < \mu^*(E) + \epsilon$. Let $U = \bigcup_n I_n^o$. Then $U$ is open, $E \subset U$, and

$$\mu^*(U) \leq \sum_n \mu^*(I_n^o) \leq \sum_n \alpha(I_n) < \mu^*(E) + \epsilon.$$

Since we always have $\mu^*(E) \leq \mu^*(U)$, this proves (5).

The result (5) is also true with $\bar{\mu}^*$ in place of $\mu^*$, of course. Hence, to prove that $\mu^* = \bar{\mu}^*$, it suffices to show that $\mu^*(U) = \bar{\mu}^*(U)$ for every open set. Since every open set in $R$ is the union of an increasing sequence of bounded open sets, it suffices (by Theorem 4–4 III) to prove $\mu^*(U) = \bar{\mu}^*(U)$ for bounded open sets. But a nonempty bounded open set is a countable union of disjoint finite open intervals (see Theorem 2–3 IV), and we know that $\mu^*$ and $\bar{\mu}^*$ agree on open intervals. Therefore $\mu^* = \bar{\mu}^*$.

## PROBLEMS

1. Let $\lambda$ and $\mathscr{G}$ be as in Theorem 4–10 I. Prove the following assertions.

(a) If $G \in \mathscr{G}$ and $G_1, \ldots, G_n$ are disjoint members of $\mathscr{G}$ such that $\bigcup_{i=1}^{n} G_i \subset G$, then $\sum_{i=1}^{n} \lambda(G_i) \leq \lambda(G)$. For this the right continuity of $v$ is not needed. The proof is made easy by assuming the notation is such that $G_1, \ldots, G_n$ are arranged in order from left to right.

(b) Suppose $G, G_1, \ldots, G_n$ are elements of $\mathscr{G}$ such that $F \subset \bigcup_{i=1}^{n} H_i$, where $F$ is the closure of $G$ and $H_i$ is the interior of $G_i$. Then $\lambda(G) \leq \sum_{i=1}^{n} \lambda(G_i)$. Observe that, by a change of notation if necessary, one may assume that $H_1, \ldots, H_n$ are arranged in order from left to right in the following sense: If $F = [a, b]$ and $H_i = (a_i, b_i)$, then $a_1 < a < b_1$, $a_n < b < b_n$, and $a_{i+1} < b_i < b_{i+1}$ when $1 \leq i \leq n - 1$ if $n > 1$. Here also the right continuity of $v$ is not needed.

(c) If $G \in \mathscr{G}$ and if $\{G_i\}$ is a $\mathscr{G}$-covering of $G$, then $\lambda(G) \leq \sum_i \lambda(G_i)$. Here the right-continuity of $v$ will be used. [*Suggestion*. Let $G = (a, b]$, $G_i = (a_i, b_i]$. With $0 < \epsilon < b - a$ and $\delta_i > 0$ let $F = [a + \epsilon, b]$, $H_i = (a_i, b_i + \delta_i)$. Then $F \subset \bigcup_i H_i$. Now use the Borel theorem and (b). A judicious choice of the $\delta_i$'s is to be made in advance, with the right-continuity of $v$ as a guide.]

(d) Show that $\lambda$ is countably additive. Give an example to show that this may be false if $v$ is not right-continuous.

2. Prove as asserted in Theorem 4–10 I that $\mu^*(F) = v(c) - v(c-)$ if $F = \{c\}$. If $a < b$, evaluate $\mu^*$ at each of the sets $[a, b]$, $[a, b)$, and $(a, b)$.

3. Let $\mu^*$ be determined by $v$ as in Theorem 4–10 I. Let $\mu = \mu^*$ on the $\mu^*$-measurable sets.

(a) Show that, for any $E$, $\mu^*(E)$ is the infimum of $\mu(U)$ as $U$ varies over the class of all open sets which contain $E$. Begin by showing that, if $G \in \mathscr{G}$ and $\epsilon > 0$. there exists an open interval $H$ such that $G \subset H$ and $\mu(H) < \lambda(G) + \epsilon$. Compare with (1) in Section 4–8.

(b) Show that $E$ is $\mu^*$-measurable if and only if to each $\epsilon > 0$ corresponds a pair of sets $F$, $G$ such that $F$ is closed, $G$ is open, $F \subset E \subset G$ and $\mu(G - F) < \epsilon$. See Theorem 4–8 V.

(c) Show that, if $E$ is $\mu^*$-measurable, $\mu(E)$ is the supremum of $\mu(C)$ as $C$ varies over the class of all compact subsets of $E$.

(d) Show that, if $E$ is $\mu^*$-measurable, it is the union of disjoint $\mu^*$-measurable sets $B$, $A$, with $B$ a Borel set and $\mu^*(A) = 0$. Show also that there exists a Borel set $H$ such that $E \subset H$ and $\mu^*(E) = \mu(H)$. Compare with Theorem 4–8 II (a). Use (a) of the present problem in place of (1) in Section 4–8.

4. If $\mu$ is the measure generated by the arbitrary nondecreasing function $v$, using Method II, find the measure of the following sets: $R$, $\{x : a < x\}$, $\{x : x < b\}$. Under what conditions on $v$ is each of these measures finite?

## 4–11 The completion of a measure

The definition of a complete measure was given at the end of Section 4–3. It is useful to know that a measure on a $\sigma$-ring can be extended in a minimal way to form a complete measure. We shall see how this is done.

Let $\mathbf{S}$ be a $\sigma$-ring, and let $\mu$ be a measure on $\mathbf{S}$. Let $\mathbf{Z}$ be the class of all sets $N$ such that to each $N$ corresponds some $F \in \mathbf{S}$ with $N \subset F$ and $\mu(F) = 0$. Let $\bar{\mathbf{S}}$ be the class of all sets of the form $E \cup N$ with $E \in \mathbf{S}$, $N \in \mathbf{Z}$.

THEOREM 4–11 I. *The class $\bar{\mathbf{S}}$ is a $\sigma$-ring which includes all members of $\mathbf{S}$. If $E_1 \cup N_1$ and $E_2 \cup N_2$ are two representations of the same member of $\bar{\mathbf{S}}$, then $\mu(E_1) = \mu(E_2)$. The function $\bar{\mu} : \bar{\mathbf{S}} \to R^*$ defined by $\bar{\mu}(E \cup N) = \mu(E)$ is a complete measure on $\bar{\mathbf{S}}$.*

*Proof.* It is obvious that $\mathbf{S} \subset \bar{\mathbf{S}}$, because $\varnothing \in \mathbf{Z}$. Since

$$\bigcup_n (E_n \cup N_n) = \left\{\bigcup_n E_n\right\} \cup \left\{\bigcup_n N_n\right\},$$

it is clear that $\bar{\mathbf{S}}$ is closed under the formation of countable unions. To see that $\bar{\mathbf{S}}$ is closed under the formation of differences, we first observe that $E - N \in \bar{\mathbf{S}}$ if $E \in \mathbf{S}$ and $N \in \mathbf{Z}$. For, suppose $N \subset F$, where $F \in \mathbf{S}$ and $\mu(F) = 0$. Let $M = F - N$. Then

$$E - N = (E - F) \cup (E \cap M) \in \bar{\mathbf{S}}. \tag{1}$$

If $E_1, E_2 \in \mathbf{S}$ and $N_1, N_2 \in \mathbf{Z}$, an easy calculation shows that

$$(E_1 \cup N_1) - (E_2 \cup N_2) = [(E_1 - E_2) - N_2] \cup [(N_1 - N_2) - E_2]. \tag{2}$$

This result in conjunction with (1) shows that $\bar{\mathbf{S}}$ is closed under differences. Therefore $\bar{\mathbf{S}}$ is a $\sigma$-ring.

Formula (2) shows that if $E_1 \cup N_1 = E_2 \cup N_2$, then $(E_1 - E_2) - N_2 = \varnothing$, whence $E_1 - E_2 = (E_1 - E_2) \cap N_2$, from which we readily infer that $\mu(E_1 - E_2) = 0$. From $E_1 = (E_1 \cap E_2) \cup (E_1 - E_2)$ we then infer that $\mu(E_1) = \mu(E_1 \cap E_2)$. By symmetry, then, $\mu(E_1) = \mu(E_2)$. It is now easy to see that the uniquely defined function $\bar{\mu}$ is a measure on $\bar{\mathbf{S}}$. It is furthermore quite easy to verify that $\bar{\mu}$ is a complete measure. We leave details to the reader.

The measure $\bar{\mu}$ derived from $\mu$ as in Theorem 4–11 I is called *the completion* of $\mu$.

The measure $\bar{\mu}$ is a minimal extension of $\mu$ in the following sense: If $\mu_1$ is a complete measure on a $\sigma$-ring $\mathbf{S}_1$, such that $\mathbf{S} \subset \mathbf{S}_1$ and $\mu_1(E) = \mu(E)$ if $E \in \mathbf{S}$, then $\bar{\mathbf{S}} \subset \mathbf{S}_1$ and $\mu_1(G) = \bar{\mu}(G)$ when $G \in \bar{\mathbf{S}}$. For, suppose $N \in \mathbf{Z}$, with $N \subset F$, $F \in \mathbf{S}$, $\mu(F) = 0$. Then $\mu_1(F) = 0$, and hence $N \in \bar{\mathbf{S}}_1$, $\mu_1(N) = 0$, because $\mu_1$ is complete. We now see that an arbitrary element $E \cup N$ of $\bar{\mathbf{S}}$ belongs to $\mathbf{S}_1$. Moreover, $\mu_1(E) \leq \mu_1(E \cup N) \leq \mu_1(E) + \mu_1(N) = \mu_1(E)$, so that $\mu_1(E \cup N) = \mu_1(E) = \mu(E) = \bar{\mu}(E \cup N)$. This proves what was asserted.

The results of this section are needed in Sections 6–10, 7–5, and 7–6. In Section 5–10 we discuss a situation involving $\mu$ and $\bar{\mu}$ in the theory of integration.

## PROBLEM

Let $\mathscr{G}$ be a ring of sets in $X$ and a sequential covering class for $X$. Let $\lambda$ be a measure on $\mathscr{G}$. Let $\mu^*$ be the outer measure defined by (1) in Section 4–9, and let $\mathbf{S}$ be the $\sigma$-ring of all $\mu^*$-measurable sets. Denote the restriction of $\mu^*$ to $\mathbf{S}$ by $\mu$. Let $\sigma(\mathscr{G})$ be the $\sigma$-ring generated by $\mathscr{G}$, and denote the restriction of $\mu^*$ to $\sigma(\mathscr{G})$ by $\lambda_1$. Observe that $\lambda_1$ is an extension of $\lambda$. Let $\bar{\lambda}_1$ be the completion of $\lambda_1$, and denote the domain of $\bar{\lambda}_1$ by $\overline{\sigma(\mathscr{G})}$. Show that $\mu$ is an extension of $\bar{\lambda}_1$. Prove that $\mathbf{S} = \overline{\sigma(\mathscr{G})}$ and $\mu = \bar{\lambda}_1$, if it is assumed that $\mathbf{S} \subset \overline{\sigma(\mathscr{G})}$. Finally, *prove* that $\mathbf{S} = \overline{\sigma(\mathscr{G})}$, assuming that the original measure $\lambda$ is $\sigma$-finite. For this one can use the idea of a measurable cover and constructions somewhat analogous to those in the proof of Theorem 4–8 I. (The reader may wish to refer to Halmos [1], pp. 54–56.)

## SUGGESTED READING FOR CHAPTER 4

Borel [1], Chapter 3. In the 3rd ed., Chapter 3 and Note VI.
Caratheodory [1], Chapters 5, 6.
Goffman [1], Chapter 13.
Halmos [1], Chapters 1, 2, 3.
Hobson [1], Vol. 1. Chapter 3.
Lebesgue [2], Chapter 7.
Munroe [1], Chapters 1, 2.
Natanson [1], Vol. 1. Chapter 3.
Rogosinski [1], Chapter 3.
Thielman [1], Chapter 8.
Titchmarsh [1], Section 10.2.
de la Vallée-Poussin, [1], Chapter 2, pp. 16–29.
Zaanen [1], Chapter 2.

CHAPTER FIVE

# The Lebesgue Integral

## 5–0 Introduction

In this chapter we shall present a modernized version of what may be called the classical method of developing the Lebesgue integral. The arrangement of the exposition has been selected with several important considerations in mind. We want ultimately to attain a degree of generality and abstraction adequate for the needs of students who are being introduced to modern functional analysis. We want an exposition with a substantial intuitive appeal. And we want to make it possible for the bulk of the theory to be read in the context of Lebesgue measure in $R^k$ and integrals of functions of the type $f : R^k \to R$ or $f : R^k \to R^*$.

What we actually consider are functions $f : X \to R^*$, where $X$ is an abstract space in which there is a $\sigma$-ring of sets and a measure defined on the $\sigma$-ring. The assumptions are general enough to allow us to interpret $X$ either as $R^k$ or as any $L$-measurable subset of $R^k$; the measure can then be interpreted as Lebesgue measure on the $L$-measurable subsets of $X$. The general theory is for the most part not essentially different or more complicated than it would be if we restricted ourselves to the classical case of Lebesgue measure in $R^k$. Since there are other important interpretations and applications of the theory (for example, to the case of Lebesgue-Stieltjes measures in $R$), there is a distinct economy in the abstract presentation.

Let us consider for a moment the aim of the Lebesgue theory of integration for functions of the type $f : R^k \to R^*$. It aims to extend the scope of the process of integration as it is conceived in elementary calculus. From elementary calculus we have a definition of $\int_a^b f(x)\,dx$ for continuous functions of the type $f : [a, b] \to R$, where $[a, b]$ is a compact interval on the real line. This elementary calculus definition can be extended without difficulty to give a definition of the integral of a continuous function $f : E \to R$, where $E$ is the closure of a finite open interval in $R^k$. In these classical situations, if we keep to one fixed domain and consider the value of the integral as depending on the function, we may use a notation such as $I(f)$ for the value of the integral. Then the mapping $I : f \to I(f)$ is a mapping of a certain class of functions into $R$. This mapping has certain important properties, among them the following:

$$(1) \qquad I(f+g) = I(f) + I(g),$$

$$(2) \qquad I(cf) = cI(f) \quad (c \text{ a real number}),$$

$$(3) \qquad I(f) \leq I(g) \quad \text{if} \quad f(x) \leq g(x) \text{ for each } x,$$

$$(4) \qquad |I(f)| \leq I(|f|).$$

In (4) $|f|$ denotes the function whose value at $x$ is $|f(x)|$.

In the case of the continuous $f : [a, b] \to R$, if $m$ and $M$ are respectively the smallest and largest values of $f$ on $[a, b]$, we have

$$(5) \qquad m(b - a) \leq I(f) \leq M(b - a).$$

There is a corresponding inequality in the case $f : E \to R$; here $b - a$ is replaced in (5) by the content of the interval $E$.

There are other important properties of these elementary integrals, having to do with splitting the domain of the function into parts. Thus, for example, if $a < b < c$ and if we have a continuous function $f : [a, c] \to R$, then

$$(6) \qquad \int_a^c f(x)\,dx = \int_a^b f(x)\,dx + \int_b^c f(x)\,dx.$$

The integration process, as conceived in elementary calculus, is too restrictive in many ways. The restriction to continuous functions is a severe one. So also is the restriction to functions having compact intervals as their domains of definition. It would be better to have a definition of an integral applicable to a larger class of functions, with a larger class of sets admissible as the domains of definition of the functions. Suppose $f$ is a function and $E$ is a subset of the domain of definition of $f$. Then we would like to be able to define the integral of $f$ over $E$ for a large class of $f$'s and $E$'s. If we denote the value of such an integral by $I(f; E)$, we want it to have properties (1)–(4) when $E$ is kept fixed. As a generalization of (6) we shall want

$$(7) \qquad I(f; E) = I(f; E_1) + I(f; E_2)$$

if $E = E_1 \cup E_2$ when $E_1$ and $E_2$ are disjoint sets of an admissible type. We shall want $I(f; E)$ to be the same as the classical integral of calculus if $E$ is a compact interval in $R^k$ and if $f$ is continuous in $E$. As a generalization of (5) we shall want

$$(8) \qquad m\mu(E) \leq I(f; E) \leq M\mu(E)$$

if $E$ is a measurable set of finite measure in $R^k$ and if $f$ is bounded on $E$, with

$$m = \inf \{f(x) : x \in E\}, \qquad M = \sup \{f(x) : x \in E\}.$$

Another unsatisfactory aspect of the integral of elementary calculus appears in connection with convergent sequences of functions. A useful elementary theorem asserts that if $f$ and $f_1, f_2, \ldots$ are all continuous on $[a, b]$ and if $f_n(x)$ converges to $f(x)$ uniformly on $[a, b]$, then $\int_a^b f_n(x)\,dx \to \int_a^b f(x)\,dx$. There are many situations in analysis where we want this kind of conclusion, but where we have neither continuity nor uniform convergence. One goal of an extended theory of integration is to make the conclusion $I(f_n; E) \to I(f; E)$ follow from the assumption $f_n(x) \to f(x)$ for each $x$ in $E$, with a minimum of additional assumptions.

The Riemann theory of integration was constructed as a generalization of the integration of continuous functions in elementary calculus. But the Riemann theory is inadequate for some of the purposes of higher analysis. It suffers from defects in connection with convergence theorems. It is also too restrictive in that it does not deal adequately with the definition and properties of $I(f; E)$ if $f$ is an unbounded function or if $E$ is an unbounded set. The Lebesgue theory, on the other hand, meets and overcomes all these difficulties in the Riemann theory.

Since the successful completion of Lebesgue's program of generalizing the theory of integration, it has been found possible to rearrange and reconstruct the original treatment so that the theory is, to a great extent, susceptible to immediate generalization far beyond the situation originally envisaged, that of functions $f: R^k \to R$. To describe the nature of this generalization we must begin by defining the concept of a measure space.

## MEASURE SPACES

Let $X$ be a nonempty set, and let $\mathbf{S}$ be a nonempty class of subsets of $X$ which is a $\sigma$-ring. We assume that the union of all the members of $\mathbf{S}$ is $X$; that is, if $x \in X$, there is some $E \in \mathbf{S}$ such that $x \in E$. We also assume the existence of a measure function $\mu$ defined on $\mathbf{S}$ (see Sections 4–2, 4–3 for the relevant definitions). The elements of $\mathbf{S}$ will be referred to as measurable sets (or as $\mu$-measurable sets). We call $X$ a *measure space* when it is thus provided with the $\sigma$-ring $\mathbf{S}$ and the measure $\mu$. Strictly speaking, it is not $X$ alone, but the triple $(X, \mathbf{S}, \mu)$ which is the measure space.

For us at this stage the most important example of a measure space is $R^k$, with the $\sigma$-ring of Lebesgue-measurable sets in $R^k$, and with Lebesgue measure as the $\mu$. We may also consider the case when $X$ is a Lebesgue-measurable set in $R^k$, $\mathbf{S}$ is the $\sigma$-ring of all measurable subsets of $X$, and $\mu$ is Lebesgue measure, with attention confined to elements of $\mathbf{S}$.

Once we are provided with a measure space $(X, \mathbf{S}, \mu)$, a theory of integration can be developed. In these preliminary remarks we wish to indicate the large features of this theory, without going into details. The theory is to be concerned with functions $f: X \to R^*$. The first step is to restrict attention to a certain class of such functions, called *the class of measurable functions*. This class includes, for instance, the characteristic function of $E$ if $E \in \mathbf{S}$. The *characteristic function* of $E$, denoted by $\chi_E$, is defined by

(9)
$$\chi_E(x) = \begin{cases} 1 & \text{if } x \in E \\ 0 & \text{if } x \notin E. \end{cases}$$

The class of measurable functions is also of such a nature that functions constructed from measurable functions are themselves measurable, when the methods of construction are the usual ones of algebra and analysis (addition, multiplication, formation of limits, least upper bounds, and so on). The theory then proceeds to a subclass of the class of measurable functions. The functions of this subclass are called *summable*, and with each summable function $f$ there is associated a real number, called the *integral* of $f$ and denoted by $\int f\,d\mu$. If $f$ is summable and $E \in \mathbf{S}$, the product of $f$ and $\chi_E$ turns out to be summable. The integral of this function is denoted by $\int_E f\,d\mu$. Thus,

(10)
$$\int_E f\,d\mu = \int f\chi_E\,d\mu.$$

It may happen that $f\chi_E$ is summable, even if $f$ is not; in this case $\int_E f\,d\mu$ is defined by (10).

If we denote the class of summable functions by $\mathscr{L}(\mu)$ and write

$$I(f; E) = \int_E f\,d\mu, \tag{11}$$

we can look upon $I$ as a function, with range in $R$, whose domain consists of all pairs $(f, E)$ such that $f\chi_E \in \mathscr{L}(\mu)$. The domain contains all of $\mathscr{L}(\mu) \times \mathbf{S}$.

The theory of integration, as we present it in this chapter, is concerned first with the class of measurable functions, next with the definition and structure of the class $\mathscr{L}(\mu)$, and then with the study of the properties of $I(f; E)$ as a function of $f$ and $E$.

It is worth mentioning specifically at this point that the general theory does not require any topology for $X$. We do use the topology of $R^*$, however.

In Chapter 6 we present an entirely different way of developing a generalization of the integral of elementary calculus, with attention focused on the properties of the integral as a linear functional. In this process no use is made of a prior theory of measure. Instead, a theory of measure is a consequence of the theory of the integral. Under certain conditions this alternative procedure leads ultimately to a body of theory equivalent to that of Chapter 5. The results of the classical Lebesgue theory for functions $f: R^k \to R^*$ can be attained in this way.

## 5–1 Measurable functions

Throughout this section $(X, \mathbf{S}, \mu)$ denotes a measure space, as defined in Section 5–0. In the most general case $X$ need not itself be a member of $\mathbf{S}$. The measure $\mu$ on the $\sigma$-ring $\mathbf{S}$ is not assumed to be the measure induced by some outer measure on $X$. Nor is $\mu$ assumed to be a complete measure.

If $\mu(E)$ is finite for each $E$ in $\mathbf{S}$, we say that $(X, \mathbf{S}, \mu)$ is a *finite* measure space. The measure space is said to be *$\sigma$-finite* if each member of $\mathbf{S}$ is expressible as a countable union of members of $\mathbf{S}$, each of finite measure. If in either the finite or the $\sigma$-finite case it happens also that $X \in \mathbf{S}$, we add the adjective *totally* in describing the space. Thus $(X, \mathbf{S}, \mu)$ is totally $\sigma$-finite if $X \in \mathbf{S}$ and the space is $\sigma$-finite. This is the situation, for example, when $X = R^k$ and $\mu$ is Lebesgue measure.

*Example 1.* Let $X$ be an $L$-measurable subset of $R^k$, of finite Lebesgue measure. Let $\mu$ be Lebesgue measure, restricted to the $\sigma$-ring $\mathbf{S}$ of all $L$-measurable subsets of $X$. Then $(X, \mathbf{S}, \mu)$ is totally finite.

*Example 2.* Let $X = X_1 \cup X_2$, where $X_1$ and $X_2$ are disjoint subsets of $R^k$, $X_1$ is $L$-measurable, and $X_2$ is not. Let $\mu$ be Lebesgue measure on the class $\mathbf{S}$ of all $L$-measurable subsets of $X$. In this case $X$ is not a member of $\mathbf{S}$.

### MEASURABLE FUNCTIONS. THE CASE WHEN $X \in \mathbf{S}$

The theory of measurable functions is in some respects more simple when $X \in \mathbf{S}$ than in the case when $X$ is not in $\mathbf{S}$. Hence we consider this case separately at first. Readers of the book who do not wish to be concerned with the case when $X$ is not in $\mathbf{S}$ may ignore our special discussions of this case.

If $(X, \mathbf{S}, \mu)$ is a measure space for which $X \in \mathbf{S}$, a function $f: X \to R^*$ is said to be *measurable* if $f^{-1}(G) \in \mathbf{S}$ whenever $G$ is an open set in $R^*$. The topology of $R^*$ is that defined in Example 1, Section 3–5. We see that the concept of a measurable function does not depend on the measure $\mu$, but only on the $\sigma$-ring $\mathbf{S}$. In a situation where some other $\sigma$-ring may be present in the discussion, we may say more explicitly "$f$ is measurable with respect to $\mathbf{S}$."

As long as there is no danger of ambiguity through the presence of other $\sigma$-rings, we may refer to the elements of $\mathbf{S}$ as *measurable sets*. For instance, where the discourse all has to do with the $\sigma$-ring of $L$-measurable sets in $R^k$, when we speak of a measurable set we mean a member of this $\sigma$-ring.

It is useful to have the criterion for measurability of a function expressed with reference to the topology of $R$ instead of to that of $R^*$.

THEOREM 5–1 I. *If $(X, \mathbf{S}, \mu)$ is a measure space with $X \in \mathbf{S}$, a function $f: X \to R^*$ is measurable if and only if* (a) *$f^{-1}(G) \in \mathbf{S}$ whenever $G$ is an open set in $R$, and* (b) *the sets $\{x : f(x) = +\infty\}$, $\{x : f(x) = -\infty\}$ are in $\mathbf{S}$.*

*Proof.* Suppose $f$ is measurable. If $G \subset R^*$, $f^{-1}(R^* - G) = X - f^{-1}(G)$. Since $X \in \mathbf{S}$, we see that $f^{-1}(H) \in \mathbf{S}$ if $H$ is a closed set in $R^*$. The sets $\{-\infty\}$ and $\{+\infty\}$ are closed in $R^*$. Hence condition (b) is satisfied. Condition (a) is satisfied, because an open set in $R$ is also open in $R^*$.

Now suppose that $f$ satisfies conditions (a) and (b). An open set in $R^*$ can be expressed in the form $G \cup H$, where $G$ is an open set in $R$ and $H$ is either empty, or a set consisting of one or both of the points $-\infty$, $+\infty$. Since $f^{-1}(G \cup H) = f^{-1}(G) \cup f^{-1}(H)$, it is clear that $f$ is measurable.

## THE GENERAL DEFINITION OF A MEASURABLE FUNCTION

When $X$ is not in $\mathbf{S}$ we have to modify the form of the definition of a measurable function. For, if $f: X \to R^*$ is given, we have $f^{-1}(R^*) = X$. Here $R^*$ is open, but $f^{-1}(R^*)$ is not in $\mathbf{S}$, so no function would be measurable if we used the former definition. As it turns out, an appropriate general definition can be formulated by taking into account the set on which $f(x) \neq 0$.

We write

(1) $$N(f) = \{x : f(x) \neq 0\}.$$

We then define $f$ to be measurable if $N(f) \cap f^{-1}(G) \in \mathbf{S}$ whenever $G$ is an open set in $R^*$. In particular, $f^{-1}(R^*) = X$, so that $N(f) \in \mathbf{S}$ when $f$ is measurable. In case $X \in \mathbf{S}$, this new form of the definition is equivalent to the one already given. Let us prove this. We observe that $N(f) = f^{-1}(G_0)$, where $G_0$ is the open set $R^* - \{0\}$. Thus, if $f^{-1}(G) \in \mathbf{S}$ whenever $G$ is an open set in $R^*$, it follows that $N(f) \cap f^{-1}(G) \in \mathbf{S}$. On the other hand, for any $G \subset R^*$ we see that

(2) $$f^{-1}(G) \cap [N(f)]^{\sim} = \begin{cases} [N(f)]^{\sim} & \text{if } 0 \in G \\ \varnothing & \text{if } 0 \notin G, \end{cases}$$

and

(3) $$f^{-1}(G) = \{f^{-1}(G) \cap N(f)\} \cup \{f^{-1}(G) \cap [N(f)]^{\sim}\}.$$

Suppose now that $X \in \mathbf{S}$ and that $N(f) \cap f^{-1}(G) \in \mathbf{S}$ whenever $G$ is open in $R^*$. By taking

$G = R^*$ we see that $N(f) \in \mathbf{S}$. Since $X \in \mathbf{S}$, it follows that $[N(f)]^{\sim} \in \mathbf{S}$. It then follows from (2) and (3) that $f^{-1}(G) \in \mathbf{S}$ if $G$ is open in $R^*$. This completes the proof that the two forms of definition of a measurable function are equivalent when $X \in \mathbf{S}$.

For the general case we have the following modification of Theorem 5–1 I:

THEOREM 5–1 I (*modified*). *If* $(X, \mathbf{S}, \mu)$ *is an arbitrary measure space, a function* $f: X \to R^*$ *is measurable if and only if* (a) $N(f) \cap f^{-1}(G) \in \mathbf{S}$ *whenever* $G$ *is an open set in* $R$, *and* (b) *the sets* $\{x : f(x) = +\infty\}$, $\{x : f(x) = -\infty\}$ *are in* $\mathbf{S}$.

We leave the proof as a problem.

## SIMPLE FUNCTIONS

An important class of measurable functions is furnished by the simple functions. A function $f$ defined on $X$ is called *simple* if the range of $f$ is a finite set of real numbers, and if $\{x : f(x) = c\} \in \mathbf{S}$ whenever $c$ is a *nonzero* real number. In particular, the characteristic function $\chi_E$ (defined in Section 5–0) is simple if and only if $E \in \mathbf{S}$. It is easy to see that a simple function is measurable. The identically zero function is simple.

If $f$ is simple and if the distinct nonzero values of $f$ are $c_1, \ldots, c_n$, let $E_i = \{x : f(x) = c_i\}$. It can be seen that

$$f = c_1\chi_{E_1} + \cdots + c_n\chi_{E_n}. \tag{4}$$

## MEASURABILITY OF CONTINUOUS FUNCTIONS

If we suppose that the $X$ of our measure space is a topological space, we can inquire into the measurability of continuous functions. The following theorem fits the situations which arise in common practice.

THEOREM 5–1 II. *Let* $(X, \mathbf{S}, \mu)$ *be a measure space, with* $X$ *a topological space such that each open set belongs to* $\mathbf{S}$. *Then* $f: X \to R^*$ *is measurable if* $f$ *is continuous.*

*Proof.* Since $f$ is continuous, $f^{-1}(G)$ is open when $G$ is open. In this case $X \in \mathbf{S}$ and it is clear that $f$ is measurable.

*Remark.* Theorem 5–1 II applies when $X$ is a metric space and $\mu$ is the measure induced by a metric outer measure $\mu^*$ on $X$, with $\mathbf{S}$ the $\sigma$-ring of $\mu^*$-measurable sets. This includes the case of Lebesgue measure in $R^k$.

## THE "ALMOST EVERYWHERE" RELATION

Given $f: X \to R^*$ and $g: X \to R^*$, we say that $f(x) = g(x)$ *almost everywhere* if the set $\{x : f(x) \neq g(x)\}$ is in $\mathbf{S}$ and has measure 0. For convenience we abbreviate "almost everywhere" as "a.e." We can also use the "almost everywhere" phraseology in other situations. Thus, we write $f(x) > 0$ a.e. to mean that $\{x : f(x) \leq 0\}$ is in $\mathbf{S}$ and has measure 0.

If $f(x) = g(x)$ a.e., we say that $f$ and $g$ are *equivalent* functions. This terminology is not wholly satisfactory, because it can happen that $f(x) = g(x)$ a.e., $g(x) = h(x)$ a.e., and yet it is *not* true that $f(x) = h(x)$ a.e. Suppose that $A = \{x : f(x) \neq g(x)\}$, $B = \{x : g(x) \neq h(x)\}$, $C = \{x : f(x) \neq h(x)\}$. Then $C \subset A \cup B$. If $\mu(A) = \mu(B) = 0$, then $\mu(A \cup B) = 0$, but $C$ may not be in $\mathbf{S}$. If this situation occurs, then it cannot be asserted that $f(x) = h(x)$ a.e. This difficulty does not arise if the measure $\mu$ is complete. When $\mu$ is complete, the relation of $f$ to $g$ expressed by $f(x) = g(x)$ a.e. is a true equivalence relation; that is, it is reflexive, symmetric, and transitive.

Even when the measure $\mu$ is not complete, the relation $f(x) = g(x)$ a.e. is a true equivalence relation within the class of measurable functions. This is because, if $f$ and $g$ are measurable, the set $\{x : f(x) \neq g(x)\}$ always belongs to $\mathbf{S}$ (see Problems 11(b) and 16(e)).

THEOREM 5–1 III. *If $f$ and $g$ are equivalent and $f$ is measurable, then $g$ also is measurable, provided that the measure $\mu$ is complete. If $\mu$ is not complete, we can still conclude that $g$ is measurable if we assume that $g(x)$ is constant on the set $\{x : f(x) \neq g(x)\}$.*

*Proof.* Let $E = \{x : f(x) \neq g(x)\}$. Then $E \in \mathbf{S}$ and $\mu(E) = 0$. If $G$ is open in $R^*$, we see that $g^{-1}(G) - E = f^{-1}(G) - E$, and hence

$$g^{-1}(G) = [g^{-1}(G) \cap E] \cup [f^{-1}(G) - E]. \tag{5}$$

Also, $N(g) - E = N(f) - E$, and so

$$N(g) \cap g^{-1}(G) = [N(g) \cap g^{-1}(G) \cap E] \cup [N(f) \cap f^{-1}(G) - E]. \tag{6}$$

The conclusion now follows if $\mu$ is complete, for then any subset of $E$ is measurable. We can use (5) directly in case $X \in \mathbf{S}$. For the case in which $\mu$ is not complete, we suppose $g(x) = c$ when $x \in E$. We see that $E \cap g^{-1}(G)$ is $E$ or $\varnothing$ according as $c \in G$ or $c \notin G$. When $X \in \mathbf{S}$ we can then see from (5) that $g$ is measurable. In the general case we use (6) and observe that $N(g) \cap E$ is $E$ or $\varnothing$ according as $c \neq 0$ or $c = 0$.

*Example 3.* When the measure $\mu$ is not complete it can happen that $f$ is measurable, $g$ is not measurable, and $f(x) = g(x)$ a.e. Let $X = R$, take for $\mathbf{S}$ the class of all Borel sets in $R$, and let $\mu$ be Lebesgue measure restricted to $\mathbf{S}$. Let $E$ be a Borel set of measure 0, and let $F$ be a subset of $E$ which is not a Borel set (see Section 4–8). Let $f$ be the characteristic function of $X - E$. Define $g$ so that $g(x) = 1$ on $X - E$, $g(x) = 2$ on $E - F$, and $g(x) = 3$ on $F$. Then $f$ and $g$ are equivalent and $f$ is measurable but $g$ is not.

The following theorem is useful for the criteria it provides for the measurability of functions. This theorem is for the case in which $X \in \mathbf{S}$.

THEOREM 5–1 IV. *Let $(X, \mathbf{S}, \mu)$ be a measure space such that $X \in \mathbf{S}$. Then, a function $f : X \to R^*$ is measurable if and only if the set $\{x : f(x) < c\}$ is measurable for each $c$ in $R^*$. The proposition remains true if $<$ is replaced by $\leq$, $\geq$, or $>$. If all the values of $f$ are finite, $f$ will be measurable provided the stated condition is satisfied for each $c$ in $R$.*

*Proof.* Let $P_1$ be the proposition: For each $c$ in $R^*$ the set $\{x : f(x) < c\}$ is measurable. Let $P_2$ be the proposition of the same form as $P_1$, except that $f(x) < c$ is replaced by $f(x) \leq c$. Likewise let $P_3$ have $f(x) \geq c$ and let $P_4$ have $f(x) > c$. Finally, let $P_+$ be the proposition: The set $\{x : f(x) = +\infty\}$ is measurable, and let $P_-$ be the corresponding proposition with $-\infty$ in place of $+\infty$.

We begin by showing that the truth of any one of the propositions $P_1, P_2, P_3, P_4$ implies the truth of the other three, and the truth of $P_+, P_-$ as well. We do this in the following order:

(7) $$P_1 \Leftrightarrow P_3,$$

(8) $$P_2 \Leftrightarrow P_4,$$

(9) $$P_3 \Rightarrow P_+,$$

(10) $$P_1 \Rightarrow P_-,$$

(11) $$P_1 \Leftrightarrow P_2.$$

The sets $\{x : f(x) < c\}$ and $\{x : f(x) \geq c\}$ are complementary. Since $X \in \mathbf{S}$, we get (7) from this remark. Likewise we get (8). We get (9) from the observation that

$$\{x : f(x) = +\infty\} = \{x : f(x) \geq +\infty\},$$

and (10) can be obtained by observing that

$$\{x : f(x) = -\infty\} = \bigcap_{n=1}^{\infty} \{x : f(x) < -n\}.$$

To see that $P_1 \Rightarrow P_2$ we observe that $P_1$ implies both $P_+$ and $P_-$ (by (7), (9), and (10)), and then we use the following relations:

$$\{x : f(x) \leq +\infty\} = \{x : f(x) < +\infty\} \cup \{x : f(x) = +\infty\},$$

$$\{x : f(x) \leq -\infty\} = \{x : f(x) = -\infty\},$$

$$\{x : f(x) \leq c\} = \bigcap_{n=1}^{\infty} \left\{x : f(x) < c + \frac{1}{n}\right\} \quad \text{if} \quad c \text{ is real.}$$

To see that $P_2 \Rightarrow P_1$ we note the relations

$$\{x : f(x) < c\} = \bigcup_{n=1}^{\infty} \left\{x : f(x) \leq c - \frac{1}{n}\right\} \quad \text{if} \quad c \text{ is real,}$$

$$\{x : f(x) < +\infty\} = \bigcup_{n=1}^{\infty} \{x : f(x) \leq n\},$$

$$\{x : f(x) < -\infty\} = \varnothing.$$

Thus we have (11).

Suppose now that $f$ is measurable. Then $P_1$ is true, for $\{x : f(x) < c\}$ is $f^{-1}(G)$, where $G$ is the open set $\{t : t < c\}$ in $R^*$. Suppose, on the other hand, that $P_1$ is true. Then $P_+$ and $P_-$ are true, and so is $P_4$, by (7)–(11). To show that $f$ is measurable it will suffice now to verify that condition (a) in Theorem 5–1 I is satisfied. If $\alpha$ and $\beta$ are real numbers such that $\alpha < \beta$, the set $\{x : \alpha < f(x) < \beta\}$ is measurable, for it is the intersection of $\{x : f(x) > \alpha\}$ and $\{x : f(x) < \beta\}$. But then $f^{-1}(G)$ is measurable if $G$ is any open set in $R$, for such a set, if nonempty, is a countable union of finite open intervals. This completes everything that is necessary for the proof of Theorem 5–1 IV.

Theorem 5–1 IV must be modified for the case of an arbitrary measure space.

THEOREM 5–1 V. *If $(X, \mathbf{S}, \mu)$ is an arbitrary measure space, a function $f : X \to R^*$ is measurable if any one of the following conditions is satisfied.*

(a) *$N(f) \cap \{x : f(x) \leq c\} \in \mathbf{S}$ for each $c$ in $R^*$;*
(b) *$N(f) \cap \{x : f(x) \geq c\} \in \mathbf{S}$ for each $c$ in $R^*$;*
(c) *$\{x : f(x) = +\infty\}$ and $N(f) \cap \{x : f(x) < c\}$ are in $\mathbf{S}$ for each $c$ in $R^*$;*
(d) *$\{x : f(x) = -\infty\}$ and $N(f) \cap \{x : f(x) > c\}$ are in $\mathbf{S}$ for each $c$ in $R^*$.*

*If $f$ is measurable, all four conditions are satisfied.*

Proof of the theorem is left to the reader. For suggestions see Problem 5.

## ELEMENTARY COMBINATIONS OF MEASURABLE FUNCTIONS

We now want to show that simple algebraic combinations of measurable functions are measurable. We remind the reader of the definitions of addition and multiplication in $R^*$; they are given in Section 4–1. In particular, we call attention to the definitions $0 \cdot (\pm\infty) = 0$, $(+\infty) + (-\infty) = 0$.

THEOREM 5–1 VI. *Let $f$ and $g$ be measurable functions on $X$ to $R^*$, and let $b$ be a real number. Then the functions $bf$, $f + g$, and $fg$ are measurable.*

*Proof for $bf$.* The conclusion is obvious if $b = 0$. When $b \neq 0$ the proof can be made easily by using Theorem 5–1 I (in the modified form, if necessary). We leave details to the reader.

*Proof for $f + g$.* We give the argument on the assumption that $X \in \mathbf{S}$, for simplicity. Suggestions for a proof valid when $X \notin \mathbf{S}$ are given in Problem 11.

First we show that $\{x : f(x) > g(x)\} \in \mathbf{S}$. For a given $x$, $f(x) > g(x)$ if and only if there is a rational number $r$ such that $g(x) < r$ and $r < f(x)$. Hence, if $\{r_n\}$ is an enumeration of the rationals, we see that

$$\{x : f(x) > g(x)\} = \bigcup_n [\{x : f(x) > r_n\} \cap \{x : g(x) < r_n\}].$$

It now follows by Theorem 5–1 IV that the set here represented is in $\mathbf{S}$.

Next, we prove that the function $h$ defined by $h(x) = c - g(x)$, where $c$ is a real number, is measurable as a consequence of the measurability of $g$. We see that $\{x : h(x) = +\infty\} = \{x : g(x) = -\infty\}$ and $\{x : h(x) = -\infty\} = \{x : g(x) = +\infty\}$ are measurable. Let $T$ be the mapping of $R$ into itself defined by $T(t) = c - t$. If $G$ is an open set in $R$, so is $T(G)$. We verify that $h^{-1}(G) = g^{-1}(T(G))$, and so $h^{-1}(G) \in \mathbf{S}$. Hence $h$ is measurable, by Theorem 5–1 I.

We come now to the proof that $f + g$ is measurable. We shall use Theorem 5–1 IV and show that $\{x : f(x) + g(x) > c\} \in \mathbf{S}$ for each $c$ in $R^*$. This set is $\varnothing$ if $c = +\infty$. If $c = -\infty$ it is $X - \{x : f(x) + g(x) = -\infty\}$, and $\{x : f(x) + g(x) = -\infty\}$ is in $\mathbf{S}$, because it is the union of $\{x : f(x) = -\infty\} \cap \{x : g(x) < +\infty\}$ and $\{x : f(x) < +\infty\} \cap \{x : g(x) = -\infty\}$. For the case when $c$ is real $\{x : f(x) + g(x) > c\}$ is the union of certain sets which are known to be in $\mathbf{S}$, namely:

$$\{x : f(x) \text{ and } g(x) \text{ finite}, f(x) > c - g(x)\},$$

$$\{x : f(x) = +\infty, g(x) > -\infty\}, \qquad \{x : f(x) > -\infty, g(x) = +\infty\},$$

and (in case $c < 0$ only)

$$\{x : f(x) = +\infty, g(x) = -\infty\}, \qquad \{x : f(x) = -\infty, g(x) = +\infty\}.$$

It is then clear that $f + g$ is measurable.

*Proof for fg.* First of all we establish that the square of a measurable function $f$ is measurable. It is clear that $N(f^2) = N(f)$, so that $N(f^2) \in \mathbf{S}$. If $c \in R^*$ and $c \leq 0$,

$$N(f^2) \cap \{x : f^2(x) \geq c\} = N(f^2).$$

If $c > 0$,

$$N(f^2) \cap \{x : f^2(x) \geq c\} = [N(f) \cap \{x : f(x) \geq \sqrt{c}] \cup [N(f) \cap \{x : f(x) \leq -\sqrt{c}\}].$$

It is then clear from (b) in Theorem 5–1 V that $f^2$ is measurable. In case $X \in \mathbf{S}$ this argument can be slightly simplified by dispensing with $N(f^2)$ and using Theorem 5–1 IV.

Now, from what has already been proved we know that $F = \frac{1}{4}(f + g)^2$ and $G = \frac{1}{4}(f - g)^2$ are measurable functions. Hence so is $H = F - G$. Let $h = fg$. If all the values of $f$ and $g$ are finite, we see that $h = H$, and thus the proof is finished in this case. To deal with the case in which some of the values of $f$ or $g$ are infinite we make a comparison of the values of $h$ and $H$ at points where one or both of $f$, $g$ have infinite values. We find that the points where $h$ and $H$ differ in value fall into two disjoint measurable sets $A$, $B$ as follows: $A$ is composed of all points where one of the functions $f$, $g$ is infinite, the other is finite and nonzero, and both have the same sign; $B$ is similarly composed, except that $f$ and $g$ have opposite signs. It is easy to see that $A$ and $B$ are measurable. For example, one of four constituent parts of $A$ is

$$\{x : 0 < f(x)\} \cap N(f) \cap \{x : f(x) < +\infty\} \cap \{x : g(x) = +\infty\},$$

which is measurable, as we can see from Theorem 5–1 V (or Theorem 5–1 IV, if $X \in \mathbf{S}$). When $x \in A$, we see that $h(x) = +\infty$ and $H(x) = 0$. For $x \in B$ we have $h(x) = -\infty$, $H(x) = 0$. If we define

$$p(x) = \begin{cases} +\infty, & x \in A \\ 0, & x \in A^{\sim} \end{cases} \qquad q(x) = \begin{cases} -\infty, & x \in B \\ 0, & x \in B^{\sim} \end{cases}$$

we can easily verify that $p$ and $q$ are measurable. Since $h = (H + p) + q$, it follows that $h$ is measurable.

## SEQUENCES OF MEASURABLE FUNCTIONS

If $\{f_n\}$ is a sequence of functions $f_n : X \to R^*$, we shall denote by $\sup_n f_n$ the function whose value at $x$ is the supremum of $f_1(x), f_2(x), \ldots$. Here $\sup_n f_n$ means $\sup_{n \geq 1} f_n$. There is an obvious meaning for $\sup_{n \geq k} f_n$. We denote by $\lim \sup f_n$ the function whose value at $x$ is $\limsup_{n \to \infty} f_n(x)$. Similar notational agreements apply to $\inf_n f_n$ and $\lim \inf f_n$. We know from Section 1–7 that

$$\text{(12)} \qquad \lim \sup f_n = \inf_n (\sup_{k \geq n} f_k),$$

$$\text{(13)} \qquad \inf_n f_n = -\sup_n (-f_n),$$

$$\text{(14)} \qquad \lim \inf f_n = -\lim \sup (-f_n).$$

THEOREM 5–1 VII. *If the functions* $f_1, f_2, \ldots$ *are measurable, so are the functions* $\sup_n f_n$, $\inf_n f_n$, $\limsup f_n$, *and* $\liminf f_n$.

*Proof.* In view of (12)–(14) it will suffice to prove that $\sup_n f_n$ is measurable. Let $f = \sup_n f_n$. If $X \in \mathbf{S}$ the proof is very simple. We observe that

$$\{x : f(x) \le c\} = \bigcap_{n=1}^{\infty} \{x : f_n(x) \le c\} \tag{15}$$

for each $c \in R^*$; then we use Theorem 5–1 IV. If $X \notin \mathbf{S}$, we have to take account of $N(f)$. From (15) we see that

$$N(f) \cap \{x : f(x) \le c\} = \bigcap_{n=1}^{\infty} [N(f) \cap \{x : f_n(x) \le c\}].$$

If we can show that $N(f) \in \mathbf{S}$, it will follow from Problem 10 that $N(f) \cap \{x : f_n(x) \le c\} \in \mathbf{S}$ for each $n$, and then we can use (a) in Theorem 5–1 V to conclude that $f$ is measurable.

Now, $\{x : f_n(x) > 0\} = N(f_n) \cap \{x : f_n(x) > 0\} \in \mathbf{S}$, and

$$\{x : f_n(x) \le c\} = N(f_n) \cap \{x : f_n(x) \le c\} \in \mathbf{S}$$

if $c < 0$. We see then from (15) that $\{x : f(x) \le c\} \in \mathbf{S}$ if $c < 0$. From

$$\{x : f(x) > 0\} = \bigcup_n \{x : f_n(x) > 0\}$$

and

$$\{x : f(x) < 0\} = \bigcup_{k=1}^{\infty} \left\{x : f(x) \le -\frac{1}{k}\right\}$$

we see that $N(f) \in \mathbf{S}$. This completes the proof.

Suppose the functions $f_1, f_2, \ldots$ are measurable and that the sequence $\{f_n(x)\}$ converges to a limit $f(x)$ in $R^*$ for each $x$. Then $f = \limsup f_n$, and it follows that $f$ is measurable. If we have a function $g$ such that $\lim_{n\to\infty} f_n(x) = g(x)$ a.e., and if we know that the measure $\mu$ is complete, we can infer from Theorem 5–1 III that $g$ is measurable. But if $\mu$ is not complete, it can happen that $g$ is not measurable. See Problem 15.

## THE FUNCTIONS $f^+$, $f^-$

Given a function $f : X \to R^*$, we define $f^+$ and $f^-$ as follows:

$$f^+(x) = \begin{cases} f(x) & \text{if } f(x) \ge 0 \\ 0 & \text{if } f(x) < 0, \end{cases} \tag{16}$$

$$f^-(x) = \begin{cases} -f(x) & \text{if } f(x) \le 0 \\ 0 & \text{if } f(x) > 0. \end{cases} \tag{17}$$

Observe that

$$f^+(x) = \max\{f(x), 0\}, \qquad f^-(x) = -\min\{f(x), 0\}, \tag{18}$$

and that

$$f^- = (-f)^+. \tag{19}$$

Both $f^+$ and $f^-$ have nonnegative values; if one of them has a nonzero value at $x$, the other has the value 0 at $x$. Observe that

(20) $$f = f^+ - f^-.$$

The function whose value at $x$ is $|f(x)|$ is denoted by $|f|$. We see that

(21) $$|f| = f^+ + f^-.$$

The functions $f^+, f^-$ are very useful. By means of them and the formula in (20) many demonstrations and arguments relating to arbitrary functions can be made to depend on simpler considerations having to do with nonnegative functions.

THEOREM 5–1 VIII. *If $f: X \to R^*$ is measurable, so are $f^+$ and $f^-$. If $f^+$ and $f^-$ are measurable, so are $f$ and $|f|$.*

*Proof.* The second assertion follows from Theorem 5–1 VI, because of (20) and (21). In view of (19) it suffices to prove that $f^+$ is measurable if $f$ is measurable. We leave this to the reader.

## APPROXIMATION BY SIMPLE FUNCTIONS

A constantly recurring theme in analysis is the approximation of things by simpler things. We approximate irrational numbers by rational numbers. We approximate a circle by inscribed regular polygons, to study its area and perimeter. In certain circumstances we approximate continuous functions by polynomials. Now we shall see that it is possible to approximate measurable functions by measurable functions of an elementary type, the *simple* functions defined earlier in this section.

First we remark on some matters of notation. If $f(x) \geq 0$ for each $x$, we abbreviate by writing $f \geq 0$ or $0 \leq f$. If $f(x) \leq g(x)$ for each $x$, we write $f \leq g$. Likewise, $f_n \to g$ means that $f_n(x) \to g(x)$ for each $x$.

THEOREM 5–1 IX. *Let $f: X \to R^*$ be measurable. Then there exists a sequence $\{f_n\}$ of simple functions such that $f_n \to f$. If $f \geq 0$, the sequence $\{f_n\}$ can be constructed so that $0 \leq f_n$ and $f_n \leq f_{n+1}$ for each $n$. If $N(f)$ is expressible as a countable union of measurable sets of finite measure, there exists a sequence $\{g_n\}$ of simple functions such that $\mu[N(g_n)] < +\infty$ for each $n$, $g_n \to f$, and furthermore, in the case $f \geq 0$, such that $0 \leq g_n \leq g_{n+1}$.*

*Comment.* For the case in which the measure space is that of $R^k$ with Lebesgue measure, the condition on $N(f)$ is automatically fulfilled. More generally, this condition is always satisfied when the measure $\mu$ is $\sigma$-finite.

*Proof of the theorem.* We deal first with the case in which $f \geq 0$. With $f$ given, for each positive integer $n$ and each positive integer $i$ such that $1 \leq i \leq n2^n$, let

$$E_{in} = \left\{x : \frac{i-1}{2^n} \leq f(x) < \frac{i}{2^n}\right\},$$

$$F_n = \{x : n \leq f(x)\}.$$

Observe that for each fixed $n$ the sets $F_n$ and $E_{1n}, E_{2n}, \ldots$ are disjoint sets whose union is $X$. The sets $F_n$ are measurable, for $F_n \subset N(f)$, whence $F_n = N(f) \cap F_n$, and the measurability follows from Theorem 5–1 V. Likewise $E_{in}$ is measurable if $i > 1$. If $X \in \mathbf{S}$ we can use Theorem 5–1 IV instead of 5–1 V. In this case the sets $E_{1n}$ also are measurable. We define $f_n : X \to R$ by the specifications

$$f_n(x) = \begin{cases} \dfrac{i-1}{2^n} & \text{if } x \in E_{in}, \quad i = 1, 2, \ldots, n2^n, \\ n & \text{if } x \in F_n. \end{cases}$$

Evidently $f_n \geq 0$, and $f_n$ is simple. If $f(x) < n$ for a certain $x$ and $n$, we see that

$$0 \leq f(x) - f_n(x) < \frac{1}{2^n}.$$

If $f(x) = +\infty$, then $f_n(x) = n$. Therefore $f_n \to f$. In the definition of $f_n$ we consider the division of $[0, n]$ into $n2^n$ equal subintervals, the interval between two consecutive integers being divided into $2^n$ parts. When we consider the corresponding process in the definition of $f_{n+1}$, it becomes clear that $f_n \leq f_{n+1}$. Consider separately the cases $f(x) < n$, $n \leq f(x) < n+1$, $n+1 \leq f(x)$.

Now suppose that $f$ is an arbitrary measurable function. We write $f = f^+ - f^-$ and apply the foregoing construction to obtain sequences $\{p_n\}$, $\{q_n\}$ of nonnegative simple functions such that $p_n \to f^+$, $q_n \to f^-$. Let $f_n = p_n - q_n$. Then $f_n$ is simple and $f_n \to f^+ - f^-$.

Finally, suppose that $N(f) = \bigcup_n A_n$, where $A_n \in \mathbf{S}$ and $\mu(A_n) < +\infty$. We can assume that $A_n \subset A_{n+1}$. (In the case of Lebesgue measure in $R^k$ we can take $A_n = N(f) \cap \{x : \|x\| \leq n\}$, for example.) Let $\varphi_n$ be the characteristic function of $A_n$, and let $g_n = f_n\varphi_n$, where the sequence $\{f_n\}$ is related to $f$ in the manner already described. Then $g_n$ is simple and $g_n \to f$. To see that $g_n \to f$, note that $f(x) \neq 0$ implies that $x \in A_n$ for all sufficiently large values of $n$, whence $g_n(x) = f_n(x)$ for such values of $n$. On the other hand, $f(x) = 0$ implies $\varphi_n(x) = 0$ for each $n$, so again $g_n(x) \to f(x)$. We have $N(g_n) \subset N(\varphi_n) = A_n$; therefore $\mu[N(g_n)] < +\infty$. The fact that $A_n \subset A_{n+1}$ implies that $0 \leq g_n \leq g_{n+1}$ if $0 \leq f_n \leq f_{n+1}$. The proof of Theorem 5–1 IX is now complete.

## PROBLEMS

1. Prove the modified version of Theorem 5–1 I.
2. Prove that a simple function $f$ is measurable. If $f$ has nonzero values $c_1, \ldots, c_n$ and $E_i = \{x : f(x) = c_i\}$, describe the set $N(f) \cap f^{-1}(G)$ when $G \subset R$.
3. If $f$ and $g$ are simple functions, prove that $fg$ and $f + g$ are simple.
4. If $E$ and $F$ are in $\mathbf{S}$, show that any linear combination of $\chi_E$ and $\chi_F$ is a simple function.
5. Prove Theorem 5–1 V. [*Suggestions:* Show that (a) $\Leftrightarrow$ (c) and (b) $\Leftrightarrow$ (d). Show that the measurability of $f$ implies (c) and (d), and that either (c) or (d) implies the measurability of $f$.]
6. To show that explicit mention of the sets $\{x : f(x) = +\infty\}$, $\{x : f(x) = -\infty\}$ cannot be omitted in Theorem 5–1 V, consider the following example. Let $X_1$ be a nonempty compact set in $R^k$, and let $X_2$ be a subset of $R^k - X_1$ which is not L-measurable. Let $X = X_1 \cup X_2$ and let $\mathbf{S}$ be the class of L-measurable subsets of $X$. Define $f : X \to R^*$ by letting $f(x) = +\infty$ if $x \in X_2$ and letting $f$ map $X_1$ continuously into $R$. Show that $f$ is not measurable, but that, nevertheless, $N(f) \cap \{x : f(x) < c\} \in \mathbf{S}$ for each $c$ in $R^*$.
7. Show that Theorem 5–1 V remains true if modified as follows: Suppose all the values of $f$ are finite; remove the references to the sets $\{x : f(x) = +\infty\}$, $\{x : f(x) = -\infty\}$ in (c) and (d), and change $R^*$ to $R$ in the phrase "for each $c$ in $R^*$."

8. Prove: (a) If $f$ is a measurable function, $\{x : f(x) = 0\} \in \mathbf{S}$ if and only if $X \in \mathbf{S}$.
(b) A nonzero constant function is measurable if and only if $X \in \mathbf{S}$.

9. If the measure space $(X, \mathbf{S}, \mu)$ is such that $X \in \mathbf{S}$, show that a measurable function $f$ has the property that $f^{-1}(G) \in \mathbf{S}$ whenever $G$ is a Borel set in $R$.

10. If $f$ is measurable and $E \in \mathbf{S}$, then $E \cap f^{-1}(G) \in \mathbf{S}$ for each $G \subset R^*$ such that $N(f) \cap f^{-1}(G) \in \mathbf{S}$. Prove this, using (2). Note that this implies $E \cap \{x : f(x) < c\} \in \mathbf{S}$ for each $c$ in $R^*$, and other similar assertions.

11. If $f$ and $g$ are measurable, prove that $f + g$ is measurable without assuming that $X \in \mathbf{S}$. One of the important facts to be used is noted in the preceding problem.
[*Suggestion*. Give the proof in stages, as follows.
(a) If $E \in \mathbf{S}$ and $G$ is open in $R^*$, $E \cap f^{-1}(G) \in \mathbf{S}$.
(b) The set $\{x : f(x) > g(x)\}$ is in $\mathbf{S}$. For this use (a) and the fact that $\{x : f(x) > r\} \subset N(f)$ if $r \geq 0$, while $\{x : g(x) < s\} \subset N(g)$ if $s \leq 0$.
(c) $N(f + g) \in \mathbf{S}$. Use (b).
(d) $\{x : f(x) + g(x) = -\infty\}$ and $N(f + g) \cap \{x : f(x) + g(x) > -\infty\}$ are in $\mathbf{S}$.
(e) If $c$ is real and $\{r_n\}$ is an enumeration of the rationals,

$$\{x : f(x) > c - g(x)\} = \bigcup_n [\{x : f(x) > r_n\} \cap \{x : c - r_n < g(x)\}].$$

Also, $\{x : f(x) + g(x) > c\}$ is $\{x : f(x) > c - g(x)\}$ if $c \geq 0$. When $c < 0$ we must allow for $f(x) + g(x) = 0$ occurring with $f(x) = +\infty$, $g(x) = -\infty$, or vice versa.
(f) Show by condition (d) in Theorem 5–1 V that $f + g$ is measurable.]

12. Given the measure space $(X, \mathbf{S}, \mu)$, let $X_1$ be a nonempty subset of $X$, not necessarily in $\mathbf{S}$. Let $\mathbf{S}_1$ be the class of all elements of $\mathbf{S}$ which are contained in $X_1$. Note that $\mathbf{S}_1$ is a $\sigma$-ring. If $f : X \to R^*$ is given, let $f_1$ be the restriction of $f$ to $X_1$. If $f$ is measurable with respect to $\mathbf{S}$, show that $f_1$ is measurable with respect to $\mathbf{S}_1$ provided that either $X_1$ or $X - X_1$ is in $\mathbf{S}$.

13. With $X$, $\mathbf{S}$ and $X_1$, $\mathbf{S}_1$ as in Problem 12, suppose $f_1 : X_1 \to R^*$ is measurable with respect to $\mathbf{S}_1$. Define $f : X \to R^*$ by setting $f(x) = f_1(x)$ if $x \in X_1$, $f(x) = 0$ if $x \in X - X_1$. Show that $f$ is measurable with respect to $\mathbf{S}$. Neither $X_1$ nor $X - X_1$ need be in $\mathbf{S}$.

14. Prove that $f^+$ is measurable if $f$ is.

15. Suppose $\{f_n\}$ is a sequence of measurable functions. Let $E$ be a set of measure 0 in $\mathbf{S}$, and let $g$ be a function which is constant on $E$ and such that $f_n(x) \to g(x)$ if $x \in X - E$. Show that $g$ is measurable. Give an example to show that this conclusion is false if $g$ is not constant on $E$ and the measure $\mu$ is not complete.

16. Prove the following:
(a) If $f : X \to R$ is measurable, $f \geq 0$, and $0 < p < +\infty$, $f^p$ is measurable.
(b) If $f : X \to R^*$ is measurable and if $f(x)$ is never 0, $X \in \mathbf{S}$.
(c) If $f : X \to R^*$ is measurable and $0 < f(x)$ for each $x$, then $g$ is measurable, where

$$g(x) = \frac{1}{f(x)} \left(\text{with } \frac{1}{+\infty} = 0\right).$$

(d) If $f : X \to R^*$ is measurable and $f(x) \neq 0$ for each $x$, then $g = 1/f$ is measurable.
(e) If $f$ and $g$ are measurable, $\{x : f(x) \neq g(x)\}$ is measurable.

17. Suppose $f : X \to R^*$ is measurable and that $f(x)$ is finite a.e. Suppose also that $\mu(\{x : |f(x)| > n\}) < +\infty$ for some positive integer $n$. Prove that, if $\epsilon > 0$, there exists a bounded and measurable function $g : X \to R$ such that $\mu(\{x : f(x) \neq g(x)\}) < \epsilon$. Is the assumption of finite measure for $\{x : |f(x)| > n\}$ essential?

18. Let $(X, \mathbf{S}, \mu)$ be a measure space such that (a) $\mu$ is a complete measure and (b) $X$ is a topological space and the open subsets of $X$ are in $\mathbf{S}$. Let $f : X \to R^*$ be continuous a.e. Prove that $f$ is measurable.

## 5–2 The integral of a bounded function

In this section we consider a totally finite measure space $(X, \mathbf{S}, \mu)$ and bounded measurable functions $f: X \to R$. The condition on the space means that $X \in \mathbf{S}$ and $\mu(X) < +\infty$. We define the integral $\int_X f\, d\mu$ in this situation by the process used originally by Lebesgue. The procedure is no more and no less complicated than if we were to restrict ourselves to the classical case in which $\mathbf{S}$ is the class of all $L$-measurable subsets of $X$, $\mu$ is Lebesgue measure, and $X$ is a set of finite measure in $R^k$.

Eventually we want to define the integral without the restriction to a totally finite measure space and also without the restriction to bounded functions. Some restriction must remain on the function $f$ however. The general definition (in Section 5–4) involves the use of approximation by functions of a special type and the convergence of a sequence of integrals of such functions. The present section serves to define the integral and establish its properties for an extensive class of functions. In Section 5–3 we consider some preliminary convergence theorems which are needed when we come to Section 5–4.

It would be possible to restrict the present section to the consideration of integrals of simple functions and to use such functions exclusively in the approximation procedures later on, when we give the general definition of the integral. We have decided not to do this, however, since there are interesting and instructive aspects of our alternative procedure.

### NOTATION

In all the theorems of this section, $(X, \mathbf{S}, \mu)$ denotes an arbitrary totally finite measure space. If $f: X \to R$ is bounded and measurable, we shall write

(1) $$m = \inf_{x \in X} f(x), \qquad M = \sup_{x \in X} f(x).$$

If $a, b \in R$ and $a < b$, by a *partition* of $[a, b]$ we mean a finite ordered set of numbers $(y_0, y_1, \ldots, y_n)$ such that

$$a = y_0 < y_1 < \cdots < y_n = b.$$

If $\Delta$ denotes this partition, we define

(2) $$\|\Delta\| = \max_i |y - y_{i-1}|,$$

and call this the *mesh-fineness* of $\Delta$. Another partition of $[a, b]$, say $\Delta' = (z_0, z_1, \ldots, z_p)$, is called a *refinement* of $\Delta$ if each of the $y_i$'s in $\Delta$ occurs among the $z_j$'s in $\Delta'$. The refinement is called *proper* if some $z_j$ does not occur among the $y_i$'s.

Now suppose $M_0 > M$, and let $\Delta = (y_0, \ldots, y_n)$ denote any partition of $[m, M_0]$. We define the following subsets of $X$:

(3) $$E_j = \{x : y_{j-1} \leq f(x) < y_j\}, \qquad j = 1, \ldots, n.$$

From the discussion in 5–1 it is clear that $E_j$ is measurable (see Theorem 5–1 IV). Moreover, the sets $E_1, \ldots, E_n$ are disjoint and their union is $X$. Therefore

(4) $$\mu(E_1) + \cdots + \mu(E_n) = \mu(X).$$

Now let

$$(5)\qquad s(\Delta)=\sum_{j=1}^{n} y_{j-1}\mu(E_j), \qquad S(\Delta)=\sum_{j=1}^{n} y_j\mu(E_j).$$

We call $s(\Delta)$ the *lower sum* (for $f$) associated with $\Delta$; $S(\Delta)$ is called the *upper sum* associated with $\Delta$. Since $m \leq y_j \leq M_0$, it is clear from (4) and (5) that

$$(6)\qquad m\mu(X) \leq s(\Delta) \leq S(\Delta) \leq M_0\mu(X).$$

## THE DEFINITION OF THE INTEGRAL

Now let us consider $s(\Delta)$ and $S(\Delta)$ as $\Delta$ varies over the class of all partitions of $[m, M_0]$. From (6) we see that $\sup_\Delta s(\Delta)$ and $\inf_\Delta S(\Delta)$ are both finite. As we shall see, it turns out that

$$(7)\qquad \sup_\Delta s(\Delta) = \inf_\Delta S(\Delta).$$

We shall denote this common value by $\int f\,d\mu$ or $\int_X f\,d\mu$. (We put the $X$ on the integral or leave it off as convenience and clarity make appropriate.) We shall show that if $\epsilon > 0$ both $s(\Delta)$ and $S(\Delta)$ will differ from each other, and hence from $\int f\,d\mu$, by less than $\epsilon$ provided merely that $\|\Delta\|$ is sufficiently small. In this sense, then we have

$$s(\Delta)\to\int f\,d\mu \quad\text{and}\quad S(\Delta)\to\int f\,d\mu$$

as $\|\Delta\| \to 0$.

To start the proof of (7) we consider a refinement $\Delta'$ of $\Delta$. Let $\Delta' = (z_0, \ldots, z_p)$. We shall show that

$$(8)\qquad s(\Delta) \leq s(\Delta') \quad\text{and}\quad S(\Delta') \leq S(\Delta).$$

In proving this it is enough to consider the case in which there is just one $z$, say $z_i$, which is different from all the $y$'s. For, if (8) is true in such a case it is true for any refinement, as we see by applying the reasoning a finite number of times. Suppose $y_{j-1} < z_i < y_j$ for some $j$. Let

$$F_j = \{x : y_{j-1} \leq f(x) < z_i\},$$
$$G_j = \{x : z_i \leq f(x) < y_j\}.$$

We see that $F_j \cup G_j = E_j$ and $\mu(E_j) = \mu(F_j) + \mu(G_j)$. Therefore

$$y_{j-1}\mu(E_j) \leq y_{j-1}\mu(F_j) + z_i\mu(G_j),$$

and from this it follows that $s(\Delta) \leq s(\Delta')$. The proof that $S(\Delta') \leq S(\Delta)$ is similar.

Now consider any two partitions $\Delta_1, \Delta_2$. We shall prove that

$$(9)\qquad s(\Delta_1) \leq S(\Delta_2).$$

We know this from (6) if $\Delta_1 = \Delta_2$. If $\Delta_1 \neq \Delta_2$, and if $\Delta$ is the partition which is obtained by superimposing $\Delta_1$ and $\Delta_2$, that is, by taking (in the proper order) all the distinct points represented in $\Delta_1$ and $\Delta_2$, then $\Delta$ is a refinement of both $\Delta_1$ and $\Delta_2$. Therefore, by (6) and (8),

$$s(\Delta_1) \leq s(\Delta) \leq S(\Delta) \leq S(\Delta_2).$$

Thus (9) is proved.

It follows from (9) that $\sup_\Delta s(\Delta) \leq S(\Delta_2)$, where $\Delta_2$ is any partition. Hence also, by letting $\Delta_2$ vary, we deduce that

$$(10)\qquad \sup_\Delta s(\Delta) \leq \inf_\Delta S(\Delta).$$

But, from (5) and (6) we see that, for any $\Delta$,

$$0 \le S(\Delta) - s(\Delta) \le \|\Delta\| \, \mu(X). \tag{11}$$

Since $\|\Delta\|$ can be as small as we please, it is clear from (11) that the equality must hold in (10). This proves (7). We then define

$$\int_X f \, d\mu = \int f \, d\mu = \sup_\Delta s(\Delta) = \inf_\Delta S(\Delta). \tag{12}$$

Our statement about $s(\Delta)$ and $S(\Delta)$ converging to $\int f \, d\mu$ as $\|\Delta\| \to 0$ is now justified by (11).

In the definition of the integral we began with an interval $[m, M_0]$, where $M < M_0$. The choice of $M_0$ was arbitrary, and it might seem that this choice could affect the value of the integral. This is not the case, however. See Problem 1. It is also worthy of notice that if we had chosen $m_0 < m$ and considered partitions of $[m_0, M_0]$ instead of partitions of $[m, M_0]$, we would have arrived at the same value of the integral. This remark is useful in connection with the proof of Theorem 5–2 IV.

## PROPERTIES OF THE INTEGRAL

We must now establish certain basic properties of the integral.

THEOREM 5–2 I. *With $m$ and $M$ related to $f$ as specified in* (1) *we have*

$$m\mu(X) \le \int f \, d\mu \le M\mu(X). \tag{13}$$

*Proof.* This is an obvious consequence of (6) and the freedom we have in choosing $M_0$.

COROLLARY 5–2 II. $\int_X f \, d\mu = 0$ *if* $\mu(X) = 0$.

COROLLARY 5–2 III. $\int_X f \, d\mu = c\mu(X)$ *if $f$ is a constant function:* $f(x) = c$ *for each* $x$.

If $T$ is a measurable subset of $X$ (that is, if $T \in \mathbf{S}$), we define $\int_T f \, d\mu$ by regarding $f$ as though it were defined only on $T$. That is, we consider the measure space $(T, \mathbf{S}_1, \mu)$, where $\mathbf{S}_1$ consists of all members of $\mathbf{S}$ which are contained in $T$. The restriction of $f$ to $T$ is obviously measurable with respect to $\mathbf{S}_1$.

With $f$ fixed, we can consider $\int_T f \, d\mu$ as the value of a set function defined on the $\sigma$-ring $\mathbf{S}$.

THEOREM 5–2 IV. *The set function $m$ defined by $m(T) = \int_T f \, d\mu$ is countably additive. That is, if $\{T_n\}$ is a countable disjoint family of elements of* $\mathbf{S}$, *and if $T = \bigcup_n T_n$, we have*

$$\int_T f \, d\mu = \sum_n \int_{T_n} f \, d\mu. \tag{14}$$

*(This implies that, if the number of $T_n$'s is infinite, the series on the right in* (14) *is unconditionally convergent.)*

*Proof.* Consider the case of two disjoint sets: $T_1 \cup T_2 = T$. Suppose $\alpha < f(x) < \beta$ on $T$. Then, using partitions $\Delta$ of $[\alpha, \beta]$ we proceed to define lower sums $s_1(\Delta)$, $s_2(\Delta)$, $s(\Delta)$ corresponding, respectively, to the integrals of $f$ over $T_1$, $T_2$, and $T$. In view of the remarks made after (12) we can use this one interval $[\alpha, \beta]$ in the construction of all three integrals. If $\Delta = (y_0, \ldots, y_n)$ it is clear that

$$\{x : x \in T_1, y_{j-1} \leq f(x) < y_j\} \quad \text{and} \quad \{x : x \in T_2, y_{j-1} \leq f(x) < y_j\}$$

are disjoint sets whose union is the set

$$\{x : x \in T, y_{j-1} \leq f(x) < y_j\}.$$

Therefore $s(\Delta) = s_1(\Delta) + s_2(\Delta)$. On making $\|\Delta\| \to 0$ we see that

$$\int_T f\, d\mu = \int_{T_1} f\, d\mu + \int_{T_2} f\, d\mu.$$

By induction we now obtain the validity of (14) for the case of any *finite* disjoint family of $T_n$'s.

For the countably infinite case let

$$V_n = T_1 \cup \cdots \cup T_n, \qquad R_n = T - V_n.$$

Then

$$\int_T f\, d\mu = \int_{V_n} f\, d\mu + \int_{R_n} f\, d\mu$$

and

(15)
$$\int_{V_n} f\, d\mu = \sum_{j=1}^{n} \int_{T_j} f\, d\mu.$$

But, by Theorem 5–2 I,

$$\alpha\mu(R_n) \leq \int_{R_n} f\, d\mu \leq \beta\mu(R_n).$$

Now, $\mu(R_n) \to 0$ as a result of the countable additivity of $\mu$ (see Theorem 4–4 III). Therefore

$$\int_{R_n} f\, d\mu \to 0,$$

and, in view of (15), the truth of (14) follows.

As a consequence of the additivity of the set function $m$, we see that it is monotone if $f \geq 0$. That is, under this condition on $f$, $S \subset T \subset X$ implies

$$\int_S f\, d\mu \leq \int_T f\, d\mu.$$

THEOREM 5–2 V. *If $f : X \to R$ and $g : X \to R$ are measurable and bounded, and if $f \leq g$, then*

(16)
$$\int f\, d\mu \leq \int g\, d\mu.$$

*Proof.* Let $\Delta$ and $E_1, \ldots, E_n$ have the significance ascribed to them in connection with (3). We know that

$$\int_X g\, d\mu = \sum_{j=1}^{n} \int_{E_j} g\, d\mu.$$

Also, $g(x) \geq y_{j-1}$ if $x \in E_j$, because $g(x) \geq f(x) \geq y_{j-1}$. Therefore

$$\int_{E_j} g\, d\mu \geq y_{j-1}\mu(E_j)$$

and thus

$$\int_X g\, d\mu \geq \sum_{j=1}^{n} y_{j-1}\mu(E_j) = s(\Delta).$$

From this we get (16) by the definition of the integral of $f$.

THEOREM 5–2 VI. *For two bounded measurable functions $f$ and $g$ on $X$ to $R$ we have*

$$\int (f+g)\, d\mu = \int f\, d\mu + \int g\, d\mu. \tag{17}$$

*Proof.* As a first step it may be proved that the assertion (17) is true in the special case when one of the functions is constant in value on $X$. Suppose $g(x)$ is the constant $c$ on $X$, and let $\Delta = (y_0, \ldots, y_n)$ and $E_1, \ldots, E_n$ have the meanings given in connection with (3). Then $m + c \leq f(x) + g(x) < M_0 + c$ for each $x$. Now, $(y_0 + c, y_1 + c, \ldots, y_n + c)$ is a partition of the interval $[m + c, M_0 + c]$, and

$$E_j = \{x : y_{j-1} + c \leq f(x) + g(x) < y_j + c\},$$

so that

$$\sum_{j=1}^{n} (y_{j-1} + c)\mu(E_j)$$

is a lower sum for $f + g$. But this sum has the value

$$s(\Delta) + c\mu(X) = s(\Delta) + \int_X g\, d\mu$$

(as we see by Corollary 5–2 III). On letting $\|\Delta\| \to 0$ we obtain (17) in this special case when $g$ is constant.

We go now to the general case of the theorem. Continuing with the same notational meanings for $y_j$ and $E_j$, we have (by Theorem 5–2 IV)

$$\int_X (f+g)\, d\mu = \sum_{j=1}^{n} \int_{E_j} (f+g)\, d\mu.$$

Then, since $f(x) + g(x) \geq y_{j-1} + g(x)$ if $x \in E_j$, Theorem 5–2 V implies

$$\int_{E_j} (f+g)\, d\mu \geq \int_{E_j} (y_{j-1} + g)\, d\mu.$$

The last integral here, on the right, has the value

$$y_{j-1}\mu(E_j) + \int_{E_j} g\, d\mu,$$

as a consequence of the special case of (17) which has already been proved. Therefore

$$\int_X (f+g)\, d\mu \geq \sum_{j=1}^{n} y_{j-1}\mu(E_j) + \sum_{j=1}^{n} \int_{E_j} g\, d\mu,$$

or

$$\int_X (f+g)\, d\mu \geq s(\Delta) + \int_X g\, d\mu.$$

From this we conclude that

$$\int f\,d\mu + \int g\,d\mu \le \int (f+g)\,d\mu.$$

A similar argument, with $y_j$ in place of $y_{j-1}$, shows that

$$\int_X (f+g)\,d\mu \le S(\Delta) + \int_X g\,d\mu,$$

whence

$$\int (f+g)\,d\mu \le \int f\,d\mu + \int g\,d\mu.$$

The combination of these results gives us (17).

THEOREM 5–2 VII. *For the kind of $f$ here considered, and $c$ real, we have*

$$\int cf\,d\mu = c\int f\,d\mu. \tag{18}$$

*Proof.* The result is clearly correct if $c = 0$. It is also correct if $c = -1$, for $f + (-1)f$ is the zero function, and therefore

$$0 = \int [f + (-1)f]\,d\mu = \int f\,d\mu + \int (-1)f\,d\mu,$$

or

$$\int (-1)f\,d\mu = -\int f\,d\mu.$$

Therefore, in proving (18) it now suffices to assume that $c > 0$. Using $y_j$ and $E_j$ as before, we observe that $cy_{j-1} \le cf(x) < cy_j$ if $x \in E_j$. Therefore, by Theorem 5–2 I,

$$cy_{j-1}\,\mu(E_j) \le \int_{E_j} cf\,d\mu \le cy_j\,\mu(E_j).$$

Adding, we get

$$cs(\Delta) \le \int_X cf\,d\mu \le cS(\Delta).$$

Letting $\|\Delta\| \to 0$, we obtain (18).

THEOREM 5–2 VIII. *For the kind of $f$ considered here,*

$$\left|\int_X f\,d\mu\right| \le \int_X |f|\,d\mu. \tag{19}$$

*Proof.* We know from Section 5–1 that $|f|$ is measurable. Let $E$ and $F$ be the subsets of $X$ on which $f(x) \ge 0$ and $f(x) < 0$, respectively. Then $f(x) = -|f(x)|$ on $F$, and so

$$\int_X f\,d\mu = \int_E f\,d\mu - \int_F |f|\,d\mu,$$

while

$$\int_X |f|\,d\mu = \int_E f\,d\mu + \int_F |f|\,d\mu.$$

Since all the integrals on the right in the last two formulas are nonnegative, and since $|\alpha - \beta| \le \alpha + \beta$ if $\alpha$ and $\beta$ are nonnegative, we have the proof of (19).

If $f$ and $g$ are bounded measurable functions on $X$ to $R$ such that $f(x) = g(x)$ a.e., then $\int f\,d\mu = \int g\,d\mu$. This is easily proved; we leave it as a problem. The meaning of "a.e." is explained immediately after Theorem 5–1 II.

The following theorem is very important.

THEOREM 5–2 IX. *If $f : X \to R$ is bounded and measurable, if $f(x) \geq 0$ for each $x$, and if $\int_X f\,d\mu = 0$, then $f(x) = 0$ a.e.*

*Proof.* We can assume that $\sup_x f(x) = M > 0$, for otherwise there is nothing to prove. Let

$$F_n = \left\{x : \frac{M}{n+1} < f(x) \leq \frac{M}{n}\right\}, \qquad n = 1, 2, \ldots.$$

Then $\bigcup_n F_n$ is the set on which $f(x) > 0$, and the measure of this set is $\sum_n \mu(F_n)$. The theorem will be proved if we show that $\mu(F_n) = 0$ for each $n$. Now, by the remark preceding Theorem 5–2 V we see that

$$\int_{F_n} f\,d\mu \leq \int_X f\,d\mu = 0.$$

Also, then

$$\frac{M}{n+1}\mu(F_n) \leq \int_{F_n} f\,d\mu \leq 0,$$

and consequently $\mu(F_n) = 0$. This finishes the proof.

## THE INTEGRAL OF A CONTINUOUS FUNCTION

Consider the special case in which $X$ is a compact interval in $R^k$, $f : X \to R$ is continuous on $X$, and we use Lebesgue measure on the measurable subsets of $X$. We know that $f$ is measurable (Theorem 5–1 II), and it is bounded because $X$ is compact. We wish to show that $\int f\,d\mu$ is equal to the integral of $f$ over $X$ as defined classically in calculus. Let us denote the value of this latter integral by $J$. For simplicity of exposition let us deal with the case $k = 1$; we take $X = [a, b]$. The principles are the same for $k > 1$. Let $\Delta = (x_0, \ldots, x_n)$ be a partition of $[a, b]$, and let

$$\left.\begin{aligned} m_i &= \inf f(x) \\ M_i &= \sup f(x) \end{aligned}\right\} \quad \text{for} \quad x_{i-1} \leq x \leq x_i.$$

Let $E_i = \{x : x_{i-1} \leq x < x_i\}$ if $i = 1, \ldots, n-1$, and let $E_n = \{x : x_{n-1} \leq x \leq x_n\}$. Then

$$\int_X f\,d\mu = \sum_{i=1}^{n} \int_{E_i} f\,d\mu,$$

and

$$m_i\,\mu(E_i) \leq \int_{E_i} f\,d\mu \leq M_i\,\mu(E_i).$$

Since $\mu(E_i) = x_i - x_{i-1}$ we see that

$$\sum_{i=1}^{n} m_i(x_i - x_{i-1}) \leq \int_X f\,d\mu \leq \sum_{i=1}^{n} M_i(x_i - x_{i-1}). \tag{20}$$

Now, as is well known, the two sums which appear in (20) both approach $J$ (from below and above, respectively) as $\|\Delta\| \to 0$. We see therefore that we necessarily have $\int_X f\,d\mu = J$.

The foregoing argument shows, in fact, that $\int_X f\,d\mu$ is equal to the Riemann integral of $f$ for any $f: X \to R$ which is integrable in the Riemann sense and also Lebesgue-measurable. Actually, it can be proved that any Riemann-integrable function *is* measurable (see Theorem 5–3 V). Therefore the theory of the Lebesgue integral, as conceived in this section, is an extension and generalization of the Riemann theory of integration.

*Example.* As a simple function which is integrable in the Lebesgue sense, but not in the Riemann sense, consider $f: [0, 1] \to R$ defined as follows:

$$f(x) = \begin{cases} 1 & \text{if } x \text{ is irrational} \\ 0 & \text{if } x \text{ is rational.} \end{cases}$$

As is well known, $f$ is not integrable in Riemann's sense. But $f(x) = g(x)$ a.e., where $g$ is the constant function with value 1 at all points of $[0, 1]$. Therefore $f$ is measurable and its integral over $[0, 1]$ is the same as that of $g$.

### THE INTEGRAL OF A SIMPLE FUNCTION

If $g: X \to R$ is a simple function, with distinct values $a_1, \ldots, a_n$, let $A_i = \{x : g(x) = a_i\}$. Then the $A_i$'s are disjoint, measurable, and their union is $X$. Results earlier in this section show that $\int_{A_i} g\,d\mu = a_i\mu(A_i)$ and

$$\int_X g\,d\mu = \sum_{i=1}^{n} a_i\mu(A_i). \tag{21}$$

We can interpret the $s(\Delta)$ and $S(\Delta)$ of (5) as integrals of simple functions. For instance, if the partition $\Delta$ is fixed, let $g$ be defined by setting $g(x) = y_{j-1}$ on $E_j$, $j = 1, \ldots, n$. Then $g$ is a simple function, and

$$\int_X g\,d\mu = s(\Delta).$$

Since $0 \le f(x) - y_{j-1} < y_j - y_{j-1}$ if $x \in E_j$, we see that $|f(x) - g(x)| \le \|\Delta\|$ for each $x$. Thus we approximate $f$ by $g$, and at the same time we approximate $\int_X f\,d\mu$ by $\int_X g\,d\mu$.

### PROBLEMS

1. (a) Show that the value of $\int_X f\,d\mu$ obtained in (12) is independent of the choice of $M_0$, so long as $M < M_0$. [*Suggestion.* If $M < M_0 < M_0'$, show that to each partition $\Delta$ of $[m, M_0]$ corresponds a partition of $[m, M_0']$ for which the associated upper and lower sums are the same as $S(\Delta)$ and $s(\Delta)$, respectively. Explain how this leads at once to the desired conclusion.]

(b) Show that, in defining the integral, we would get the same value for the integral in (12) if, instead of using partitions of $[m, M_0]$, we used partitions of $[m_0, M_0]$, where $m_0$ is any real number such that $m_0 < m$.

2. Let $f, g$, be as in Theorem 5–2 VI, and suppose $f(x) = g(x)$ a.e. Prove that $\int_X f\,d\mu = \int_X g\,d\mu$.

3. A great deal of the development of theory in this section can be made with weaker assumptions about **S** and $\mu$. Suppose **S** is merely a ring, not a $\sigma$-ring, and $\mu$ is a finitely additive nonnegative set function on **S**. As before, assume $X \in \mathbf{S}$ and $\mu(X) < +\infty$. Examine in detail what should be assumed about $f$ in order to be able to define $\int_X f\, d\mu$, and investigate the extent to which the theorems remain true.

## 5–3 Preliminary convergence theorems

In this section we discuss some convergence theorems relating to sequences of measurable functions and to sequences of integrals of the type defined in Section 5–2. These theorems are needed in connection with the work of Section 5–4.

### EGOROFF'S THEOREM

The following theorem is of fundamental importance in the study of convergence of sequences of measurable functions. It is called Egoroff's (or Egorov's) theorem, after D. F. Egoroff (1869–1931); he published the original version of the theorem in 1911.

THEOREM 5–3 I. *Let $(X, \mathbf{S}, \mu)$ be a totally finite measure space. Suppose $f$ and $f_1, f_2, \ldots$ are measurable functions on $X$ to $R$ such that $f_n(x) \to f(x)$ a.e. Then to each $\epsilon > 0$ corresponds a measurable set $E$ with $\mu(E) < \epsilon$ such that $f_n(x)$ converges to $f(x)$ uniformly on $X - E$.*

*Proof.* Let $X_0$ be the subset (of measure 0) on which $f_n(x)$ does not converge to $f(x)$. For each pair of positive integers $i$, $n$ let

$$E_{in} = \{x : x \in X - X_0,\ |f_m(x) - f(x)| < 2^{-i} \text{ if } m \geq n\}.$$

These sets $E_{in}$ are measurable, $E_{in} \subset E_{i,n+1}$, and since $f_n(x)$ converges to $f(x)$ on $X - X_0$, we see that for each $i$ we have

$$\bigcup_n E_{in} = X - X_0.$$

Then, by Theorem 4–4 III,

$$\lim_{n\to\infty} \mu(E_{in}) = \mu(X - X_0) = \mu(X).$$

Consequently, given $\epsilon > 0$, there is some $n$ depending on $i$ [we denote it by $n(i)$] such that

$$\mu[E_{i,n(i)}] > \mu(X) - \frac{\epsilon}{2^i}, \qquad \mu[X - E_{i\ n(i)}] < \frac{\epsilon}{2^i}.$$

Let

$$E = X - \bigcap_i E_{i,n(i)} = \bigcup_i [X - E_{i,n(i)}].$$

We see that

$$\mu(E) \leq \sum_i \frac{\epsilon}{2^i} = \epsilon.$$

Now, $X - E = \bigcap_i E_{i,n(i)}$, and so, if $x \in X - E$ we have

$$|f_m(x) - f(x)| < \frac{1}{2^i} \quad \text{if} \quad m \geq n(i),$$

this being valid for $i = 1, 2, \ldots$. Therefore $f_n(x) \to f(x)$ uniformly on $X - E$.

Egoroff's theorem and the theorem which follows are closely related to the concept of convergence in measure (see Section 5–6). However, for the sake of simplicity we do not wish to introduce this concept at this place in the text. Moreover, we have not given Egoroff's theorem here in quite as general a form as it can have. In Problem 3 (a) and (b), Section 5–6, will be found another discussion which can logically take the place of Theorems 5–3 I, II as here stated. Nothing about convergence in measure is needed except the definition.

THEOREM 5–3 II. *Under the hypotheses of the preceding theorem, for each* $\epsilon > 0$ *and each n let*

$$A_n = A_n(\epsilon) = \{x : |f_n(x) - f(x)| \geq \epsilon\}.$$

*Then* $\mu(A_n) \to 0$.

*Proof.* Corresponding to an arbitrarily assigned positive $\delta$ Egoroff's theorem permits us to choose a measurable subset $E$ of $X$ such that $\mu(E) < \delta$ and such that $f_n(x) \to f(x)$ uniformly on $X - E$. Then, given $\epsilon > 0$, choose $N$ so that $|f_n(x) - f(x)| < \epsilon$ if $n \geq N$ and $x \in X - E$. We see that $A_n(\epsilon) \subset E$ if $n \geq N$, and so certainly $\mu(A_n) < \delta$ if $n \geq N$. This proves the theorem.

LEMMA 5–3 III. *Suppose that* $(X, \mathbf{S}, \mu)$ *is a totally finite measure space. Let* $f$ *and* $f_1, f_2, \ldots$ *be bounded measurable functions on* $X$ *to* $R$ *such that* $f_n(x) \to f(x)$ *a.e. and such that, for a certain positive constant* $M$ *and for each* $n$, $|f_n(x)| \leq M$ *a.e. Then*

$$\lim_{n\to\infty} \int f_n \, d\mu = \int f \, d\mu.$$

*Proof.* We note first of all that, since the set $E_n$ on which $|f_n(x)| > M$ is a set of measure 0, the union of all these sets $E_1, E_2, \ldots$ is also of measure zero. Then, since $f_n(x) \to f(x)$ a.e., it follows that there is a certain set $E$ of measure zero such that $|f_n(x) - f(x)| \leq 2M$ for all $n$ if $x \in X - E$. If $\epsilon > 0$, choose $\delta > 0$ so that $\delta\mu(X) < \frac{\epsilon}{2}$, and let

$$A_n(\delta) = A_n = \{x : |f_n(x) - f(x)| \geq \delta\}.$$

Also let $B_n = X - A_n$. Then

$$\left|\int (f_n - f) \, d\mu\right| \leq \int |f_n - f| \, d\mu, \tag{1}$$

and the integral on the right is the sum of the integrals of $|f_n - f|$ over the three sets $A_n \cap E^\sim$, $A_n \cap E$, $B_n$. We have

$$\int_{A_n \cap E^\sim} |f_n - f| \, d\mu \leq 2M\mu(A_n),$$

$$\int_{A_n \cap E} |f_n - f| \, d\mu = 0, \qquad \text{because} \quad \mu(E) = 0,$$

$$\int_{B_n} |f_n - f| \, d\mu \leq \delta\mu(B_n) \leq \delta\mu(X) < \frac{\epsilon}{2}.$$

By Theorem 5–3 II we can choose $N$ so that $2M\mu(A_n) < \frac{\epsilon}{2}$ if $n \geq N$. We then have $\int_X |f_n - f| \, d\mu < \epsilon$ if $n \geq N$. In view of (1), this completes the proof.

Lemma 5–3 III is sometimes called Lebesgue's *bounded* convergence theorem. It is a special case of the general *dominated* convergence theorem (Theorem 5–5 IV), which is one of the triumphs of Lebesgue's theory of integration.

If $(X, \mathbf{S}, \mu)$ is an arbitrary measure space (not necessarily totally finite) and $f: X \to R$ is a measurable function, we can define $\int_E f\,d\mu$ for any measurable set $E$ of finite measure on which $f$ is bounded. To do this we let $f_1$ be the restriction of $f$ to $E$ and let $\mathbf{S}_1$ be the $\sigma$-ring composed of those elements of $\mathbf{S}$ which are contained in $E$. Then $(E, \mathbf{S}_1, \mu)$ is a totally finite measure space. It can be shown that $f_1$ is measurable with respect to $\mathbf{S}_1$. (See Problem 12, Section 5–1.) This is obvious if $X \in \mathbf{S}$. We can define $\int_E f_1\,d\mu$ as in Section 5–2. We define $\int_E f\,d\mu = \int_E f_1\,d\mu$.

If, in particular, $f$ is bounded on $X$ and $N(f)$ is of finite measure, we clearly have $\int_E f\,d\mu = \int_{N(f)} f\,d\mu$ for any measurable $E$ such that $N(f) \subset E$ and $\mu(E) < +\infty$.

LEMMA 5–3 IV. *Let $g$ and $f_1, f_2, \ldots$ be bounded measurable functions on $X$ to $R$, where $(X, \mathbf{S}, \mu)$ is an arbitrary measure space. Suppose $0 \le g$ and $0 \le f_n \le f_{n+1}$ for each $n$. Let $F_n = N(f_n)$, $G = N(g)$, and suppose that the measures of $G$ and $F_n$ are finite. Finally, suppose that*

(2) $$g(x) \le \lim_{n\to\infty} f_n(x) \quad a.e.$$

*Then*

(3) $$\int_G g\,d\mu \le \lim_{n\to\infty} \int_{F_n} f_n\,d\mu.$$

*(The limits in* (2) *and* (3) *are not required to be finite.)*

*Proof.* We see that $F_n \subset F_{n+1}$. It is then easily seen from the results in Section 5–2 that the sequence of integrals $\int_{F_n} f_n\,d\mu$ is nondecreasing. We now define $g_n(x) = \min\{f_n(x), g(x)\}$. Then $g_n$ is bounded and measurable, and $0 \le g_n \le g_{n+1}$. From (2) and the definition of $g_n$ it is now easy to prove that $g_n(x) \to g(x)$ a.e. If $M = \sup_x g(x)$, we have $0 \le g_n(x) \le M$ for all $x$. Let $G_n = N(g_n)$. Since $g_n \le g$ we have $G_n \subset G$. The integral of $g_n$ over $G - G_n$ is 0, and therefore

$$\int_{G_n} g_n\,d\mu = \int_G g_n\,d\mu.$$

Also, $g_n \le f_n$, and hence $G_n \subset F_n$. We have

(4) $$\int_{F_n} f_n\,d\mu \ge \int_{F_n} g_n\,d\mu \ge \int_{G_n} g_n\,d\mu = \int_G g_n\,d\mu.$$

But $\int_G g_n\,d\mu \to \int_G g\,d\mu$ by Lemma 5–3 III. Thus (4) implies (3).

## FUNCTIONS INTEGRABLE IN RIEMANN'S SENSE

By refining somewhat the argument in Section 5–2 about the integral of a continuous function we can prove the following theorem.

THEOREM 5–3 V. *Let $f : [a, b] \to R$ be a bounded function. If $f$ is integrable in the sense of Riemann, it is measurable, and the Riemann integral of $f$ over $[a, b]$ has the same value as the Lebesgue integral. In order that $f$ be Riemann-integrable, it is necessary and sufficient that the points at which $f$ is discontinuous form a set of measure zero.*

*Proof.* We use the notations $\Delta$, $m_i$, $M_i$, $E_i$ as in the discussion preceding (20) in Section 5–2. With the partition $\Delta$ we associate the functions

$$g_\Delta = \sum_i m_i \chi_{E_i}, \qquad G_\Delta = \sum_i M_i \chi_{E_i}.$$

These are bounded measurable functions, and we have the Lebesgue integrals

$$\int g_\Delta \, d\mu = \sum_i m_i \mu(E_i), \qquad \int G_\Delta \, d\mu = \sum_i M_i \mu(E_i). \tag{5}$$

Suppose now that $\{\Delta_k\}$ is a sequence of partitions of $[a, b]$ such that $\|\Delta_k\| \to 0$ and such that $\Delta_{k+1}$ is a refinement of $\Delta_k$. Let $f_k = g_{\Delta_k}$, $F_k = G_{\Delta_k}$. Then it is easy to see that $f_k \le f_{k+1}$, $F_{k+1} \le F_k$. We also have $-\|f\| \le f_k(x) \le f(x) \le F_k(x) \le \|f\|$, where $\|f\|$ is the least upper bound of $|f(x)|$ on $[a, b]$. Let $f_k(x) \to h(x)$ and $F_k(x) \to H(x)$. Both $h$ and $H$ are bounded measurable functions, and $h(x) \le f(x) \le H(x)$. By Lemma 5–3 III we know that

$$\int f_k \, d\mu \to \int h \, d\mu, \qquad \int F_k \, d\mu \to \int H \, d\mu. \tag{6}$$

Now suppose that $f$ is Riemann integrable, and let the value of the Riemann integral of $f$ over $[a, b]$ be $J$. We know from the Riemann theory that both of the sums in (5) approach $J$ as $\|\Delta\| \to 0$. It then follows from (6) that

$$\int h \, d\mu = \int H \, d\mu = J, \tag{7}$$

and hence, by Theorem 5–2 IX, we conclude that $H(x) - h(x) = 0$ a.e. This implies $h(x) = f(x) = H(x)$ a.e. Hence $f$ is measurable, and its Lebesgue integral is equal to $J$, by (7).

Let $S$ be the set of points at which $f$ is discontinuous. We shall show that

$$S \subset \{x : H(x) - h(x) > 0\} \cup S_0, \tag{8}$$

where $S_0$ is a certain countable set of points. It will then follow that $\mu(S) = 0$ if $f$ is Riemann-integrable. In what follows, when we refer to a neighborhood of a point in $[a, b]$, we mean a neighborhood in the relative topology of $[a, b]$ as a subset of $R$. If $x \in S$, there is an $\epsilon > 0$ such that for any neighborhood $V$ of $x$,

$$\sup_{y \in V} f(y) - \inf_{y \in V} f(y) \ge \epsilon.$$

Now, if $x$ is not one of the points $x_1, \ldots, x_{n-1}$ in the partition $\Delta$, and if $x \in E_i$, there is some neighborhood $V$ of $x$ such that $V \subset E_i$. It then follows that

$$g_\Delta(x) = m_i \le \inf_{y \in V} f(y), \qquad \sup_{y \in V} f(y) \le M_i = G_\Delta(x).$$

Let $S_0$ be the countable set of all the points except $a$, $b$ in the partitions $\Delta_1, \Delta_2, \ldots$. From the foregoing we see that $x \in S - S_0$ implies $F_n(x) - f_n(x) \ge \epsilon$ and hence $H(x) - h(x) \ge \epsilon$. This proves (8).

Now let us assume that $\mu(S) = 0$, and prove from this that $f$ is Riemann integrable. Let $\{\Delta_k\}$ be any sequence of partitions as specified in the paragraph following (5). We wish to show that

(9) $$\{x : H(x) - h(x) > 0\} \subset S.$$

This will imply that $\int h\, d\mu = \int H\, d\mu$. Then (6) and (5) will imply that $f$ is Riemann integrable. We suppose $x$ is a point such that $H(x) - h(x) > 0$. Choose $\epsilon > 0$ so that $2\epsilon < H(x) - h(x)$ and assume $f$ is continuous at $x$. Choose $\delta > 0$ so that $|y - x| \leq \delta$ and $a \leq y \leq b$ imply $|f(y) - f(x)| < \epsilon$. Choose $k$ so that $\|\Delta_k\| \leq \delta$. Then $x$ lies in a certain one of the closed subintervals determined by the partition $\Delta_k$, and it is easy to see that

$$f(x) - \epsilon \leq f_k(x), \qquad F_k(x) \leq f(x) + \epsilon.$$

From this we see that

$$f(x) - \epsilon \leq h(x), \qquad H(x) \leq f(x) + \epsilon,$$

whence we arrive at the contradiction

$$H(x) - h(x) \leq 2\epsilon.$$

Thus (9) is proved and the proof is complete.

### PROBLEM

Suppose that $f_n : [a, b] \to R$ and $f : [a, b] \to R$ are integrable in the Riemann sense, that $|f_n(x)| \leq M < +\infty$ for each $n$ and $x$, and that $f_n(x) \to f(x)$ for each $x$. It is true that

$$\int_a^b f_n(x)\, dx \to \int_a^b f(x)\, dx,$$

where the integrals are Riemann integrals? Explain. What can be said if the hypothesis that $f$ is Riemann integrable is omitted?

## 5–4 The general definition of an integral

We now wish to generalize the definition of an integral, so as to include a much larger class of functions than those considered in Section 5–2. The procedure we use involves beginning with nonnegative functions. Arbitrary functions are then treated by using the decomposition $f = f^+ - f^-$. As in previous sections, the theory is basically the same in the context of a general space as it is for the context of Lebesgue measure in $R^k$, so we deal with the general case. There are some complications which could be avoided by the assumption that $X \in \mathbf{S}$, but we do not make this assumption in general.

### REGULAR APPROXIMATING SEQUENCES

Let $(X, \mathbf{S}, \mu)$ be a measure space, and suppose $f : X \to R^*$ is a measurable function such that $f(x) \geq 0$ for each $x$. By *a regular approximating sequence* $\{f_n\}$ for $f$ we mean a sequence of functions $f_n : X \to R$ (note that it is $R$, not $R^*$) with the following properties:

(a) $0 \leq f_n \leq f_{n+1}$ for each $n$,
(b) each $f_n$ is bounded and measurable,
(c) each of the sets $N(f_n)$ has finite measure,
(d) $f_n(x) \to f(x)$ a.e.

As we see from Theorem 5–1 IX, there will certainly exist a regular approximating sequence for $f$ provided that the set $N(f)$ can be expressed as a countable union of measurable sets of finite measure. This condition on $f$ is automatically satisfied in case our measure space is $R^k$ with Lebesgue measure. We can even obtain a regular approximating sequence which converges to $f$ at all points, and the members of the sequence can be taken to be simple functions.

It is interesting to observe that the process of defining $\int_X f\,d\mu$ in Section 5–2 provides us in a natural way with a regular approximating sequence for $f$ in that special situation. With the meanings of $\Delta$ and $E_1, \ldots, E_n$ as given in connection with (3) in Section 5–2 we define a function $f_\Delta$ as follows: $f_\Delta(x) = y_{j-1}$ if $x \in E_j$. Then $f_\Delta$ is a simple function, and we clearly have $0 \leq f(x) - f_\Delta(x) \leq \|\Delta\|$ for each $x$. If $\Delta'$ is a refinement of $\Delta$ it is easy to see that $f_\Delta(x) \leq f_{\Delta'}(x)$. Now let $\{\Delta_n\}$ be a sequence of partitions such that $\Delta_{n+1}$ is a refinement of $\Delta_n$ and $\|\Delta_n\| \to 0$. Let $g_n = f_{\Delta_n}$. We see that $g_n(x) \to f(x)$ uniformly on $X$; also, $g_n \leq g_{n+1}$. for each $n$. If $f$ is a nonnegative function, so is $g_n$, and $\{g_n\}$ is a regular approximating sequence for $f$. We observe the following:

$$(1) \qquad \int_X f_\Delta\,d\mu = \sum_{j=1}^{n} \int_{E_j} f_\Delta\,d\mu = \sum_{j=1}^{n} y_{j-1}\mu(E_j) = s(\Delta).$$

Thus, the regular approximating sequence $\{g_n\}$ has the property that

$$(2) \qquad \int g_n\,d\mu \to \int f\,d\mu.$$

This observation helps to motivate the general definition of an integral to which we shall come presently.

The following important lemma is concerned with two regular approximating sequences for the same function.

LEMMA 5–4 I. *Let $f$ be a nonnegative measurable function on $X$ to $R^*$, where $(X, \mathbf{S}, \mu)$ is an arbitrary measure space. If $\{f_n\}$ and $\{g_n\}$ are two regular approximating sequences for $f$, and if $F_n = N(f_n)$, $G_n = N(g_n)$, then*

$$\lim_{n\to\infty} \int_{F_n} f_n\,d\mu = \lim_{n\to\infty} \int_{G_n} g_n\,d\mu.$$

*(The common value of the limits need not be finite.)*

*Proof.* Concerning the integrals which occur here we call attention to remarks made just prior to Lemma 5–3 IV. By symmetry it will suffice to prove that

$$(3) \qquad \lim_{n\to\infty} \int_{G_n} g_n\,d\mu \leq \lim_{n\to\infty} \int_{F_n} f_n\,d\mu.$$

But the truth of this follows with the aid of Lemma 5–3 IV. In fact, for any $j$ we have a.e.

$$g_j(x) \leq \lim_{n\to\infty} g_n(x) = f(x) = \lim_{n\to\infty} f_n(x),$$

and so

$$\int_{G_j} g_j\,d\mu \leq \lim_{n\to\infty} \int_{F_n} f_n\,d\mu.$$

The truth of (3) now follows.

## DEFINITION OF THE CLASS OF SUMMABLE FUNCTIONS

We come now to the basic definition. A nonnegative measurable function $f: X \to R^*$ is called *summable* if there exists a regular approximating sequence $\{f_n\}$ for $f$ such that

$$\lim_{n\to\infty} \int_{F_n} f_n \, d\mu < +\infty. \tag{4}$$

Here $F_n = N(f_n)$. It follows from Lemma 5–4 I that the limit in (4) is independent of the particular regular approximating sequence. We define this finite limit to be the integral of $f$ (over $X$):

$$\int f \, d\mu = \lim_{n\to\infty} \int_{F_n} f_n \, d\mu. \tag{5}$$

For an arbitrary measurable function $f: X \to R^*$ we decompose $f$ into $f = f^+ - f^-$. Then $f$ is called summable if both $f^+$ and $f^-$ are summable. The integral of $f$ is, by definition,

$$\int f \, d\mu = \int f^+ \, d\mu - \int f^- \, d\mu. \tag{6}$$

If the measure space is totally finite, and if $f: X \to R$ is measurable, nonnegative, and bounded, the sequence $\{f_n\}$ obtained by taking $f_n = f$ for each $n$ is a regular approximating sequence for $f$. From this remark we can easily establish that every bounded measurable $f: X \to R$ is summable if the measure space is totally finite, and that the integral here defined by (6) has the same value as the integral of $f$ defined in Section 5–2.

For a given measure space $(X, \mathbf{S}, \mu)$ we denote the class of summable functions by $\mathscr{L}(\mu)$, leaving the dependence of this class on $X$ and $\mathbf{S}$ to be kept in mind from the context.

## FUNCTIONS SUMMABLE OVER A MEASURABLE SET

If $E$ is a measurable subset of $X$, a function $f: X \to R^*$ is called *summable over $E$* if the product $f\chi_E$ is summable, where $\chi_E$ is the characteristic function of $E$. In this case the integral of $f$ over $E$ is defined by

$$\int_E f \, d\mu = \int f\chi_E \, d\mu. \tag{7}$$

If $f$ is any measurable function, the set $N(f)$ is measurable. Obviously, $f$ is summable if and only if it is summable over $N(f)$; when this is the case we have

$$\int f \, d\mu = \int_{N(f)} f \, d\mu.$$

There is another way of looking at the situation when we speak of the integral of $f$ over $E$. We may consider $(E, \mathbf{S}_1, \mu)$ as a measure space, where $\mathbf{S}_1$ is composed of all members of $\mathbf{S}$ which are contained in $E$. Then, if $f_1$ is the restriction of $f$ to $E$, it turns out that $f$ is summable over $E$ if and only if $f_1$ is summable with reference to $(E, \mathbf{S}_1, \mu)$. Moreover, the integral in (7) is then the same as the integral of $f_1$.

## SOME EASILY PROVED FACTS

We shall list a number of useful facts. When referring to some of these simple propositions we call them "fact A," "fact B," and so on. Proofs are left to the reader.

A. *The identically zero function is summable and its integral is* 0.

B. *If $f$ is summable, it is summable over every measurable set. If $f$ is summable over the measurable set $E$, it is summable over every measurable subset of $E$.*

C. *If $f$ is measurable and $E$ is a set of measure* 0, *$f$ is summable over $E$ and* $\int_E f\,d\mu = 0$.

D. *If $f$ is summable and $f(x) \geq 0$ a.e., then* $\int f\,d\mu \geq 0$.

E. *If $f$ is summable, if $g$ is measurable, and $f(x) = g(x)$ a.e., then $g$ is summable and* $\int g\,d\mu = \int f\,d\mu$.

## PROPERTIES OF THE INTEGRAL

The assumption that $f$ is summable places a restriction on $N(f)$, as we see in the following theorem.

THEOREM 5–4 II. *If $f \in \mathscr{L}(\mu)$, the set $N(f)$ is expressible as a countable union of measurable sets, each of finite measure.*

*Proof.* Since $N(f) = \{x : f^+(x) > 0\} \cup \{x : f^-(x) > 0\}$, it is clearly sufficient to give the proof on the assumption that $f \geq 0$. Let $\{f_n\}$ be a regular approximating sequence for $f$. Let $X_0$ be the set on which $f_n(x)$ does not converge to $f(x)$, and let $F_n = N(f_n)$. We see readily that

$$N(f) - X_0 \subset \bigcup_{i=1}^{\infty} \bigcap_{n \geq i} F_n.$$

Let $G_0 = N(f) \cap X_0$, and

$$G_i = N(f) \cap \bigcap_{n \geq i} F_n \qquad \text{if} \quad i \geq 1.$$

Then let $A_n = G_0 \cup G_1 \cup \cdots \cup G_n$, $n \geq 1$. We see that $A_n \subset A_{n+1}$, $\mu(A_n) < +\infty$, and

(8) $$N(f) = \bigcup_n A_n.$$

This gives the required expression of $N(f)$.

One consequence of Theorem 5–4 II is that we would not change the class $\mathscr{L}(\mu)$ or the value of the integral of a member of the class if, in the definition of a summable nonnegative function $f$, we were to demand of the regular approximating sequence $\{f_n\}$ that $f_n(x) \to f(x)$ for every $x$ (instead of a.e.) and that each $f_n$ be a simple function. These demands could be added to the conditions already imposed without restricting the class of summable functions. For, as we now see by Theorems 5–1 IX and 5–4 II, such a regular approximating sequence exists for every nonnegative $f$ in $\mathscr{L}(\mu)$.

Another important consequence of Theorem 5–4 II is expressed in Theorem 5–7 III. This latter theorem could well come at this point in the text, since all the methods for its proof are at our disposal. But we prefer to put it in Section 5–7 in order to emphasize its significance in connection with the metric space $L(\mu)$ which is there constructed from $\mathscr{L}(\mu)$.

The next theorem shows the limitation which necessarily exists on infinite values of a summable function.

THEOREM 5–4 III. *If $f \in \mathscr{L}(\mu)$, the sets $\{x : f(x) = +\infty\}$ and $\{x : f(x) = -\infty\}$ are of measure* 0, *so that $f(x)$ is finite a.e.*

*Proof.* It is enough to treat the case in which $f \geq 0$, for the result can then be applied to $f^+$ and $f^-$. We express $N(f)$ as in (8). If $E = \{x : f(x) = +\infty\}$, let $E_n = E \cap A_n$. Now, $\{n\chi_{E_n}\}$ is a regular approximating sequence for $f\chi_E$, which is summable; therefore

$$\int n\chi_{E_n}\, d\mu = n\mu(E_n) \to \int_E f\, d\mu.$$

But $\mu(E_n) \to \mu(E)$, by Theorem 4–4 III. We must then conclude that $\mu(E) = 0$, for $\mu(E) > 0$ would imply $n\mu(E_n) \to +\infty$, which is false.

We now begin the investigation of $\int_E f\, d\mu$ as a function of $E$ and $f$.

THEOREM 5–4 IV. *Suppose f is measurable, and that it is summable over each of the measurable sets F, G. Then it is summable over H = F ∪ G. If F and G are disjoint,*

(9) $$\int_H f\, d\mu = \int_F f\, d\mu + \int_G f\, d\mu.$$

*Proof.* It is enough to give the proof for the case in which $f \geq 0$, so we consider this case. Since $F \cup G = F \cup (G - F)$ and $f$ is summable over $G - F$ (see fact $B$), we may as well assume at the outset that $F \cap G = \varnothing$. Let $\{f_n\}$ and $\{g_n\}$ be regular approximating sequences for $f\chi_F$ and $f\chi_G$, respectively. We can assume that $\{f_n\}$ is chosen so that $f_n$ converges pointwise to $f\chi_F$ everywhere; likewise for $\{g_n\}$ and $f\chi_G$. Let $h_n = f_n + g_n$. Evidently $\{h_n\}$ is a regular approximating sequence for $f\chi_H$. Let $F_n = N(f_n)$, and define $G_n$, $H_n$ likewise. Clearly $F_n \cap G_n = \varnothing$, $H_n = F_n \cup G_n$. From results in Section 5–2 we can see that

$$\int_{H_n} h_n\, d\mu = \int_{F_n} f_n\, d\mu + \int_{G_n} g_n\, d\mu.$$

From this we can deduce that $f$ is summable over $H$ and that (9) holds.

In Theorem 5–5 II we shall have an extension of the foregoing theorem for the case of a countable union of measurable sets.

The next theorem deals with linear combinations of summable functions.

THEOREM 5–4 V. *If $f$, $g$ are in $\mathscr{L}(\mu)$ and $c \in R$, then $cf$ and $f + g$ are in $\mathscr{L}(\mu)$, and*

(10) $$\int cf\, d\mu = c\int f\, d\mu,$$

(11) $$\int (f + g)\, d\mu = \int f\, d\mu + \int g\, d\mu.$$

*Proof of* (10). We develop the argument in stages as follows: (a) The result is evident if $c = 0$. (b) If $c > 0$ and $f \geq 0$, we appeal to the definition of summability and use Theorem 5–2 VII for the integrals of the approximating functions. (c) If $f$ is summable, we use $(-f)^+ = f^-$, $(-f)^- = f^+$ to obtain (10) for the case $c = -1$. (d) For arbitrary summable $f$ and $c > 0$, $(cf)^+ = cf^+$, $(cf)^- = cf^-$. We can then use (b). If $c < 0$, we write $cf = (-c)(-f)$ and use previous results. We leave details to the reader.

*Proof of* (11). A little checking shows that

$$f + g = (f^+ + g^+) - (f^- + g^-). \tag{12}$$

(This is not simply a matter of rearranging $(f^+ - f^-) + (g^+ - g^-)$, because, as we pointed out in Section 4–1, addition is not always associative in $R^*$.) On account of (12) we see that it suffices to prove (11) in two special cases: ($\alpha$) $f \geq 0$ and $g \geq 0$, ($\beta$) $f \geq 0$ and $-g \geq 0$. We consider case ($\alpha$) first. If $\{f_n\}$ and $\{g_n\}$ are regular approximating sequences for $f$ and $g$, respectively, and if $h_n = f_n + g_n$, then $\{h_n\}$ is a regular approximating sequence for $f + g$. Let $F_n = N(f_n)$, and define $G_n$, $H_n$ likewise. We see that $H_n = F_n \cup G_n$. By the results of Section 5–2 we know that

$$\int_{H_n} f_n \, d\mu = \int_{F_n} f_n \, d\mu$$

and likewise for $g_n$, whence

$$\int_{H_n} h_n \, d\mu = \int_{F_n} f_n \, d\mu + \int_{G_n} g_n \, d\mu.$$

From this we draw the desired conclusion in case ($\alpha$).

Now consider case ($\beta$). Let $h = f + g$, and let $E_0 = \{x : h(x) = 0\}$, $E_1 = \{x : h(x) > 0\}$, $E_2 = \{x : h(x) < 0\}$, $E = E_1 \cup E_2$. We observe that $E = N(h)$. We know that $h$ is measurable (Theorem 5–1 VI). Hence $N(h) \in \mathbf{S}$. Since $E_1 = E_1 \cap N(h)$, we see by Theorem 5–1 V that $E_1 \in \mathbf{S}$; likewise $E_2 \in \mathbf{S}$. If $X \in \mathbf{S}$, $E_0$, $E_1$, and $E_2$ are all measurable, as we can see by Theorem 5–1 IV. When $X \notin \mathbf{S}$ we cannot conclude that $E_0 \in \mathbf{S}$, but it is nevertheless true that $E_0$ has a measurable intersection with every measurable set (see Problem 10, Section 5–1).

First we show that $h$ is summable over $E_1$. Since $f \geq 0$ and $g \leq 0$, $h(x) > 0$ implies that $g(x)$ is finite and $f(x) = h(x) + (-g(x)) > 0$. Thus $E_1 \subset N(f)$. It follows that $E_1$ is expressible as a countable union of measurable sets of finite measure. By Theorem 5–1 IX, then, there exists a regular approximating sequence $\{h_n\}$ for $h\chi_{E_1}$. Now, $-g$ is summable over $E_1$; let $\{-g_n\}$ be a regular approximating sequence for $-g\chi_{E_1}$. Let $f_n = h_n - g_n$. Then $\{f_n\}$ is a regular approximating sequence for $f\chi_{E_1}$. We know that

$$\int f_n \, d\mu \to \int_{E_1} f \, d\mu, \qquad \int (-g_n) \, d\mu \to \int_{E_1} (-g) \, d\mu = -\int_{E_1} g \, d\mu.$$

Therefore

$$\int h_n \, d\mu \to \int_{E_1} f \, d\mu + \int_{E_1} g \, d\mu.$$

This establishes that $h$ is summable over $E_1$, and gives us

$$\int_{E_1} h \, d\mu = \int_{E_1} f \, d\mu + \int_{E_1} g \, d\mu. \tag{13}$$

In a similar way we prove that $h$ is summable over $E_2$, with a formula corresponding to (13). For this we write $-g(x) = f(x) + (-h(x))$ on $E_2$, and observe that $E_2 \subset N(g)$. From Theorem 5–4 IV we can now infer that $h$ is summable over $E$, and that

$$\int_E h \, d\mu = \int_E f \, d\mu + \int_E g \, d\mu. \tag{14}$$

Since $E = N(h)$, $h$ is summable and the integral on the left in (14) is the same as $\int h\,d\mu$. It now remains to identify the sum of the two integrals on the right in (14) with the sum of the two integrals on the right in (11).

From Theorem 5–4 IV and the remarks in the paragraph following (7) we see that $\int f\,d\mu = \int_F f\,d\mu$, where $F$ is any member of **S** such that $N(f) \subset F$. We shall take $F = E \cup F_0$, where $F_0 = E_0 \cap N(f)$. Clearly

$$N(f) = [N(f) \cap E] \cup [N(f) \cap E_0] \subset E \cup F_0.$$

Thus

$$\int f\,d\mu = \int_E f\,d\mu + \int_{F_0} f\,d\mu.$$

A similar equation holds for $g$, with $F_0$ replaced by $G_0 = E_0 \cap N(g)$. But it is easy to see that $F_0 = G_0$ and that $f(x) = -g(x)$ if $x \in F_0$, because then $h(x) = 0$. Hence, using (10), we have

$$\int_{G_0} g\,d\mu = -\int_{F_0} f\,d\mu.$$

In this way we see that

$$\int f\,d\mu + \int g\,d\mu = \int_E f\,d\mu + \int_E g\,d\mu. \tag{15}$$

This is what was needed to complete the proof of the theroem.

As an easy corollary of Theorem 5–4 V we have:

THEOREM 5–4 VI. *If $f \in \mathscr{L}(\mu)$, then $|f| \in \mathscr{L}(\mu)$ and*

$$\left|\int f\,d\mu\right| \leq \int |f|\,d\mu. \tag{16}$$

The proof is left to the reader.

Theorem 5–2 IX has the following generalization:

THEOREM 5–4 VII. *If $f$ is summable over $E$, if $f(x) \geq 0$ when $x \in E$, and if $\int_E f\,d\mu = 0$, then $f(x) = 0$ a.e. in $E$.*

*Proof.* Let $\{f_n\}$ be a regular approximating sequence for $f\chi_E$, and let $F_n = N(f_n)$. Then

$$0 \leq \int_{F_n} f_n\,d\mu \leq \int_E f\,d\mu = 0.$$

We can apply Theorem 5–2 IX with $f_n$ and $F_n$ in place of $f$ and $X$. But $f_n(x) > 0$ if $x \in F_n$, and so $f_n(x) = 0$ a.e. on $F_n$ implies $\mu(F_n) = 0$. Let $E_0$ be the subset of $E$ on which $f_n(x)$ does not converge to $f(x)$, and let $F = \bigcup_i F_i$. Then $\mu(E_0 \cup F) = 0$, and $0 = f_n(x) \to f(x)$ if $x \in E - (E_0 \cup F)$. Hence $f(x) = 0$ a.e. in $E$.

The next theorem is very useful.

THEOREM 5–4 VIII. *Suppose that $f$ is measurable, that $g$ is summable, and that $|f(x)| \leq g(x)$ a.e. Then $f$ is summable.*

*Proof.* The hypothesis implies that $f^+(x) \leq g(x)$ a.e. and likewise for $f^-$. Hence it suffices to give the proof on the assumption that $0 \leq f$ and $f(x) \leq g(x)$ a.e. Let us suppose at first that $f(x) \leq g(x)$ for every $x$. Then $N(f) \subset N(g)$. By Theorem 5–4 II we can conclude that $N(f)$ is expressible as a countable union of measurable sets of finite measure. Accordingly, by Theorem 5–1 IX, there exists a regular approximating sequence $\{f_n\}$ for $f$. But then $f_n \leq f \leq g$, and so $\int f_n \, d\mu \leq \int g \, d\mu < +\infty$, and we conclude that $f$ is summable.

We go now to the general case. Let $E_0 = \{x : g(x) < f(x)\}$; by hypothesis $\mu(E_0) = 0$. Define $h(x) = +\infty$ if $x \in E_0$, $h(x) = 0$ otherwise. Then $h$ is measurable; it is also summable, because $\mu(E_0) = 0$. Hence $g + h$ is summable. But $f \leq g + h$, and therefore $f$ is summable, by the first part of our proof.

## PROBLEMS

1. Prove the validity of the remarks about $f_1$ and $(E, \mathbf{S}_1, \mu)$ made in the second paragraph after (7).

2. Suppose $f : X \to R^*$ is measurable. Suppose $X_0$ is a measurable subset of $X$. Let $X_1 = X - X_0$ and let $\mathbf{S}_1$ be the $\sigma$-ring of all measurable subsets of $X_1$. Let $f_1$ be the restriction of $f$ to $X_1$. It is measurable with respect to $\mathbf{S}_1$ (see Problem 12, Section 5–1).

(a) Show that $f_1$ is summable if $f$ is summable.

(b) Assume $\mu(X_0) = 0$. For this case, show that $f$ is summable if $f_1$ is, and that then $\int f \, d\mu = \int f_1 \, d\mu$.

3. Prove "facts" A–E, listed prior to Theorem 5–4 II.

4. Prove Theorem 5–4 VI.

5. Prove the following assertions:

(a) Theorem 5–4 VII remains true if instead of $f(x) \geq 0$ for each $x \in E$ we assume $f(x) \geq 0$ a.e. in $E$.

(b) If $f$ is summable over $E$, if $f(x) > 0$ a.e. in $E$, and if $\int_E f \, d\mu = 0$, then $\mu(E) = 0$.

(c) If $f$ is summable over $E$ and if $f(x) \geq c > 0$ when $x \in E$ (where $c$ is a constant), then $\mu(E) < +\infty$.

(d) If $f$ is measurable and $|f| \in \mathscr{L}(\mu)$, then $f \in \mathscr{L}(\mu)$. Is the assumption that $f$ is measurable an essential one?

(e) If $f$ and $g$ are summable, and if $\int_E f \, d\mu = \int_E g \, d\mu$ for each $E$ in $\mathbf{S}$, then $f(x) = g(x)$ a.e.

(f) If $E, F \in \mathbf{S}$ and $F \subset E$, if $f$ is summable over $E$ and $f(x) \geq 0$ a.e. on $E$, then $\int_F f \, d\mu \leq \int_E f \, d\mu$.

(g) If $f$ and $g$ are summable and $f(x) \leq g(x)$ a.e., then $\int f \, d\mu \leq \int g \, d\mu$.

(h) If $g$ and $h$ are summable, if $f$ is measurable, and if $g(x) \leq f(x) \leq h(x)$ a.e., then $f$ is summable.

6. Use Problem 2 to give an alternative argument, replacing the last paragraph in the proof of Theorem 5–4 VIII.

7. Suppose $f \in \mathscr{L}(\mu)$, where the measure space is $R^k$ with Lebesgue measure $\mu$. For fixed $y \in R^k$ define $f_y$ by $f_y(x) = f(x + y)$. Prove that $\int |f_y - f| \, d\mu \to 0$ as $y \to 0$. One method of proof, involving approximation by continuous functions, is suggested in Problem 10, Section 5–6. A more direct and elementary method is outlined in the following suggestions. Show, by consideration of $f = f^+ - f^-$, that the problem can be reduced to the case in which $f \geq 0$. Then, by use of a regular approximating sequence, the problem can be reduced to the case in which $f$ is a nonnegative summable simple function, and so finally to the case in which $f$ is the characteristic function of a set $E$ of finite measure. If $E(y) = \{x : x + y \in E\}$, the problem is reduced to showing that $\mu(E \,\Delta\, E(y)) \to 0$ as $y \to 0$. This may be dealt with by Theorem 4–8 VI.

## 5–5 Some basic convergence theorems

In this section we present some of the most important convergence theorems pertaining to the Lebesgue integral. The first of these theorems is often referred to as *the monotone convergence theorem for integrals.*

THEOREM 5–5 I. *Let $(X, \mathbf{S}, \mu)$ be an arbitrary measure space. Suppose $\{f_n\}$ is a sequence of functions on $X$ to $R^*$ such that each $f_n$ is in $\mathscr{L}(\mu)$ and $f_n \leq f_{n+1}$ for each $n$. Let $f(x) = \lim_{n\to\infty} f_n(x)$. Then $f$ is summable if and only if $\lim_{n\to\infty} \int f_n \, d\mu < +\infty$. When this condition is satisfied, we have*

$$\int f \, d\mu = \lim_{n\to\infty} \int f_n \, d\mu. \tag{1}$$

*Proof.* Suppose first that $f$ is summable. Then $f_n \leq f$ for each $n$, and therefore $\int f_n \, d\mu \leq \int f \, d\mu$, whence

$$\lim_{n\to\infty} \int f_n \, d\mu \leq \int f \, d\mu. \tag{2}$$

We shall see later that the reverse inequality also holds, and thus we shall have (1).

We now assume that $\lim_{n\to\infty} \int f_n \, d\mu < +\infty$, and from this we shall deduce that $f$ is summable. To begin with we make the additional assumption that $0 \leq f_n$ for each $n$. Let $f_{n1}, f_{n2}, \ldots$ be a regular approximating sequence for $f_n$, and let

$$g_{nj}(x) = \max\,[f_{1j}(x), \ldots, f_{nj}(x)]. \tag{3}$$

Our aim is to show that if $h_j = g_{jj}$, then $\{h_j\}$ is a regular approximating sequence for $f$, with $h_n(x) \leq f_n(x)$ a.e. Once this has been done we can conclude that $\int h_n \, d\mu \leq \int f_n \, d\mu$, from which it will follow that $f$ is summable and that

$$\int f \, d\mu = \lim_{n\to\infty} \int h_n \, d\mu \leq \lim_{n\to\infty} \int f_n \, d\mu. \tag{4}$$

From this, in conjunction with (2), we shall have (1) (for the case in which all the $f_n$'s are nonnegative).

From (3) and Theorem 5–1 VII we see that $g_{nj}$ is measurable. Clearly $g_{nj}(x)$ is nondecreasing as $n$ increases, and also as $j$ increases. Since $g_{nj}(x) = f_{ij}(x)$ for some $i$ (depending on $x$) such that $1 \leq i \leq n$, we see that $N(g_{nj})$ is of finite measure, for it is contained in the union of $N(f_{1j}), \ldots, N(f_{nj})$. Let $M_{nj} = \sup_x f_{nj}(x)$. Then (3) shows that $\sup_x g_{nj}(x) \leq \max\,[M_{1j}, \ldots, M_{nj}]$, so that each $g_{nj}$ is bounded. With the foregoing notation (as regards $i$) we see that

$$g_{nj}(x) = f_{ij}(x) \leq f_i(x) \leq f_n(x)$$

if $x$ is not in the set $E_n$ on which $\lim_{j\to\infty} f_{nj}(x) \neq f_n(x)$. Now let $h_j = g_{jj}$. If $j \geq n$ and $x \notin E_j$, we have

$$f_{nj}(x) \leq g_{nj}(x) \leq h_j(x) \leq f_j(x).$$

Letting $j \to \infty$, we see that
$$f_n(x) \le \lim_{j\to\infty} h_j(x) \le f(x)$$
if $x$ is not in $\bigcup_n E_n$. Since this latter set has measure 0, we see that
$$f(x) = \lim_{j\to\infty} h_j(x) \text{ a.e.}$$
Thus $\{h_j\}$ is a regular approximating sequence for $f$. We thus have everything that is needed to obtain (4), and the proof is thus finished for the case under consideration.

We have yet to deal with the situation if some of the $f_n$'s have negative values. For this case let $g_n = f_n - f_1$. Then $g_n \in \mathscr{L}(\mu)$, $g_n \ge 0$, and $g_n \le g_{n+1}$, so what has been proved applies to the sequence $\{g_n\}$ and its limit function $g$. It is clear that $\lim_{n\to\infty} \int g_n \, d\mu < +\infty$ if and only if $\lim_{n\to\infty} \int f_n \, d\mu < +\infty$. If all the values of the $f_n$'s were finite, we could infer that $g = f - f_1$ and $f = g + f_1$, whence $g \in \mathscr{L}(\mu)$ if and only if $f \in \mathscr{L}(\mu)$. From these facts we could then finish the proof for $\{f_n\}$ and $f$. But it can happen that $f(x) \ne g(x) + f_1(x)$ at some points. Suppose, for instance, that $f_1(x) = -\infty$, $f_n(x) = 1 - \dfrac{1}{n}$ if $n \ge 2$. In this case $f(x) = 1$, $g(x) = +\infty$, $g(x) + f_1(x) = 0$. But the situation can be rescued by showing that $g(x) = f(x) - f_1(x)$ and $f(x) = g(x) + f_1(x)$ at all points where $f_1(x)$ is finite. These relations are therefore valid a.e., and that is sufficient. The details are left to the reader (see Problem 1).

The next theorem extends Theorem 5–4 IV to the case of a countable family of sets.

THEOREM 5–5 II. *Let $E = \bigcup_{n=1}^{\infty} E_n$, where $\{E_n\}$ is a disjoint sequence of measurable sets. Let $f$ be measurable, and summable over $E_n$ for each $n$. Then $f$ is summable over $E$ if and only if*

(5) $$\sum_{n=1}^{\infty} \int_{E_n} |f| \, d\mu < +\infty.$$

*If this condition* (5) *is satisfied, we have*

(6) $$\int_E f \, d\mu = \sum_{n=1}^{\infty} \int_{E_n} f \, d\mu.$$

*Proof.* Suppose at first that $f(x) \ge 0$ for each $x$. In this case $f = |f|$, of course. Let $F_n = \bigcup_{j=1}^{n} E_j$, and define $f_n = f\chi_{F_n}$. Then, for each $x$,
$$0 \le f_n(x) \le f_{n+1}(x), \qquad f_n(x) \to f(x)\chi_E(x).$$
Using Theorem 5–4 IV and induction, we see that
$$\int f_n \, d\mu = \int_{F_n} f \, d\mu = \sum_{j=1}^{n} \int_{E_j} f \, d\mu.$$
Thus, in this case, $\lim_{n\to\infty} \int f_n \, d\mu < +\infty$ is equivalent to (5), and we draw the desired conclusions by applying Theorem 5–5 I.

For the general case we observe that the measurable function $f$ is summable over $E$ if and only if $|f|$ is summable over $E$; this follows from results in Section 5–4. Hence, by what has been shown, (5) is a necessary and sufficient condition for $f$ to be summable over $E$. The truth of (6) when (5) holds is then proved by writing what corresponds to (6) for $f^+$ and $f^-$ separately, and combining the results.

With a given measurable $f: X \to R^*$ we can associate the class of all measurable sets $E$ such that $f$ is summable over $E$. What we now know enables us to assert that this class is a ring of sets and that the set function $m$ defined on the ring by

$$m(E) = \int_E f\, d\mu \tag{7}$$

is countably additive. The ring is $\mathbf{S}$ itself if $f$ is summable.

## THE ABSOLUTE CONTINUITY OF THE INTEGRAL

As an important application of the fact that the integral defines a countably additive set function we have the following result.

THEOREM 5–5 III. *Suppose $f \in \mathscr{L}(\mu)$. Then to each $\epsilon > 0$ corresponds a $\delta > 0$ such that $\left|\int_E f\, d\mu\right| < \epsilon$ if $E \in \mathbf{S}$ and $\mu(E) < \delta$.*

*Proof.* Let $m(E) = \int_E |f|\, d\mu$. From preceding remarks we see that $m$ is a measure on $\mathbf{S}$. Now suppose the theorem false. Then there is some $\epsilon > 0$ such that for each $n$ there exists a set $E_n$ in $\mathbf{S}$ with $\mu(E_n) < 2^{-n}$ and $\left|\int_{E_n} f\, d\mu\right| \geq \epsilon$. Let

$$G_n = \bigcup_{k \geq n} E_k, \qquad G = \bigcap_{n=1}^{\infty} G_n.$$

We see that

$$\mu(G) \leq \mu(G_n) \leq \sum_{k=n}^{\infty} \mu(E_k) < \frac{1}{2^{n-1}},$$

so that $\mu(G) = 0$. Therefore $m(G) = 0$. On the other hand, $m(G_n) \to m(G)$, by Theorem 4–4 IV. Since $m(G_n) \geq m(E_n) \geq \left|\int_{E_n} f\, d\mu\right| \geq \epsilon$, it follows that $m(G) \geq \epsilon$. This contradiction ends the proof.

The property of the integral described in the theorem is sometimes expressed by saying that $\int_E f\, d\mu$, as a function of $E$, is absolutely continuous. This is a special case of a general concept of absolute continuity which occurs in the study of set functions (see Section 8–2, especially Theorem 8–2 II). There is also a related concept of absolute continuity for point functions (see Section 9–8).

## LEBESGUE'S DOMINATED CONVERGENCE THEOREM

One of the main convergence theorems in the theory of integration, often called *Lebesgue's dominated convergence theorem*, is the following.

THEOREM 5–5 IV. *Let $(X, \mathbf{S}, \mu)$ be a measure space. Let $\{f_n\}$ be a sequence of summable functions. Let $f$ be a measurable function and $g$ a summable function such that $\lim_{n\to\infty} f_n(x) = f(x)$ a.e. and $|f_n| \leq g$ for each $n$. Then $f$ is summable, and*

$$\int f_n\, d\mu \to \int f\, d\mu. \tag{8}$$

We remark at the outset that the assumption that $f$ is measurable is superfluous if $f_n(x) \to f(x)$ for every $x$, for in this case $f$ must be measurable, by Theorem 5–1 VII. We can also omit the hypothesis that $f$ is measurable, even with merely $f_n(x) \to f(x)$ a.e., provided the measure $\mu$ is complete. See the remarks following the proof of Theorem 5–1 VII.

*Proof of the theorem.* Let us define

$$F_{nj}(x) = \max \{f_n(x), f_{n+1}(x), \ldots, f_{n+j}(x)\}.$$

Since $F_{nj}(x) = f_{n+i}(x)$ for some $i$ (depending on $x$) such that $1 \leq i \leq j$, we see that $|F_{nj}(x)| \leq g(x)$. Evidently $F_{nj}$ is summable (Theorem 5–4 VIII). We see that $F_{nj}(x)$ is nondecreasing as $j$ increases, and that

$$\lim_{j\to\infty} F_{nj}(x) = \sup_{j\geq n} f_j(x).$$

Therefore, defining $F_n(x) = \lim_{j\to\infty} F_{nj}(x)$, we have $F_1(x) \geq F_2(x) \geq \cdots$ and

$$\lim_{n\to\infty} F_n(x) = \limsup_{n\to\infty} f_n(x). \tag{9}$$

Because $F_{nj}(x) \leq g(x)$, we can apply the monotone convergence theorem to deduce that $F_n$ is summable, with

$$\lim_{j\to\infty} \int F_{nj}\, d\mu = \int F_n\, d\mu.$$

Now, $-g(x) \leq F_n(x)$, or $-F_n(x) \leq g(x)$. Applying the monotone convergence theorem to the nondecreasing sequence $\{-F_n\}$, we deduce that the function whose value at $x$ is $\lim_{n\to\infty} [-F_n(x)]$ is summable. Hence, the negative of this function is also summable. In view of (9) and the hypothesis we see that

$$f(x) = \lim_{n\to\infty} F_n(x) \text{ a.e.}$$

Therefore $f$ is summable. We see that $\int F_n\, d\mu$ converges downward to $\int f\, d\mu$.

Next, $f_n(x) \leq F_{nj}(x) \leq F_n(x)$, and so

$$\int f_n\, d\mu \leq \int F_n\, d\mu.$$

If $\epsilon > 0$, there is an $N$ such that

$$\int F_N\, d\mu < \int f\, d\mu + \epsilon.$$

Consequently,

$$\int f_n\, d\mu < \int f\, d\mu + \epsilon \tag{10}$$

if $n \geq N$. The whole chain of reasoning may be applied with $\{-f_n\}$ in place of $\{f_n\}$. Then, in place of (10), we get

$$-\int f_n\, d\mu < -\int f\, d\mu + \epsilon$$

for all sufficiently large values of $n$. But then

$$\int f\, d\mu - \epsilon < \int f_n\, d\mu < \int f\, d\mu + \epsilon$$

for all sufficiently large values of $n$. This proves (8).

## FATOU'S LEMMA

There is another important consequence of the monotone convergence theorem which is useful as a tool in many arguments. It is called Fatou's lemma. It occurs incidentally in a remarkable paper by Pierre Fatou (1878–1929) published in 1906.

THEOREM 5–5 V. *Suppose $g$ and $f_1, f_2, \ldots$ are summable functions such that $g(x) \le f_n(x)$ for each $n$ and $x$. Suppose that*

$$\liminf_{n\to\infty} \int f_n \, d\mu < +\infty, \tag{11}$$

*and let $f(x) = \liminf_{n\to\infty} f_n(x)$. Then $f$ is summable, and*

$$\int f \, d\mu \le \liminf_{n\to\infty} \int f_n \, d\mu. \tag{12}$$

*Proof.* We remark that in many applications $g$ is the zero function. Let

$$g_n(x) = \inf \{f_n(x), f_{n+1}(x), \ldots\}.$$

By definition, $g_n(x) \to f(x)$. We have $g_n(x) \le g_{n+1}(x)$, and $g(x) \le g_n(x) \le f_n(x)$. We can then deduce that $g_n$ is summable (see Problem 5 (h) in Section 5–4). But, since $\int g_n \, d\mu \le \int f_n \, d\mu$, it follows from (11) that $\lim_{n\to\infty} \int g_n \, d\mu \le \liminf \int f_n \, d\mu < +\infty$. Theorem 5–5 I then shows that $f$ is summable and gives us (12).

## PROBLEMS

1. Finish up the details of the proof of Theorem 5–5 I for the case in which the $f_n$'s may have negative values. Take note of fact $E$, preceding Theorem 5–4 II. The crucial facts are these: (1) $g \le f - f_1$ and $f_n - f_1 \le g$; (2) if $a \in R^*$ and $b \in R$, $(a - b) + b = a$ and $(a + b) - b = a$.

2. State and prove a theorem analogous to Theorem 5–5 I for a sequence $\{f_n\}$ such that $f_{n+1} \le f_n$.

3. Let $X$ be $R$, and let $\mu$ be Lebesgue measure on $X$. Suppose $f : R^2 \to R$ is such that the function $x \to f(x, y)$ is in $\mathscr{L}(\mu)$ for each $y$ in $R$. Suppose the partial derivative $f_2(x, y) = \dfrac{\partial f(x, y)}{\partial y}$ exists for each $(x, y)$ in $R^2$, and that $|f_2(x, y)| \le g(x)$ for each $(x, y)$, where $g$ belongs to $\mathscr{L}(\mu)$. Let $F(y) = \int_{-\infty}^{\infty} f(x, y) \, dx$. (The integral denotes the Lebesgue integral over $R$.) Prove that $F$ has a derivative at each $y$ given by

$$F'(y) = \int_{-\infty}^{\infty} f_2(x, y) \, dx.$$

4. Theorem 5–5 IV may be proved in an entirely different way. To show the essential plan of the proof with a minimum of complications, suppose at first that all the values of $f$ are finite and that $f_n(x) \to f(x)$ for every $x$. Once the basic scheme of the proof is understood, the reader will be able to make the few necessary modifications in details to make the proof valid for the general case. It is left to the reader to work the proof out completely with the help of the following sketch. The key to the proof is the fact that $m(E) = \int_E g \, d\mu$ defines a measure $m$ on **S**. Let $\{E_n\}$ be a sequence of measurable sets such that $E_n \subset E_{n+1}$ and $\bigcup_n E_n = N(g)$. Explain why $\int_{E_n} g \, d\mu \to \int g \, d\mu$. With

$\epsilon > 0$ given, choose $i$ so that $0 \leq \int g\,d\mu - \int_{E_i} g\,d\mu < \frac{\epsilon}{6}$. Since $|f(x)| \leq g(x)$ a.e., $f$ is summable. The plan is to prove (8) by showing that $\int |f_n - f|\,d\mu \to 0$. Now choose $\delta > 0$ so that $\delta\mu(E_i) < \frac{\epsilon}{3}$ and define

$$H_n = \bigcup_{j \geq n} \{x : |f_j(x) - f(x)| \geq \delta\}, \qquad H = \bigcap_n H_n.$$

Show that $\int_{H_n} g\,d\mu \to \int_H g\,d\mu = 0$. The integral $\int |f_n - f|\,d\mu$ is now to be estimated by expressing it as an integral over the set.

$$(B_n \cap E_i \cap H_n) \cup [B_n \cap (E_i - H_n)] \cup (B_n \cap F_i),$$

where $B_n = N(|f_n - f|)$ and $F_i = N(g) - E_i$. Observe that $|f_n(x) - f(x)| \leq 2g(x)$.

## 5–6 Convergence in measure

In Theorem 5–3 II we found it desirable to call attention explicitly to a relation which sometimes exists between a sequence $\{f_n\}$ of measurable functions and another measurable function $f$. In Section 5–3 we were intent on proceeding toward the definition of summable functions and their integrals with a minimum of diversionary considerations. Now, however, it is useful for us to examine more closely the kind of situation which was revealed in Theorem 5–3 II. There is an important concept to be recognized, that of convergence in measure. Although this concept relates to measurable functions, and can be discussed without reference to integrals, it has important uses in the theory of integration. We shall see this especially in Section 5–7.

Let $(X, \mathbf{S}, \mu)$ be an arbitrary measure space. Suppose $f$ and $f_1, f_2, \ldots$ are measurable functions on $X$ to $R^*$, and that each function is finite in value a.e. For each $\epsilon > 0$ and each $n$ we consider the set

$$F_n(\epsilon) = \{x : |f_n(x) - f(x)| \geq \epsilon\}. \tag{1}$$

This set is measurable. If $\mu(F_n(\epsilon)) \to 0$ as $n \to \infty$, for each $\epsilon > 0$, we say that $\{f_n\}$ *converges in measure* to $f$. We use the notation $f_n \xrightarrow{\mu} f$ to express this state of affairs.

The concept of convergence in measure is called *asymptotic convergence* by some authors. Other terms are also used. The concept was introduced and studied by F. Riesz and E. Fischer in 1906–07. One of its most important uses is in connection with the notion convergence in mean; we shall see this connection in Theorem 5–7 I.

Much of the usefulness of the concept of convergence in measure lies in the fact that there is for such convergence a principle comparable to the principle which relates Cauchy sequences to convergent sequences in a complete metric space. In fact, under suitable circumstances it is possible to define a metric space formed from measurable functions, in which convergence corresponds to convergence in measure, and this metric space is complete as a consequence of one of the basic theorems about convergence in measure (see Problem 5). This construction of a metric space is due to Fréchet.

A sequence $\{f_n\}$ of measurable functions on $X$ to $R^*$, each function finite a.e., is called *a Cauchy sequence in measure* if

$$\mu(\{x : |f_n(x) - f_m(x)| \geq \epsilon\}) \to 0 \qquad \text{as} \quad m \text{ and } n \to \infty$$

for each $\epsilon > 0$.

THEOREM 5–6 I. *Let $(X, \mathbf{S}, \mu)$ be an arbitrary measure space, and let $f, g, f_1, f_2, \ldots$ be measurable functions on $X$ to $R^*$, each function finite a.e. Then:*

(a) *If $f_n \xrightarrow{\mu} f$ and $f(x) = g(x)$ a.e., $f_n \xrightarrow{\mu} g$.*

(b) *If $f_n \xrightarrow{\mu} f$ and $f_n \xrightarrow{\mu} g$, $f(x) = g(x)$ a.e.*

(c) *If $f_n \xrightarrow{\mu} f$, $\{f_n\}$ is a Cauchy sequence in measure.*

*Proof of* (a). We see that $\{x : |f_n(x) - g(x)| \geq \epsilon\}$ is contained in the union

$$\{x : |f_n(x) - f(x)| \geq \epsilon\} \cup \{x : f(x) \neq g(x)\};$$

the asserted result follows.

*Proof of* (b). Let $G_n(\epsilon)$ be the set corresponding to the set $F_n(\epsilon)$ in (1) when $f$ is replaced by $g$. We can see that

$$\{x : |f(x) - g(x)| \geq \epsilon\} \subset F_n\left(\frac{\epsilon}{2}\right) \cup G_n\left(\frac{\epsilon}{2}\right). \tag{2}$$

This is a result of the inequality

$$|f(x) - g(x)| \leq |f_n(x) - f(x)| + |f_n(x) - g(x)|.$$

(This is true even in the case of infinite functional values; see (8) in Section 4–1.) It follows from (2) that $\mu(\{x : |f(x) - g(x)| \geq \epsilon\}) = 0$ for each $\epsilon > 0$. But

$$\{x : |f(x) - g(x)| > 0\} = \bigcup_n \left\{x : |f(x) - g(x)| \geq \frac{1}{n}\right\},$$

and therefore $f(x) = g(x)$ a.e.

*Proof of* (c). We leave this to the reader. The key argument is like the one leading to (2).

It is possible to have $f_n \xrightarrow{\mu} f$ and yet for $f_n(x) \to f(x)$ to be false for every $x$.

*Example 1.* Take $X = [0, 1]$ in $R$, with $\mu$ as Lebesgue measure. Let $F_{nj} = \left[\frac{j-1}{n}, \frac{j}{n}\right]$, $j = 1, 2, \ldots, n$, and let $\{E_n\}$ be the sequence

$$F_{11}, F_{21}, F_{22}, F_{31}, F_{32}, F_{33}, F_{41}, \ldots$$

Let $f_n = \chi_{E_n}$. Then $\mu(E_n) \to 0$ and $\{x : |f_n(x)| > 0\} = E_n$, so that $f_n \xrightarrow{\mu} 0$. But, for each $x$, $f_n(x) = 1$ for infinitely many values of $n$, so $f_n(x) \to 0$ is always false.

Under certain circumstances $f_n(x) \to f(x)$ a.e. implies $f_n \xrightarrow{\mu} f$. See Problem 3(a). But this is not true without qualification.

*Example 2.* Take $X = R$, with $\mu$ as Lebesgue measure. Define $f_n$ so that

$$f_n(x) = \begin{cases} 0 & \text{if } |x| \leq n \text{ or } |x| > n + 1 \\ 1 & \text{if } n < |x| \leq n + 1. \end{cases}$$

Then $f_n(x) \to 0$ for each $x$, but the measure of the set $\{x : |f_n(x)| \geq \epsilon\}$ is 2 for each $n$ if $0 < \epsilon \leq 1$.

The following theorem sets forth what we shall need most to apply in connection with convergence in measure.

THEOREM 5–6 II. *Suppose $(X, \mathbf{S}, \mu)$ is an arbitrary measure space and $\{f_n\}$ is a Cauchy sequence in measure. Then there exists a measurable function $f$ with all its values finite such that $f_n \xrightarrow{\mu} f$ and such that a subsequence of $\{f_n(x)\}$ converges to $f(x)$ a.e. Moreover, to each $\epsilon > 0$ corresponds a measurable set $E$ such that $\mu(E) < \epsilon$ and such that the subsequence converges uniformly on $X - E$.*

*Proof.* Let $\sum_1^\infty \epsilon_n$ be any convergent series of positive numbers. Choose a positive integer $N_i$ so that

$$\mu(\{x : |f_n(x) - f_m(x)| \geq \epsilon_i\}) < \epsilon_i \qquad \text{if} \quad m \geq N_i \text{ and } n \geq N_i.$$

Let $n_1, n_2, \ldots$ be a sequence of integers such that $n_1 < n_2 < \cdots$ and $n_i \geq N_i$. Let $g_i = f_{n_i}$, and let

$$G_i = \{x : |g_i(x) - g_{i+1}(x)| \geq \epsilon_i\}.$$

Then $G_i$ is measurable and $\mu(G_i) < \epsilon_i$. Let $X_0$ be a set of measure 0 such that $f_n(x)$ is finite for each $n$ if $x \in X - X_0$. Let

$$E_k = X_0 \cup \bigcup_{i \geq k} G_i.$$

Then $\mu(E_k) \leq \sum_{i \geq k} \epsilon_i \to 0$ as $k \to \infty$. If $x$ is not in $E_k$ we have $|g_i(x) - g_{i+1}(x)| < \epsilon_i$ when $i \geq k$. Therefore, if $k \leq i < j$, we have

$$|g_i(x) - g_j(x)| = \left| \sum_{n=i}^{j-1} [g_n(x) - g_{n+1}(x)] \right| < \sum_{n \geq i} \epsilon_n.$$

From this it is clear that $\{g_n(x)\}$ converges uniformly to a finite limit at each point of $X - E_k$.

We can now deduce that $\{g_n(x)\}$ converges to a finite limit a.e. In fact, let

$$F = \bigcap_{k=1}^{\infty} E_k.$$

Then $\mu(F) \leq \mu(E_k)$ for each $k$, so $\mu(F) = 0$. Also,

$$X - F = \bigcup_k (X - E_k),$$

and so we see that $\{g_n(x)\}$ converges to a finite limit if $x \in X - F$.

Now let $g = \limsup g_n$; this function is measurable (Theorem 5–1 VII) and $g_n(x) \to g(x)$ if $x \in X - F$. The function $g\chi_F$ is measurable, and so is $g - g\chi_F$, by Theorem 5–1 VI. Let $f = g - g\chi_F$. We see that $f(x) = g(x)$ if $x \in X - F$ and $f(x) = 0$ if $x \in F$, so that $f(x)$ is always finite.

It remains only to prove that $f_n \xrightarrow{\mu} f$. First we prove that $g_i \xrightarrow{\mu} f$. Suppose $\epsilon > 0$ and $\delta > 0$. Choose $k$ so that $\mu(E_k) < \delta$ and $j$ so that $|g_i(x) - f(x)| < \epsilon$ if $i \geq j$ and $x \in X - E_k$. Thus $i \geq j$ implies

$$\mu(\{x : |g_i(x) - f(x)| \geq \epsilon\}) \leq \mu(E_k) < \delta;$$

this proves $g_i \xrightarrow{\mu} f$. Next, from

$$|f_n(x) - f(x)| \leq |f_n(x) - g_i(x)| + |g_i(x) - f(x)|$$

we see that the set $\{x : |f_n(x) - f(x)| \geq \epsilon\}$ is contained in

$$\left\{x : |f_n(x) - g_i(x)| \geq \frac{\epsilon}{2}\right\} \cup \left\{x : |g_i(x) - f(x)| \geq \frac{\epsilon}{2}\right\}.$$

Then, from the fact that $\{f_n\}$ is a Cauchy sequence in measure and that $g_i \xrightarrow{\mu} f$, we can see that $f_n \xrightarrow{\mu} f$. This completes the proof.

*Remark.* From the foregoing and Theorem 5–6 I (b) and (c) we see that if $\{f_n\}$ comes to us as a sequence which converges in measure to a function $h$, then a certain subsequence of $\{f_n(x)\}$ converges to $h(x)$ a.e.

## PROBLEMS

1. If $f_n \xrightarrow{\mu} f$ and $g_n \xrightarrow{\mu} g$, then $f_n + g_n \xrightarrow{\mu} f + g$. Also, $cf_n \xrightarrow{\mu} cf$.

2. Let the members of the sequence $\{f_n\}$ be measurable and finite in value a.e. Let $f$ be a function of the same kind such that for each $\delta > 0$ there is a measurable set $E$ with $\mu(E) < \delta$ such that $f_n(x)$ converges to $f(x)$ uniformly on $X - E$. Then $f_n \xrightarrow{\mu} f$.

3. (a) When the measure space $(X, \mathbf{S}, \mu)$ is totally finite, convergence almost everywhere implies convergence in measure, and even more. This is shown in the following theorem: *Let $f$ and $f_1, f_2, \ldots$ be measurable functions on $X$ to $R^*$ which are finite a.e. Suppose $f_n(x) \to f(x)$ a.e. For $\epsilon > 0$ let $E_n(\epsilon)$ be the set of points $x$ for which $|f_n(x) - f(x)| \geq \epsilon$. Let $F_n(\epsilon) = \bigcup_{k \geq n} E_k(\epsilon)$. Then $\mu(F_n(\epsilon)) \to 0$.* [*Hint.* Use Theorem 4–4 IV and show that $\bigcap_{n=1}^{\infty} F_n(\epsilon)$ is a set of measure 0.]

(b) Prove the slightly more general form of Egoroff's theorem (Theorem 5–3 I) which is obtained by assuming $f$ and $f_1, f_2, \ldots$ are functions on $X$ to $R^*$ (but finite a.e.) instead of functions on $X$ to $R$. This can be done by using the result in (a) and considering the sets $\bigcup_{i \geq k} F_{n(i)}(2^{-i})$, where $n_i = n(i)$ is chosen so as to make $\mu(F_{n(i)}(2^{-i})) < 2^{-i}$.

(c) With $(X, \mathbf{S}, \mu)$ an arbitrary measure space let $f, f_1, f_2, \ldots$ be measurable functions on $X$ to $R^*$ such that $f_n(x) \to f(x)$ a.e. Suppose there exists a summable function $g : X \to R^*$ such that $|f_n(x)| \leq g(x)$ for each $x$ (note that this implies that $f$ and each $f_n$ are finite a.e.). With $E_n(\epsilon)$ and $F_n(\epsilon)$ defined as in (a), show that $\mu(F_n(\epsilon)) \to 0$. The proof can be made as in (a), except that a special argument is needed to show that $\mu(F_n(\epsilon)) < +\infty$.

4. (a) Let $f$ and $f_1, f_2, \ldots$ be measurable functions which are finite a.e. Suppose $\{f_n\}$ has the property that every subsequence of $\{f_n\}$ contains a further subsequence which converges to $f$ a.e. Suppose $G \in \mathbf{S}$, $\mu(G) < +\infty$, $\epsilon > 0$, and let $E_n = \{x : x \in G, |f_n(x) - f(x)| \geq \epsilon\}$. Prove that $\mu(E_n) \to 0$.

(b) Suppose the measure space $(X, \mathbf{S}, \mu)$ is $\sigma$-finite. Suppose that $f$ and $f_1, f_2, \ldots$ are measurable and finite a.e., and that $\mu(E_n) \to 0$ for arbitrary $G$ and $\epsilon$ as specified in (a). Deduce that $\{f_n\}$ fulfills the hypothesis in (a).

5. (a) If $\varphi(t) = \dfrac{t}{1+t}$, $\varphi$ is an increasing function of the real variable $t$ when $t > -1$. Use this fact to deduce that

$$\frac{|a+b|}{1+|a+b|} \leq \frac{|a|}{1+|a|} + \frac{|b|}{1+|b|}$$

if $a$ and $b$ are arbitrary real or complex numbers.

(b) Let $(X, \mathbf{S}, \mu)$ be a totally finite measure space. Let $\mathscr{M}$ be the class of measurable functions $f : X \to R^*$ which are finite a.e. If $f$ and $g$ are in $\mathscr{M}$, the function

$$\frac{|f-g|}{1+|f-g|}$$

is well-defined a.e. and, since its values are bounded, we may consider the integral

$$\delta(f,g) = \int \frac{|f-g|}{1+|f-g|}\, d\mu.$$

Clearly, $\delta(f, g) = 0$ if and only if $f \sim g$, where $f \sim g$ means $f(x) = g(x)$ a.e. Let $M$ be the set of equivalence classes in $\mathscr{M}$ determined by the equivalence relation $\sim$. If $[f]$ is the equivalence class containing $f$, define $D([f_1], [f_2]) = \delta(f_1, f_2)$. Show that $M$ is a metric space in which $D([f_n], [f]) \to 0$ if and only if $f_n \xrightarrow{\mu} f$. Why is $M$ complete? *Suggestion.* I $\epsilon > 0$ and $E_n(\epsilon) = \{x : |f_n(x) - f(x)| \geq \epsilon\}$, show that

$$\delta(f_n, f) \leq \mu(E_n(\epsilon)) + \epsilon\mu(X)$$

and

$$\frac{\epsilon}{1 + \epsilon}\mu(E_n(\epsilon)) \leq \delta(f_n, f).$$

(c) The considerations in (b) can be modified and generalized in various ways, the aim remaining that of obtaining a metric space of equivalence classes in which convergence corresponding to convergence in measure. We can avoid the use of integrals by defining $\delta(f, g)$ in the following way (not equivalent to the definition of $\delta(f, g)$ in (a)) and then defining $D([f_1], [f_2]$ as before:

$$\delta(f, g) = \inf_{\epsilon > 0} [\epsilon + \mu(\{x : |f(x) - g(x)| > \epsilon\})].$$

We leave it for the reader to verify that things work out in the desired manner. As a clue to proving the triangular inequality for the metric, observe that when $\alpha > 0$ and $\beta > 0$ the measure of $\{x : |f(x) - g(x)| > \alpha + \beta\}$ is not less than the measure of $\{x : |f(x) - h(x)| > \alpha\}$ plus the measure of $\{x : |h(x) - g(x)| > \beta\}$. For part of the work of showing the relation between convergence in the metric sense and convergence in measure, it may be shown that

$$\delta(f_n, f) \geq \min [\epsilon, \mu(\{x : |f_n(x) - f(x)| > \epsilon\})].$$

Where in all this is use made of the condition that $\mu(X) < +\infty$?

For the case of an arbitrary measure space we can define

$$\delta(f, g) = \inf_{\epsilon > 0} \varphi[\epsilon + \mu(\{x : |f(x) - g(x)| > \epsilon\})],$$

where $\varphi(t) = t(1 + t)^{-1}$. Then, as before, we obtain a metric for $M$, and convergence in $M$ has the desired relation to convergence in measure. The reader may be interested in consulting Dunford and Schwartz [1] pp. 101–104, where there is a discussion of convergence in measure in a rather more general context.

6. Suppose $(X, \mathbf{S}, \mu)$ is a measure space with $X \in \mathbf{S}$, $\mu(X)$ finite, and $X$ a metric space. Suppose further that each closed set belongs to $\mathbf{S}$ and that, for each $E \in \mathbf{S}$, $\mu(E)$ is the supremum of $\mu(A)$ as $A$ ranges over the class of closed subsets of $E$. Prove the following theorem: *If $f : X \to R^*$ is measurable, if $f(x)$ is finite a.e., and if $\epsilon$ and $\delta$ are given positive numbers, there exists a bounded continuous function $g : X \to R$ such that $\mu(\{x : |g(x) - f(x)| \geq \delta\}) < \epsilon$.*

[*Suggestions.* Suppose at first that $f$ is bounded. If $|f(x)| < M$ for each $x$, choose a positive integer $n$ so that $M/n < \delta$. Let

$$G_i = \left(\frac{i-1}{n}M, \frac{i}{n}M\right), \qquad i = -n + 1, -n + 2, \ldots, n,$$

and let $E_i = f^{-1}(G_i)$. Choose a closed set $A_i \subset E_i$ so that $\mu(A_i) > \mu(E_i) - \frac{\epsilon}{2n}$. Let $A = \bigcup_i A_i$ and define a function $h : A \to R$ by setting $h(x) = \frac{i}{n}M$ if $x \in A_i$. Explain why $h \in C(A)$. What can be said about $\mu(X - A)$? By Problem 7, Section 3–15, there exists $g \in C(X)$ such that $g(x) = h(x)$ if $x \in A$. Show that $g$ meets the requirements of the theorem. Now deal with the case when $f$ is not bounded. Begin by using Problem 17, Section 5–1 to get a bounded function $h : X \to R$ such that $\mu(\{x : f(x) \neq h(x)\}) < \frac{\epsilon}{2}$.]

7. Let $(X, \mathbf{S}, \mu)$ be as in Problem 6. If $f : X \to R^*$ is measurable and if $f(x)$ is finite a.e., prove that there exists a sequence $\{g_n\}$ of bounded continuous functions $g_n : X \to R$ such that $g_n \xrightarrow{\mu} f$. It then follows (why?) that some subsequence of $\{g_n(x)\}$ converges to $f(x)$ a.e.

8. Let $(X, \mathbf{S}, \mu)$ and $f$ be as in Problem 7. Prove that to each $\epsilon > 0$ corresponds a continuous function $g : X \to R$ such that $\mu(\{x : f(x) \neq g(x)\}) < \epsilon$. Show, moreover, that if $f$ is bounded, with $m \leq f(x) \leq M$ when $x \in X$, $g$ can be chosen so that $m \leq g(x) \leq M$ if $x \in X$. This is known as Lusin's theorem, after the Russian mathematician N. N. Lusin (1883–1952).

[*Suggestions.* Use Problem 7 to obtain a sequence of continuous functions $g_n : X \to R$ such that $g_n(x) \to f(x)$ a.e. Then use Egoroff's theorem to obtain a set $E$ such that $\mu(E) < \frac{\epsilon}{2}$ and $g_n(x) \to f(x)$ uniformly on $X - E$. Choose a closed set $A \subset X - E$ such that $\mu(A) > \mu(X - E) - \frac{\epsilon}{2}$. The restriction of $f$ to $A$ is continuous on $A$. Why? Now use Problem 7, Section 3–15 to get a continuous function $g : X \to R$ which agrees with $f$ on $A$ and meets all the requirements.]

9. Let $X$ be a metric space, and let $(X, \mathbf{S}, \mu)$ be a measure space with the following properties: All open sets are in $\mathbf{S}$, and to each $E \in \mathbf{S}$ with $\mu(E)$ finite, and to each $\epsilon > 0$, correspond sets $A$, $U$ with $A \subset E \subset U$, $A$ closed, $U$ open, and $\mu(U - A) < \epsilon$. Then the following is true. *If* $f \in \mathscr{L}(\mu)$ *and* $\epsilon > 0$, *there exists a bounded continuous function* $h : X \to R$ *such that* $\int |f - h| \, d\mu < \epsilon$ *and the set on which* $h(x) \neq 0$ *has finite measure.* Prove this, with the aid of the following suggestions. Let $\{f_n\}$ and $\{g_n\}$ be regular approximating sequences for $f^+$ and $f^-$, respectively. For any $h \in \mathscr{L}(\mu)$ it is true that

$$\int |f - h| \, d\mu \leq \int (f^+ - f_n) \, d\mu + \int (f^- - g_n) \, d\mu + \int |f_n - g_n - h| \, d\mu.$$

Therefore, by a suitable fixed choice of $n$, the problem is reduced to choosing $h$ so that $\int |f_n - g_n - h| \, d\mu < \frac{\epsilon}{3}$ and so that $h$ is continuous and $\mu(N(h)) < +\infty$. Let $E = N(f_n) \cup N(g_n)$. After a suitable choice of $A$ and $U$, apply Lusin's theorem (Problem 8) to obtain a member of $C(A)$ which coincides with $f_n - g_n$ on most of $A$. Then extend this function to all of $X$ so as to yield the required $h$. For this use Problems 7, 8, Section 3–15.

10. If $X = R^k$ and $\mu$ is Lebesgue measure, show that to each $f \in \mathscr{L}(\mu)$ and each $\epsilon > 0$ corresponds a continuous $h : X \to R$ such that $h(x) = 0$ outside of some compact set, and $\int |f - h| \, d\mu < \epsilon$. The argument is similar to that in Problem 9. Use this result to give another proof of the proposition in Problem 7, Section 5–4. The existence of the required $h$ can be demonstrated by an entirely different method, using the methods of Chapter 6. See Theorems 6–4 VI, 6–11 I, and the remarks following the proof of Theorem 6–11 I.

## 5–7 Convergence in mean

In this section we deal with the class $\mathscr{L}(\mu)$ of summable functions $f : X \to R^*$, where $(X, \mathbf{S}, \mu)$ is an arbitrary measure space. If $f$ and $f_1, f_2, \ldots$ are in $\mathscr{L}(\mu)$, the sequence $\{f_n\}$ is said to be *convergent in mean* (of order 1) to $f$ if $\int |f_n - f| \, d\mu \to 0$. Later we shall consider convergence in mean of order $p$, where $p > 1$, but for the present we consider only $p = 1$ and we shall not keep repeating the phrase "of order 1." A sequence $\{f_n\}$ from $\mathscr{L}(\mu)$ such that

$$\int |f_n - f_m| \, d\mu \to 0 \quad \text{as } m \text{ and } n \to \infty$$

is called *a Cauchy sequence in mean.* If $\{f_n\}$ converges in mean to $f$, it is a Cauchy sequence in mean; this is evident from the inequality

$$\int |f_n - f_m| \, d\mu \leq \int |f_n - f| \, d\mu + \int |f_m - f| \, d\mu.$$

THEOREM 5–7 I. *If $\{f_n\}$ converges in mean to $f$, then $f_n \xrightarrow{\mu} f$. If $\{f_n\}$ is a Cauchy sequence in mean, it is a Cauchy sequence in measure.*

*Proof.* All of the functions in question are finite a.e., by Theorem 5–4 III. For the proof of the first assertion, suppose $\epsilon > 0$ is given, and let $E_n = \{x : |f_n(x) - f(x)| \geq \epsilon\}$. Then $\mu(E_n)$ is finite (see Problem 5(c), Section 5–4), and

$$\int |f_n - f| \, d\mu \geq \int_{E_n} |f_n - f| \, d\mu \geq \epsilon\mu(E_n),$$

and so $\mu(E_n) \to 0$. Therefore $f_n \xrightarrow{\mu} f$. The proof of the second assertion is made in the same way.

The next theorem is a completeness theorem for convergence in mean.

THEOREM 5–7 II. *If $\{f_n\}$ is a Cauchy sequence in mean, there exists an $f$ in $\mathscr{L}(\mu)$ such that $\{f_n\}$ converges in mean to $f$.*

*Proof.* By the preceding theorem $\{f_n\}$ is a Cauchy sequence in measure. We can then apply Theorem 5–6 II. We adopt the notations used in the proof of this theorem. We shall show that $\{f_n\}$ converges in mean to $f$. The first step is to show that $f$ is summable and that $\{g_n\}$ converges in mean to $f$. For this purpose we use Fatou's lemma (Theorem 5–5 V). Suppose $\epsilon > 0$. Since $\{g_n\}$ is a subsequence of $\{f_n\}$, there is an $N$ such that

$$\int |g_n - g_m| \, d\mu < \epsilon \quad \text{if } m \geq N \text{ and } n \geq N.$$

We fix $m$ ($m \geq N$) and consider the sequence $\{|g_n - g_m|\}$ ($n = 1, 2, \ldots$). By Fatou's lemma the function $h$ defined as

$$h(x) = \liminf_{n\to\infty} |g_n(x) - g_m(x)|$$

is summable, and

$$\int h \, d\mu \leq \liminf_{n\to\infty} \int |g_n - g_m| \, d\mu \leq \epsilon.$$

But we know that

$$|g_n(x) - g_m(x)| \to |f(x) - g_m(x)| \text{ a.e. as } n \to \infty.$$

Therefore $h(x) = |f(x) - g_m(x)|$ a.e. We conclude that $f - g_m$ is summable, and hence that $f$ is summable. Moreover,

$$\int |f - g_m| \, d\mu \leq \epsilon \quad \text{if } m \geq N.$$

This finishes the first step in the proof. Next,

$$\int |f_n - f| \, d\mu \leq \int |f_n - g_i| \, d\mu + \int |g_i - f| \, d\mu,$$

where the index $i$ is at our disposal. Both integrals on the right can be made as small as we please merely by requiring $i$ and $n$ to be sufficiently large. From this we see that $\{f_n\}$ converges in mean to $f$.

## THE SPACE $L(\mu)$

We can define an equivalence relation $\sim$ in $\mathscr{L}(\mu)$ as follows: $f \sim g$ if and only if $f(x) = g(x)$ a.e. We shall denote the set of all the equivalence classes thus formed in $\mathscr{L}(\mu)$ by $L(\mu)$. If $f \in \mathscr{L}(\mu)$, the equivalence class which contains $f$ will be denoted by $[f]$. Evidently $f \sim g$ if and only if $\int |f - g| \, d\mu = 0$. The set $L(\mu)$ becomes a metric space if we define the distance between two elements of $L(\mu)$ by

$$D([f_1], [f_2]) = \int |f_1 - f_2| \, d\mu.$$

Convergence in $L(\mu)$ corresponds to convergence in mean in $\mathscr{L}(\mu)$. Theorem 5–7 II shows that the space $L(\mu)$ is complete.

We can make $L(\mu)$ into a Banach space (see Section 3–13). We define the norm by

$$\|[f]\| = \int |f| \, d\mu. \tag{1}$$

The zero element of $L(\mu)$ is composed of all $f$ such that $f(x) = 0$ a.e. We define

$$c[f] = [cf], \qquad [f] + [g] = [f + g].$$

We see that

$$D([f], [g]) = \|[f] - [g]\|.$$

We must of course verify that $\|[f]\| = \|[g]\|$ if $f \sim g$, and similar verifications must be made for the other definitions.

It is common practice to ignore the notational distinction between $\mathscr{L}(\mu)$ and $L(\mu)$, and to write $f$ in place of $[f]$, regarding $f$ as if it were an element of $L(\mu)$.

A simple function $f : X \to R$ belongs to $\mathscr{L}(\mu)$ if and only if the set $N(f) = \{x : f(x) \neq 0\}$ has finite measure. One of the important facts in the theory of summable functions is that the elements of $L(\mu)$ which correspond to summable simple functions are everywhere dense in $L(\mu)$. This fact is a consequence of the following theorem.

THEOREM 5–7 III. *If $f \in \mathscr{L}(\mu)$, there exists a sequence $\{h_n\}$ of summable simple functions such that $\{h_n\}$ converges in mean to $f$ and $|h_n(x)| \leq |f(x)|$ for each $x$.*

*Proof.* For the case in which $f(x) \geq 0$ for each $x$, this assertion is an immediate consequence of the remarks which follow the proof of Theorem 5–4 II. The sequence $\{h_n\}$ can be taken as a regular approximating sequence for $f$ consisting of summable simple functions. Since $h_n(x) \leq f(x)$ and $\int h_n \, d\mu \to \int f \, d\mu$, it follows that $\int |f - h_n| \, d\mu \to 0$.

In the general case we write $f = f^+ - f^-$ and obtain regular approximating sequences $\{f_n\}$ and $\{g_n\}$ of the sort just described for $f^+$ and $f^-$, respectively. Then $h_n = f_n - g_n$ is a summable simple function. We see that $|h_n(x)| \leq f_n(x) + g_n(x) \leq f^+(x) + f^-(x) = |f(x)|$. Finally,

$$|f(x) - h_n(x)| \leq (f^+(x) - f_n(x)) + (f^-(x) - g_n(x)),$$

from which it is clear that $\int |f - h_n| \, d\mu \to 0$.

*Remark.* We observe, furthermore, that $h_n(x) \to f(x)$ for each $x$. The fact that $|h_n(x)| \leq |f(x)|$ then enables us to conclude that $h_n \xrightarrow{\mu} f$. See Problem 3 (c), Section 5–6.

## AN ALTERNATIVE APPROACH TO THE INTEGRAL

As an alternative to the plan followed in Sections 5–2 and 5–4, we could have developed the theory of summable functions in a very different way, on the basis of the following definitions:

A simple function $f: X \to R$ will be called summable if the set $\{x : f(x) \neq 0\}$ has finite measure. If then $f = \sum_{i=1}^{n} c_i \chi_{E_i}$, where $E_1, \ldots, E_n$ are disjoint sets of finite measure, the integral of $f$ will be, by definition,

$$\int f\,d\mu = \sum_{i=1}^{n} c_i \mu(E_i).$$

Next, a measurable function $f: X \to R^*$ which is finite a.e. will be called summable if there exists a sequence $\{f_n\}$ of summable simple functions such that $f_n \xrightarrow{\mu} f$ and $\{f_n\}$ is a Cauchy sequence in mean. The integral of $f$ is then defined as

$$\int f\,d\mu = \lim_{n\to\infty} \int f_n\,d\mu.$$

This is the way in which summable functions and their integrals are defined in the book by Halmos [1]. This approach has some advantages over the one we have used earlier in this chapter. It avoids the necessity of beginning with nonnegative functions and then going to the general case via the decomposition $f = f^+ - f^-$. It also has the advantage that it can be adapted to much more general situations. For example, one can construct a theory of integration for functions which, instead of having real values, have values in a Banach space (with either real or complex scalars). Of course, one must first have a suitable theory of measurable functions. One may also generalize the nature of the set function $\mu$. See, for instance, Dunford and Schwartz [1], Chapter III.

In order to discuss this alternative procedure in relation to the development of the theory as we have given it, let us temporarily denote by $N\mathscr{L}(\mu)$ the class of functions summable by the new definition. Also, let us denote the newly defined integral by $N\int f\,d\mu$. It is easy to see that $N\mathscr{L}(\mu) \subset \mathscr{L}(\mu)$ and $N\int f\,d\mu = \int f\,d\mu$ if $f \in N\mathscr{L}(\mu)$. Theorems 5–7 I, II play an important role in the argument. Conversely, it follows easily from earlier results in this section that $\mathscr{L}(\mu) \subset N\mathscr{L}(\mu)$. We leave details of these arguments to the reader. The consequence is that $N\mathscr{L}(\mu) = \mathscr{L}(\mu)$ and $N\int f\,d\mu = \int f\,d\mu$; in other words the two different procedures for developing the theory are actually equivalent.

## PROBLEMS

1. If $\int |f_n - f|\,d\mu \to 0$ and $f_n(x) \to g(x)$ a.e., prove that $f(x) = g(x)$ a.e.

2. Suppose $\{f_n\}$ is a sequence from $\mathscr{L}(\mu)$ and that $f: X \to R^*$ is measurable. Suppose also that $f_n \xrightarrow{\mu} f$ and that $|f_n(x)| \le g(x)$ a.e., where $g \in \mathscr{L}(\mu)$. Deduce that $f \in \mathscr{L}(\mu)$ and that $\{f_n\}$ converges in mean to $f$. [*Suggestions*. Explain why $F = \bigcup_n N(f_n)$ can be expressed as $F = \bigcup_n F_n$, where $F_n \subset F_{n+1}$, $F_n \in \mathbf{S}$, and $\mu(F_n) < +\infty$. Let $G_n = F - F_n$. For given $\delta > 0$ let $H_{mn} = H_{mn}(\delta) = \{x : |f_n(x) - f_m(x)| \ge \delta\}$. Express the integral of $|f_n - f_m|$ as the sum of integrals over the sets $F_k \cap H_{mn}$, $F_k - H_{mn}$, $G_k$, and note that

$$\int |f_n - f_m|\,d\mu \le 2\int_{H_{mn}} g\,d\mu + \delta\mu(F_k) + 2\int_{G_k} g\,d\mu.$$

Now, complete the proof.]

3. Write out in full the proof that $N\mathscr{L}(\mu) = \mathscr{L}(\mu)$ and that $N\int f\,d\mu = \int f\,d\mu$ when $f \in N\mathscr{L}(\mu)$ (notation explained in the text).

## 5–8 The $L^p$ spaces

Let $(X, \mathbf{S}, \mu)$ be a measure space. For a given positive real number $p$, we denote by $\mathscr{L}^p(\mu)$ the class of measurable functions $f: X \to R^*$ such that $|f|^p$ is in $\mathscr{L}(\mu)$. If $p = 1$, then $\mathscr{L}^p(\mu)$ is the same as $\mathscr{L}(\mu)$. If $f$ and $g$ are in $\mathscr{L}^p(\mu)$, so is $f + g$, because of the inequality

$$|f(x) + g(x)|^p \leq 2^p\{|f(x)|^p + |g(x)|^p\} \tag{1}$$

which is always valid. (It is obviously valid if $f(x)$ or $g(x)$ is infinite. If they are both finite, we can apply (1), Section 3–12.) To obtain the best inequalities relating the integrals of $|f + g|^p$, $|f|^p$, and $|g|^p$, it is necessary to consider the cases $p \geq 1$, $0 < p < 1$ separately.

We begin with Hölder's inequality, which we state as a theorem.

THEOREM 5–8 I. *Suppose $p > 1$, $p' = \dfrac{p}{p-1}$, $f \in \mathscr{L}^p(\mu)$, $g \in \mathscr{L}^{p'}(\mu)$. Then the product $fg$ is in $\mathscr{L}(\mu)$, and*

$$\int |fg|\,d\mu \leq \left(\int |f|^p\,d\mu\right)^{1/p}\left(\int |g|^{p'}\,d\mu\right)^{1/p'}. \tag{2}$$

*Proof.* We know that $fg$ is measurable. Let

$$a = \left(\int |f|^p\,d\mu\right)^{1/p}, \qquad b = \left(\int |g|^{p'}\,d\mu\right)^{1/p'}.$$

If either $a = 0$ or $b = 0$, (2) is clearly true, because in that case $f(x)g(x) = 0$ a.e. Hence suppose $a > 0$, $b > 0$. Now, $f(x)$ and $g(x)$ are finite a.e. If they are both finite, let

$$A = a^{-p}\,|f(x)|^p, \qquad B = b^{-p'}\,|g(x)|^{p'}.$$

Then, by Problem 9 (a), Section 3–6, with $\alpha = 1/p$, $\beta = 1/p'$, we have

$$\frac{|f(x)g(x)|}{ab} \leq \frac{1}{p}\frac{|f(x)|^p}{a^p} + \frac{1}{p'}\frac{|g(x)|^{p'}}{b^{p'}}.$$

It follows from this that $fg$ is summable, and that

$$\frac{1}{ab}\int |fg|\,d\mu \leq \frac{1}{pa^p}\int |f|^p\,d\mu + \frac{1}{p'b^{p'}}\int |g|^{p'}d\mu = \frac{1}{p} + \frac{1}{p'} = 1.$$

That is, (2) is valid.

We can now deduce Minkowski's inequality, which asserts that, if $f$ and $g$ are in $\mathscr{L}^p(\mu)$ and $p \geq 1$, then

$$\left(\int |f + g|^p\,d\mu\right)^{1/p} \leq \left(\int |f|^p\,d\mu\right)^{1/p} + \left(\int |g|^p\,d\mu\right)^{1/p}. \tag{3}$$

This is evidently valid if $p = 1$. For $p > 1$ the proof is made by using Hölder's inequality. See Problem 1.

When $0 < p < 1$, (3) is replaced by the inequality

$$\int |f + g|^p \, d\mu \leq \int |f|^p \, d\mu + \int |g|^p \, d\mu. \tag{4}$$

See Problem 2.

If $p \neq q$, there is no general containment relation between $\mathscr{L}^p(\mu)$ and $\mathscr{L}^q(\mu)$. A function may belong to $\mathscr{L}^p(\mu)$ for just one value of $p$. But if the measure space $(X, \mathbf{S}, \mu)$ is totally finite, $0 < p < q$ implies $\mathscr{L}^q(\mu) \subset \mathscr{L}^p(\mu)$. In particular, $\mathscr{L}^2(\mu) \subset \mathscr{L}(\mu)$ in this case. See Problem 6.

## THE SPACE $L^p(\mu)$

Just as we formed $L(\mu)$ from $\mathscr{L}(\mu)$ (see Section 5–7), so we can form $L^p(\mu)$ from $\mathscr{L}^p(\mu)$. We use the notation $[f]$ for the class of functions in $\mathscr{L}^p(\mu)$ equivalent to $f$. If $p \geq 1$, $L^p(\mu)$ is a normed linear space with norm

$$\|[f]\|_p = \left(\int |f|^p \, d\mu\right)^{1/p}, \qquad p \geq 1. \tag{5}$$

Minkowski's inequality shows that the norm satisfies the triangular inequality. If $0 < p < 1$, $L^p(\mu)$ is a linear space, but we do not get a norm from (5), because Minkowski's inequality is not valid. Nevertheless, we can define a metric in $L^p(\mu)$ when $0 < p < 1$, by setting

$$D([f_1], [f_2]) = \int |f_1 - f_2|^p \, d\mu, \qquad 0 < p < 1. \tag{6}$$

We use (4) to show that the triangular inequality is satisfied. The topological properties of the spaces $L^p(\mu)$ are remarkably different for $0 < p < 1$ from what they are for $p \geq 1$.

## THE HILBERT SPACE $L^2(\mu)$

When $p = 2$, the $p'$ in Theorem 5–8 I is 2 also. This fact makes the space $L^2(\mu)$ especially interesting. If $f, g \in \mathscr{L}^2(\mu)$, we see that $fg \in \mathscr{L}(\mu)$. If we write

$$([f], [g]) = \int fg \, d\mu, \tag{7}$$

we see that we have an inner product defined on $L^2(\mu) \times L^2(\mu)$ such that

$$([f], [f]) = (\|[f]\|_2)^2.$$

Therefore $L^2(\mu)$ is a real Hilbert space.

To get a complex Hilbert space we use complex-valued functions and use $f\bar{g}$ in place of $fg$ in the integral in (7).

## MEAN CONVERGENCE OF ORDER $p$

If $f$ and $f_1, f_2, \ldots$ are in $\mathscr{L}^p(\mu)$, the sequence $\{f_n\}$ is said to be convergent in mean (of order $p$) to $f$ if $\int |f_n - f|^p \, d\mu \to 0$. This concept, for the case $p = 1$, was discussed in Section 5–7. A sequence $\{f_n\}$ in $\mathscr{L}^p(\mu)$ is said to be a Cauchy sequence in mean of order $p$ if $\int |f_n - f_m|^p \, d\mu \to 0$, as $m$ and $n \to \infty$.

Much as in Section 5–7 we can prove that if $\{f_n\}$ is a Cauchy sequence in mean of order $p$, there is an $f$ in $\mathscr{L}^p(\mu)$ such that $\{f_n\}$ converges in mean of order $p$ to $f$. This means that $L^p(\mu)$ is complete as a metric space if $p > 0$, and that it is a Banach space if $p \geq 1$.

We have the following counterpart of Theorem 5–7 III. It is valid for any $p > 0$.

THEOREM 5–8 II. *If $f \in \mathscr{L}^p(\mu)$, there exists a sequence $\{h_n\}$ of simple functions in $\mathscr{L}^p(\mu)$ such that $|h_n(x)| \leq |f(x)|$ for each $x$, and $\int |h_n - f|^p \, d\mu \to 0$.*

*Proof.* Suppose at first that $f \geq 0$. Since $f$ is measurable and $N(f)$ is contained in a countable union of sets of finite measure, there exists a nondecreasing sequence $\{h_n\}$ of nonnegative simple functions such that $\mu[N(h_n)] < +\infty$ and $h_n \to f$. Then $h_n^p \leq f^p$, so $h_n \in \mathscr{L}^p(\mu)$. Since $|f - h_n|^p$ is a monotone sequence converging downward to 0, we conclude that $\int |f - h_n|^p \, d\mu \to 0$ (by the monotone convergence theorem).

In the general case we deal with $f = f^+ - f^-$ as in the proof of Theorem 5–7 III. Then, with notation as in this earlier proof, and writing $f - h_n = (f^+ - h_n) + (g_n - f^-)$, we use the metric in $L^p(\mu)$ to write

$$D([f], [h_n]) \leq D([f^+], [f_n]) + D([g_n], [f^-]).$$

Since $D([f], [h_n]) \to 0$ is equivalent to $\int |f - h_n|^p \, d\mu \to 0$, we have what is required. If we wish to avoid explicit reference to the metric, we can say that we use (3) if $p \geq 1$ and (4) if $0 < p < 1$.

## THE SPACE $L^\infty(\mu)$

A measurable function $f: X \to R^*$ is called *essentially bounded* (with respect to $\mu$) if there is some positive real number $M$ such that the set $\{x : |f(x)| > M\}$ has measure zero. The infimum of all such numbers $M$ is itself such a number; we call it the *essential supremum* of $|f|$ and denote it by $\sup^\circ |f(x)|$. We denote the class of all essentially bounded functions by $\mathscr{L}^\infty(\mu)$. We form $L^\infty(\mu)$ from $\mathscr{L}^\infty(\mu)$ just as we formed $L(\mu)$ from $\mathscr{L}(\mu)$. If $f \in \mathscr{L}^\infty(\mu)$, we define

$$\|[f]\|_\infty = \sup{}^\circ |f(x)|. \tag{8}$$

This defines a norm on $L^\infty(\mu)$, and we obtain a Banach space. It is easy to see that for $f_n$ and $f$ in $\mathscr{L}^\infty(\mu)$, $\|[f_n] - [f]\|_\infty \to 0$ is equivalent to the assertion: There is some set $E$ of measure zero such that $f_n(x)$ converges to $f(x)$ uniformly on $X - E$.

Observe that integrals are not used in defining $\mathscr{L}^\infty(\mu)$. If $(X, \mathbf{S}, \mu)$ is totally finite, $\mathscr{L}^\infty(\mu) \subset \mathscr{L}(\mu)$. In general all we can say is that if $f \in \mathscr{L}^\infty(\mu)$, then $f$ is summable over every set of finite measure.

## A CONVERSE OF HÖLDER'S INEQUALITY

The following theorem will be useful to us in Section 8–4. Insofar as it deals with the case $1 < p < +\infty$, it is in a way a converse of Theorem 5–8 I.

To enable us to make statements in a form applicable to $\mathscr{L}^\infty(\mu)$ as well as to $\mathscr{L}^p(\mu)$ when $p$ is finite, we adopt the conventions that

$$p' = \begin{cases} \dfrac{p}{p-1} & \text{if } 1 < p < \infty \\ \infty & \text{if } p = 1 \\ 1 & \text{if } p = \infty. \end{cases}$$

Also, we shall for simplicity write $\|f\|_p$ instead of $\|[f]\|_p$, using the definitions (5) and (8).

THEOREM 5–8 III. *Suppose the measure space $(X, \mathbf{S}, \mu)$ is totally $\sigma$-finite. Let $g : X \to R^*$ be measurable, and let $M$ be a positive constant such that $fg \in \mathscr{L}(\mu)$ and*

$$\left|\int fg \, d\mu\right| \le M \, \|f\|_x \tag{9}$$

*whenever $f$ is a bounded measurable function such that $\mu[N(f)] < +\infty$. Then $g \in \mathscr{L}^{p'}(\mu)$ and*

$$\|g\|_{p'} \le M. \tag{10}$$

*Proof.* We give the proof on the assumption that $1 < p < \infty$. The proofs for $p = 1$, $p = \infty$ are left as problems. Suppose $E$ is a set of finite measure. We shall prove that $g\chi_E \in \mathscr{L}^{p'}(\mu)$ and that

$$\left(\int_E |g|^{p'} \, d\mu\right)^{1/p'} \le M. \tag{11}$$

We use the notation

$$\operatorname{sgn} c = \begin{cases} \dfrac{c}{|c|} & \text{if } c \ne 0 \\ 0 & \text{if } c = 0, \end{cases} \tag{12}$$

where $c$ is any real number. Let us write $\alpha_n = n^{1/p}$ for convenience. We define $f_n(x) = 0$ if $x \in X - E$, and for $x \in E$ we define

$$f_n(x) = \begin{cases} |g(x)|^{p'-1} \operatorname{sgn} g(x) & \text{if } |g(x)|^{p'-1} \le \alpha_n \\ \alpha_n \operatorname{sgn} g(x) & \text{if } |g(x)|^{p'-1} > \alpha_n. \end{cases}$$

Then $f_n$ is measurable, $|f_n(x)| \le \alpha_n$, and $\mu[N(f_n)] \le \mu(E) < +\infty$. When $x \in E$ we have

$$|f_n(x)|^p = \begin{cases} |g(x)|^{p'} & \text{if } |g(x)|^{p'} \le n \\ n & \text{if } |g(x)|^{p'} > n. \end{cases}$$

and

$$f_n(x)g(x) = \begin{cases} |g(x)|^{p'} & \text{if } |g(x)|^{p'} \le n \\ \alpha_n |g(x)| & \text{if } |g(x)|^{p'} > n. \end{cases}$$

Observe that $|f_n(x)|^p \le f_n(x)g(x)$ for every $x$. By our hypothesis, $f_n g \in \mathscr{L}(\mu)$ and

$$\int |f_n|^p \, d\mu \le \int f_n g \, d\mu \le M\left(\int |f_n|^p \, d\mu\right)^{1/p}. \tag{13}$$

If the coefficient of $M$ on the right in (13) is not 0, we can divide both sides of (13) by it and obtain

$$\left(\int |f_n|^p \, d\mu\right)^{1/p'} \le M.$$

Now, $|f_n(x)|^p$ converges upward to $|g(x)|^{p'}\chi_E$ as $n \to \infty$. Therefore, by the monotone convergence theorem we conclude that $|g|^{p'}\chi_E$ is summable and that (11) holds.

Now we use the assumption that the measure space is totally $\sigma$-finite. Let $\{E_n\}$ be an expanding sequence of sets of finite measure such that their union is $X$. Then $|g|^{p'}\chi_{E_n}$ converges upward to $|g|^{p'}$. Using (11) with $E$ replaced by $E_n$ and applying the monotone convergence theorem again, we obtain (10).

## PROBLEMS

1. Assume $p > 1$ and prove Minkowski's inequality (3). [*Suggestion.* Write

$$|f(x) + g(x)|^p \leq |f(x)|\,|f(x) + g(x)|^{p-1} + |g(x)|\,|f(x) + g(x)|^{p-1}$$

and observe that $p'(p - 1) = p$. Use Hölder's inequality.]

2. Show that $(a + b)^p \leq a^p + b^p$ if $0 < p < 1$ and $a \geq 0, b \geq 0$. Then prove (4). [*Suggestion.* Consider $(1 + t)^p$, where $0 \leq t \leq 1$, and note the comparative sizes of $c^p$ and $c$ in the two cases $c \geq 1, 0 \leq c \leq 1$.]

3. (a) Prove that Theorem 5–7 I remains true for convergence in mean of order $p, p > 0$. (b) Prove the counterpart of Theorem 5–7 II for $\mathscr{L}^p(\mu)$ and convergence in mean of order $p$.

4. If $X \in \mathbf{S}$ and $\mu(X)$ is finite, $\mathscr{L}^\infty(\mu) \subset \mathscr{L}^p(\mu)$ for each $p > 0$. If $f \in \mathscr{L}^\infty(\mu)$, $(\int |f|^p\, d\mu)^{1/p} \to \sup^\circ |f(x)|$ as $p \to \infty$. Prove these assertions.

5. If $f \in \mathscr{L}^\infty(\mu) \cap \mathscr{L}^p(\mu)$ for some $p > 0$, then $f \in \mathscr{L}^q(\mu)$ if $q > p$. Moreover, $(\int |f|^q\, d\mu)^{1/q} \to \sup^\circ |f(x)|$ as $q \to \infty$. Prove these assertions.

6. If $0 < p < q$ and if $(X, \mathbf{S}, \mu)$ is such that $X \in \mathbf{S}$ and $\mu(X) < +\infty$, $\mathscr{L}^q(\mu) \subset \mathscr{L}^p(\mu)$ and $(\int |f|^p\, d\mu)^{1/p} \leq (\int |f|^q\, d\mu)^{1/q}\, |\mu(X)|^{(q-p)/pq}$ when $f \in \mathscr{L}^q(\mu)$. Prove this. [*Suggestion.* Let $\alpha = q/p$ and observe that $|f|^p \in \mathscr{L}^\alpha(\mu)$.]

7. Verify in detail that $L^\infty(\mu)$ is a Banach space.

8. The statement: "to each $\epsilon > 0$ corresponds an $N(\epsilon)$ such that $\sup^\circ |f_n(x) - f(x)| < \epsilon$ if $n \geq N(\epsilon)$" is equivalent to the statement: "to each $\epsilon > 0$ corresponds an $N(\epsilon)$ such that if $n \geq N(\epsilon)$ then $|f_n(x) - f(x)| < \epsilon$ except on a set $E_n(\epsilon)$ of measure zero." Show that it is also equivalent to the statement: "there exists a set $E$ of measure zero such that to each $\epsilon > 0$ corresponds an $N(\epsilon)$ for which $n \geq N$ implies that $|f_n(x) - f(x)| < \epsilon$ except when $x \in E$." Consider

$$F(\epsilon) = \bigcup_n E_n(\epsilon) \quad \text{and} \quad E = \bigcup_k F\left(\frac{1}{k}\right).$$

9. Prove Theorem 5–8 III for the cases $p = 1, \infty$.

10. Prove the following assertions.
   (a) If $f \in \mathscr{L}^p(\mu) \cap \mathscr{L}^q(\mu)$, where $0 < p < q$, then $f \in \mathscr{L}^r(\mu)$ if $p < r < q$.
   (b) It can happen that $\mathscr{L}^p(\mu)$ is a proper subset of $\mathscr{L}(\mu)$ if $p > 1$. Suppose, for instance, that $\mu$ is Lebesgue measure on the L-measurable subsets of [0, 1]. Consider $f(x) = \left[x\left(\log \dfrac{2}{x}\right)^2\right]^{-1}$.
   (c) It can happen that a function belongs to $\mathscr{L}^q(\mu)$ but not to $\bigcup_{p \neq q} \mathscr{L}^p(\mu)$. Consider $f(x) = [x(1 + |\log x|)^2]^{-1}$ with $q = 1$, using ordinary Lebesgue integrals over $[0, \infty)$.

## 5–9 Integration with respect to the completion of a measure

Let $(X, \mathbf{S}, \mu)$ be a measure space, and let $(X, \bar{\mathbf{S}}, \bar{\mu})$ be the measure space obtained by completing the measure $\mu$ (see Section 4–11). If $f : X \to R^*$ is measurable with respect to $\bar{\mathbf{S}}$, it is natural to wonder if it has the same property with respect to $\mathbf{S}$; the same question arises with respect to summability. The answer to these questions involves the construction of another function $g : X \to R^*$ which differs from $f$ only on a set of $\bar{\mu}$-measure zero.

THEOREM 5–9 I. *Suppose $f : X \to R^*$ is measurable with respect to $\bar{\mathbf{S}}$. Then there exists a function $g : X \to R^*$ which is measurable with respect to $\mathbf{S}$ and such that $\bar{\mu}(\{x : f(x) \neq g(x)\}) = 0$. Furthermore, $g$ can be so constructed that $g(x) = 0$ if $f(x) \neq g(x)$.*

*Proof.* Let $\{r_n\}$ be an enumeration of all the rational numbers. Since $f$ is measurable with respect to $\bar{\mathbf{S}}$, we know that the sets $\{x : f(x) = +\infty\}$ and $N(f) \cap \{x : f(x) < r_n\}$ are in $\bar{\mathbf{S}}$ (Theorem 5–1 V). Using the notation $\mathbf{Z}$ as in Section 4–11, we can write

$$\{x : f(x) = +\infty\} = E_0 \cup N_0, \quad E_0 \in \mathbf{S}, \quad N_0 \in \mathbf{Z},$$

$$N(f) \cap \{x : f(x) < r_n\} = E_n \cup N_n, \quad E_n \in \mathbf{S}, \quad N_n \in \mathbf{Z}, \qquad n = 1, 2, \ldots.$$

By the nature of $\mathbf{Z}$, there exist sets $F_i \in \mathbf{S}$ with $N_i \subset F_i$, $\mu(F_i) = 0$, $i = 0, 1, 2, \ldots$. Let $F = \bigcup_i F_i$. Then $F \in \mathbf{S}$ and $\mu(F) = 0$. We define $g : X \to R^*$ by

$$g(x) = \begin{cases} f(x) & \text{if } x \in X - F \\ 0 & \text{if } x \in F. \end{cases}$$

Clearly, $\{x : f(x) \neq g(x)\}$ is a subset of $F$, so that it is in $\bar{\mathbf{S}}$ and has $\bar{\mu}$-measure zero. We have to show that $g$ is measurable with respect to $\mathbf{S}$. For this we shall use the criterion of Theorem 5–1 V (c).

We see that

$$\{x : g(x) = +\infty\} = \{x : f(x) = +\infty\} - F = E_0 - F \in \mathbf{S}.$$

Likewise,

$$N(g) \cap \{x : g(x) < r_n\} = N(f) \cap \{x : f(x) < r_n\} - F = E_n - F \in \mathbf{S}.$$

Now,

$$N(g) \cap \{x : g(x) < c\} = \bigcup_{r_n < c} [N(g) \cap \{x : g(x) < r_n\}] \in \mathbf{S}$$

if $c \in R^*$ and $c \neq -\infty$. If $c = -\infty$, $\{x : g(x) < c\} = \varnothing$. It is now clear that $g$ is measurable with respect to $\mathbf{S}$. This ends the proof.

It is of course clear that $g$ is also measurable with respect to $\bar{\mathbf{S}}$, because $\mathbf{S} \subset \bar{\mathbf{S}}$. Hence, if $f$ is summable with respect to $\bar{\mu}$, so is $g$, and $\int g \, d\bar{\mu} = \int f \, d\bar{\mu}$. It is thus natural to ask whether $g$ is summable with respect to $\mu$, and whether in that case, the integrals of $g$ with respect to $\mu$ and $\bar{\mu}$ are equal. This is in fact true.

THEOREM 5–9 II. *If the $f$ of Theorem 5–9 I is $\bar{\mu}$-summable, the $g$ defined in the proof of that theorem is $\mu$-summable, and*

$$\int f \, d\bar{\mu} = \int g \, d\bar{\mu} = \int g \, d\mu.$$

*Proof.* First we consider the case in which $f \geq 0$, so that $g \geq 0$. Since $g$ is $\bar{\mu}$-summable, there exists a nondecreasing sequence $\{g_n\}$ such that $g_n \to g$ and each $g_n$ is a summable function, simple with respect to $\bar{\mathbf{S}}$. That is, each $g_n$ is a finite linear combination of characteristic functions of sets of finite measure in $\bar{\mathbf{S}}$. If $E \cup N$ is a typical one of these sets for $g_n$, where $E \in \mathbf{S}$ and $N \in \mathbf{Z}$, and if we replace this set by $E$, we in this way convert $g_n$ into a function $h_n$ which is summable with respect to $\mathbf{S}$. Since $\bar{\mu}(E \cup N) = \mu(E)$, we see that $\int g_n \, d\bar{\mu} = \int h_n \, d\mu$. Now, the set on which $h_n$ differs in value from $g_n$ has $\bar{\mu}$-measure zero. Hence there is a set $N_0$ of $\bar{\mu}$-measure zero such that $h_n(x) = g_n(x)$ for every $n$ if $x \in X - N_0$. There is a set $F_0 \in \mathbf{S}$ with $\mu(F_0) = 0$ and $N_0 \subset F_0$. We see then that $0 \leq h_n \leq g_n \leq g$ and that $h_n(x) \to g(x)$ if $x \in X - F_0$. We are not sure that $h_n \leq h_{n+1}$. We therefore let $h(x) = \liminf_{n\to\infty} h_n(x)$. Certainly $h(x) = g(x)$ if $x \in X - F_0$. Since $\int h_n \, d\mu \to \int g \, d\bar{\mu}$, we are assured by Fatou's lemma (Theorem 5–5 V) that $h$ is $\mu$-summable. But then $g$ is $\mu$-summable. This being established, from $0 \leq h_n \leq g$ and $h_n(x) \to g(x)$ a.e. we can infer (by Theorem 5–5 IV) that $\int h_n \, d\mu \to \int g \, d\mu$. Thus $\int g \, d\bar{\mu} = \int g \, d\mu$, and the proof is complete for the case in which $f \geq 0$.

In the general case we write $f = f^+ - f^-$. Applying Theorem 5–9 I to $f^+$, we obtain a function $g_1$ and a set $F_1$ related to $f^+$ just as $g$ and $F$ are related to $f$. Likewise, related to $f^-$ we have $g_2$ and $F_2$. By what has been proved we know that

$$\int g_1 \, d\mu = \int f^+ \, d\bar{\mu}, \qquad \int g_2 \, d\mu = \int f^- \, d\bar{\mu}.$$

But it is clear that $g(x) = g_1(x) - g_2(x)$ if $x$ is not in $F \cup F_1 \cup F_2$. Therefore $g$ is summable, and

$$\int g \, d\mu = \int g_1 \, d\mu - \int g_2 \, d\mu = \int f \, d\bar{\mu}.$$

This ends the proof.

## SUGGESTED READING FOR CHAPTER 5

Bliss [1].
Burkill [1].
Caratheodory [1], Chapters 7, 8.
Goffman [1], Chapters 15–18.
Hahn and Rosenthal [1], Chapters 3, 4.
Halmos [1], Chapters 4, 5.
Hildebrandt [1].
Hobson [1], Vol. 1, parts of Chapter 7; Vol. 2, Sections 99, Sections 201–218.
Kestelman [1], Chapters 5, 6.
Kolmogorov and Fomin [1], Chapters 2, 3, 4.
Lebesgue [2], Chapter 7.
Munroe [1], Chapters 4, 5, 6.
Natanson [1], Vol. 1, Chapters 5, 6, 7; Vol. 2, Chapter 12.
Riesz and Nagy [1], Chapter 2.
Saks [1], Chapter 1, 3.
Titchmarsh [1], Chapter 10.
Williamson [1], Chapters 3, 4.

CHAPTER SIX

# Integration by the Daniell Method

## 6–0 Introduction

The classical theory of the Lebesgue integral is based on the theory of measure. As is shown in Chapter 5, a complete theory of integration can be developed for functions defined on an abstract measure space. But when we want to use integration as a technique in some part of analysis, if we are to depend on the classical theory, we must first of all obtain a measure suitable for our purpose. Thus, we must be familiar with general methods for constructing measures. In Chapter 4 we have seen that the classical theory of Lebesgue measure in $R^k$ is developed by first constructing an outer measure. More generally, we saw in Section 4–7 how to obtain a measure from an outer measure, and in Section 4–9 we discussed a general method of constructing outer measures.

The theory of outer measures and measures is important on its own account, and not merely to provide stepping stones on the way to a theory of integration. But it is a simple fact that in some parts of analysis our attention is much more on integrals than on measures. It is therefore quite natural to seek a way of developing a theory of integration which focuses attention on functions and their integrals at the outset, and does not require discussion of outer measures and measures as a preliminary to the main business. In this chapter we shall see how to develop a theory of integration in this way. The basic method stems from the work of P. J. Daniell (1889–1946) [1, 2]. M. H. Stone's formulation of the theory (see Stone [2]) has heavily influenced its current form. In particular, through Stone's work we know how to relate this "direct" theory of integration to the theory of integration via measure theory.

Roughly, the first half of this chapter (through Section 6–6) can be read without prior knowledge of the theory of integration as presented in Chapter 5. Some familiarity with the early part of Chapter 4 is needed. For an understanding of the rest of the chapter, the reader should be familiar with the core material from Chapters 4, 5.

Before starting Section 6–2, the reader should be acquainted with Section 4–1.

## 6–1 Elementary integrals on a vector lattice of functions

In this section we describe axiomatically the type of mathematical structure which serves as a base for the development of the theory of integration in this chapter. This structure consists of a family of real-valued functions and a real-valued function, called an elementary integral, defined on this family of functions. The family of functions is of a special kind, which merits the name *vector lattice*. The *elementary integral*, so-called, is a real-valued function defined on the vector lattice. Its postulated properties are among the properties possessed by integrals of various types.

Let $X$ be a nonempty set of elements of unspecified nature. We consider functions $f : X \to R$, with the usual definitions of $f + g$ and $cf$ ($c \in R$). Since we shall often make use of the functions defined as having the values $\max \{f(x), g(x)\}$ and $\min \{f(x), g(x)\}$ at $x$, we shall use a convenient brief notation for these functions. We define $f \vee g$ by

(1) $$(f \vee g)(x) = \max \{f(x), g(x)\};$$

likewise, we define $f \wedge g$ by

(2) $$(f \wedge g)(x) = \min \{f(x), g(x)\}.$$

The operations $\vee$ and $\wedge$ are commutative and associative. Because of the associativity we can write $f_1 \vee f_2 \vee \cdots \vee f_n$ and $f_1 \wedge f_2 \wedge \cdots \wedge f_n$ without parentheses.

Observe that

(3) $$f^+ = f \vee 0, \qquad f^- = (-f) \vee 0 = -(f \wedge 0),$$

and therefore that

(4) $$|f| = (f \vee 0) - (f \wedge 0).$$

Here, of course, 0 refers to the function all of whose values are zero.

It is useful to note that

(5) $$f \wedge g = -[(-f) \vee (-g)], \qquad f \vee g = -[(-f) \wedge (-g)].$$

We can also define $f \vee g$ and $f \wedge g$ for functions defined on $X$ with values in $R^*$. In this case we apply the operations $\vee$ and $\wedge$ to arbitrary (nonempty) collections of functions, not merely to pairs of functions. To do this we must change *maximum* to *supremum* and *minimum* to *infimum*. If $A$ is a nonempty index set and if $f_\alpha : X \to R^*$ is given for each $\alpha \in A$, we can define $\sup_\alpha f_\alpha$ as the function whose value at $x$ is $\sup_\alpha f_\alpha(x)$. Sometimes we shall denote this function by $\bigvee_\alpha f_\alpha$:

(6) $$\bigvee_\alpha f_\alpha = \sup_\alpha f_\alpha.$$

We define $\inf_\alpha f_\alpha$ in the corresponding way and write

(7) $$\bigwedge_\alpha f_\alpha = \inf_\alpha f_\alpha.$$

Corresponding to (5) we have

(8) $$\bigwedge_\alpha f_\alpha = -\bigvee_\alpha(-f_\alpha), \qquad \bigvee_\alpha f_\alpha = -\bigwedge_\alpha(-f_\alpha).$$

In case $A$ is the finite set $\{1, 2, \ldots, n\}$ we may write

$$\bigvee_{i=1}^n f_i = f_1 \vee \cdots \vee f_n.$$

In the class of all functions $f: X \to R^*$ there is a partial order relation $\leq$, where $f \leq g$ means that $f(x) \leq g(x)$ for each $x$. With respect to this partial order relation $f \vee g$ is the least upper bound of $f$ and $g$. That is, $f \leq f \vee g$, $g \leq f \vee g$, and if $h$ is any function such that $f \leq h$ and $g \leq h$, then $f \vee g \leq h$. Likewise, $f \wedge g$ is the greatest lower bound of $f$ and $g$.

It is a property of the class of *all* $f: X \to R$ that $f \vee g$ and $f \wedge g$ belong to this class when $f$ and $g$ do. But this property may also pertain to more restricted classes of such $f$'s.

## VECTOR LATTICES

A nonempty class $\mathscr{F}$ of functions $f: X \to R$ is called a *vector lattice* of functions if it is such that $f + g$, $f \vee g$, $f \wedge g$ and $cf$ are in $\mathscr{F}$ when $f, g \in \mathscr{F}$ and $c \in R$. Note that we are now ruling out functions with infinite values, so far as the vector lattice is concerned. In the sense of abstract algebra, $\mathscr{F}$ is a vector space, or linear space, and it is also a lattice with the partial order relation $\leq$.

*Example 1.* The class of all continuous functions $f: R \to R$ is a vector lattice, but the subclass of all these functions which have a derivative continuous at each point is not a vector lattice. Consider, for instance, $f(x) = x$, $g(x) = -x$. Here, $(f \vee g)(x) = |x|$ and $(f \wedge g)(x) = -|x|$. Both $f \vee g$ and $f \wedge g$ are continuous but do not meet the requirement of differentiability.

*Example 2.* If $X$ is a topological space, the class of all continuous functions $f: X \to R$ is a vector lattice.

## MONOTONE CONVERGENCE

For functions on $X$ to $R^*$ we write $f_n \to f$ to indicate that $f_n(x) \to f(x)$ for each $x$. If $f_n \leq f_{n+1}$ for each $n$, there is a unique limit function $f: X \to R^*$ such that $f_n \to f$. In this case we use the notation $f_n \nearrow f$ to express both $f_1 \leq f_2 \leq \cdots$ and $f_n \to f$. Likewise, $f_n \searrow f$ means that $f_1 \geq f_2 \geq \cdots$ and $f_n \to f$. In either of the two cases, $f_n \nearrow f$ and $f_n \searrow f$, we say that the convergence is *monotone*.

## ELEMENTARY INTEGRALS

If $\mathscr{F}$ is a vector lattice of functions on $X$ to $R$, a function $I: \mathscr{F} \to R$ is called an *elementary integral* on $\mathscr{F}$ if it has the following properties:

(a) $$I(f + g) = I(f) + I(g),$$

(b) $$I(cf) = cI(f) \quad \text{if} \quad c \in R,$$

(c) $$I(f) \geq 0 \quad \text{if} \quad f \geq 0,$$

(d) $$\text{if } f_n \searrow 0, \quad \text{then} \quad I(f_n) \to 0.$$

The two properties (a), (b) express the fact that $I$ is a *linear functional* on $\mathscr{F}$. From (b) we see that $I(0) = 0$. Because of property (c) we say that $I$ is a *positive* linear functional. In this general situation we have no topology for $\mathscr{F}$, so there is no concept of continuity for functions defined on $\mathscr{F}$. The condition (d) does, however, serve as a kind of continuity condition on $I$, expressed in terms of the partial order relation in $\mathscr{F}$ and the topology of $R$. It is significant that the topology of $R$ is intimately related to the fact that $R$ is an ordered set, for we shall be considering infima and suprema of certain collections of values of $I$.

From (a), (b), and (c) it follows that $f \leq g$ implies $I(f) \leq I(g)$. If $f_n$ and $f$ are in $\mathscr{F}$, with $f_n \nearrow f$ or $f_n \searrow f$, it is easy to see with the aid of (d) that $I(f_n) \to I(f)$.

*Example* 3. Let $X$ be a compact interval in $R$ and take $\mathscr{F}$ to be $C[a, b]$ (see Section 3–15). We define $I$ by

$$I(f) = \int_a^b f(x)\,dx,$$

the integral being that of elementary calculus, the Riemann integral. To see that this is an example of an elementary integral we must check property (d). Now, if $f_n \in C[a, b]$ and $f_n \searrow 0$, it follows from Dini's theorem (Theorem 3–15 I) that the convergence is not merely pointwise, but uniform. Therefore, $I(f_n) \to 0$.

*Example 4*. Let $X = R^k$ and let $\mathscr{F}$ be the class of all continuous functions $f : R^k \to R$ such that the set $\{x : f(x) \neq 0\}$ has a compact closure. Using the notation $N(f) = \{x : f(x) \neq 0\}$ as in Section 5–1, we can express this last condition equivalently by requiring that $N(f)$ be contained in some compact set. We denote this class $\mathscr{F}$ by $C_\infty(R^k)$. (The subscript $\infty$ is to suggest that each $f$ is zero in some neighborhood of the "point at infinity" of the one-point compactification of $R^k$. See Section 3–5.) It is easy to see that $C_\infty(R^k)$ is a vector lattice.

We define $I$ on $C_\infty(R^k)$ as follows. If $f \in C_\infty(R^k)$, let $E$ be a compact interval (a closed box in the sense of Sections 2–3, 2–4) such that $N(f) \subset E$. Then let

$$I(f) = \int_E f(x)\,dx,$$

where the integral is the ordinary Riemann integral. It is easily seen that the value of the integral is independent of the choice of $E$. It is easily verified that $I$ is an elementary integral. To verify property (d), suppose $f_n \searrow 0$. Since $0 \leq f_n \leq f_1$, we see that $N(f_n) \subset N(f_1)$. In computing $I(f_n)$ let us use a compact interval $E$ which contains $N(f_1)$. Then we see by Dini's theorem that $f_n(x)$ converges to 0 uniformly on $E$; therefore $I(f_n) \to 0$.

Examples 3 and 4 are among the important special cases for the application of the theory which we shall develop, starting from an elementary integral $I$ on a vector lattice $\mathscr{F}$. As we shall see in Section 6–8, the application of the theory in the case of Example 4 leads to Lebesgue measure and Lebesgue integration by a route entirely different from that of Chapter 5.

We point out explicitly that, in the general definition of an elementary integral, we do not require the elements of the vector lattice $\mathscr{F}$ to be bounded functions. In the foregoing examples the functions are bounded, however. Not until Theorem 6–11 I do we find it necessary in the general theory to assume boundedness of the functions in the vector lattice.

## 6–2 Over-functions and under-functions

In this section we define a class $\mathscr{F}^\circ$ of functions $f : X \to R^*$ associated with a given vector lattice $\mathscr{F}$ of functions. These functions are called *over-functions* (relative to $\mathscr{F}$). This class includes $\mathscr{F}$. We also define a class $\mathscr{F}_u$, whose elements are called *under-functions*; $\mathscr{F}_u$ is composed of all $f$ such that $-f \in \mathscr{F}^\circ$. We extend the definition of $I$ in a natural way so that $I(f)$ acquires a meaning for each $f$ in $\mathscr{F}^\circ \cup \mathscr{F}_u$, in agreement with its original value in case $f \in \mathscr{F}$. This procedure is preliminary to the work of Section 6–3, where we shall define a class of functions on $X$ to $R^*$ which are said to be summable with respect to $I$.

## OVER-FUNCTIONS

Given the vector lattice $\mathscr{F}$ of functions on $X$ to $R$, a function $f : X \to R^*$ is called an over-function if there exists a sequence $\{f_n\}$ such that $f_n \in \mathscr{F}$ and $f_n \nearrow f$. The class of over-functions is denoted by $\mathscr{F}^\circ$. The basic simple facts about over-functions are expressed in the following theorem.

THEOREM 6–2 I. (a) $\mathscr{F} \subset \mathscr{F}^\circ$. (b) *If* $f, g \in \mathscr{F}^0$ *then* $f + g \in \mathscr{F}^\circ$. (c) *If* $f \in \mathscr{F}^\circ$ *and* $0 \leq c < +\infty$, *then* $cf \in \mathscr{F}^\circ$. (d) *If*, $f, g \in \mathscr{F}^\circ$, *then* $f \vee g$ *and* $f \wedge g$ *are in* $\mathscr{F}^\circ$.

*Proof.* We leave the proofs of (a), (b), and (c) to the reader. For (d) we observe that if $f_n \nearrow f$ and $g_n \nearrow g$, then $f_n \vee g_n \nearrow f \vee g$ and $f_n \wedge g_n \nearrow f \wedge g$. Let us deal with the first of these assertions. The proof in the other case is left to the reader. Let $h_n = f_n \vee g_n$. First we shall show that $h_n \leq h_{n+1}$. Because of symmetry we may assume that, for a given $n$ and $x, f_n(x) \geq g_n(x)$. Then $h_n(x) = f_n(x) \leq f_{n+1}(x) \leq h_{n+1}(x)$; hence $h_n \leq h_{n+1}$. Let $h = f \vee g$. We shall show that $h_n \to h$. Clearly, $f_n \leq f \leq h$ and $g_n \leq g \leq h$, so that $f_n \vee g_n \leq h$. For a given $x$ we may suppose that $f(x) \geq g(x)$. Suppose $c < f(x)$. Then $c < f_n(x)$ for some $n$. But $f_n(x) \leq h_n(x)$, and therefore $c < h_i(x) \leq h(x)$ if $i \geq n$. Thus $h_i \to h$. In the future we shall leave the details of most such arguments to the reader.

We observe that if $f \in \mathscr{F}^\circ, f(x)$ may be $+\infty$ for a given $x$, but it can never be $-\infty$.

*Example 1.* Let $\mathscr{F} = C[0, 1]$. Define $f_n(x) = x^{1/n}$, $g_n(x) = nx$. The corresponding over-functions $f$ and $g$ are given by $f(0) = 0$, $f(x) = 1$ if $0 < x \leq 1$, $g(0) = 0$, $g(x) = +\infty$ if $0 < x \leq 1$. The function $h$ defined by $h(x) = 0$ if $0 \leq x < \frac{1}{2}$, $h(\frac{1}{2}) = -\frac{1}{2}$, $h(x) = \frac{1}{2}$ if $\frac{1}{2} < x \leq 1$ is an over-function. For example, $h_n \nearrow h$, where $h_n$ is defined so that its graph is that shown in Figure 37.

We shall not stop now to try to discover the properties which are characteristic of over-functions for particular choices of the vector lattice $\mathscr{F}$. In Section 6–9 we shall see that the concept of semicontinuity plays an important role in describing over-functions for the case

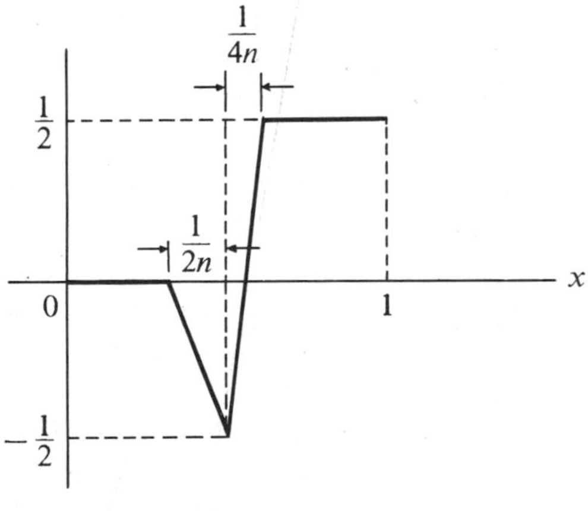


Graph of $h_n$

FIGURE 37

$\mathscr{F} = C_\infty(R^k)$ (see Example 4, Section 6–1). In this case or in the case $\mathscr{F} = C[0, 1]$, the value of $f(x)$ at a point of discontinuity of the over-function $f$ is definitely restricted.

*Example* 2. Suppose $\mathscr{F} = C[0, 1]$. Let $f$ be defined by

$$f(x) = \begin{cases} 0 & \text{if } 0 \le x < \frac{1}{2} \\ c & \text{if } x = \frac{1}{2} \\ 1 & \text{if } \frac{1}{2} < x \le 1. \end{cases}$$

Then $f$ is an over-function if and only if $c \le 0$. We leave the proof of this to the reader.

If $f \in \mathscr{F}^\circ$ and $f_n \nearrow f$, where $f_n \in \mathscr{F}$, the sequence $\{I(f_n)\}$ converges upward to a limit which may be either finite or $+\infty$. The following lemma shows that the limit depends only on $f$, not on the particular sequence $\{f_n\}$.

LEMMA 6–2 II. *If $\{f_n\}$ and $\{g_n\}$ are sequences from $\mathscr{F}$ such that $f_n \nearrow f$ and $g_n \nearrow f$, where $f \in \mathscr{F}^\circ$, then* $\lim I(f_n) = \lim I(g_n)$.

*Proof.* We make the argument in three steps.

*Step 1.* With $\{f_n\}$ as given, let $A = \lim I(f_n)$. Consider any $h \in \mathscr{F}$ such that $h \le f$. We shall prove that $I(h) \le A$. We see that $I(f_n \wedge h) \le I(f_n)$, because $f_n \wedge h \le f_n$. Now, $f_n \wedge h \nearrow f \wedge h = h$, and, therefore, $h - (f_n \wedge h) \searrow 0$. It follows that $I(h) - I(f_n \wedge h) \to 0$ and $I(h) = \lim I(f_n \wedge h) \le \lim I(f_n) = A$.

*Step 2.* Now, let $B = \lim I(g_n)$. We show that $B \le A$. Since $g_n \le f$, Step 1 implies that $I(g_n) \le A$, whence $B \le A$.

*Step 3.* The reasoning applies with the roles of $\{f_n\}$ and $\{g_n\}$ reversed. Therefore $A \le B$, and so $A = B$.

Relying on the foregoing lemma, we now define $I(f)$ when $f \in \mathscr{F}^\circ - \mathscr{F}$ by

$$I(f) = \lim I(f_n), \tag{1}$$

where $\{f_n\}$ is any sequence in $\mathscr{F}$ such that $f_n \nearrow f$. This formula is valid as well if $f \in \mathscr{F}$, for in that case we can take $f_n = f$ for every $n$.

Observe that, as a mapping of $\mathscr{F}^\circ$ into $R^*$, $I$ may have $+\infty$ in its range, but not $-\infty$.

THEOREM 6–2 III. *The mapping $I : \mathscr{F}^\circ \to R^*$ has the following properties:* (a) $I(f+g) = I(f) + I(g)$*;* (b) $I(cf) = cI(f)$ *if* $c \ge 0$*;* (c) $I(g) \le I(f)$ *if* $g \le f$*;* (d) *if* $f_n \in \mathscr{F}^\circ$ *and* $f_n \nearrow f$, *then* $f \in \mathscr{F}^\circ$ *and* $I(f_n) \to I(f)$.

*Proof.* We leave the proofs of (a) and (b) to the reader. We prove (c) by the argument of Steps 1 and 2 in the proof of Lemma 6–2 II. To prove (d) suppose $\{g_{nm}\}$ is a sequence in $\mathscr{F}$ such that $g_{nm} \nearrow f_m$ as $n \to \infty$, $m$ being fixed. Let $g_n = g_{n1} \vee \cdots \vee g_{nn}$. To a given $x$ corresponds some $j$ with $1 \le j \le n$ such that $g_n(x) = g_{nj}(x)$. Thus $g_n(x) \le f_j(x) \le f_n(x)$. Also, $g_n(x) \le g_{n+1,j}(x) \le g_{n+1}(x)$. If $i \le n$, we have $g_{ni} \le g_n \le f_n$. Writing $g = \lim g_n$, we see on letting $n \to \infty$ in the preceding inequality that $f_i \le g \le f$. But then $f \le g \le f$, so $f = g$. Since $g_n \in \mathscr{F}$, we know that $f \in \mathscr{F}^\circ$ and $I(g_n) \to I(f)$. We also have $I(g_{ni}) \le I(g_n) \le I(f_n)$. In the limit as $n \to \infty$ we have $I(f_i) \le I(f) \le \lim I(f_n)$. Finally, letting $i \to \infty$, we get $\lim I(f_n) = I(f)$, as desired.

## UNDER-FUNCTIONS

A function $f : X \to R^*$ such that $-f \in \mathscr{F}^\circ$ is called an *under-function* (relative to $\mathscr{F}$). The class of under-functions is denoted by $\mathscr{F}_u$. If $f \in \mathscr{F}_u$, we may have $f(x) = -\infty$ but not $f(x) = +\infty$. It is easy to see that $f \in \mathscr{F}_u$ if and only if there exists a sequence $\{f_n\}$ in $\mathscr{F}$ such that $f_n \searrow f$. Theorem 6–2 I remains true with $\mathscr{F}^\circ$ replaced by $\mathscr{F}_u$, as the reader may easily verify. Observe (5) in Section 6–1, for instance, to see that $f \vee g$ and $f \wedge g$ are in $\mathscr{F}_u$ when $f, g \in \mathscr{F}_u$.

A function $f$ may belong to both $\mathscr{F}^\circ$ and $\mathscr{F}_u$; in this case $f$ has no infinite values. We have $\mathscr{F} \subset \mathscr{F}^\circ \cap \mathscr{F}_u$, but in general $\mathscr{F}_u$ may contain elements which are not in $\mathscr{F}$ or $\mathscr{F}^\circ$. If $f \in \mathscr{F}^\circ \cap \mathscr{F}_u$, then $-f \in \mathscr{F}^\circ$ and $f + (-f) = 0$, so that, by (a) in Theorem 6–2 III, $I(f) + I(-f) = I(0) = 0$, or $I(f) = -I(-f)$. We use this relation as a definition when $f \in \mathscr{F}_u - \mathscr{F}^\circ$. Thus we always have

$$I(f) = -I(-f) \tag{2}$$

if $f \in \mathscr{F}^\circ \cup \mathscr{F}_u$.

For the properties of $I$ as a function on $\mathscr{F}_u$ we have (a)–(c) the same as in Theorem 6–2 III. Instead of (d) we have a corresponding property with $f_n \searrow f$ in place of $f_n \nearrow f$.

THEOREM 6–2 IV. *Suppose $f \in \mathscr{F}_u$, $g \in \mathscr{F}^\circ$, and $f \le g$. Then $g - f \in \mathscr{F}^\circ$ and $I(g - f) = I(g) - I(f) \ge 0$.*

This result is stated formally so that we may refer to it later. The simple proof is left to the reader.

We give one simple but interesting example in which it is not difficult to describe $\mathscr{F}^\circ$ and $\mathscr{F}_u$ directly.

*Example 3.* Let $X$ be the class of positive integers, and let $\mathscr{F}$ be the class of functions $f : X \to R$ (real sequences) such that $f(n) = 0$ for all except a finite number of values of $n$. Define $I : \mathscr{F} \to R$ by

$$I(f) = \sum_n f(n). \tag{3}$$

We leave it for the reader to verify that $\mathscr{F}$ is a vector lattice and that $I$ is an elementary integral on $\mathscr{F}$. If $f : X \to R^*$ is such that $f(n)$ is never $-\infty$ and $f(n) \ge 0$ when $n > N$, where $N$ depends on $f$, then $f \in \mathscr{F}^\circ$, and $\mathscr{F}^\circ$ is composed precisely of all such functions. The reader can prove this for himself. The extension of $I$ to $\mathscr{F}^\circ$ is still defined by (3), with the usual interpretations of sums and infinite series when each term is either a real number or $+\infty$.

The next example shows that the class $\mathscr{F}^\circ$ may not be a very substantial enlargement of $\mathscr{F}$.

*Example 4.* Let $X = [0, \pi]$. Let $\mathscr{F}$ consist of all $f : X \to R$ of the form $f(x) = a \sin x$ where $a \in R$, and let $I(f)$ be the Riemann integral $\int_0^\pi f(x)\, dx$. In this case the only element of $\mathscr{F}^\circ - \mathscr{F}$ is given by $f(0) = f(\pi) = 0$, $f(x) = +\infty$ if $0 < x < \pi$, and for this $f$, $I(f) = +\infty$.

PROBLEMS

1. Show that $f_n \nearrow f$ and $g_n \nearrow g$ imply $f_n \wedge g_n \nearrow f \wedge g$.
2. Prove (a), (b), and (c) in Theorem 6–2 I.
3. Prove (a) and (b) in Theorem 6–2 III.
4. Prove Theorem 6–2 IV.
5. Verify the assertions made in connection with Examples 3 and 4.

## 6–3 Summable functions

In this section we have the core of the theory of integration, insofar as the strictly abstract development of the present method is concerned. We define the class of functions which are called summable, and we define the integral of each such function. We then develop the properties of the integral as a function on the class of summable functions. These developments include the basic convergence theorems which are characteristic of the Lebesgue theory of integration in its various forms and generalizations.

### UPPER AND LOWER INTEGRALS

If $f : X \to R^*$ is such that there exists an $h$ in $\mathscr{F}^\circ$ for which $f \leq h$, we define

$$\bar{I}(f) = \inf \{I(h) : h \in \mathscr{F}^\circ, f \leq h\}. \tag{1}$$

We call $\bar{I}(f)$ the *upper integral* of $f$. The class of $f$'s for which $\bar{I}(f)$ is defined includes all of $\mathscr{F}^\circ$; $\bar{I}(f) = I(f)$ if $f \in \mathscr{F}^\circ$, as we see from Theorem 6–2 III (c).

If $f$ is such that there exists a $g$ in $\mathscr{F}_u$ for which $g \leq f$, we define

$$\underline{I}(f) = \sup \{I(g) : g \in \mathscr{F}_u, g \leq f\}. \tag{2}$$

We call $\underline{I}(f)$ the lower integral of $f$. The class of $f$'s for which $\underline{I}(f)$ is defined includes all of $\mathscr{F}_u$, and $\underline{I}(f) = I(f)$ if $f \in \mathscr{F}_u$.

By Theorem 6–2 IV we see that $I(g) \leq I(h)$ if $g \in \mathscr{F}_u$, $h \in \mathscr{F}^\circ$, and $g \leq f \leq h$. From this it follows that

$$\underline{I}(f) \leq \bar{I}(f) \tag{3}$$

when both $\underline{I}(f)$ and $\bar{I}(f)$ are defined.

### SUMMABLE FUNCTIONS

If $f : X \to R^*$ is such that $\underline{I}(f)$ and $\bar{I}(f)$ are defined, finite, and equal, $f$ is said to be *summable* (with respect to the elementary integral $I$). We denote the class of summable functions by $\mathscr{L}$. If $f \in \mathscr{L}$ we define the *integral* $I(f)$ of $f$ as

$$I(f) = \underline{I}(f) = \bar{I}(f). \tag{4}$$

In the following theorem we shall see that this definition of $I(f)$ is consistent with meanings of $I(f)$ already available in case $f \in \mathscr{F}_u \cup \mathscr{F}^\circ$.

THEOREM 6–3 I. (a) *A function $f : X \to R^*$ is summable if and only if to each $\epsilon > 0$ corresponds some pair of functions $g$, $h$ with $g \in \mathscr{F}_u$, $h \in \mathscr{F}^\circ$, $g \leq f \leq h$, $I(g)$ and $I(h)$*

*finite, and* $I(h) - I(g) < \epsilon$. (b) *If* $f \in \mathscr{F}^\circ$, $f$ *is summable if and only if* $I(f) < +\infty$, *where* $I(f)$ *is given by* (1), *Section* 6–2. *In all cases of* $f \in \mathscr{F}^\circ$, *whether* $I(f)$ *is finite or not, we have* $\underline{I}(f) = \bar{I}(f) = I(f)$. (c) *If* $f \in \mathscr{F}_u$, $f$ *is summable if and only if* $-\infty < I(f)$, *where* $I(f)$ *is given as in Section* 6–2. *In all cases of* $f \in \mathscr{F}_u$, *whether* $I(f)$ *is finite or not, we have* $\underline{I}(f) = \bar{I}(f) = I(f)$.

*Proof.* Suppose that to each $\epsilon > 0$ corresponds a pair of functions $g, h$ with the specified properties. Since $I(g)$ and $I(h)$ are finite, we infer that $-\infty < \underline{I}(f)$ and $\bar{I}(f) < +\infty$, whence both $\underline{I}(f)$ and $\bar{I}(f)$ are finite, by (3). From $I(h) < I(g) + \epsilon$ we infer that $\bar{I}(f) < \underline{I}(f) + \epsilon$, whence $\bar{I}(f) \leq \underline{I}(f)$. In view of (3), we see that $f \in \mathscr{L}$. We leave the proof of the other part of (a) to the reader.

Suppose now that $f \in \mathscr{F}^\circ$. Clearly, $\bar{I}(f) \leq I(f)$, by (1). Suppose $f_n \nearrow f$, where $f_n \in \mathscr{F}$. Then $I(f_n) \to I(f)$. Since $f_n \in \mathscr{F}_u$ and $f_n \leq f$, we infer that $I(f) \leq \bar{I}(f)$. In view of (3) we conclude that $\underline{I}(f) = \bar{I}(f) = I(f)$ if $f \in \mathscr{F}^\circ$. It then follows that $f$ is summable if and only if $I(f) < +\infty$.

The proof of (c) is analogous.

We emphasize that the value of $I(f)$ is finite when $f \in \mathscr{L}$. The class $\mathscr{L}$ includes the original vector lattice $\mathscr{F}$ and all elements of $\mathscr{F}^\circ$ and $\mathscr{F}_u$ for which $I(f)$ is finite; $\mathscr{L}$ may also contain elements which are not in $\mathscr{F}^\circ \cup \mathscr{F}_u$.

## PROPERTIES OF $I$ AND $\mathscr{L}$

The principal algebraic properties of the class $\mathscr{L}$ and of $I$ as a function on $\mathscr{L}$ to $R$ are summarized in the next theorem.

THEOREM 6–3 II. *Suppose* $f, g \in \mathscr{L}$ *and* $c \in R$. *Then:*

(a) $f + g \in \mathscr{L}$ *and* $I(f + g) = I(f) + I(g)$.

(b) $cf \in \mathscr{L}$ *and* $I(cf) = cI(f)$.

(c) $f \vee g$ *and* $f \wedge g$ *are in* $\mathscr{L}$.

(d) *If* $f \leq g$, *then* $I(f) \leq I(g)$.

(e) $|f| \in \mathscr{L}$ *and* $|I(f)| \leq I(|f|)$.

*Proof of* (a). Suppose $\epsilon > 0$. Choose $f_1$ and $g_1$ in $\mathscr{F}_u$ and $f_2, g_2$ in $\mathscr{F}^\circ$ so that $f_1 \leq f \leq f_2$, $g_1 \leq g \leq g_2$ and so that $I(f_1)$ and $I(f_2)$ each differ from $I(f)$ by less than $\epsilon/2$, while $I(g_1)$ and $I(g_2)$ each differ from $I(g)$ by less than $\epsilon/2$. Then $f_1 + g_1 \leq f + g \leq f_2 + g_2$. We know that $f_1 + g_1 \in \mathscr{F}_u$ and

$$I(f) + I(g) - \epsilon < I(f_1) + I(g_1) = I(f_1 + g_1).$$

Therefore $I(f) + I(g) - \epsilon < \underline{I}(f + g)$. Likewise, we see that $\bar{I}(f + g) < I(f) + I(g) + \epsilon$. Thus $\underline{I}(f + g)$ and $\bar{I}(f + g)$ are finite, and each differs from $I(f) + I(g)$ by less than $\epsilon$. Since $\epsilon$ is arbitrary we can draw the desired conclusion (see Theorem 6–3 I (a)).

*Proof of* (b). This is divided into three cases: $c = 0$, $c > 0$, $c < 0$. We leave the details to the reader.

*Proof of* (c). Choose $f_1, f_2, g_1, g_2$ as in the proof of (a). Then $f_1 \vee g_1 \leq f \vee g \leq f_2 \vee g_2$. Now,

$$f_2 \vee g_2 - (f_1 \vee g_1) \leq (f_2 - f_1) + (g_2 - g_1).$$

To see this, consider any $x$. Because of symmetry we may suppose $(f_2 \vee g_2)(x) = f_2(x)$ for this $x$. But $f_1(x) \leq (f_1 \vee g_1)(x)$ and $g_2(x) - g_1(x) \geq 0$, and so

$$(f_2 \vee g_2)(x) - (f_1 \vee g_1)(x) \leq f_2(x) - f_1(x) \leq [f_2(x) - f_1(x)] + [g_2(x) - g_1(x)].$$

Using the results of Section 6–2, we see that

$$I(f_2 \vee g_2) - I(f_1 \vee g_1) \leq I(f_2) - I(f_1) + I(g_2) - I(g_1) < 2\epsilon.$$

Since $f_2 \vee g_2 \in \mathscr{F}^\circ$ and $f_1 \vee g_1 \in \mathscr{F}_u$, it follows from Theorem 6–3 I (a) that $f \vee g \in \mathscr{L}$. The proof for $f \wedge g$ is similar.

*Proof of* (d). There exist functions $f_1 \in \mathscr{F}_u$, $g_1 \in \mathscr{F}^\circ$ such that $f_1 \leq f$, $g \leq g_1$. Since $f \leq g$, we see that $f_1 \leq g_1$, whence $I(f_1) \leq I(g_1)$. It follows from this, by letting $f_1$ vary, that $\underline{I}(f) \leq I(g_1)$. Then, letting $g_1$ vary, we see that $\underline{I}(f) \leq \bar{I}(g)$. Since $f$ and $g$ are summable, this is equivalent to (d).

*Proof of* (e). We know that $|f| = f^+ + f^-$, and that $f^+, f^-$ are in $\mathscr{L}$, by (c) (see (4), Section 6–1). Thus, (a) implies that $|f| \in \mathscr{L}$ and $I(|f|) = I(f^+) + I(f^-)$. But also, $f = f^+ - f^-$ and $I(f) = I(f^+) - I(f^-)$. We can then conclude that $|I(f)| \leq I(|f|)$, because $|a - b| \leq a + b$ if $a$ and $b$ are nonnegative real numbers. The inequality in (e) can also be deduced by (d) and the fact that $-f \leq |f| \leq f$.

The following example shows that the summing of an absolutely convergent series is an instance of an integration process.

*Example 1.* Let $X$, $\mathscr{F}$, and $I$ be as in Example 3, Section 6–2. It is not difficult to show that $f : X \to R^*$ is summable if and only if $f(n)$ is finite for each $n$ and

$$\sum_n |f(n)| < +\infty.$$

When $f$ is summable,

$$I(f) = \sum_{n=1}^{\infty} f(n).$$

## CONVERGENCE THEOREMS

We now have *the monotone convergence theorem*. The corresponding theorem in Chapter 5 is 5–5 I.

THEOREM 6–3 III. *Suppose $f : X \to R^*$ is given. Suppose $\{f_n\}$ is a sequence in $\mathscr{L}$ such that $f_n \nearrow f$ and* $\lim I(f_n) < +\infty$. *Then $f \in \mathscr{L}$ and $I(f_n) \to I(f)$. The same conclusions can be drawn if $f_n \in \mathscr{L}$, $f_n \searrow f$, and* $\lim I(f_n) > -\infty$.

*Proof.* Since $f_n \nearrow f$, $I(f_n)$ converges upward to a limit $A$; we are assuming $A < +\infty$. If $g \in \mathscr{F}_u$ and $g \leq f_n$, then also $g \leq f$. From this we can conclude that $\underline{I}(f_n) \leq \underline{I}(f)$. But we know that $\underline{I}(f_n) = I(f_n)$. We see then that $A \leq \underline{I}(f)$. To finish the proof that $f \in \mathscr{L}$ and that $A = I(f)$, it will suffice to show that $\bar{I}(f) \leq A$.

Now, suppose that $\epsilon > 0$, and choose $g_n \in \mathscr{F}_u$, $h_n \in \mathscr{F}^\circ$ in such a way that $g_n \leq f_n \leq h_n$ and

$$I(f_n) - \frac{\epsilon}{2^{n+1}} < I(g_n),\ I(h_n) < I(f_n) + \frac{\epsilon}{2^{n+1}}.$$

Then $I(h_n) - I(g_n) < \frac{\epsilon}{2^n}$. Now, let

$$p_n = g_1 \vee \cdots \vee g_n, \qquad q_n = h_1 \vee \cdots \vee h_n.$$

Observe that $p_n \in \mathscr{F}_u$ and $q_n \in \mathscr{F}^\circ$. The remainder of the proof is divided up into steps as follows.

*Step 1.* $q_n \leq q_{n+1}$. Therefore $q_n \nearrow q$, where, as shown by Theorem 6–2 III (d), $q \in \mathscr{F}^\circ$ and $I(q_n) \to I(q)$.

*Step 2.* $f_n \leq q_n$. Therefore, $f \leq q$. It follows that $\bar{I}(f) \leq I(q)$.

*Step 3.* For a given $x$, $q_n(x) = h_i(x)$ for some $i \leq n$. For this $i$ and $x$, $p_n(x) \geq g_i(x)$, so $q_n(x) - p_n(x) \leq h_i(x) - g_i(x)$. But $h_j(x) - g_j(x) \geq 0$, for every $j$ and $x$, and so we see that

$$q_n - p_n \leq (h_1 - g_1) + \cdots + (h_n - g_n).$$

It follows that

$$I(q_n) - I(p_n) \leq \sum_{j=1}^{n} [I(h_j) - I(g_j)] < \sum_{j=1}^{n} \frac{\epsilon}{2^j} < \epsilon.$$

Now, $p_n \leq f_n$ (because to each $x$ corresponds some $i \leq n$ such that $p_n(x) = g_i(x) \leq f_i(x) \leq f_n(x)$). Therefore $I(p_n) \leq I(f_n) \leq A$. It then follows that $I(q_n) < A + \epsilon$, whence $I(q) \leq A + \epsilon$, and so finally $I(q) \leq A$.

*Step 4.* From Steps 2 and 3 we have $\bar{I}(f) \leq A$.

If $\{f_n\}$ is a sequence in $\mathscr{L}$ such that $f_n \searrow f$ and $\lim I(f_n) > -\infty$, we observe that $-f_n \nearrow -f$ and $\lim I(-f_n) < +\infty$. Hence $-f$ is summable and $I(-f_n) \to I(-f)$, by what has been proved. The conclusion then follows from Theorem 6–3 II (b).

The next theorem deals with sequences which may not be monotonic.

THEOREM 6–3 IV. *Suppose $\{f_n\}$ is a sequence in $\mathscr{L}$. Let $p = \liminf f_n$, $q = \limsup f_n$. Then:*

(a) *If there exists $h \in \mathscr{L}$ such that $f_n \leq h$ for all $n$, and if $\limsup I(f_n) \neq -\infty$, then $q \in \mathscr{L}$ and $\limsup I(f_n) \leq I(q)$.*

(b) *If there exists $g \in \mathscr{L}$ such that $g \leq f_n$ for all $n$, and if $\liminf I(f_n) \neq +\infty$, then $p \in \mathscr{L}$ and $I(p) \leq \liminf I(f_n)$.*

(c) *If there exists $g \in \mathscr{L}$ such that $|f_n| \leq g$ for all $n$, and if $f : X \to R^*$ is such that $f_n \to f$, then $f \in \mathscr{L}$ and $I(f_n) \to I(f)$.*

*Proof of* (a). Let $F_{nj} = f_n \vee \cdots \vee f_{n+j}$, $F_n = \sup_{i \geq n} f_i$. We see readily that for fixed $n$ and increasing $j$, $F_{nj} \nearrow F_n$. Since $F_{nj} \leq h$, we have $I(F_{nj}) \leq I(h)$, and so $F_n \in \mathscr{L}$, by Theorem 6–3 III. Next, $F_n \searrow q$, by definition. We see that $f_n \leq F_n$, whence $I(f_n) \leq I(F_n)$. It now follows from the given hypothesis that $\lim I(F_n) > -\infty$. Therefore, again by Theorem 6–3 III, we see that $q \in \mathscr{L}$ and $I(F_n) \to I(q)$. The desired conclusion now follows, because $I(f_n) \leq I(F_n)$.

*Proof of* (b) is analogous to that of (a).

*Proof of* (c). Here we have $-g \leq f_n \leq g$, with $-g$ and $g$ in $\mathscr{L}$. We can now apply (a) and (b). But $f_n \to f$ implies $f = p = q$, and so it follows that $I(f_n) \to I(f)$.

*Remark.* In Chapter 5, Lebesgue's dominated convergence theorem (Theorem 5–5 IV) corresponds to (c), and Fatou's lemma (Theorem 5–5 V) corresponds to (b).

The next theorem will prove useful later on.

THEOREM 6–3 V. *Suppose $f \in \mathscr{L}$. Then there exist functions $g$, $h$ in $\mathscr{L}$ and sequences $\{g_n\}$ in $\mathscr{F}_u$, $\{h_n\}$ in $\mathscr{F}^\circ$ such that $g \le f \le h$, $I(g) = I(f) = I(h)$, and $g_n \nearrow g$, $h_n \searrow h$.*

*Proof.* Choose a sequence $\{f_n\}$ in $\mathscr{F}^\circ$ such that $f \le f_n$ and $I(f_n) \to I(f)$. Let $h_1 = f_1$, $h_n = h_{n-1} \wedge f_n$ if $n \ge 2$. Then $h_n \in \mathscr{F}^\circ$ and it is readily verified that $f \le h_n$ and $h_{n+1} \le h_n$. Hence there exists a function $h$ such that $h_n \searrow h$ and $f \le h$. Since $h_n \le f_n$, we see that $I(f) \le I(h_n) \le I(f_n)$. Therefore, $h \in \mathscr{L}$ and $I(h) = I(f)$.

The construction and proof as regards $g_n$ and $g$ is similar.

*Remark.* The function $h$ need not be identical with $f$. Later, after we have introduced the notion of sets of measure zero, we shall be able to say that $h(x) = f(x)$ except on a set of measure zero. Likewise, for $g$ and $f$.

## PROBLEMS

1. Finish the proof of Theorem 6–3 I (a) (that is, prove the "only if" part of the assertion).
2. Prove Theorem 6–3 I (c).
3. Prove Theorem 6–3 II (b).
4. Show that $I(f \vee g) + I(f \wedge g) = I(f) + I(g)$ if $f, g \in \mathscr{L}$.
5. Show that $\mathscr{L} = \mathscr{F}$ in the situation of Example 4, Section 6–2.
6. Work out in detail the claim made about $\mathscr{L}$ and $I$ in Example 1.
7. Take $X$ and $\mathscr{F}$ as in Example 3, Section 6–2, but define the elementary integral $I$ on $\mathscr{F}$ by $I(f) = \sum_n \frac{f(n)}{n}$. Find $\mathscr{F}^\circ$, $\mathscr{F}_u$, $\mathscr{L}$, and the value of $f$ when $f \in \mathscr{L}$.
8. Let $X = (0, a]$, where $0 < a < +\infty$. Let $\mathscr{F}$ consist of all functions of the form $f(x) = cx$, $c \in R$. Define $I(f) = \frac{1}{2} a^2 c$. Show that this provides an example of the theory in which $\mathscr{L} = \mathscr{F}$. What is $\mathscr{F}^\circ$?
9. Let $\mathscr{G}$ be the class of all those $f \in \mathscr{L}$ such that all the values of $f$ are finite. Write $\mathscr{L} = \mathscr{L}(\mathscr{F}, I)$ to show the dependence of $\mathscr{L}$ on $\mathscr{F}$ and $I$. Define $J(f) = I(f)$ if $f \in \mathscr{G}$. Note that $\mathscr{G}$ is a vector lattice and that $J$ is an elementary integral on $\mathscr{G}$. Proceed from $\mathscr{G}$ and $J$ as we did from $\mathscr{F}$ and $I$, obtaining $\mathscr{G}^\circ$, $\mathscr{G}_u$, and $\mathscr{L}(\mathscr{G}, J)$. Prove that $\mathscr{L}(\mathscr{G}, J) = \mathscr{L}(\mathscr{F}, I)$ and that $J(f) = I(f)$ if $f \in \mathscr{L}(\mathscr{G}, J)$.

## 6–4 Sets of measure zero

In this section we introduce the notion of a set in $X$ of measure zero. This can be done without the necessity of developing a theory of measure. One of the very important consequences of the availability of the notion of a set of measure zero is the fact that we can use the class $\mathscr{L}$ to construct a Banach space $L$, each element of which is represented by an element $f \in \mathscr{L}$; the norm of this element is $I(|f|)$. Two different functions $f_1, f_2$ which represent the same element of $L$ are such that $I(|f_1 - f_2|) = 0$. This happens if and only if the set $\{x : f_1(x) \ne f_2(x)\}$ is a set of measure zero.

If $E \subset X$, we call *$E$ a set of measure zero* (relative to the elementary integral $I$) if the characteristic function $\chi_E$ is summable and $I(\chi_E) = 0$. For the definition of $\chi_E$ see (9) in Section 5–0. We shall denote the class of all sets of measure zero by **SZ**.

A number of important facts about sets of measure zero are contained in the following theorem.

THEOERM 6–4 I. (a) *If $E \in$ **SZ** and $F \subset E$, then $F \in$ **SZ**.* (b) $\varnothing \in$ **SZ**. (c) *A countable union of sets of measure zero is a set of measure zero.* (d) *Suppose $E \subset X$, and let*

*$f = +\infty \cdot \chi_E$ (that is, $f(x) = +\infty$ if $x \in E$, $f(x) = 0$ if $x \in X - E$). Then $f \in \mathscr{L}$ if and only if $E \in \mathbf{SZ}$, and in this case $I(f) = 0$.* (e) *If $g \in \mathscr{L}$, then $\{x : |g(x)| = +\infty\} \in \mathbf{SZ}$.*

*Proof of* (a). Since $0 \in \mathscr{F}_u$, $0 \leq \chi_F$, and $I(0) = 0$, we see that $0 \leq \underline{I}(\chi_F)$. Suppose $\epsilon > 0$. Since $E \in \mathbf{SZ}$, there exists $h \in \mathscr{F}^\circ$ such that $\chi_E \leq h$ and $I(h) < \epsilon$. But $\chi_F \leq \chi_E$. Hence $\chi_F \leq h$, and it follows that $\bar{I}(\chi_F) < \epsilon$. It now follows that $\chi_F \in \mathscr{L}$ and $I(\chi_F) = 0$.

*Proof of* (b). A consequence of (a).

*Proof of* (c). Suppose $E_n \in \mathbf{SZ}$, $n = 1, 2, \ldots$. Let $E = \bigcup_n E_n$, $F_n = E_1 \cup \cdots \cup E_n$. We see that $\chi_{F_n} = \chi_{E_1} \vee \cdots \vee \chi_{E_n}$, whence $\chi_{F_n} \in \mathscr{L}$. Also, $0 \leq \chi_{F_n} \leq \chi_{E_1} + \cdots + \chi_{E_n}$, so that $0 \leq I(\chi_{F_n}) \leq I(\chi_{E_1}) + \cdots + I(\chi_{E_n}) = 0$. Since $\chi_{F_n} \nearrow \chi_E$, we can conclude from Theorem 6–3 III that $E \in \mathbf{SZ}$.

*Proof of* (d). We see that $n\chi_E \nearrow f$. If $E \in \mathbf{SZ}$, we have $I(n\chi_E) = nI(\chi_E) = 0$. Then $f \in \mathscr{L}$ and $I(f) = 0$, by the monotone convergence theorem. On the other hand, if we assume $f \in \mathscr{L}$, we see that $f = 2f$, $I(f) = 2I(f)$, and $I(f) = 0$. Since $0 \leq \chi_E \leq f$, we can then deduce as in the proof of (a) that $\chi_E \in \mathscr{L}$ and $I(\chi_E) = 0$.

*Proof of* (e). Let $E = \{x : |g(x)| = +\infty\}$, and let $h = +\infty \cdot \chi_E$. We see that $\frac{1}{n}|g| \searrow h$ and $I\left(\frac{1}{n}|g|\right) = \frac{1}{n}I(|g|) \to 0$. Applying Theorem 6–3 III, we conclude that $h \in \mathscr{L}$ and $I(h) = 0$. It follows from (d) that $E \in \mathbf{SZ}$.

## NULL FUNCTIONS

A function $f : X \to R^*$ is called a *null function* if $|f| \in \mathscr{L}$ and $I(|f|) = 0$.

THEOREM 6–4 II. (a) *If $f$ is a null function, any function $g$ such that $|g| \leq |f|$ is also a null function.*

(b) *If $f$ and $g$ are null functions and $c \in R$, $cf$, and $f + g$ are null functions.*

(c) *$f$ is a null function if and only if the set $\{x : f(x) \neq 0\}$ is of measure zero.*

(d) *If $\{f_n\}$ is a sequence of null functions and if $f_n \to f$, then $f$ is a null function.*

*Proofs of* (a) *and* (b). These are left to the reader.

*Proof of* (c). Let $E = \{x : f(x) \neq 0\}$. It is clear that $0 \leq |f| \leq +\infty \cdot \chi_E$. If $E \in \mathbf{SZ}$, we see by (a) and Theorem 6–4 I (d) that $f$ is a null function. Suppose, on the other hand, that $f$ is a null function. Let $E_n = \left\{x : |f(x)| \geq \frac{1}{n}\right\}$. Observe that $0 \leq \frac{1}{n}\chi_{E_n} \leq |f|$ and $E = \bigcup_n E_n$. It follows by (a), (b) and Theorem 6–4 I (c) that $E \in \mathbf{SZ}$.

*Proof of* (d). Define $E$ as in the proof of (c), and let $F_n = \{x : f_n(x) \neq 0\}$. Note that $E \subset \bigcup_n F_n$. The conclusion $E \in \mathbf{SZ}$ follows from (c) applied to each $f_n$, along with Theorem 6–4 I (a) and (c).

## ALMOST EVERYWHERE EQUALITY OF FUNCTIONS

Following customary terminology, if $f : X \to R^*$ and $g : X \to R^*$ are given, we say that $f(x) = g(x)$ *almost everywhere* if $\{x : f(x) \neq g(x)\}$ is a set of measure zero. The phrase "almost everywhere" is regularly abbreviated as "a.e." Since $\{x : f(x) \neq g(x)\} = \{x : f(x) - g(x) \neq 0\}$, we see by Theorem 6–4 II (c) that $f(x) = g(x)$ a.e. if and only if $f - g$ is a null function.

The "almost everywhere" notion is applied in other situations as well. Thus, we may have $f_n(x) \to f(x)$ a.e., which means that the set of those $x$'s for which $f_n(x) \to f(x)$ is false is a set of measure zero. Likewise, we may have $f(x) \leq g(x)$ a.e., and so on.

THEOREM 6–4 III. *If $f(x) = g(x)$ a.e., and if $g \in \mathscr{L}$, then $f \in \mathscr{L}$ and $I(f) = I(g)$.*

*Proof.* Let $E = \{x : f(x) \neq g(x)\}$ and let $f_0 = +\infty \cdot \chi_E$. Then $f_0 \in \mathscr{L}$ and $I(f_0) = 0$. If $\epsilon > 0$, there exist functions $h_1, h_2$ in $\mathscr{F}^\circ$ such that $g \leq h_1$, $0 \leq f_0 \leq h_2$, $I(h_1) < I(g) + \epsilon$, $I(h_2) < \epsilon$. Then $h_1 + h_2 \in \mathscr{F}^\circ$ and $I(h_1 + h_2) < I(g) + 2\epsilon$. By considering the cases $x \in E$, $x \notin E$ separately we can see that $f \leq h_1 + h_2$. It follows that $\bar{I}(f) < I(g) + 2\epsilon$, whence $\bar{I}(f) \leq I(g)$. By a similar argument, using the summability of $-f_0$, we can show that $\underline{I}(f) \geq I(g)$. The desired conclusion now follows.

Theorem 6–4 III makes it possible to weaken the assumptions in certain of the earlier theorems and yet retain all the conclusions. For example, in Theorem 6–3 III the hypothesis $f_n \nearrow f$ may be weakened to read $f_n(x) \nearrow f(x)$ a.e. The proof is reduced to the previous case with the aid of the following definitions: Let $E$ be the set of measure zero on which $f_n(x) \nearrow f(x)$ is false. Define $g_n(x) = f_n(x)$ and $g(x) = f(x)$ if $x \in X - E$, $g_n(x) = g(x) = 0$ if $x \in E$. Then $g_n \nearrow g$. Then $g_n(x) = f_n(x)$ a.e., and $g(x) = f(x)$ a.e. From Theorem 6–4 III and the original form of Theorem 6–3 III, as applied to $\{g_n\}$ and $g$, we conclude that $f \in \mathscr{L}$ and $I(f_n) \to I(f)$.

A similar change may be made in the dominated convergence theorem (Theorem 6–3 IV (c)); see Problem 2.

### THE BANACH SPACE $L$

Let us write $f \sim g$ if $f$ and $g$ are in $\mathscr{L}$ and $f(x) = g(x)$ a.e. Then $\sim$ is an equivalence relation in $\mathscr{L}$, as we can see from Theorem 6–4 I (a). Therefore, $\mathscr{L}$ is divided into equivalence classes by this relation. Let $[f]$ denote the equivalence class which contains $f$. If $f \in \mathscr{L}$ and if we define $g$ by setting $g(x) = f(x)$ when $f(x)$ is finite and $g(x) = 0$ when $f(x)$ is infinite, we see by Theorems 6–4 I (e) and 6–4 III that $g \in \mathscr{L}$ and $g \sim f$. Hence, in discussing $[f]$, we may always suppose that $f$ is chosen so that all of the values of $f$ are finite.

We can construct a normed linear space with elements $[f]$. For any $f$ and $g$ in $\mathscr{L}$ and any real $c$ we define

$$[f] + [g] = [f + g], \tag{1}$$

$$c[f] = [cf], \tag{2}$$

$$\|[f]\| = I(|f|). \tag{3}$$

It is easy to verify that these are unambiguous definitions. We must know, for instance, that if $f \sim f_1$ and $g \sim g_1$, then $[f + g] = [f_1 + g_1]$ and $I(|f|) = I(|f_1|)$.

The equivalence class containing the zero function consists of all the null functions. It is the zero element of the normed linear space we are constructing.

We leave it for the reader to verify that we do in this way obtain a normed linear space with norm given by (3). We shall denote the space by $L$.

As we shall see, the space $L$ is complete. In proving this, we obtain certain detailed results which contain more information than the mere assertion that $L$ is complete. We present these results in the following theorem.

THEOREM 6–4 IV. *Let $\{f_n\}$ be a sequence in $\mathscr{L}$ such that $I(|f_n - f_m|) \to 0$ as $m \to \infty$ and $n \to \infty$. Then there exist functions $f$ and $h$ in $\mathscr{L}$ and a subsequence $\{g_n\}$ of $\{f_n\}$ such that $I(|f_n - f|) \to 0$, while, except on a certain set $E$ of measure zero we have $g_n(x) \to f(x)$ and $|g_n(x)| \le h(x)$ for each $n$. In particular, the space $L$ is complete.*

*Proof.* As a typographical convenience we shall use the notation

$$\|f\| = I(|f|) \tag{4}$$

when $f \in \mathscr{L}$; this is suggested by (3), but we wish to deal with $f$ rather than with $[f]$.

We first establish a preliminary result: If $\{g_n\}$ is a sequence in $\mathscr{L}$ such that $g_n \ge 0$ and $\sum_1^\infty \|g_n\| < +\infty$, then the series $\sum_1^\infty g_n$ defines a function in $\mathscr{L}$, and $\|\sum_1^\infty g_n\| \le \sum_1^\infty \|g_n\|$. The proof is by a direct application of the monotone convergence theorem to the sequence $\{h_n\}$, where $h_n = g_1 + \cdots + g_n$.

Coming now to the theorem, we choose $N_1$ so that $\|f_n - f_{N_1}\| < 2^{-1}$, if $n \ge N_1$. Then we choose $N_2 > N_1$ so that $\|f_n - f_{N_2}\| < 2^{-2}$, if $n \ge N_2$. In general we have $N_k > N_{k-1}$ and $\|f_n - f_{N_k}\| < 2^{-k}$, if $n \ge N_k$. Now, let $g_k = f_{N_k}$. Observe that $\|g_{n+1} - g_n\| < 2^{-n}$. Let $h_n = \sum_{i \ge n} |g_{i+1} - g_i|$. The preliminary result shows that $h_n \in \mathscr{L}$ and $\|h_n\| \le 2^{1-n}$. Let $A_n = \{x : h_n(x) = +\infty\}$, $B_n = \{x : |g_n(x)| = +\infty\}$, $E = \bigcup_n (A_n \cup B_n)$. Then $E$ is a set of measure zero. Observe that

$$h_n = |g_{n+1} - g_n| + h_{n+1}, \; h_n \ge h_{n+1}. \tag{5}$$

On the set $X - E$ we have

$$h_{n+1}(x) - h_n(x) = -|g_{n+1}(x) - g_n(x)| \le g_{n+1}(x) - g_n(x),$$

and thus also

$$g_n(x) - h_n(x) \le g_{n+1}(x) - h_{n+1}(x). \tag{6}$$

Likewise, on $X - E$,

$$g_{n+1}(x) - g_n(x) \le |g_{n+1}(x) - g_n(x)| = h_n(x) - h_{n+1}(x),$$

so that

$$g_{n+1}(x) + h_{n+1}(x) \le g_n(x) + h_n(x). \tag{7}$$

Let us define

$$G_n(x) = \begin{cases} g_n(x) - h_n(x) & \text{if } x \in X - E \\ 0 & \text{if } x \in E, \end{cases}$$

$$H_n(x) = \begin{cases} g_n(x) + h_n(x) & \text{if } x \in X - E \\ 0 & \text{if } x \in E. \end{cases}$$

Then $G_n$ and $H_n$ are in $\mathscr{L}$, by Theorem 6–4 III. Since $h_n \ge 0$, we see that $G_n \le H_n$. By (6) and (7) we see that $G_n \le G_{n+1}$ and $H_{n+1} \le H_n$. Hence, $G_n \le H_1$. Let $f(x) = \lim G_n(x)$. By Theorem 6–3 III we see that $f \in \mathscr{L}$. Since $G_n \le H_m$ if $n \ge m$, we see that $G_m \le f \le H_m$ for every $m$. In view of the definitions of $G_n$ and $H_n$ it follows that

$$-h_n(x) \le f(x) - g_n(x) \le h_n(x) \tag{8}$$

if $x \in X - E$. Thus $|f(x) - g_n(x)| \le h_n(x)$ a.e., and it follows that

$$\|f - g_n\| \le \|h_n\| < 2^{1-n}. \tag{9}$$

From this it is easy to conclude that $\|f - f_n\| \to 0$, for

$$\|f - f_n\| \le \|f - g_i\| + \|g_i - f_n\|$$
$$< 2^{1-n} + 2^{-i} \quad \text{if} \quad n \ge N_i.$$

Now, $h_n(x)$ is finite when $x \in X - E$. The definition of the $h_n$'s then shows that we must have $h_n(x) \to 0$ if $x \in X - E$. From (8) we therefore have $g_n(x) \to f(x)$ if $x \in X - E$.

For the last point in the proof, we observe from (8) that

$$f(x) - h_n(x) \le g_n(x) \le f(x) + h_n(x)$$

and therefore also

$$f(x) - h_1(x) \le g_n(x) \le f(x) + h_1(x)$$

if $x \in X - E$. If we define $h = |f + h_1| \vee |f - h_1|$, we therefore have $h \in \mathscr{L}$ and $|g_n(x)| \le h(x)$ a.e. This completes the proof.

For convenience we record the following easy consequence of the foregoing theorem:

THEOREM 6–4 V. *If $g \in \mathscr{L}$ and if $\{f_n\}$ is a sequence in $\mathscr{L}$ such that $\|f_n - g\| \to 0$, then $\{f_n\}$ contains a subsequence $\{g_n\}$ such that $g_n(x) \to g(x)$ a.e.*

*Proof.* Because $\|f_n - f_m\| \le \|f_n - g\| + \|g - f_m\|$, the conditions of Theorem 6–4 IV are fulfilled. If $f$ and $g_n$ are as in this preceding theorem, we have

$$\|f - g\| \le \|f - f_n\| + \|f_n - g\|,$$

and therefore $\|f - g\| = 0$. This implies $f(x) = g(x)$ a.e. We know that $g_n(x) \to f(x)$ a.e. Hence, $g_n(x) \to g(x)$ a.e.

The next theorem shows that each element of $\mathscr{L}$ can be approximated as closely as we please, in the sense of the norm, by an element of $\mathscr{F}$. Or, to put the matter in another way, suppose $F$ is the class of all $[f]$ as $f$ varies over $\mathscr{F}$. Then $F$ is dense in $L$.

THEOREM 6–4 VI. *If $f \in \mathscr{L}$ and $\epsilon > 0$, there exists an element $h \in \mathscr{F}$ such that $\|f - h\| < \epsilon$. If $f \ge 0$, $h$ may be chosen so that $h \ge 0$.*

*Proof.* Suppose at first that $f \ge 0$. There exists $g \in \mathscr{F}^\circ$ such that $f \le g$ and $I(g) < I(f) + \epsilon/2$. There also exists a sequence $\{h_n\}$ in $\mathscr{F}$ such that $h_n \nearrow g$ and $I(h_n) \to I(g)$; therefore, $0 \le I(g) - I(h_n) < \epsilon/2$ if $n$ is sufficiently large. We may assume $h_n \ge 0$; otherwise, we replace $h_n$ by $0 \vee h_n$. Then $\|f - g\| = I(g - f) < \epsilon/2$ and $\|g - h_n\| = I(g - h_n) < \epsilon/2$. Hence,

$$\|f - h_n\| \le \|f - g\| + \|g - h_n\| < \epsilon.$$

This proves the theorem for the case in which $f \ge 0$. For the general case we write $f = f^+ - f^-$ and apply what we have just learned to $f^+$ and $f^-$. If $g$ and $h$ are in $\mathscr{F}$ and $\|f^+ - g\| < \epsilon/2$, $\|f^- - h\| < \epsilon/2$, then $\|f - (g - h)\| < \epsilon$. This finishes the proof.

## PROBLEMS

1. Prove (a) and (b) in Theorem 6–4 II.
2. Prove the following modification of Theorem 6–3 IV(c): *Suppose $f_n$, $f$, and $g$ are functions such that $f_n$ and $g$ are in $\mathscr{L}$, $|f_n(x)| \le g(x)$ a.e. for each $n$, and $f_n(x) \to f(x)$ a.e. Then $f \in \mathscr{L}$ and $I(f_n) \to I(f)$.*

3. Give an alternative proof of Theorem 6–4 IV, starting as follows: Let $h_1 = |g_1|$, and define

$$h_n = |g_1| + \sum_{i \le n-1} |g_{i+1} - g_i|,$$

if $n \geq 2$. Show that, except on a certain set of measure zero,

$$|g_n(x) - g_m(x)| \leq h_n(x) - h_m(x),$$

if $2 \leq m < n$.

## 6–5 Measurable functions and measurable sets

A function $f: X \to R^*$ is called *measurable* (in the context of this chapter) if the function $g \vee (f \wedge h)$ is summable for every choice of summable functions $g$, $h$ such that $g \leq 0 \leq h$. The meaning of this definition is easier to grasp if one observes that, with the notation $F = g \vee (f \wedge h)$,

$$(1) \qquad F(x) = \begin{cases} f(x) & \text{if } g(x) \leq f(x) \leq h(x) \\ h(x) & \text{if } h(x) < f(x) \\ g(x) & \text{if } f(x) < g(x). \end{cases}$$

From this we can see that $g \vee (f \wedge h) = (g \vee f) \wedge h$ and that $g \leq F \leq h$.

We denote the class of measurable functions by $\mathcal{M}$. Some important facts about $\mathcal{M}$ and $\mathcal{L}$ are given in the following theorem.

THEOREM 6–5 I. *(a) If $f_1(x) = f_2(x)$ a.e. and if $f_1 \in \mathcal{M}$, then $f_2 \in \mathcal{M}$. (b) If $f \in \mathcal{L}$, then $f \in \mathcal{M}$. (c) If $f \in \mathcal{M}$ and $h \in \mathcal{L}$, and if $|f| \leq h$, then $f \in \mathcal{L}$. (d) If $f_n \in \mathcal{M}$ and $f_n(x) \to f(x)$ a.e., then $f \in \mathcal{M}$.*

*Proofs of* (a) *and* (b) are left to the reader.

*Proof of* (c). With $f$ and $h$ as given we see that $-h \leq f \leq h$, and so $(-h) \vee (f \wedge h) = f$, which implies that $f \in \mathcal{L}$, by the definition of measurability.

*Proof of* (d). Let $F_n = g \vee (f_n \wedge h)$, $F = g \vee (f \wedge h)$, where $g$ and $h$ are arbitrary elements of $\mathcal{L}$ such that $g \leq 0 \leq h$. Then $F_n(x) \to F(x)$ a.e. This is true because, if $\{a_n\}$ is a sequence in $R^*$ such that $a_n \to a$, then $a_n \wedge b \to a \wedge b$ and $a_n \vee b \to a \vee b$ for each $b$ in $R^*$. Now, $g \leq F_n \leq h$, so $|F_n| \leq (-g) \vee h$. It then follows that $F$ is summable; for this we use Theorem 6–3 IV (c), as extended to allow for convergence a.e. (See the remarks following the proof of Theorem 6–4 III.)

The next theorem shows that simple algebraic operations on elements of $\mathcal{M}$ lead to elements of $\mathcal{M}$.

THEOREM 6–5 II. *Suppose that $f, f_1, f_2 \in \mathcal{M}$ and $c \in R$. Then:* (a) $cf_1 \in \mathcal{M}$. (b) $f_1 \wedge f_2$ *and* $f_1 \vee f_2$ *are in* $\mathcal{M}$. (c) $f^+$ *and* $f^-$ *are in* $\mathcal{M}$. (d) $f_1 + f_2 \in \mathcal{M}$.

*Proof of* (a). If $g, h \in \mathcal{L}$ and $g \leq 0 \leq h$, it may be verified directly that

$$(2) \qquad g \vee (cf_1 \wedge h) = c\left[\frac{g}{c} \vee \left(f_1 \wedge \frac{h}{c}\right)\right] \quad \text{if } c > 0,$$

$$(3) \qquad g \vee (cf_1 \wedge h) = c\left[\frac{h}{c} \vee \left(f_1 \wedge \frac{g}{c}\right)\right] \quad \text{if } c < 0.$$

It follows that $cf_1 \in \mathcal{M}$ if $f_1 \in \mathcal{M}$ and $c \neq 0$. The result is of course trivial if $c = 0$.

*Proof of* (b). When $g \leq 0 \leq h$, we have the identity

$$(4) \qquad [g \vee (f_1 \wedge f_2)] \wedge h = [(g \vee f_1) \wedge h] \wedge [(g \vee f_2) \wedge h].$$

Once (4) has been established, we see from Theorem 6–3 II (c) that $f_1 \wedge f_2 \in \mathscr{M}$ if $f_1$ and $f_2$ are in $\mathscr{M}$. To see that $f_1 \vee f_2$ is in $\mathscr{M}$, we use (a) along with (5), Section 6–1.

Among other possibilities for ways of verifying (4) there is the following. For a given $x$ one may by symmetry assume that $f_1(x) \leq f_2(x)$. There are then four cases to consider: $h(x) \leq f_1(x)$, $f_2(x) \leq g(x)$, the case in which $f_1(x) < h(x) \leq f_2(x)$, and the case in which $g(x) < f_2(x) < h(x)$. It is easy to verify the identity (4) for the given $x$ in each case.

*Proof of* (c). Use (3) from Section 6–1, and (b).

*Proof of* (d). We suppose $g, h \in \mathscr{L}$, $g \leq 0 \leq h$, and $f_1, f_2 \in \mathscr{M}$. Let $p_n = n(h - g)$, $F_{n1} = (-p_n) \vee (f_1 \wedge p_n)$, $F_{n2} = (-p_n) \vee (f_2 \wedge p_n)$, $F_n = F_{n1} + F_{n2}$. Observe that $0 \leq p_n$ and $p_n \in \mathscr{L}$. It then follows that $F_{n1}$ and $F_{n2}$ are in $\mathscr{L}$, and hence $F_n \in \mathscr{L}$, by Theorem 6–3 II (a). Hence, also, $g \vee (F_n \wedge h) \in \mathscr{L}$, by Theorem 6–3 II (c). Observe that $g \leq g \vee (F_n \wedge h) \leq h$, and hence that $|g \vee (F_n \wedge h)| \leq (-g) \vee h$. We shall see that

$$(5) \qquad g \vee (F_n \wedge h) \to g \vee [(f_1 + f_2) \wedge h].$$

It will then follow by Theorem 6–3 IV (c) that $g \vee [(f_1 + f_2) \wedge h] \in \mathscr{L}$, and hence that $f_1 + f_2 \in \mathscr{M}$.

The verification of (5) is a trifle tedious. Let $f = f_1 + f_2$. If $x$ is such that $h(x) - g(x) = 0$, then $h(x) = g(x) = 0$ (because $g \leq 0 \leq h$), and both $g \vee (F_n \wedge h)$ and $g \vee (f \wedge h)$ have the value 0 at $x$; hence this case is disposed of. If $x$ is such that $h(x) - g(x) > 0$, we see that $p_n(x) \to +\infty$. It is then easy to see that $F_{n1}(x) = f_1(x)$ for sufficiently large values of $n$ if $f_1(x)$ is finite, while $F_{n1}(x) = p_n(x)$ if $f_1(x) = +\infty$ and $F_{n1}(x) = -p_n(x)$ if $f_1(x) = -\infty$. Likewise for $F_{n2}$. These observations enable us to compute $F_n(x)$ and to proceed with the verification. Details are left to the reader.

## MEASURABLE SETS

Suppose $E \subset X$. We say that $E$ is a *measurable set* if $\chi_E \in \mathscr{M}$. Let **S** denote the class of all measurable sets. Concerning **S** we first prove:

THEOREM 6–5 III. *The family* **S** *of all measurable sets is a* $\sigma$*-ring.*

*Proof.* To see that $\varnothing \in$ **S**, we observe that the characteristic function of $\varnothing$ is the zero function, which is summable, and therefore measurable. Next, we show that **S** is a ring. For ease in printing let $f_i = \chi_{E_i}$. Suppose $E_1, E_2 \in$ **S**. It is easy to verify that

$$\chi_{E_1 \cup E_2} = f_1 \vee f_2,$$

$$\chi_{E_1 \cap E_2} = f_1 \wedge f_2,$$

$$\chi_{E_1 - E_2} = f_1 - (f_1 \wedge f_2).$$

It is then clear from Theorem 6–5 II that **S** is a ring. To see that **S** is a $\sigma$-ring, suppose $E_1, E_2, \ldots$ are in **S**, and let

$$G_n = E_1 \cup \cdots \cup E_n, \qquad G = \bigcup_{n=1}^{\infty} E_n.$$

Also, let $g_n = \chi_{G_n}, g = \chi_G$. It is easy to see that $g_n \nearrow g$. But $G_n \in \mathbf{S}$, because $\mathbf{S}$ is a ring, and therefore $g_n \in \mathscr{M}$. It follows from Theorem 6–5 I (d) that $g \in \mathscr{M}$, whence $G \in S$.

At this point we are unable to say anything more specific about **S**. As we shall see in Section 6–7, $X$ itself need not belong to **S**. There is nothing in the general situation to guarantee that **S** contains enough sets to be very interesting. It can even happen that $\varnothing$ is the only member of **S**.

### THE MEASURE INDUCED BY $I$

We shall now show that it is possible to use the integral $I$ to define a measure on **S**. We define a function $\mu : \mathbf{S} \to R^*$ as follows:

(6)
$$\mu(E) = \begin{cases} I(\chi_E) & \text{if } \chi_E \in \mathscr{L} \\ +\infty & \text{if } \chi_E \in \mathscr{M} - \mathscr{L}. \end{cases}$$

We see by referring back to Section 6–4 that the class **SZ** of sets of measure zero is a subset of **S**, and that $\mu(E) = 0$ if and only if $E \in \mathbf{SZ}$. We are going to prove that $\mu$ is a measure; hence our earlier terminology concerning sets of measure zero is consistent with the present situation.

THEOREM 6–5 IV. *The function $\mu$ defined in* (6) *is a measure on* **S**. *Moreover, it is a complete measure.*

*Proof.* Obviously, all the values of $\mu$ are nonnegative. It is clear that $\mu(\varnothing) = 0$, for $I(\chi_\varnothing) = I(0) = 0$. Suppose that $\{E_n\}$ is a countable disjoint family of members of $S$. Let us use the notations $f_i, G_n, G, g_n, g$ as in the proof of Theorem 6–5 III.

First, we establish that $\mu$ is finitely additive. It is sufficient to show that $\mu(G_2) = \mu(E_1) + \mu(E_2)$. Because $E_1 \cap E_2 = \varnothing$, we see that $g_2 = f_1 + f_2$. If $f_1$ and $f_2$ are in $\mathscr{L}$, so is their sum, and $I(g_2) = I(f_1) + I(f_2)$, by Theorem 6–3 II (a). Thus $\mu(G_2) = \mu(E_1) + \mu(E_2)$ in this case. If $g_2$ is in $\mathscr{L}$, so are both $f_1$ and $f_2$. For, all three functions are in $\mathscr{M}$, $0 \leq f_1 \leq g_2$, $0 \leq f_2 \leq g_2$, and we can use Theorem 6–5 I (c). We see then that $\mu(G_2) = +\infty$ if and only if at least one of the values $\mu(E_1), \mu(E_2)$ is $+\infty$; in this case, of course, $\mu(G_2) = \mu(E_1) + \mu(E_2)$.

To complete the proof of the theorem we must now show that

$$\mu(G) = \sum_{n=1}^{\infty} \mu(E_n).$$

Because $\mu$ is known to be finitely additive, this is equivalent to showing that

(7)
$$\mu(G_n) \to \mu(G).$$

Now, as we saw in the proof of Theorem 6–5 III, $g_n \nearrow g$. By definition, $\mu(G) < +\infty$ and $\mu(G) = I(g)$ if and only if $g \in \mathscr{L}$; likewise for $G_n$ and $g_n$ in place of $G$ and $g$. Since $\mu$ is non-negative and finitely additive, it is monotone; hence, $\mu(G_n) \leq \mu(G_{n+1})$. There are now two cases. If $\mu(G)$ is finite, $g$ and $g_n$ are in $\mathscr{L}$, and we obtain (7) from the monotone convergence theorem for integrals (Theorem 6–3 III). If $\mu(G) = +\infty$, $g$ is not in $\mathscr{L}$. From the monotone convergence theorem we conclude either that some $g_n$ is not in $\mathscr{L}$ (whence $\mu(G_n) = +\infty$ for this and all succeeding values of $n$), or that every $g_n$ is in $\mathscr{L}$, but $I(g_n) = \mu(G_n) \to +\infty$. Thus (7) is valid in this second case also. This completes the proof.

*Example.* Let $X, \mathscr{F}$ and $I$ be as in Example 3, Section 6–2 and Example 1, Section 6–3. It is easy to see that $\mathscr{M}$ consists of all functions on $X$ to $R^*$ and that **S** consists of all subsets of $X$. If $E \subset X$, $\mu(E)$ is the number of elements in $E$.

## PROBLEMS

1. Prove parts (a) and (b) of Theorem 6–5 I.

2. Assuming that $\{f_n\}$ is a sequence in $\mathscr{M}$, prove that $\sup_n f_n$ and $\inf_n f_n$ are in $\mathscr{M}$, and also that $\limsup f_n$ and $\liminf f_n$ are in $\mathscr{M}$.

3. (a) If $f \in \mathscr{M}$, $g \in \mathscr{L}$, $h \in \mathscr{L}$, and $g \leq f \leq h$, prove that $f \in \mathscr{L}$.

(b) If $f \in \mathscr{M}$, $g \in \mathscr{L}$, and $h \in \mathscr{L}$, show that $g \vee (f \wedge h) \in \mathscr{L}$ (without assuming $g \leq 0 \leq h$). [*Hint.* Let $g_1 = 0 \wedge g$, $h_1 = 0 \vee h$, and show that $g_1 \wedge h \leq g \vee (f \wedge h) \leq g \vee h_1$.]

4. Suppose there exists a function $g \in \mathscr{L}$ such that $0 < g(x) \leq 1$ for each $x$. Then, if $f$ is a given element of $\mathscr{M}$, prove that there exists a sequence $\{f_n\}$ in $\mathscr{L}$ such that $|f_n(x)| \leq n$ for each $x$ and each $n$, and such that $f_n \to f$. If $f \geq 0$, show that it can also be arranged to have $0 \leq f_n \leq f_{n+1}$ for each $n$. [*Suggestion.* Consider the functions $(-ng) \vee (f \wedge ng)$.]

5. The following problem is designed to show one aspect of a connection between the ideas developed in Chapter 5 and the approach to integration and measure used in the present chapter. Let $(X, \mathbf{S}, \mu)$ be an arbitrary measure space, as defined in Section 5–0. Let $\mathscr{F}$ be the class of all simple functions $f$ such that $\mu[N(f)] < +\infty$. The term "simple function" is used as in Section 5–1, and $N(f) = \{x : f(x) \neq 0\}$. An element of **S** is referred to as a $\mu$-measurable set. A function measurable with respect to **S** is called $\mu$-measurable. If it is summable in the sense of Section 5–4 we call it $\mu$-summable.

(a) Show that $\mathscr{F}$ is a vector lattice.

(b) If $f \in \mathscr{F}$ and if $E_1, \ldots, E_n$ is a finite disjoint collection of $\mu$-measurable sets of finite measure such that $f = \sum_i c_i \chi_{E_i}$, where $c_1, \ldots, c_n$ are in $R$, show that $I(f) = \sum_i c_i \mu(E_i)$ defines $I : \mathscr{F} \to R$ unambiguously, and that $I$ is an elementary integral on $\mathscr{F}$. Suggestions for showing that $f_n \searrow 0$ implies $I(f_n) \to 0$: Let $A = \sup_x f_1(x)$ and let $B = \mu(\{x : f_1(x) > 0\})$. If $\delta > 0$, let $F_n = \{x : f_n(x) \geq \delta\}$ and deduce that $\mu(F_n) \to 0$. Then show that $I(f_n) \leq \delta(A + B)$ if $n$ is sufficiently large.

(c) If $f$ is $\mu$-summable, show that $f$ is in the class $\mathscr{L}$ as determined by $I$ in Section 6–3, and that $I(f) = \int f\, d\mu$. Hereafter, in this problem we shall refer to elements of $\mathscr{L}$ as $I$-summable functions.

(d) If $h \in \mathscr{F}^\circ \cap \mathscr{L}$, show that $h$ is $\mu$-summable and that $\int h\, d\mu = I(h)$. If $f$ is $I$-summable, show that there exists an $h$ such that $f \leq h$ and such that $h$ is both $I$-summable and $\mu$-summable, with $I(f) = I(h) = \int h\, d\mu$.

(e) The integral $I$ determines a class $\mathbf{S}_1$ of measurable sets and a measure $\mu_1$ on $\mathbf{S}_1$, as in Section 6–5. Show that $E \in \mathbf{S}$ and $\mu(E) = 0$ implies $E \in \mathbf{S}_1$ and $\mu_1(E) = 0$. Show that the converse is true if the measure $\mu$ is complete. In this latter case, show that the $f$ in (d) is $\mu$-summable, with $\int f\, d\mu = I(f)$.

(f) Assume that $\mu$ is a complete measure and show that the class of $E$'s in **S** with $\mu(E)$ finite is the same as the class of $E$'s in $\mathbf{S}_1$ with $\mu_1(E)$ finite, with $\mu(E) = \mu_1(E)$ for such a set.

## 6–6 The N-norm

The results of this section are not needed until we come to the proof of the Fubini-Stone theorem, in Section 7–2.

We continue the general discussion in the framework established in the preceding sections of this chapter. We shall define a function **N** whose domain is the class of all functions

$f : X \to R^*$. We define

(1) $$\mathbf{N}(f) = \inf \{I(h) : h \in \mathscr{F}^\circ, |f| \leq h\}$$

if there exists an $h$ in $\mathscr{F}^\circ$ for which $|f| \leq h$. This is equivalent to

(2) $$\mathbf{N}(f) = \bar{I}(|f|)$$

for such an $f$ (see (1) in Section 6–3). If no $h$ of the required sort exists, we define

(3) $$\mathbf{N}(f) = +\infty.$$

We observe that

(4) $$\mathbf{N}(f) = I(f)$$

if $f \in \mathscr{F}^\circ$ and $f \geq 0$. This is clear from Theorem 6–2 III (c).

As we shall see, the function **N** has properties which make it suitable for constructing a norm in a linear space formed from functions $f$ for which $\mathbf{N}(f) < +\infty$, in the same way that $I(|f|)$ was used for defining a norm in the space $L$ (see Section 6–4).

THEOREM 6–6 I. *The function* **N** *defined by* (1) *and* (3) *has the following properties:*

(a) $\mathbf{N}(f) = \mathbf{N}(|f|)$;
(b) $\mathbf{N}(f_1) \leq \mathbf{N}(f_2)$ *if* $|f_1| \leq |f_2|$;
(c) $|f| \leq \sum_n |f_n|$ *implies* $\mathbf{N}(f) \leq \sum_n \mathbf{N}(f_n)$;
(d) $\mathbf{N}(cf) = |c|\, \mathbf{N}(f)$ *if* $c \in R$;
(e) $\mathbf{N}(f) = I(|f|)$ *if* $f \in \mathscr{L}$;
(f) $\mathbf{N}(f) = 0$ *if and only if* $f$ *is a null-function* (*defined in Section* 6–4);
(g) *if* $\mathbf{N}(f) < +\infty$, $f(x)$ *is finite a.e.*

*Proof.* The properties (a) and (b) are obvious. Properties (c) and (d) are easily proved with the aid of properties of over-functions from Section 6–2; we leave details to the reader. Property (e) follows from (2), and the same is true of (f), because we always have $0 \leq \underline{I}(|f|)$. If $\mathbf{N}(f) < +\infty$, there exists an $h \in \mathscr{F}^\circ$ with $|f| \leq h$ and $I(h) < +\infty$. Then $h(x)$ is finite a.e., by Theorem 6–4 I (e). This implies the truth of (g).

LEMMA 6–6 II. *Let* $f$ *and* $g$ *be functions on* $X$ *to* $R^*$. *Then*

(a) $f(x) = g(x)$ *a.e. implies* $\mathbf{N}(f) = \mathbf{N}(g)$;
(b) $|f(x)| \leq |g(x)|$ *a.e. implies* $\mathbf{N}(f) \leq \mathbf{N}(g)$.

*Proof of* (a). Let $E = \{x : f(x) \neq g(x)\}$. Define $p(x) = g(x)$ if $x \in E$, $p(x) = 0$ if $x \in E^\sim$; also, define $q(x) = 0$ if $x \in E$, $q(x) = f(x)$ if $x \in E^\sim$. Then $g = p + q$, $p$ is a null function, and $|q| \leq |f|$. Therefore $\mathbf{N}(g) \leq \mathbf{N}(p) + \mathbf{N}(q) \leq \mathbf{N}(f)$. We get $\mathbf{N}(f) \leq \mathbf{N}(g)$ by symmetry, and this completes the proof.

*Proof of* (b). Let $f_1(x) = f(x)$ and $g_1(x) = g(x)$ when $|f(x)| \leq |g(x)|$, and let $f_1(x) = g_1(x) = 0$, otherwise. Now, use what has just been proved, together with Theorem 6–6 I (b).

## THE CLASS $\mathscr{T}$

Let us denote by $\mathscr{T}$ the class of all functions $f : \mathbf{X} \to R^*$ such that $\mathbf{N}(f) < +\infty$. There is a completeness theorem for $\mathscr{T}$ similar to Theorem 6–4 IV.

THEOREM 6–6 III. *Let $\{f_n\}$ be a sequence in $\mathscr{T}$ such that* $\mathbf{N}(f_n - f_m) \to 0$ *as $m \to \infty$ and $n \to \infty$. Then there exists a function $f$ in $\mathscr{T}$ such that $N(f_n - f) \to 0$.*

*Proof.* We can select a subsequence $\{g_n\}$ from $\{f_n\}$ so that $\mathbf{N}(g_{n+1} - g_n) < 2^{-n}$ for each $n$. Then

$$N(g_1) + \sum_{i=1}^{\infty} N(g_{i+1} - g_i) < +\infty.$$

It follows by Theorem 6–6 I (c) and (g) that the function

$$h = |g_1| + \sum_{i=1}^{\infty} |g_{i+1} - g_i|$$

is such that the set $E = \{x : h(x) = +\infty\}$ has measure zero. We define $f(x) = 0$ if $x \in E$ and

$$f(x) = g_1(x) + \sum_{i=1}^{\infty} [g_{i+1}(x) - g_i(x)]$$

if $x \in E^{\sim}$. Since $|f| \leq h$, we have $\mathbf{N}(f) \leq \mathbf{N}(h) < +\infty$.

We now show that $\mathbf{N}(g_n - f) \to 0$. If $x \in E^{\sim}$,

$$f(x) - g_n(x) = \sum_{i=n}^{\infty} [g_{i+1}(x) - g_i(x)],$$

from which it follows that

$$N(f - g_n) \leq \sum_{i=n}^{\infty} N(g_{i+1} - g_i) < \frac{1}{2^{n-1}}.$$

The last step is to show that $\mathbf{N}(f_n - f) \to 0$. This is easy, for

$$\mathbf{N}(f_n - f) \leq \mathbf{N}(f_n - g_k) + \mathbf{N}(g_k - f),$$

and $\{g_k\}$ is a subsequence of $\{f_n\}$, so that $\mathbf{N}(f_n - g_k) \to 0$, as $n \to \infty$ and $k \to \infty$.

An important relation between $\mathscr{L}$ and $\mathscr{T}$ is expressed in the following theorem, which we state formally for future reference.

THEOREM 6–6 IV. *Suppose $f_n \in \mathscr{L}$, $f \in \mathscr{T}$, and* $\mathbf{N}(f_n - f) \to 0$. *Then $f \in \mathscr{L}$.*

*Proof.* The hypothesis implies that $\mathbf{N}(f_n - f_m) \to 0$. But $\mathbf{N}(f_n - f_m) = I(|f_n - f_m|)$. By Theorem 6–4 IV we know that there exists $g \in \mathscr{L}$ such that $\mathbf{N}(f_n - g) = I(|f_n - g|) \to 0$. Then

$$\mathbf{N}(f - g) \leq \mathbf{N}(f - f_n) + \mathbf{N}(f_n - g),$$

from which we see that $\mathbf{N}(f - g) = 0$ and $f(x) = g(x)$ a.e., so that $f \in \mathscr{L}$, by Theorem 6–4 III.

## THE SPACE $T$

If two elements $f$ and $g$ of $\mathscr{T}$ are such that $\mathbf{N}(f - g) = 0$, $f - g$ is a null function, and conversely. An equivalent condition is that the set $\{x : f(x) \neq g(x)\}$ be of measure zero. It is then clear that we can form a family $T$ of equivalence classes in $\mathscr{T}$ in just the same way that we formed the family $L$ of equivalence classes in $\mathscr{L}$. We can make $T$ into a normed linear space, the norm of the equivalence class $[f]$ being

(5) $$\|[f]\| = N(f).$$

Theorem 6–6 I (e) shows that $\mathscr{L} \subset \mathscr{T}$, and Lemma 6–6 II (a) shows that, if $f \in \mathscr{L}$, all the members of the equivalence class $[f]$ are in $\mathscr{L}$. Thus we see that $L \subset T$. Theorem 6–6 III shows that the space $T$ is complete, and Theorem 6–6 IV shows that $L$ is a closed subspace of $T$. Theorem 6–4 VI shows that $L$ is the closed subspace of $T$ generated by elements corresponding to functions which belong to the original vector lattice $\mathscr{F}$.

**PROBLEMS**

1. Prove (c) and (d) of Theorem 6–6 I.
2. (a) Given $f_n, f, g_n, g$, all on $X$ to $R^*$, with $\mathbf{N}(f_n - f) \to 0$ and $\mathbf{N}(g_n - g) \to 0$, prove that $\mathbf{N}(f \wedge g_n - f \wedge g) \to 0$, $\mathbf{N}(g_n \vee f - g \vee f) \to 0$, and $\mathbf{N}(g_n \vee f_n - g_n \vee f) \to 0$.

(b) Given $g_n, g, h_n, h, f$, all on $X$ to $R^*$, with $\mathbf{N}(g_n - g) \to 0$ and $\mathbf{N}(h_n - h) \to 0$, let $F_n = g_n \vee (f \wedge h_n)$ and $F = g \vee (f \wedge h)$. Then show that $\mathbf{N}(F_n - F) \to 0$.

## 6–7 Connections with Chapter 5

Thus far in this chapter we have developed a theory of summable functions and their integrals without any use of a theory of measure. We have then used the theory of summable functions to construct a theory of measurable functions and of measurable sets. Theorems 6–5 III and 6–5 IV show that we obtain from the original elementary integral $I$ a measure space $(X, \mathbf{S}, \mu)$ such that $\mu$ is a complete measure. The theory up to this point says nothing about whether $X \in \mathbf{S}$, nor about the possible finiteness or $\sigma$-finiteness of the measure space.

We now wish to compare the theory of the present chapter with the theory of integration developed in Chapter 5. In Chapter 5 the procedure is quite different. We start with an arbitrary measure space, and from this beginning we construct, first a theory of measurable functions and then a theory of summable functions and their integrals. The question to which we now address ourselves is this: Suppose we take the measure space $(X, \mathbf{S}, \mu)$ determined by the elementary integral $I$, as explained in Section 6–5, and use the methods of Chapter 5. Will the resulting classes of measurable functions and summable functions be the same as those arrived at in Sections 6–5 and 6–3, respectively? And will the integral $\int f\,d\mu$ of Section 5–4 be the same as the $I(f)$ of Section 6–3?

In order to keep our ideas clear we need to make some agreements on terminology, so that we may distinguish between summability and measurability of functions in the sense of Chapter 5 and these same terms in the sense of Chapter 6. A function summable in the sense of Section 6–3 will be called *I-summable*. Likewise, a function measurable in the sense of Section 6–5 will be called *I-measurable*. A function which is measurable in the sense of Section 5–1, where $\mathbf{S}$ is the basic $\sigma$-ring, will be called **S**-*measurable*. A function which is summable in the sense of Section 5–4, where $(X, \mathbf{S}, \mu)$ is the basic measure space, will be called $\mu$-*summable*.

The following example shows that we cannot expect affirmative answers to our questions unless we make some further assumption about the ingredients of our mathematical structure.

*Example 1.* Suppose $X = (0, 1] = \{x : 0 < x \leq 1\}$. Let $\mathscr{F}$ be the class of all functions $f : X \to R$ of the form $f(x) = ax$, $a \in R$. Define $I : \mathscr{F} \to R$ by $I(f) = \dfrac{a}{2}$. Let us see what the theory of Sections 6–1 – 6–6 yields in this case.

The only $h$ in $\mathscr{F}^\circ - \mathscr{F}$ is defined by $h(x) = +\infty$ for each $x$. For this $h$ we have $I(h) = +\infty$. The upper and lower integrals $\bar{I}(f)$ and $\underline{I}(f)$ are defined for every $f : X \to R^*$;

$\bar{I}(f) < +\infty$ if and only if $f \leq h$ for some $h \in \mathscr{F}$, and $-\infty < \underline{I}(f)$ if and only if $g \leq f$ for some $g \in \mathscr{F}$. It is not difficult to see that $\mathscr{L} \subset \mathscr{F}$, whence $\mathscr{L} = \mathscr{F}$ (one can use Theorem 6–3 V, for instance). Knowing that $\mathscr{L} = \mathscr{F}$, it is rather easy to see that if $f \geq 0$ and $f \in \mathscr{M}$ then either $f(x) = +\infty$ for every $x$, or $f \in \mathscr{F}$. For, otherwise there exist two distinct points $x_1$, $x_2$ and some $h \in \mathscr{F}$ such that $h \geq 0$ and $h(x_1) < f(x_1)$, $f(x_2) < h(x_2)$. Then, taking $g = 0$ and $F = g \vee (f \wedge h)$ as in (1), Section 6–5, we see that $F = f \wedge h$, $F(x_1) = h(x_1)$, $F(x_2) = f(x_2)$. But, since $f \in \mathscr{M}$ implies $F \in \mathscr{L} = \mathscr{F}$, we have a contradiction. For, by the nature of $\mathscr{F}$, $F(x_1) = h(x_1)$ implies $F = h$, whereas $F(x_2) \neq h(x_2)$. It now follows easily that $\mathscr{M}$ is composed of $\mathscr{F}$ and the two functions $\pm f_0$, where $f_0(x) = +\infty$ for every $x$. Thus the only characteristic function in $\mathscr{M}$ is the zero function, which is $\chi_{\varnothing}$; that is, **S** consists solely of $\varnothing$.

## THE SITUATION WHEN $X \in \mathbf{S}$

It turns out that by assuming $X \in \mathbf{S}$, we can obtain a satisfactory answer to the questions raised at the beginning of this section. It is convenient to denote by 1 the function $f : X \to R$ such that $f(x) = 1$ for each $x$. We observe that 1 is the characteristic function of $X$. Hence $X \in \mathbf{S}$ is equivalent to $1 \in \mathscr{M}$.

From some points of view it is unsatisfactory to use $X \in \mathbf{S}$ as a hypothesis, because this hypothesis does not bear directly on the original vector lattice $\mathscr{F}$ and the elementary integral $I$. There is a simple condition bearing on $\mathscr{F}$ only which is sufficient to guarantee that $X \in \mathbf{S}$. This is the condition that $1 \wedge f$ be in $\mathscr{F}$ whenever $f$ is in $\mathscr{F}$. The assumption of this condition, known as *Stone's axiom*, is discussed later in the present section. This axiom is fulfilled in the most important applications of the theory.

THEOREM 6–7 I. (a) *Suppose that* $X \in \mathbf{S}$. *Then* $f \in \mathscr{L}$ *implies* $1 \wedge f \in \mathscr{L}$, *and* $f \in \mathscr{M}$ *implies* $1 \wedge f \in \mathscr{M}$. (b) *Suppose that* $1 \wedge f \in \mathscr{L}$ *whenever* $f \geq 0$ *and* $f \in \mathscr{L}$. *Then* $X \in \mathbf{S}$.

*Proof of* (a). We observe that

$$1 \wedge f = (1 \wedge f^+) - f^- \tag{1}$$

is true for all functions $f$. If $f \in \mathscr{L}$, then $f^+$ and $f^-$ are in $\mathscr{L}$. Now $0 \vee (1 \wedge f^+) = 1 \wedge f^+$. Since $1 \in \mathscr{M}$, it follows by definition that $1 \wedge f^+ \in \mathscr{L}$. We then see by (1) that $1 \wedge f \in \mathscr{L}$.

Suppose now that $f \in \mathscr{M}$. Since $1 \in \mathscr{M}$, we have $1 \wedge f \in \mathscr{M}$ by Theorem 6–5 II (b).

*Proof of* (b). We wish to prove that $1 \in \mathscr{M}$, or equivalently, that $g \vee (1 \wedge h) \in \mathscr{L}$ if $g$ and $h$ are in $\mathscr{L}$ and $g \leq 0 \leq h$. Under these conditions $0 \leq 1 \wedge h$ and $g \vee (1 \wedge h) = 1 \wedge h$. But $1 \wedge h \in \mathscr{L}$ as a result of the hypothesis. Hence the proof is complete.

We can now deal with the two notions of a measurable function.

THEOREM 6–7 II. *Suppose that* $X \in \mathbf{S}$. *Then* $f \in \mathscr{M}$ *if and only if* $f$ *is* **S**-*measurable in the sense of Section* 5–1.

*Proof.* We use the various criteria for **S**-measurability expressed in Theorem 5–1 IV. Suppose first that $f \in \mathscr{M}$. For a given $c$ in $R$ let $E = \{x : f(x) > c\}$. Define $f_n$ by $f_n = n[f - (f \wedge c)]$, where $c$ is also used to denote the constant function with value $c$. Since $X \in \mathbf{S}$, we have $1 \in \mathscr{M}$ and also $c \in \mathscr{M}$. Hence, $f \wedge c \in \mathscr{M}$ and $f_n \in \mathscr{M}$. Let $g_n = 1 \wedge f_n$. We shall see that $g_n \nearrow \chi_E$. Since $g_n \in \mathscr{M}$, we can conclude that $E \in \mathbf{S}$, by Theorem 6–5 I (d). If $x \in E$, we have $f_n(x) = n[f(x) - c] \to +\infty$ as $n \to \infty$. Hence $g_n(x) = 1$ if $n$ is sufficiently large, and $g_n(x) \to 1$. If $x \in X - E$, the value of $f \wedge c$ at $x$ is $f(x)$, and $g_n(x) = f_n(x) = 0$ for all $n$. We now have the proof that $E \in \mathbf{S}$. To complete the proof that $f$ is $\mathbf{S}$-measurable, we need to show that $\{x : f(x) > +\infty\}$ and $\{x : f(x) > -\infty\}$ are in $\mathbf{S}$. The first of these sets is empty and the second one is the union of the sets $\{x : f(x) > -n\}$, $n = 1, 2, \ldots,$ which are known to be in $\mathbf{S}$. Hence, $f$ is $\mathbf{S}$-measurable.

Now suppose that $f$ is $\mathbf{S}$-measurable. It follows (Theorem 5–1 VIII) that $f^+$ and $f^-$ are $\mathbf{S}$-measurable. If we can show that $f^+$ and $f^-$ are in $\mathcal{M}$, it will follow by Theorem 6–5 II (d) that $f = f^+ - f^-$ is in $\mathcal{M}$. Hence it suffices to consider the case in which $f \geq 0$. We shall finish the proof by constructing a sequence $\{g_n\}$ with $g_n \in \mathcal{M}$ and $g_n \nearrow f$.

Let $E = \{x : f(x) = 0\}$, $F = \{x : f(x) = +\infty\}$. These sets are in $\mathbf{S}$ because $X \in \mathbf{S}$ and $f$ is $\mathbf{S}$-measurable. Choose $\epsilon > 1$ and consider the sets $E_i(\epsilon) = \{x : \epsilon^i < f(x) \leq \epsilon^{i+1}\}$, $i = 0, \pm 1, \pm 2, \ldots$. These sets also belong to $\mathbf{S}$. Each point of $X$ belongs to exactly one of the sets

$$E,\ F,\ E_0(\epsilon),\ E_1(\epsilon),\ E_{-1}(\epsilon),\ E_2(\epsilon), \ldots$$

Let $h$ be the function defined by $h(x) = +\infty$, if $x \in F$, $h(x) = 0$, otherwise. We leave it for the reader to verify that $h \in \mathcal{M}$. Let $h_i$ be the characteristic function of $E_i(\epsilon)$. The function

$$h + \sum_{i=-n}^{n} \epsilon^i h_i$$

belongs to $\mathcal{M}$, and it converges upward (pointwise) to a limit function as $n \to \infty$. We denote this limit function by $f_\epsilon$. It belongs to $\mathcal{M}$. Clearly, $f_\epsilon$ has values $0$, $+\infty$, and $\epsilon^i$ on $E$, $F$, and $E_i(\epsilon)$, respectively.

The next step is to choose a sequence of values of $\epsilon$ converging downward to 1. We choose some fixed $\delta > 1$ and put $\epsilon_n = \delta^{\alpha_n}$, where $\alpha_n = 2^{1-n}$. Observe that $\epsilon_{n+1} = \epsilon_n^{1/2}$. Then $\epsilon_{n+1}^{2i} = \epsilon_n^i$, and $\epsilon_{n+1}^{2i+1}$ is between $\epsilon_n^i$ and $\epsilon_n^{i+1}$. This means that $E_i(\epsilon_n)$ is the union of $E_{2i}(\epsilon_{n+1})$ and $E_{2i+1}(\epsilon_{n+1})$. Now, let $g_n = f_{\epsilon_n}$. From the construction it is clear that $g_n(x) = f(x)$ if $x \in E \cup F$, that $g_n \leq g_{n+1}$, and that

$$0 < f(x) - g_n(x) < \epsilon_n^{i+1} - \epsilon_n^i = \epsilon_n^i(\epsilon_n - 1) < f(x)(\epsilon_n - 1)$$

if $0 < f(x) < +\infty$. Thus we see that $g_n \nearrow f$, whence $f \in \mathcal{M}$, and the proof is complete.

*Remark.* An $\mathbf{S}$-measurable function is also $I$-measurable, even if $X$ is not in $\mathbf{S}$. The only change in the foregoing proof is that we use Theorem 5–1 V instead of Theorem 5–1 IV to be assured that the sets $F$ and $E_i(\epsilon)$ are in $\mathbf{S}$. We cannot assert $E \in \mathbf{S}$, but this is not essential.

We proceed next to the question of summability.

THEOREM 6–7 III. *Suppose $X \in \mathbf{S}$. Then $f$ is $I$-summable if and only if $f$ is $\mu$-summable; in that case*

$$I(f) = \int f\, d\mu. \tag{2}$$

*Proof.* It is enough to prove the theorem for the case $f \geq 0$. The general case then follows by using the decomposition $f = f^+ - f^-$.

For convenience we denote by $\mathcal{L}(I)$ the class of $I$-summable functions and by $\mathcal{L}(\mu)$ the class of $\mu$-summable functions. By Theorem 6–7 II the class of $\mathbf{S}$-measurable functions is the same as the class of $I$-measurable functions, so we may simply refer to functions of this class as measurable functions.

Suppose now that $f \geq 0$ and that either $f \in \mathscr{L}(I)$ or $f \in \mathscr{L}(\mu)$. Then $f$ is measurable, and we can construct the functions $h$, $h_i$, $f_\epsilon$, $g_n$ as in the proof of Theorem 6–7 II. Either hypothesis on $f$ implies that $\mu(F) = 0$. Therefore $h$ belongs to both $\mathscr{L}(I)$ and $\mathscr{L}(\mu)$, and $I(h) = \int h \, d\mu = 0$. We observe that $0 \leq h_i \leq \epsilon^{-i} f$. Since $h_i$ is measurable, we conclude that $h_i \in \mathscr{L}(I)$ if $f \in \mathscr{L}(I)$ and that $h_i \in \mathscr{L}(\mu)$ if $f \in \mathscr{L}(\mu)$. In either case, since $h_i$ is a characteristic function, we see that $\mu(E_i(\epsilon)) < +\infty$; in fact; $h_i$ belongs to both $\mathscr{L}(I)$ and $\mathscr{L}(\mu)$ with either hypothesis on $f$, and

$$I(h_i) = \int h_i \, d\mu = \mu(E_i(\epsilon)).$$

Thus, if we write $H_n = h + \sum_{i=-n}^{n} h_i$, we see that $H_n$ belongs to both $\mathscr{L}(I)$ and $\mathscr{L}(\mu)$, $H_n \nearrow f_\epsilon \leq f$, $I(H_n) = \int H_n \, d\mu$, and the sequence $\{I(H_n)\}$ is bounded above by $I(f)$ if $f \in \mathscr{L}(I)$, and by $\int f \, d\mu$ if $f \in \mathscr{L}(\mu)$. We can then use the monotone convergence theorems (Theorems 6–3 III and 5–5 I) to conclude that $f_\epsilon$ belongs to both $\mathscr{L}(I)$ and $\mathscr{L}(\mu)$ and that

$$I(f_\epsilon) = \int f_\epsilon \, d\mu.$$

Finally, putting $\epsilon = \epsilon_n$, so that $f_\epsilon$ becomes $g_n$, we note that $g_n \nearrow f$. The same mode of reasoning then assures us that $f$ is summable in both senses and that (2) is true.

## STONE'S AXIOM

In his investigations of the theory of integration M. H. Stone [2] imposed the following condition on the initial vector lattice $\mathscr{F}$:

(3) $$f \in \mathscr{F} \quad \text{implies} \quad 1 \wedge f \in \mathscr{F}.$$

In many examples of importance this axiom holds, even though the function 1 is not always in $\mathscr{F}$, or even in $\mathscr{L}$. For instance in the case of Example 4, Section 6–1, Stone's axiom holds.

For the purposes of this book the main importance of Stone's axiom is that it guarantees that $X \in \mathbf{S}$. This is shown in the next theorem. There are situations in which Stone's axiom does not hold, but nevertheless $X \in \mathbf{S}$; see Example 2, after the proof of Theorem 6–7 IV.

Explicit uses of Stone's axiom occur in Section 6–11 and in Theorem 8–6 IV.

THEOREM 6–7 IV. *Suppose Stone's axiom holds. Then:*

(a) *$f \in \mathscr{F}$ implies $(-1) \vee f \in \mathscr{F}$, and it implies $c \wedge f \in \mathscr{F}$ if $c > 0$.*

(b) *$f \in \mathscr{F}^\circ$ implies that $1 \wedge f$ and $(-1) \vee f$ are in $\mathscr{F}^\circ$. The same is true with $\mathscr{F}_u$ in place of $\mathscr{F}^\circ$.*

(c) $X \in \mathbf{S}$.

*Proof of* (a). Suppose $f \in \mathscr{F}$. Then $1 \wedge (-f)$ is in $\mathscr{F}$, and hence so is $(-1) \vee f$, which equals $-[1 \wedge (-f)]$. If $c > 0$, we see that $c \wedge f = c[1 \wedge g]$, where $g = c^{-1}f$. Hence $c \wedge f \in \mathscr{F}$.

*Proof of* (b). If $f \in \mathscr{F}^\circ$, there exists a sequence $\{f_n\}$ in $\mathscr{F}$ such that $f_n \nearrow f$. One sees easily that $1 \wedge f_n \nearrow 1 \wedge f$, so that $1 \wedge f \in \mathscr{F}^\circ$. The proof for $(-1) \vee f$ is similar. If $f \in \mathscr{F}_u$, $-f \in \mathscr{F}^\circ$, and so $1 \wedge (-f) = -[(-1) \vee f]$ and $(-1) \vee (-f) = -[1 \wedge f]$ both belong to $\mathscr{F}^\circ$. This means that $(-1) \vee f$ and $1 \wedge f$ are in $\mathscr{F}_u$.

*Proof of* (c). By Theorem 6–7 I (b) it suffices to show that $f \geq 0$ and $f \in \mathscr{L}$ imply $1 \wedge f \in \mathscr{L}$. Suppose $\epsilon > 0$; then $f \in \mathscr{L}$ implies the existence of $g \in \mathscr{F}_u$ and $h \in \mathscr{F}^\circ$ such that $g \leq f \leq h$, $I(h) - I(f) < \epsilon/2$, and $I(f) - I(g) < \epsilon/2$. Then $1 \wedge f \leq 1 \wedge h \leq h$. We know from (b) that $1 \wedge h \in \mathscr{F}^\circ$; then $I(1 \wedge h) \leq I(h)$. Let $G = (-1) \vee (g \wedge 1)$. We see from (b) that $G \in \mathscr{F}_u$. It is easily checked that $G \leq 1 \wedge f$. (We use the fact that $f \geq 0$ to make the verification at a point where $g(x) < -1$.) We shall establish that

$$(1 \wedge h) - G \leq h - g. \tag{4}$$

Since $1 \wedge h \leq h$, it suffices to verify (4) at points where $G(x) < g(x)$. But $G(x) < g(x)$ occurs only when $G(x) = 1$ and $1 < g(x)$. In that case $1 < h(x)$ also, because $g \leq h$. Then the value of $(1 \wedge h) - G$ at $x$ is 0, while the value of $h - g$ is nonnegative. This proves (4). We know that $G \leq 1 \wedge f \leq 1 \wedge h$. From (4), Theorem 6–2 IV, and Theorem 6–2 III (c) we see that

$$I(1 \wedge h) - I(G) \leq I(h) - I(g) < \epsilon.$$

Theorem 6–3 I (a) now shows that $1 \wedge f \in \mathscr{L}$. This completes the proof of the theorem.

*Example 2.* Let $X = [0, 1]$, and let $\mathscr{F}$ be the class of all functions of the form $f(x) = ax$, $a \in R$. It is clear that Stone's axiom is not satisfied; consider $1 \wedge f$ when $a = 2$, for instance. Let $I(f) = 0$ for each $f$ in $\mathscr{F}$. In this case the only element of $\mathscr{F}^\circ - \mathscr{F}$ is the function $f_0$ defined by $f_0(0) = 0$, $f_0(x) = +\infty$ if $0 < x \leq 1$. We have $I(f_0) = 0$. For an arbitrary function $f : X \to R^*$, $\bar{I}(f)$ is defined if and only if $f(0) \leq 0$ and $\underline{I}(f)$ is defined if and only if $f(0) \geq 0$. Since $\underline{I}(f)$ and $\bar{I}(f)$ are zero when they are defined, $\mathscr{L}$ consists of all $f$ such that $f(0) = 0$, and $I(f) = 0$ for such an $f$. It is easily verified that any nonnegative function is $I$-measurable; hence every function is $I$-measurable, and **S** consists of all subsets of $X$. If $E \subset X$, $\chi_E \in \mathscr{L}$ if and only if the point 0 is not in $E$. For such an $E$, $\mu(E) = 0$. If $0 \in E$, $\mu(E) = +\infty$. The measure space is not $\sigma$-finite.

Some assumptions equivalent to the assumption of $\sigma$-finiteness of the measure space are discussed in Problem 5.

## OUTER MEASURE FROM $I$

Not only does $I$ determine **S** and the measure $\mu$; it also induces an outer measure on the class of all subsets of $X$. Using the function **N** defined in Section 6–6, let us define a function $\nu^*$ on the class of all subsets of $X$ by

$$\nu^*(E) = \mathbf{N}(\chi_E). \tag{5}$$

That is, $\nu^*(E) = +\infty$ if there is no $h \in \mathscr{F}^\circ$ such that $\chi_E \leq h$, and

$$\nu^*(E) = \inf\{I(h) : h \in \mathscr{F}^\circ, \chi_E \leq h\}, \tag{6}$$

if the class of relevant $h$'s is not empty.

THEOREM 6–7 V. (a) *The function $\nu^*$ is an outer measure on $X$.* (b) *If $E \in$* **S**, *then $E$ is $\nu^*$-measurable in the sense of Section 4–7, and $\nu^*(E) = \mu(E)$.*

*Proof of* (a). This is left to the reader. Consult Theorem 6–6 I.

*Proof of* (b). Suppose $E \in$ **S**. We see from Theorem 6–6 I (e) that $\mu(E) = \nu^*(E)$ if $\chi_E \in \mathscr{L}$. If $\chi_E$ is not in $\mathscr{L}$, then $\mu(E) = +\infty$, and we must prove that $\nu^*(E) = +\infty$ also. If the contrary were true, there would exist $h \in \mathscr{F}^\circ$ such that $0 \leq \chi_E \leq h$ and $I(h) < +\infty$.

This implies $h \in \mathscr{L}$ and hence also $\chi_E \in \mathscr{L}$, by results earlier in this chapter. Therefore $\nu^*(E) = +\infty$.

To show that $E$ is $\nu^*$-measurable, let $T$ be any set for which $\nu^*(T) < +\infty$. We wish to show that

(7) $$\nu^*(T \cap E) + \nu^*(T \cap E^\sim) \leq \nu^*(T).$$

By the method used in proving Theorem 6–3 V we may assert the existence of $h \in \mathscr{L}$ such that $\chi_T \leq h$ and $I(h) = \nu^*(T)$. Let $h_n = (n\chi_E) \wedge h$. It is easy to verify that $h_n \to \chi_E h$, whence $\chi_E h \in \mathscr{M}$. But $0 \leq \chi_E h \leq h$, and so $\chi_E h \in \mathscr{L}$. Now, $\chi_{E \cap T} = \chi_E \chi_T \leq \chi_E h$; from this it follows that

(8) $$\nu^*(E \cap T) \leq N(\chi_E h) = I(\chi_E h).$$

Also, $\chi_{T \cap E^\sim} = \chi_T(1 - \chi_E) \leq h(1 - \chi_E)$, whence

(9) $$\nu^*(T \cap E^\sim) \leq I(h) - I(h\chi_E) = \nu^*(T) - I(\chi_E h).$$

Adding (8) and (9), we obtain (7).

The question naturally arises as to whether every $\nu^*$-measurable set is in **S**. This is not always true. It is true if and only if $X \in \mathbf{S}$. To get at this we need the following lemma.

LEMMA 6–7 VI. *Suppose $X \in \mathbf{S}$. Then, if $E \subset X$ and $\nu^*(E) < +\infty$, there exists a set $F \in \mathbf{S}$ such that $E \subset F$ and $\nu^*(E) = \mu(F)$, or, what is the same, $\chi_E \leq \chi_F$, $\chi_F \in \mathscr{L}$, and $\mathbf{N}(\chi_E) = I(\chi_F)$.*

*Proof.* We may use the method of the proof of Theorem 6–3 V to obtain $g \in \mathscr{L}$ such that $\chi_E \leq g$ and $\mathbf{N}(\chi_E) = I(g)$. Let $f_1 = 1 \wedge g$. We know that $f_1 \in \mathscr{L}$, by Theorem 6–7 I (a). Evidently $\chi_E \leq f_1 \leq 1$. Let $f_n = (f_1)^n$. We see that $f_n \in \mathscr{M}$, by Theorems 6–7 II and 5–1 VI. Clearly, $\chi_E \leq f_{n+1} \leq f_n \leq f_1$. Writing $f = \lim f_n$, we conclude that $\chi_E \leq f \leq g$. Moreover, $f_n \in \mathscr{L}$, whence $f \in \mathscr{L}$ and $I(f) = \mathbf{N}(\chi_E)$. It is obvious that $f$ is a characteristic function, from the facts that $0 \leq f_1 \leq 1$ and $(f_1)^n \to f$. Letting $F$ be the set such that $f = \chi_F$, we obtain the desired result.

THEOREM 6–7 VII. *In order that **S** coincide with the class of $\nu^*$-measurable sets, it is necessary and sufficient that $X \in \mathbf{S}$.*

*Proof.* The necessity is immediate, since $X$ is $\nu^*$-measurable (Theorem 4–7 II).

Suppose that $X \in \mathbf{S}$ and that $E$ is $\nu^*$-measurable. We have to show that $\chi_E \in \mathscr{M}$. Since $\chi_E \geq 0$, the definition of the class $\mathscr{M}$ shows that we must prove that $\chi_E \wedge h \in \mathscr{L}$ if $h \geq 0$ and $h \in \mathscr{L}$. Let $H_n = \left\{x : \frac{1}{n} \leq h(x)\right\}$. Using Theorem 6–7 II, we find that $H_n \in \mathbf{S}$. Let $h_n = \chi_{H_n}$. Then $h_n \in \mathscr{L}$, because $h_n \in \mathscr{M}$ and $0 \leq h_n \leq nh$. We observe that $\nu^*(H_n) = \mu(H_n) = I(h_n) < +\infty$. It is easy to verify that $(\chi_E h_n) \wedge h \to \chi_E \wedge h$ (consider separately the points of $E^\sim$, the points of $E$ where $h(x) > 0$, and the remaining points). Thus we see that our goal will be attained if we prove that $\chi_E h_n \in \mathscr{L}$, because we can then apply Theorem 6–3 IV (c) to conclude that $\chi_E \wedge h \in \mathscr{L}$.

Now, $\chi_E h_n$ is the characteristic function of $E \cap H_n$, and $\nu^*(E \cap H_n) \leq \nu^*(H_n) < +\infty$. By Lemma 6–7 VI there exists a set $F_n \in \mathbf{S}$ such that $E \cap H_n \subset F_n$ and $\nu^*(E \cap H_n) = \mu(F_n)$. Let $G_n = F_n \cap H_n$ and $g_n = \chi_{G_n}$. Then $g_n \in \mathscr{L}$. We see that

(10) $$G_n \cap E = H_n \cap E,$$

because $H_n \cap E \subset F_n$. We obviously have $\nu^*(G_n \cap E) \leq \nu^*(G_n) \leq \nu^*(F_n)$. But $\nu^*(F_n) = \mu(F_n) = \nu^*(E \cap H_n)$. In view of (10) we have $\nu^*(F_n) = \nu^*(G_n \cap E)$. The result is that

(11) $$\nu^*(G_n) = \nu^*(G_n \cap E).$$

Because $E$ is $\nu^*$-measurable we can write

$$\nu^*(G_n) = \nu^*(G_n \cap E) + \nu^*(G_n \cap E^\sim).$$

From (11) we conclude that $\nu^*(G_n \cap E^\sim) = 0$. By Theorem 6–6 I (f) this implies that $G_n \cap E^\sim \in S$ and $\mu(G_n \cap E^\sim) = 0$. From (10) we see that

$$G_n \cap E^\sim = G_n - (H_n \cap E).$$

We see therefore that $g_n$ and $\chi_E h_n$ differ in value only on a set of $\mu$-measure zero. Since $g_n \in \mathscr{L}$, it follows that $\chi_E h_n \in \mathscr{L}$, and the proof is complete.

## PROBLEMS

1. Let $X = [0, 1]$ and let $\mathscr{F}$ be the class of all functions of the form $f(x) = ax$, $a \in R$.

(a) Show that $\mathscr{F}^\circ$ contains just one function not in $\mathscr{F}$; denote this function by $f_0$ and describe it.

(b) Suppose that $I(f) = \dfrac{a}{2}$ when $f(x) = ax$. What is $I(f_0)$? Show that $\mathscr{L} = \mathscr{F}$.

(c) Continuing from (b), show that a nonnegative function $f$ is in $\mathscr{M}$ if and only if either $f(x) = +\infty$ for each $x$ such that $0 < x \leq 1$, or for some real $a \geq 0$ we have $f(x) = ax$ when $0 < x \leq 1$. In either case the only restriction on $f(0)$ is that $f(0) \geq 0$.

(d) Continuing from (c), observe that the only nonempty measurable set consists of the single point $x = 0$. The measure of this set is $+\infty$.

2. Take $X$ and $\mathscr{F}$ as in Example 1, but let $I$ be identically zero on $\mathscr{F}$. In this case, show that every function $f$ is summable, with $I(f) = 0$. Thus $\mu$ is the zero measure on the class of all subsets of $X$.

3. Consider an arbitrary $X$ and $\mathscr{F}$, and let $I$ be identically zero on $\mathscr{F}$.

(a) Show that $\mathscr{L}$ consists of all functions $f$ such that there exist functions $g \in \mathscr{F}_u$ and $h \in \mathscr{F}^\circ$ with $g \leq f \leq h$.

(b) Show that every function is measurable, and hence that every set is measurable, the measure being either 0 or $+\infty$.

4. Suppose $X$, $\mathscr{F}$, $I$ given, with $I(f) \neq 0$ for at least one $f \in \mathscr{F}$. Show that there exists $f \in \mathscr{F}$ with $f \geq 0$ and $I(f) > 0$. In this situation it may happen that there are no sets of positive measure. But suppose $1 \in \mathscr{M}$. Then a set of positive measure must exist, and hence $\mu(X) > 0$. Prove this.

5. Consider the following propositions concerning $X$, $\mathscr{F}$, $I$ and the associated $\mathscr{L}$, **S**, $\mu$.

(i) There exists $g \in \mathscr{L}$ such that $0 < g(x) \leq 1$ for each $x$.

(ii) There exists a sequence $\{f_n\}$ in $\mathscr{F}$ such that $\sum_n |f_n(x)| = +\infty$ for each $x$.

(iii) There exists a sequence $\{g_n\}$ in $\mathscr{F}$ such that $g_n \geq 0$ and $\mu(\bigcap_n G_n) = 0$, where $G_n = \{x : g_n(x) = 0\}$.

(iv) The measure space $(X, \mathbf{S}, \mu)$ is $\sigma$-finite.

(a) Prove that (i) implies (ii). [*Suggestion.* With $g$ from (i), there exists $h$ from $\mathscr{F}^\circ$ such that $g \leq h$. Now use the definition of $\mathscr{F}^\circ$.]

(b) Prove that (ii) implies (iii). [*Suggestion.* In fact, given $\{f_n\}$ from (ii), let $g_n = |f_n|$ and show that $\bigcap_n G_n = \varnothing$.]

(c) Prove that (iii) implies (i) if $\mu(X) > 0$ and $1 \in \mathscr{M}$. [*Suggestions.* Taking $\{g_n\}$ as in (iii), observe that $\mu(X) > 0$ implies that $I(g_n) > 0$ for at least one value of $n$. Show that $\mu(A) = 0$ if $A$ is the intersection of the $G_n$'s corresponding to the $g_n$'s for which $I(g_n) > 0$. Hence, we can assume that $I(g_n) > 0$ for every $n$. Then let $h(x) = \sum_n \frac{g_n(x)}{2^n I(g_n)}$. Show that $h \in \mathscr{L}$, and that $\mu(\{x : h(x) = 0\}) = 0$. Let $g$ be defined by

$$g(x) = \begin{cases} 1 \wedge h(x) & \text{if } h(x) > 0 \\ 1 & \text{if } h(x) = 0. \end{cases}$$

Show that $g$ has the required properties.]

(d) Show that (i) implies (iv) if $1 \in \mathscr{M}$. [*Suggestion*. Taking $g$ from (i), let $f_n = 1 \wedge ng$. Let $E_n = \{x : f_n(x) = 1\}$. Observe that $E_n$ is contained in $\left\{x : g(x) \geq \frac{1}{n}\right\}$ and that the latter set has finite measure. (Why?)]

(e) Show that (iv) implies (i) if $\mu(X) > 0$ and $1 \in \mathscr{M}$. [*Suggestion*. There exists a countable disjoint family $\{E_n\}$ with $E_n \in \mathbf{S}$, $X = \bigcup_n E_n$, and $0 < \mu(E_n) < +\infty$. Let $h = \sum_n \frac{1}{2^n \mu(E_n)} \chi_{E_n}$, $g = 1 \wedge h$.]

(f) Show that propositions (i)–(iv) are all true if $1 \in \mathscr{M}$ and $\mu(X) = 0$. Show also that when $1 \in \mathscr{M}$ and $\mu(X) > 0$, they are all true if any one of them is true.

6. Suppose proposition (ii) in Exercise 5 is true. Suppose $h \in \mathscr{M}$, $h \geq 0$, and $c < +\infty$, where $c = \sup\{I(f) : f \in \mathscr{L}, 0 \leq f \leq h\}$. Show that $h \in \mathscr{L}$ and $I(h) = c$. [*Hint*. Using $\{f_n\}$ from proposition (ii), let $h_n = (|f_1| + \cdots + |f_n|) \wedge h$].

7. For the situation of Example 1, suppose $E \subset X$ and let $e = \inf\{x : x \in E\}$ if $E \neq \varnothing$. Show that $\nu^*(E) = +\infty$ if $e = 0$ and $\nu^*(E) = \frac{1}{2e}$ if $e > 0$. What sets are $\nu^*$-measurable?

8. Prove (a) in Theorem 6–7 V.

## 6–8 Induction of Lebesgue measure in $R^k$

In this section we shall show that the method of the present chapter leads to the classical Lebesgue integral and to Lebesgue measure in $R^k$ if we choose the initial vector lattice and the elementary integral in the right way.

### THE SPACE $C_\infty(R^k)$

We consider continuous functions $f : R^k \to R$ such that to each $f$ corresponds some compact set in $R^k$ which contains the set $N(f) = \{x : f(x) \neq 0\}$. We denote the family of all such functions by $C_\infty(R^k)$. Sometimes the closure of $N(f)$ is called the *support* of $f$. Then $C_\infty(R^k)$ can be described as the class of all continuous functions on $R^k$ to $R$ having compact supports.

We define $I : C_\infty(R^k) \to R$ as follows. Given $f$, choose a compact interval $E$ which contains $N(f)$ and let

$$I(f) = \int_E f(x)\,dx, \tag{1}$$

where the integral is the Riemann integral. These definitions were given in Example 4, Section 6–1, and it was there pointed out that $C_\infty(R^k)$ is a vector lattice and that $I$ is an elementary integral. It is easy to see that Stone's axiom ((3) in Section 6–7) is satisfied. In fact, if $f \in C_\infty(R^k)$ and $g = 1 \wedge f$, then $g$ is continuous, and $g(x) = 0$ when $f(x) = 0$.

By the theory developed earlier in this chapter, $I$ induces a class $\mathscr{L}$ of summable functions, a class $\mathscr{M}$ of measurable functions, a certain $\sigma$-ring $\mathbf{S}$ of subsets of $R^k$, and a complete measure $\mu$ on $\mathbf{S}$. By Theorem 6–7 IV we know that $R^k \in \mathbf{S}$.

In what follows we shall denote by **M** the class of sets in $R^k$ which are measurable in the sense of Lebesgue ($L$-measurable sets), and we shall denote the Lebesgue measure function by $m$. A function which is summable in the Lebesgue sense is called $L$-summable. This is the class $\mathscr{L}(m)$ in the notation of Section 5–4, where the basic measure space is $(R^k, \mathbf{M}, m)$. We also speak of $L$-measurable functions. For facts about Lebesgue measure we refer to Chapter 4.

THEOREM 6–8 I. (a) *A function $f: R^k \to R^*$ is I-summable if and only if it is L-summable. In that case $I(f) = \int f\,dm$.* (b) *The classes* **S** *and* **M** *are the same, and the measures $\mu$, $m$ are the same.* (c) *A function $f$ is I-measurable if and only if it is L-measurable.*

*Proof.* First of all we assert that if $E$ is a finite open interval in $R^k$, then $E \in \mathbf{S}$ and $\mu(E) = m(E)$. To prove this it is sufficient to know that there exists a sequence $\{f_n\}$ in $C_\infty(R^k)$ such that $f_n \nearrow \chi_E$ and $I(f_n) \to m(E)$, for the monotone convergence theorem then implies that $\chi_E \in \mathscr{L}$ and $\mu(E) = I(\chi_E) = m(E)$. We construct $\{f_n\}$ as follows. Let $e$ be the minimum length of the edges of $E$. Let $d(x)$ be the distance from $x$ to $E^\sim$. Let

$$f_n(x) = \begin{cases} 0 & \text{if } x \in E^\sim \\ 1 \wedge \dfrac{2n}{e}\, d(x) & \text{if } x \in E. \end{cases}$$

This meets the requirements. If $k = 1$, $e$ is the length of $E$; the graph of a typical $f_n$ for this case is shown in Figure 38.

The result of the preceding paragraph implies that $\mu(E) < +\infty$ for any $E$ in **S** which is bounded. As a consequence of the nature of the space $R^k$, it is then easy to see that the measure space $(R^k, \mathbf{S}, \mu)$ is $\sigma$-finite.

Now suppose that $h \in \mathscr{F}^\circ \cap \mathscr{L}$, where $\mathscr{F} = C_\infty(R^k)$. We shall prove that $h$ is $L$-summable and that $\int h\,dm = I(h)$. There exists a sequence $\{f_n\}$ in $\mathscr{F}$ such that $f_n \nearrow h$ and $I(f_n) \to I(h) < +\infty$. Since the Riemann integral of $f_n$ is known to be equal to the Lebesgue integral of $f_n$ (because $f_n$ is continuous), we infer by the monotone convergence theorem for Lebesgue integrals that $h$ is $L$-summable and $\int h\,dm = I(h)$.

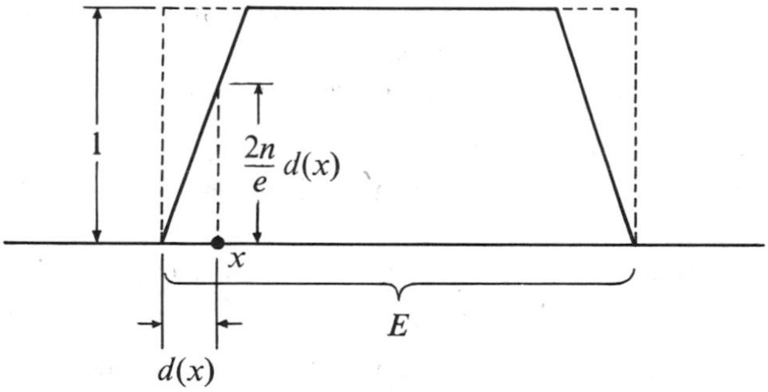


Graph of $y = f_n(x)$

FIGURE 38

Now, suppose that $f$ is $I$-summable. From Theorem 6–3 V we see that there exists a sequence $\{h_n\}$ in $\mathscr{F}^\circ \cap \mathscr{L}$ and an $h$ in $\mathscr{L}$ such that $h_n \searrow h$, $h \geq f$, $I(h_n) \to I(h)$, and $I(h) = I(f)$. By the preceding paragraph we can infer that $h$ is $L$-summable and $I(h) = \int h\, dm$. To conclude that $f$ is $L$-summable and that $I(f) = \int f\, dm$ it will suffice to show that $f(x) = h(x)$ except on a set of $m$-measure zero. From $f \leq h$ and $I(f) = I(h)$ we know that $f(x) = h(x)$ except on a set of $\mu$-measure zero. Hence, we need to prove that if $E \in \mathbf{S}$ and $\mu(E) = 0$, then $E \in \mathbf{M}$ and $m(E) = 0$. For this purpose we apply the reasoning earlier in this paragraph to the case in which $f = \chi_E$ and $I(\chi_E) = \mu(E) = 0$. We obtain a function $h$ which is $L$-summable and such that $\chi_E \leq h$ and $\int h\, dm = 0$. Thus, $E \subset \{x : h(x) \neq 0\} = N(h)$. But $m(N(h)) = 0$. Since the measure $m$ is complete, we conclude that $E \in \mathbf{M}$ and $m(E) = 0$.

We shall now show that $\mathbf{S} \subset \mathbf{M}$ and that $\mu(E) = m(E)$ if $E \in \mathbf{S}$. If $\mu(E) < +\infty$, the result follows from the preceding paragraph, taking $f = \chi_E$. Since the measure space $(R^k, \mathbf{S}, \mu)$ is $\sigma$-finite, we can obtain the result for the case in which $\mu(E) = +\infty$; this is easy to see with the aid of Theorem 4–4 III.

Next, suppose that $f$ is $L$-summable. We wish to show that $f \in \mathscr{L}$ and that $I(f) = \int f\, dm$. Because of the decomposition $f = f^+ - f^-$, it suffices to deal with the case in which $f \geq 0$. For this case we can work with a sequence $\{f_n\}$ such that $f_n \nearrow f$, where each $f_n$ is $L$-summable and simple in the $L$-sense (that is, the sets on which $f_n$ is constant are in $\mathbf{M}$). If we can show that $f_n \in \mathscr{L}$ and $I(f_n) = \int f_n\, dm$, the desired conclusion will follow by the monotone convergence theorem for $I$-integrals. Since the $f_n$'s are $L$-simple, it suffices to show that if $E \in \mathbf{M}$ and $m(E) < +\infty$, then $E \in \mathbf{S}$ and $\mu(E) = m(E)$. We shall demonstrate this in several steps. We already know the result if $E$ is an open interval.

*Step 1.* Suppose $E = E_1 \cup E_2$, where $E_1$ and $E_2$ are open intervals. It is easy to see that

$$\chi_E = \chi_{E_1} + \chi_{E_2} - \chi_{E_1 \cap E_2}.$$

Now, $E_1 \cap E_2$ is an open interval if it is not empty. Hence $\chi_E$, being a linear combination of members of $\mathscr{L}$, is in $\mathscr{L}$, and

$$\begin{aligned} I(\chi_E) &= \mu(E) = \mu(E_1) + \mu(E_2) - \mu(E_1 \cap E_2) \\ &= m(E_1) + m(E_2) - m(E_1 \cap E_2) = m(E). \end{aligned}$$

*Step 2.* We extend the result by induction to any finite union of open intervals, $E = E_1 \cup \cdots \cup E_n$. If $F = E_1 \cup \cdots \cup E_{n-1}$, we write $E = F \cup E_n$ and proceed as in Step 1, using the induction hypothesis and noting that $F \cap E_n = (E_1 \cap E_n) \cup \cdots \cup (E_{n-1} \cap E_n)$ is a union of $n - 1$ open intervals.

*Step 3.* Next, we deal with the case of a countable union of open intervals, $E = \bigcup_n E_n$. We know that $E \in \mathbf{S}$, because $\mathbf{S}$ is a $\sigma$-ring. If $F_n = E_1 \cup \cdots \cup E_n$, we know that $m(F_n) \to m(E)$ and $\mu(F_n) \to \mu(E)$ by Theorem 4–4 III. But then $m(E) = \mu(E)$, because $m(F_n) = \mu(F_n)$ by Step 2.

*Step 4.* Suppose $E \in \mathbf{M}$ and $m(E) < +\infty$. We arrange a sequence of Lebesgue coverings of $E$, say $\{E_{n1}\}, \{E_{n2}\}, \ldots$ such that $\lim_{i \to \infty} \sum_n |E_{ni}| = m(E)$ and such that, if $F_i = \bigcup_n E_{ni}$, then $F_{i+1} \subset F_i$. Let $F = \bigcap_i F_i$. Now $F_i \in \mathbf{S}$, and we know from Step 3 that $\mu(F_i) = m(F_i)$. We know that $F \in \mathbf{S}$, and we use Theorem 4–4 IV to conclude that $\mu(F) = m(F)$. We also know that $E \subset F_i$ and $m(F_i) \leq \sum_n |E_{ni}|$, whence $m(F_i) \to m(E)$. Thus we have $E \subset F$, $m(E) = m(F)$, and therefore $m(F - E) = 0$. What is needed now is to know that $F - E \in \mathbf{S}$

and $\mu(E - F) = 0$, for we can then conclude from $E = F - (F - E)$ that $E \in \mathbf{S}$, and from $F = E \cup (F - E)$ we can conclude $\mu(F) = \mu(E)$, whence $\mu(E) = m(F) = m(E)$.

For this final stage in Step 4 we look again at the first part of the argument in Step 4, assuming now that $E$ denotes a set for which $m(E) = 0$. Obtaining $F$, we see that $\mu(F) = m(F) = m(E) = 0$. Then $E \subset F$ implies $E \in \mathbf{S}$ and $\mu(E) = 0$, because the measure $\mu$ is complete.

We have now completed the proof of (a). To complete the proof of (b) we need only show that if $E \in \mathbf{M}$ and $m(E) = +\infty$, then $E \in \mathbf{S}$ and $\mu(E) = +\infty$. This follows from the fact that the measure space $(R^k, \mathbf{M}, m)$ is $\sigma$-finite.

Finally, the proof of (c) is a consequence of (b) and Theorem 6–7 II.

**PROBLEM**

For the function $f_n$ defined in the first part of the proof of Theorem 6–8 I, show that if $n \geq 2$ and $E_n = \{x : x \in E, d(x) \geq e/2n\}$, then $m(E_n) \leq I(f_n) \leq m(E)$. Show also that $m(E_n) = \left(a_1 - \dfrac{e}{n}\right) \cdots \left(a_k - \dfrac{e}{n}\right)$, where $a_1, \ldots, a_k$ are the lengths of the edges of the open interval $E$. It follows that $I(f_n) \to m(E)$.

## 6–9 Arbitrary elementary integrals on $C_\infty(R^k)$

In this section we investigate in some detail the consequences of the general theory of Section 6–1, . . . , Section 6–5 for the case in which the vector lattice is $\mathscr{F} = C_\infty(R^k)$ and the elementary integral $I$ on $\mathscr{F}$ is arbitrary. The first point to be noted is that in the list of properties (a)–(d) characterizing an elementary integral in Section 6–2, property (d) is a logical consequence of (a)–(c) when $\mathscr{F} = C_\infty(R^k)$. We recall that a linear functional on $\mathscr{F}$ is called positive if its value at $f$ is nonnegative when $f \geq 0$, (property (c)). Also, we write

(1) $$\|f\| = \sup\{|f(x)| : x \in R^k\}.$$

THEOREM 6–9 I. *Let $I$ be a positive linear functional on $C_\infty(R^k)$. Then, to each compact set $T$ in $R^k$ corresponds a constant $M$ such that*

(2) $$|I(f)| \leq M\,\|f\|$$

*for each $f$ such that $N(f) \subset T$. Moreover, $I$ is an elementary integral on $C_\infty(R^k)$.*

*Proof.* With $T$ given, it is possible to construct a bounded open set $E$ and an element $g$ in $C_\infty(R^k)$, in such a way that $T \subset E$, $g(x) = 1$ if $x \in T$, $g(x) = 0$ if $x \in E^\sim$, and $0 \leq g(x) \leq 1$ for each $x$. For instance, we may choose $r > 0$ so that $\|x\| \leq r$ for each $x$ in $T$, and let $E = \{x : \|x\| < r + 1\}$. Then define $g$ by

(3) $$g(x) = \begin{cases} 1 & \text{if } \|x\| \leq r \\ 1 + r - \|x\| & \text{if } r < \|x\| < r + 1 \\ 0 & \text{if } r + 1 \leq \|x\|. \end{cases}$$

Now, let $M = I(g)$. If $f \in C_\infty(R^k)$ and $N(f) \subset T$, the properties of $E$ and $g$ assure that

$$-\|f\|\,g(x) \leq f(x) \leq \|f\|\,g(x)$$

for each $x$. Since $I$ is a positive linear functional, it follows that

$$-\|f\| \, I(g) \leq I(f) \leq \|f\| \, I(g),$$

so that (2) is satisfied.

Now, suppose that $f_n \searrow 0$, where $f_n \in C_\infty(R^k)$. Let $T$ be a compact set such that $N(f_1) \subset T$. Then $N(f_n) \subset T$ for each $n$. By Dini's theorem (Theorem 3–15 I) we see that $f_n(x) \to 0$ uniformly on $T$, and hence uniformly on $R^k$. But this means that $\|f_n\| \to 0$. It follows from (2) that $I(f_n) \to 0$. Therefore $I$ is an elementary integral.

It was pointed out in Section 6–8 that Stone's axiom ((3) in Section 6–7) is satisfied in the vector lattice $C_\infty(R^k)$. Therefore, if we denote by **S** the class of $I$-measurable sets in $R^k$ and by $\mu$ the measure on **S** induced by $I$, the results of Section 6–7 can all be applied when $I$ is any elementary integral on $C_\infty(R^k)$. In particular, $R^k \in$ **S**, and we may look at questions of measurability, summability and integrals from the point of view of either Chapter 5 or Chapter 6, according to convenience.

In studying the measure $\mu$ induced by $I$ it is necessary in the first place to determine precisely the nature of the class of over-functions arising from $C_\infty(R^k)$. For this we must examine the concept of semicontinuity.

## SEMICONTINUOUS FUNCTIONS

A function $f : R^k \to R^*$ is said to be *lower semicontinuous* (which we abbreviate as l.s.c.) at $x_0$ if to each $c \in R^*$ such that $c < f(x_0)$ corresponds a neighborhood $V$ of $x_0$ such that $f(x) > c$ if $x \in V$. This definition applies in exactly the same form to functions $f : X \to R^*$, where $X$ is any topological space. *Upper semicontinuity* at $x_0$ is defined by reversing the sense of the inequality in both cases. It is evident that $-f$ is u.s.c. (upper semicontinuous) if and only if $f$ is l.s.c. To say that $f$ is l.s.c. on $R^k$ means that it is l.s.c. at each point of $R^k$. A function is continuous at $x_0$ if and only if it is both u.s.c. and l.s.c.

Finally, we observe that $f$ is always l.s.c. at $x_0$ if $f(x_0) = -\infty$. The condition of the definition is then satisfied vacuously.

THEOREM 6–9 II. (a) *The function $f : R^k \to R^*$ is l.s.c. on $R^k$ if and only if for each $c \in R^*$ the set $\{x : f(x) > c\}$ is open.*

(b) *If $\mathscr{G}$ is a nonempty family of l.s.c. functions $g : R^k \to R^*$ and if*

$$f(x) = \sup \{g(x) : g \in \mathscr{G}\}$$

*for each $x$, then $f$ is l.s.c. on $R^k$. In particular, if $f_n \nearrow f$, with each $f_n$ l.s.c., then $f$ is l.s.c. The theorem remains true if $R^k$ is replaced by any topological space $X$.*

*Proof of* (a). Let $E_c = \{x : f(x) > c\}$. Suppose $E_c$ is open, no matter how $c$ is chosen. If $f(x_0) \neq -\infty$, choose $c < f(x_0)$. Then $x_0 \in E_c$, so $E_c$ contains a neighborhood $V$ of $x_0$. Thus, $f(x) > c$ if $x \in V$, and $f$ is l.s.c. at $x_0$. The reader may supply the proof in the other direction.

*Proof of* (b). Consider any point $x_0$, and suppose $c < f(x_0)$. Then $c < g(x_0)$ for some $g \in \mathscr{G}$. Since $g$ is l.s.c., there exists a neighborhood $V$ of $x_0$ such that $c < g(x)$ if $x \in V$. But $g(x) \leq f(x)$, so $c < f(x)$ if $x \in V$. Hence, $f$ is l.s.c. at $x_0$. The situation when $f_n \nearrow f$ is a special case of the foregoing, for here $f(x) = \sup_n f_n(x)$.

## THE NATURE OF OVER-FUNCTIONS

In Section 6–2 we defined $f : X \to R^*$ to be an over-function (relative to the vector lattice $\mathscr{F}$ of functions on $X$ to $R$) if there exists a sequence $\{f_n\}$ in $\mathscr{F}$ such that $f_n \nearrow f$. We are now considering the situation in which $X = R^k$ and $\mathscr{F} = C_\infty(R^k)$. We see at once from Theorem 6–9 II (b) that over-functions are l.s.c. on $R^k$. Therefore an under-function is u.s.c. This information is of importance for study of the measure $\mu$ determined by an elementary integral $I$. Further information is contained in the following theorem.

THEOREM 6–9 III. *Let $\mathscr{F}^\circ$ be the class of over-functions relative to $C_\infty(R^k)$. Then $f \in \mathscr{F}^\circ$ if and only if $f$ is l.s.c. on $R^k$ and there exists $f_0 \in C_\infty(R^k)$ such that $f_0 \leq f$.*

The correctness of the "only if" assertion is evident from what has already been said. For the proof of the "if" assertion we need a general proposition about lower semicontinuous functions. We state it as a lemma.

LEMMA 6–9 IV. *Suppose $F : R^k \to R^*$ is l.s.c. and that $F \geq 0$. Then there exists a sequence $\{F_n\}$ of continuous functions on $R^k$ to $R$ such that $F_n \geq 0$ and $F_n \nearrow F$.*

*Proof.* We emphasize that the $F_n$'s have finite values. We also remark that the theorem and proof are valid if $R^k$ is replaced by any metric space.

The case in which $F(x) = +\infty$ for every $x$ is simple. Here, we can define $F_n(x) = n$ for all $x$. From now on we assume that $F$ has some finite values. We define

$$F_n(x) = \inf\{F(y) + nD(x, y) : y \in R^k\}, \tag{4}$$

where $D(x, y)$ is the distance from $x$ to $y$. Clearly, $F_n(x) \leq F(x)$, because $D(x, x) = 0$. Also, $0 \leq F_n(x) < +\infty$, because $F \geq 0$ and $F(y)$ is finite for some $y$. It is furthermore obvious that $F_n \leq F_{n+1}$. Let $G(x) = \lim F_n(x)$. Then $0 \leq G(x) \leq F(x)$.

Consider any two points $x_1$, $x_2$. By the triangular inequality for distance, for any $y$ we have

$$F_n(x_1) \leq F(y) + nD(x_1, y) \leq F(y) + n[D(x_1, x_2) + D(x_2, y)],$$

whence

$$F_n(x_1) - nD(x_1, x_2) \leq F(y) + nD(x_2, y).$$

Letting $y$ vary, we see that

$$F_n(x_1) - nD(x_1, x_2) \leq F_n(x_2).$$

Thus,

$$F_n(x_1) - F_n(x_2) \leq nD(x_1, x_2).$$

By symmetry, then,

$$|F_n(x_1) - F_n(x_2)| \leq nD(x_1, x_2).$$

This shows that $F_n$ is continuous.

We now wish to prove that $F \leq G$. This will imply that $F = G$ and complete the proof. Let $x$ be given. Suppose $c < F(x)$. Then, since $F$ is l.s.c., there is a neighborhood $V$ of $x$ such that $c < F(y)$ if $y \in V$. Choose $\epsilon > 0$ so that $y \in V$ if $D(x, y) < \epsilon$. We want to show that $F_n(x) \geq c$ if $n$ is sufficiently large, and hence that $G(x) \geq c$. Because of our freedom in choosing $c$, this will imply $F(x) \leq G(x)$. In examining the definition of $F_n(x)$ by (4), we consider $y$'s for which $D(x, y) < \epsilon$ and those $y$'s for which $D(x, y) \geq \epsilon$. When $D(x, y) < \epsilon$,

$$F(y) + nD(x, y) > c + 0 = c.$$

When $D(x, y) \geq \epsilon$,

$$F(y) + nD(x, y) \geq n\epsilon.$$

Hence, if $n$ is so large that $n\epsilon \geq c$, we see that $F_n(x) \geq c$. This completes the proof.

We now turn to the proof of Theorem 6–9 III. Assuming $f_0 \in C_\infty(R^k)$, $f : R^k \to R^*$, with $f$ l.s.c. and $f_0 \leq f$, let $F = f - f_0$. The fact that $f_0$ is continuous implies that $F$ is l.s.c. (see Problem 2). We then obtain a sequence $\{F_n\}$ as specified in Lemma 6–9 IV, with $F_n \nearrow F$. We wish to replace $\{F_n\}$ by another sequence $\{G_n\}$ having the same general properties, but with the additional property that $G_n \in C_\infty(R^k)$. Let

$$H_n(x) = \begin{cases} n & \text{if } \|x\| \leq n \\ n - n(\|x\| - n) & \text{if } n < \|x\| < n + 1 \\ 0 & \text{if } \|x\| \geq n + 1. \end{cases}$$

Then let $G_n = H_n \wedge F_n$. Then $G_n \in C_\infty(R^k)$ and $G_n \nearrow F$, as the reader may easily verify. But then $G_n + f_0 \nearrow F + f_0 = f$. This shows that $f$ is an over-function relative to $C_\infty(R^k)$.

## PROPERTIES OF THE MEASURE $\mu$

We return now to a study of the measure $\mu$ determined by an arbitrary elementary integral $I$ on $C_\infty(R^k)$; the class of measurable sets is $\mathbf{S}$.

THEOREM 6–9 V. (a) *The class* $\mathbf{S}$ *contains all Borel sets.*

(b) *Compact sets have finite measure.*

(c) *For any* $E \in \mathbf{S}$, $\mu(E)$ *is the infimum of* $\mu(U)$ *as* $U$ *varies over the class of open sets such that* $E \subset U$.

(d) *In order that a set* $E$ *be measurable and of finite measure, it is necessary and sufficient that to each* $\epsilon > 0$ *there correspond an open set* $U$ *and a compact set* $A$ *such that* $A \subset E \subset U$ *and* $\mu(U - A) < \epsilon$.

(e) *For any nonempty* $E \in \mathbf{S}$, $\mu(E)$ *is the supremum of* $\mu(A)$ *as* $A$ *varies over the class of compact subsets of* $E$.

(f) *Each* $E \in \mathbf{S}$ *can be expressed in the form* $E = B \cup F$, *where* $B$ *is a Borel set and* $F \in \mathbf{S}$, $\mu(F) = 0$.

*Proof.* We remark that there is a further property of $\mu$ and $\mathbf{S}$, similar to (d). If in (d) we delete the requirement that $\mu(E)$ be finite, and replace "compact" by "closed," we obtain a true proposition (the same as Theorem 4–8 V for Lebesgue measure). The proof of this modification of (d) is left as a problem.

*Proof of* (a). Suppose $E$ is an open set. The characteristic function $\chi_E$ is l.s.c. (as the reader may easily verify). Since $\chi_E \geq 0$, it follows by Theorem 6–9 III that $\chi_E$ is an over-function. But then it is measurable. Hence, $E$ is measurable. Since $\mathbf{S}$ is a $\sigma$-ring which contains all open sets, it must contain all Borel sets.

*Proof of* (b). It is enough to show that compact intervals have finite measure, because the measure is monotone. If $E$ is a compact interval, it is easy to see that there exists $f \in C_\infty(R^k)$ such that $f(x) \geq 1$ if $x \in E$ and $f(x) \geq 0$ everywhere (see the definition of $g$ in connection with (3), for instance). But then $0 \leq \chi_E \leq f$, whence $\chi_E$ is summable and $\mu(E) < +\infty$.

*Proof of* (c). The case when $\mu(E) = +\infty$ is obvious, so we suppose $\mu(E)$ is finite. Then $\chi_E$ is summable. Suppose $\epsilon > 0$. Choose an over-function $f$ so that $\chi_E \leq f$ and $I(f) < \mu(E) + \frac{\epsilon}{2}$. Choose $\delta > 0$, with $\delta < 1$ but $1 - \delta$ so small that $\delta^{-1}\left[\mu(E) + \frac{\epsilon}{2}\right] < \mu(E) + \epsilon$. Let $U = \{x : f(x) > \delta\}$. The set $U$ is open, by Theorem 6–9 II (a). Evidently, $\delta\chi_U \leq f$. Therefore $\delta\mu(U) \leq I(f) < \mu(E) + \epsilon/2$, and $\mu(U) < \mu(E) + \epsilon$. Since $E \subset U$, the proof is complete.

*Proof of the sufficiency in* (d). If $A$ and $U$ are related to $E$ as specified, we observe first of all that $\mu(U)$ is finite, because $\mu(A)$ is finite, by (b), and $U = A \cup (U - A)$. Hence, there exists an under-function $g$ and an over-function $h$ such that $g \leq \chi_A \leq \chi_E \leq \chi_U \leq h$, with

$$I(g) > \mu(A) - \epsilon, \qquad I(h) < \mu(U) + \epsilon.$$

Then $I(h) - I(g) < \mu(U - A) + 2\epsilon < 3\epsilon$. Since $\epsilon$ is arbitrary, Theorem 6–3 I (a) shows that $\chi_E$ is summable, which implies that $E \in \mathrm{S}$ and $\mu(E) < +\infty$.

*Proof of the necessity in* (d). We assume that $\chi_E$ is summable. Suppose $\epsilon > 0$. Let $h$ be an over-function such that $\chi_E \leq h$ and $I(h) < \mu(E) + \frac{\epsilon}{8}$. There exists a function $f \in C_\infty(R^k)$ such that $f \leq h$ and $I(f) > I(h) - \frac{\epsilon}{16}$. Now,

$$|f - \chi_E| \leq |f - h| + |h - \chi_E| = (h - f) + (h - \chi_E),$$

and so

$$I(|f - \chi_E|) < \frac{\epsilon}{16} + \frac{\epsilon}{8} = \frac{3\epsilon}{16}.$$

Therefore there exists an over-function $p$ such that $|f - \chi_E| \leq p$ and $I(p) < \frac{5\epsilon}{16}$. We see that $f - p \leq \chi_E$ and hence also $(f - p) \vee 0 \leq \chi_E$. Let $g = (f - p) \vee 0$. Then $g$ is u.s.c., because $f$ is continuous and $p$ is l.s.c. (see Problems 2 and 3). Moreover, $g(x) = 0$ if $f(x) = 0$, because $p \geq 0$. Hence there is a compact set outside of which all values of $g$ are zero. Let $A = \{x : g(x) \geq \frac{1}{4}\}$. Since $g$ is u.s.c., $A$ is the complement of an open set; hence, being a closed subset of a compact set, $A$ is compact. Moreover, $A \subset E$, because $g \leq \chi_E$. Let $B = E - A$. By checking at points of $E^\sim$, $A$, and $B$ we see that $g \leq \chi_A + \frac{1}{4}\chi_B$, whence

$$I(g) \leq \mu(A) + \tfrac{1}{4}\mu(B) = \tfrac{3}{4}\mu(A) + \tfrac{1}{4}\mu(E). \tag{5}$$

But

$$I(g) \geq I(f - p) = I(f) - I(p) > I(h) - \frac{\epsilon}{16} - \frac{5\epsilon}{16} \geq \mu(E) - \frac{3\epsilon}{8}.$$

From this and (5) we find that $\mu(E) - \frac{\epsilon}{2} < \mu(A)$.

We can use (c) to obtain an open set $U$ such that $E \subset U$ and $\mu(U) < \mu(E) + \frac{\epsilon}{2}$. Evidently then, $\mu(U - A) = \mu(U) - \mu(A) < \epsilon$, and the proof is complete.

*Proof of* (e). The case in which $\mu(E) < +\infty$ is covered in the proof of (d). If $\mu(E) = +\infty$, we can express $E$ in the form $E = \bigcup_n E_n$, where $E_n \subset E_{n+1}$, $E_n$ is measurable, and $\mu(E_n) < +\infty$ (for example, $E_n = E \cap \{x : \|x\| \leq n\}$). Then $\mu(E_n) \to \mu(E) = +\infty$. We can choose a compact set $A_n$ such that $A_n \subset E_n$ and $\mu(A_n) > \mu(E_n) - \frac{1}{n}$. Then $A_n \subset E$, $\mu(A_n) \to +\infty$, and the proof is complete.

*Proof of* (f). We can use essentially the same argument that was used in proving Theorem 4–8 II (a). This traces back to (1) in Section 4–8. In our present case we are not concerned with outer measures, and we use part (c) of the present theorem in place of (1) in Section 4–8.

### THE SPECIAL CASE $k = 1$

We shall show that when $\mu$ is the measure determined by an elementary integral $I$ on $C_\infty(R)$, it is the same as the Radon measure (= Lebesgue-Stieltjes measure) generated by a certain right-continuous nondecreasing function $v$ according to Method I in Section 4–10.

THEOREM 6–9 VI. *Let $I : C_\infty(R) \to R$ be an elementary integral, and let $\mu$ be the measure it determines, with* **S** *the $\sigma$-ring of measurable sets. Let $v : R \to R$ be defined as follows:*

$$v(x) = \begin{cases} \mu((0, x]) & \text{if } x > 0 \\ 0 & \text{if } x = 0 \\ -\mu((x, 0]) & \text{if } x < 0. \end{cases} \tag{6}$$

*Then $v$ is a right-continuous nondecreasing function. Let $\nu^*$ be the outer measure on $R$ generated by $v$ according to Method I in Section* 4–10. *Then* **S** *is precisely the class of $\nu^*$-measurable sets, and $\mu(E) = \nu^*(E)$ if $E \in$* **S**.

*Proof.* It is easily checked that $v(b) - v(a) = \mu((a, b])$ whenever $a < b$. Hence, $v$ is nondecreasing. To show that $v$ is right-continuous, observe that $v(x+) = \inf \{v(y) : y > x\}$. Since $v(y) = v(a) + \mu((a, y])$ if $a < y$, we wish to prove that $\inf_{y>x} \mu((a, y]) = \mu((a, x])$. Since $\mu$ is monotone it clearly suffices to show that if $\epsilon > 0$ there exists some $y > x$ such that $\mu((a, y]) < \mu((a, x]) + \epsilon$. By Theorem 6–9 V (c) there exists an open set $U$ such that $(a, x] \subset U$ and $\mu(U) < \mu((a, x]) + \epsilon$. Choose $y$ so that $x < y$ and $[x, y] \subset U$. Then $(a, y] \subset U$, so $\mu((a, y]) < \mu(U)$, and we have attained what was needed.

An argument similar to the foregoing shows that $\mu(E) = v(c) - v(c-)$ if $E$ consists of the single point $c$. From Theorem 4–10 I it now appears that $\nu^*(E) = \mu(E)$ if $E$ is either a half-open interval $(a, b]$ or a set consisting of a single point, and hence also if $E$ is an open interval. From this it follows that $\nu^*(E) = \mu(E)$ if $E$ is any open set (see the argument at the end of Section 4–10). Since Theorem 6–9 V (c) is valid for $\nu^*$-measurable sets with $\nu^*$ in place of $\mu$ (see Problem 3 (a) in Section 4–10), it follows that $\nu^*(E) = \mu(E)$ for any Borel set, since Borel sets are measurable in both senses.

Next, we remark that $\nu^*(E) = 0$ (and therefore $E$ is $\nu^*$-measurable) if and only if $E \in$ **S** and $\mu(E) = 0$. For, if $E \in$ **S** and $\mu(E) = 0$, then

$$0 = \inf \{\mu(U) : U \text{ open, } E \subset U\} = \nu^*(E)$$

(because $\mu(U) = \nu^*(U)$). On the other hand, if $\nu^*(E) = 0$, there exists a Borel set $H$ such that $E \subset H$ and $\nu^*(H) = 0$ (see Problem 3 (d) in Section 4–10). But then $\mu(H) = 0$. Hence, $E \in$ **S** and $\mu(E) = 0$, because $\mu$ is a complete measure (Theorem 6–5 IV). Because of

Theorem 6–9 V (f) and the corresponding proposition for $\nu^*$-measurable sets (Problem 3 (d), Section 4–10), we now see that **S** coincides with the class of $\nu^*$-measurable sets and that the restriction of $\nu^*$ to **S** is $\mu$.

### PROBLEMS

1. Let $X$ be a compact space, and suppose $f : X \to R^*$ is l.s.c. on $X$. Show that $X$ contains a point $x_0$ such that $f(x_0) \leq f(x)$ for every $x$. [*Suggestion.* Assuming $f(x) < +\infty$ for some $x$, let $m = \inf_x f(x)$, assume the proposition false, and consider the sets $E_c = \{x : f(x) \leq c\}$, where $m < c$.]

2. Prove that $f_1 + f_2$ is l.s.c. if $f_1$ and $f_2$ are each l.s.c. and if $f_1$ and $f_2$ are never infinite but of opposite sign at the same point. In particular, this applies if $f_1$ is l.s.c., $f_2$ is continuous, and one of the functions has all its values finite.

3. Prove that $f_1 \vee f_2$ is u.s.c. if both $f_1$ and $f_2$ are u.s.c.

4. In the context of Theorem 6–9 V, prove that a set $E$ is measurable if and only if to each $\epsilon > 0$ corresponds a pair of sets $A$, $U$ with $A$ closed, $U$ open, $A \subset E \subset U$, and $\mu(U - A) < \epsilon$.

## 6–10 Regular Borel measures in $R^k$

Let **B** be the $\sigma$-ring of all Borel sets in $R^k$ and let $\nu$ be a measure on **B**. Suppose that $\nu$ has the two properties

(a) $\nu(E) < +\infty$ if $E$ is compact,
(b) for any $E \in B$, $\nu(E)$ is the infimum of $\nu(U)$ as $U$ varies over the class of open sets which contain $E$.

Then we call $\nu$ *a regular Borel measure*. Property (b) is called the regularity property of $\nu$.

If $\mu$ is any measure on a $\sigma$-ring **S** in $R^k$ such that (1) **S** includes all Borel sets, (2) $\mu(E) < +\infty$ if $E$ is compact, and (3) for each $E \in$ **S**, $\mu(E)$ is the infimum of $\mu(U)$ as $U$ varies over the class of open sets which contain $E$, we call $\mu$ *a regular extension* of a Borel measure. Property (3) is called the regularity property.

Lebesgue measure in $R^k$ is a regular extension of a Borel measure (see (1) in Section 4–8). The Radon measure in $R$ determined by a right-continuous nondecreasing function (by Method I in Section 4–10) is a regular extension of a Borel measure; see Problem 3 (a) in Section 4–10. The measure determined by an arbitrary elementary integral $I$ on $C_\infty(R^k)$ is a regular extension of a Borel measure (see Theorem 6–9 V).

THEOREM 6–10 I. *If $\mu$ : **S** $\to R^*$ is a regular extension of a Borel measure (with **S** a $\sigma$-ring in $R^k$), then to every $E \in$ **S** corresponds a pair of Borel sets $H_1$, $H_2$ such that $H_1 \subset E \subset H_2$ and $\mu(E - H_1) = \mu(H_2 - E) = 0$. Consequently, each element of **S** is a disjoint union of a Borel set and a set of measure zero.*

*Proof.* We can argue exactly as in the proofs of Theorems 4–8 I (a) and 4–8 II (a), using the regularity property of $\mu$ in place of (1) in Section 4–8.

It is worthy of mention that if $\mu$ is a regular extension of a Borel measure, then for every measurable set $E$, $\mu(E)$ is the supremum of $\mu(A)$, as $A$ varies over the class of compact subsets of $E$. This can be proved by arguments used in the proof of Theorem 4–8 V.

Now, let us start from the measure space $(R^k, \mathbf{B}, \nu)$, where $\nu$ is a regular Borel measure on $R^k$, and let us apply the theory in Chapter 5 to arrive at the corresponding class of summable functions. It is easy to see that every element of $C_\infty(R^k)$ is summable. In the first place, any continuous function is measurable by Theorem 5–1 II. Next, if $f \in C_\infty(R^k)$, $f$ is bounded, with $\|f\| = \max |f(x)| < +\infty$. Also, the set $N(f) = \{x : f(x) \neq 0\}$ is measurable; it has finite measure because it is contained in a compact set. Hence, $f$ is summable, because $|f| \leq \|f\| \, \chi_{N(f)}$.

If we define $I(f) = \int f \, d\nu$ when $f \in C_\infty(R^k)$, it is clear that $I$ is an elementary integral on $C_\infty(R^k)$, in the sense of Section 6–1 (see Theorem 6–9 I). Let $\mu$ and **S** be the measure and the class of measurable sets determined by $I$ according to Section 6–5. Then we have the natural question: What is the relation between the two measures $\nu$, $\mu$? We know a good deal about $\mu$ from Theorem 6–9 V. It is a regular extension of a Borel measure. The next theorem tells us more.

THEOREM 6–10 II. *With $\mu$ and $\nu$ as here specified, $\mu(E) = \nu(E)$ for each Borel set $E$.*

*Proof.* Because of the regularity of both $\mu$ and $\nu$ it is enough to show that $\nu(E) = \mu(E)$ if $E$ is an open set. Moreover, it is enough to consider bounded open sets, for every open set is the union of an increasing sequence of bounded open sets. If $E$ is a bounded open set, $\mu(E)$ and $\nu(E)$ are both finite. By Theorem 6–7 III we know that $\mu(E) = I(\chi_E)$. Now, $\chi_E$ is lower semicontinuous, because $E$ is open. Therefore it is an over-function relative to $C_\infty(R^k)$ (Theorem 6–9 III). Hence, there is a sequence $\{f_n\}$ in $C_\infty(R^k)$ such that $f_n \nearrow \chi_E$ and $\int f_n \, d\nu \to \int \chi_E \, d\nu = \nu(E)$. But also $\int f_n \, d\nu = I(f_n) \to I(\chi_E) = \mu(E)$. Hence, $\nu(E) = \mu(E)$. This ends the proof.

There is a temptation to conjecture that $\mathbf{S} = \mathbf{B}$ and $\mu = \nu$, but this is not true in general, for $\mu$ is a complete measure (Theorem 6–5 IV), whereas $\nu$ need not be complete. For example, if $\nu$ is Lebesgue measure restricted to **B**, it is not complete (see the end of Section 4–8). There is, nevertheless, a well-defined relationship between $\mu$ and $\nu$; $\mu$ is the completion of $\nu$, in the sense of Section 4–11.

THEOREM 6–10 III. *If $\nu$ is a regular Borel measure on $R^k$ and $\mu$ is the measure determined (as in* Section 6–5*) by the elementary integral on $C_\infty(R^k)$ defined by $I(f) = \int f \, d\nu$, then $\mu$ coincides with the completion of $\nu$.*

*Proof.* Let $\bar{\nu}$ be the completion of $\nu$. It is easy to verify that $\bar{\nu}$ has the regularity property, so that it is a regular extension of a Borel measure. We leave this as an exercise for the reader. Then the situation is this: Both $\mu$ and $\bar{\nu}$ are regular extensions of Borel measures, and they are both complete. Moreover, $\mu(E) = \nu(E)$ if $E$ is a Borel set (Theorem 6–10 II). It is then an easy matter, using Theorem 6–10 I, to show that the sets of measure zero for $\bar{\nu}$ are the same as those for $\mu$. Finally, since every set either in $\bar{\mathbf{B}}$ or **S** has a representation as a disjoint union of a Borel set and a set of measure zero, we see that $\mu = \bar{\nu}$.

COROLLARY 6–10 IV. *If $\nu_1$ and $\nu_2$ are regular Borel measures on $R^k$ such that*

$$\int f \, d\nu_1 = \int f \, d\nu_2$$

*for each $f$ in $C_\infty(R^k)$, then $\nu_1 = \nu_2$.*

*Proof.* Use the preceding theorem, and observe that $\bar{\nu}_1 = \bar{\nu}_2$ implies $\nu_1 = \nu_2$.

**PROBLEMS**

1. Work out every detail of Theorem 6–10 III.

2. Suppose $\nu$ is a regular Borel measure on $R^k$. Show that, for any Borel set $E$, $\nu(E) = \sup \nu(A)$ as $A$ varies over the class of all compact subsets of $E$. Show also that, if $\nu(E)$ is finite and $\epsilon > 0$, there exist sets $A$, $U$ with $A$ compact, $U$ open, $A \subset E \subset C$, and $\nu(U - A) < \epsilon$. [*Hint*. Consider the completion $\bar{\nu}$.]

3. Let $\nu$ be a regular Borel measure on $R^k$. Show that, if $A$ is a compact set, $\nu(A)$ is the infimum of the values of $\int f\,d\nu$ as $f$ varies over the class of all $f \in C_\infty(R^k)$ such that $\chi_A \leq f$. [*Hint*. Note the construction of the function $g$ in the proof of Theorem 6–9 I.]

## 6–11 The class $\mathscr{L}^p$

We return now to the general situation considered in Sections 6–1 – 6–7. We denote by $\mathscr{L}^p$ the class of all functions $f: X \to R^*$ such that $f \in \mathscr{M}$ and $|f|^p \in \mathscr{L}$. In Section 5–8 we have already discussed this topic from the point of view of the integration theory in Chapter 5. If we assume that $1 \in \mathscr{M}$, we know from Section 6–7 that Chapters 5 and 6 simply afford us two different ways of arriving at much the same final results in the theory of measurable functions and summable functions. Hence, our purpose in this section is not to duplicate Section 5–8, but merely to discuss some matters which belong here rather than in Chapter 5.

We shall confine our attention to the case $1 \leq p < \infty$. Also, we point out that the assumption $1 \in \mathscr{M}$ is needed, because we wish to use Hölder's inequality (Theorem 5–8 I). For, the proof that the product of two elements of $\mathscr{M}$ is in $\mathscr{M}$ depends on Theorem 6–7 II and on results in Chapter 5; this fact about products is needed in the proof of Theorem 5–8 I.

We shall use the notation

$$\|f\|_p = \{I(|f|^p)\}^{1/p} \tag{1}$$

when $f \in \mathscr{L}^p$. If $f$ and $g$ are in $\mathscr{L}^p$, we have

$$\|f + g\|_p \leq \|f\|_p + \|g\|_p. \tag{2}$$

This is Minkowski's inequality ((3) in Section 5–8), which depends on Hölder's inequality in case $p > 1$.

In the specification of the vector lattice $\mathscr{F}$ in Section 6–1 it was not assumed that the elements of $\mathscr{F}$ are bounded functions. Now, however, we need this assumption. We also need Stone's axiom (see Section 6–7). This axiom, the assumption that $1 \wedge f \in \mathscr{F}$ if $f \in \mathscr{F}$, implies for $c > 0$ that $c \wedge f \in \mathscr{F}$ when $f \in \mathscr{F}$ (see Theorem 6–7 IV (a)). It also implies that $1 \in \mathscr{M}$ (Theorem 6–7 IV (c)).

THEOREM 6–11 I. *Suppose that each element of $\mathscr{F}$ is a bounded function, and that $\mathscr{F}$ satisfies Stone's axiom. Then, for $p \geq 1$ we have:* (a) $\mathscr{F} \subset \mathscr{L}^p$; (b) *if $f \in \mathscr{L}^p$ and $\epsilon > 0$, there exists $g \in \mathscr{F}$ such that $\|f - g\|_p < \epsilon$.*

*Comment*. For $p = 1$ the special assumptions on $\mathscr{F}$ are not necessary. See Theorem 6–4 VI.

*Proof of* (a). Suppose $f \in \mathscr{F}$; let $M = \sup\{|f(x)| : x \in X\}$. Then $|f|^p \leq M^{p-1}|f|$, whence $f \in \mathscr{L}^p$. Here, we use $1 \in \mathscr{M}$ and Theorem 6–7 II to show that $|f|^p \in \mathscr{M}$; then $|f|^p \in \mathscr{L}$, by Theorem 6–5 I (c).

*Proof of* (b). If $f \in \mathscr{L}^p$ and $g, h \in \mathscr{F}$, we can write $f - (g - h) = (f^+ - g) - (f^- - h)$,

$$\|f - (g - h)\|_p \leq \|f^+ - g\|_p + \|f^- - h\|_p.$$

Since $f^+$ and $f^-$ are also in $\mathscr{L}^p$, it is then clearly sufficient to prove (b) on the assumption that $f \geq 0$. We proceed on this assumption.

For each $n$ let $E_n = \left\{x : \frac{1}{n} < f(x) < n\right\}$, and let $f_n = f\chi_{E_n}$. It is clear that $f_n(x) \nearrow f(x)$ if $f(x)$ is finite; thus this is true a.e. We conclude that $\|f_n - f\|_p \to 0$. Next, observe that $\chi_{E_n} \leq nf$, whence $\chi_{E_n} \in \mathscr{L}$, because $\chi_{E_n} = (\chi_{E_n})^p \leq n^p f^p$. Moreover, $0 \leq f_n \leq n\chi_{E_n}$, and so $f_n \in \mathscr{L}$. By Theorem 6–4 VI we may choose $h_n \in \mathscr{F}$ so that $h_n \geq 0$ and $\|f_n - h_n\|_1 < n^{-p}$. Now, let $g_n = n \wedge h_n$. Then $0 \leq g_n \leq h_n$, $g_n \in \mathscr{F}$; when $g_n(x) \neq h_n(x)$, we have $g_n(x) = n < h_n(x)$. In view of these facts and the definition of $f_n$, it may be seen that $|f_n - g_n| \leq |f_n - h_n|$. Therefore, $\|f_n - g_n\|_1 < n^{-p}$. We now have $0 \leq g_n \leq n$ and $0 \leq f_n \leq n$, so that $|f_n - g_n| \leq n$. Therefore, $|f_n - g_n|^p \leq n^{p-1} |f_n - g_n|$, and hence $(\|f_n - g_n\|_p)^p \leq n^{p-1} \|f_n - g_n\|_1 < n^{-1}$. Therefore,

$$\begin{aligned} \|f - g_n\|_p &\leq \|f - f_n\|_p + \|f_n - g_n\|_p \\ &< \|f - f_n\|_p + n^{-1/p}, \end{aligned}$$

so that $\|f - g_n\|_p \to 0$. This finishes the proof, for when $\epsilon$ is given we have $\|f - g_n\|_p < \epsilon$ when $n$ is sufficiently large.

In view of Section 6–8, we conclude from Theorem 6–11 I that for the case of Lebesgue measure $\mu$ in $R^k$, if $f \in \mathscr{L}^p(\mu)$, there is for each $\epsilon > 0$ a function $g \in C_\infty(R^k)$ such that

$$\int |f - g|^p \, d\mu < \epsilon.$$

THEOREM 6–11 II. *Suppose that* $1 \in \mathscr{M}$. *Let* $\{f_n\}$ *be a sequence in* $\mathscr{L}^p$ *such that* $\|f_n - f_m\|_p \to 0$ *as* $m$ *and* $n \to \infty$. *Then there exists a function* $f \in \mathscr{L}^p$ *such that* $\|f_n - f\|_p \to 0$. *Moreover, there exists a function* $h \in \mathscr{L}^p$ *and a subsequence* $\{g_n\}$ *of* $\{f_n\}$ *such that* $g_n(x) \to f(x)$ *a.e. and* $|g_n| \leq h$.

*Proof.* The argument is very much the same as in the proof of Theorem 6–4 IV. The preliminary result in that proof is valid with $\| \quad \|_p$ in place of $\| \quad \|_1$ and $\mathscr{L}^p$ in place of $\mathscr{L}$. We then proceed in the same manner as before. When it comes to proving that $f \in \mathscr{L}^p$, the argument is slightly different. Since $G_1 \leq G_n \leq H_1$, we have $|G_n| \leq |G_1| + |H_1|$, $|G_n|^p \leq (|G_1| + |H_1|)^p$, and since $|G_n|^p \to |f|^p$, we can conclude from Theorem 6–3 IV (c) that $f \in \mathscr{L}^p$. The rest of the proof is then essentially as before.

## SUGGESTED READING FOR CHAPTER 6

References most closely related to the exposition in Chapter 6:

AUMANN [1], Chapter 9.
DANIELL [1], [2].
LOOMIS [1], Chapter 3.
NAIMARK [1], Section 6 in Chapter 1.

STONE [2].
ZAANEN [1], Chapters 3, 4.

Parts of the books of McShane [1] (Chapters 1–4) and McShane and Botts [1] (Chapter 5) are relevant here, since they employ the Daniell method of obtaining an integral by extending a positive linear functional. The treatment is not as abstract as in our exposition. Attention is limited to functions defined on $R^k$, and considerations of semicontinuity enter at the outset.

For a more abstract treatment of integration processes by McShane, see his monograph [2].

There is another method, due to F. Riesz, in which the theory of integration is developed prior to the general theory of measure. It is somewhat different from the Daniell method. For accounts of this method see:

GRAVES [1], Chapters 10, 11.
RIESZ [2].
RIESZ and NAGY [1], Chapter 2.

Chapter 10 of Halmos [1], and especially Section 56 of this reference, is related to Sections 6–9 and 6–10 of our text.

For an interesting historical essay on the subject of integration and measure, see Bourbaki [3b], pp. 113–124. This account provides a starting point for attempting to understand the contributions made by Borel, Lebesgue, Stieltjes, Riesz, and Radon. It is also pointed out that what we have called "the Daniell method" was essentially present in the work of W. H. Young [1], albeit merely in a special concrete case, where the elementary integral is the Riemann integral on $C_\infty(R^k)$.

The theory of integration as expounded in Bourbaki [3a], Chapters 3 and 4, is closely related to the developments in Section 6–9 (with one difference that $R^k$ is replaced by an arbitrary locally compact Hausdorff space). The whole point of view is very different, however.

CHAPTER SEVEN

# Iterated Integrals and Fubini's Theorem

## 7–0 Introduction

When a function of several variables is given and an operation is performed which consists of two or more successive integrations, each integration being extended over a set in a subspace generated by a proper subset of all the variables, this operation is called an *iterated integral.* A classical example is furnished by a continuous function $f$ of two real variables $x$, $y$, defined in the rectangular region

(1) $$A = \{(x, y) : a \leq x \leq b,\ \alpha \leq y \leq \beta\}.$$

We may integrate with respect to $y$, obtaining a function of $x$:

(2) $$\int_\alpha^\beta f(x, y)\, dy.$$

Integrating next with respect to $x$, we obtain

(3) $$\int_a^b \left( \int_\alpha^\beta f(x, y)\, dy \right) dx, \text{ written as} \int_a^b dx \int_\alpha^\beta f(x, y)\, dy.$$

Here each integration process is an integration of a function of one real variable.

In contrast to the iterated integral there is the direct single operation of integrating the function of several variables by a process appropriate to the product space in which the function is defined. In classical analysis it has been customary to call an integral of this kind a *multiple integral.* Thus, for example, if $f$ is defined and continuous on the rectangle $A$ in (1), the Riemann integral

(4) $$\iint_A f(x, y)\, dx\, dy$$

is called a *double integral.* It is defined as a limit of approximating sums, each term of one of the sums being of the form $f(x, y)\Delta A$, where $\Delta A$ is the area of a subregion of $A$ and $(x, y)$ is a point in the subregion. We then have the theorem that the double integral in (4) has the same value as the iterated integral in (3) for each continuous function. This theorem is very important in practice. For one thing, it enables us to reduce the problem of calculating the value of the double integral to the problem of calculating integrals of functions of one real variable. For the latter problem we can often use antiderivatives and the fundamental theorems connecting differentiation and integration.

When we turn from Riemann integrals to the more general integrals of the Lebesgue type, the distinction between iterated integrals and multiple integrals persists. Owing to the more general point of view, however, what we have previously called a "multiple" integral is not in principle a different kind of object from a "single" integral. In theories of the Lebesgue type, integration is determined by a measure space. A multiple integral is an integral in which the space underlying the measure space is a *product space* and the measure is constructed in a special way from measures on the *factor spaces.* We can regard the Euclidean space $R^2$ as the product $R \times R$. Lebesgue measure in $R^2$ can be regarded as arising in a certain way from Lebesgue measure in $R$. Likewise, we can regard $R^3$ as $R^2 \times R$ (or equally well as $R \times R^2$), and Lebesgue measure in $R^3$ can be regarded as arising in a certain way from Lebesgue measure in $R^2$ and Lebesgue measure in $R$. From this point of view we evolve the notion of a *product-measure.* In this sense we can regard a multiple Lebesgue integral as an integral in the sense of Chapter 5, with the special feature that the measure which is used is a product-measure. We then have the problem of whether an integral with respect to a product-measure is equal to an iterated integral in which we use the constituent *factor-measures.*

These questions can also be looked at from the point of view of the Daniell integral of Chapter 6, without the intervention of the notion of measure.

In this chapter we shall not use several integral signs in representing a "multiple" integral. The fact that a product space and a product-measure is involved will be shown by other notational devices.

In its original form, the theorem of G. Fubini (1879–1943), published in 1907 [1], was a theorem about expressing a multiple Lebesgue integral as an iteration of Lebesgue integrals in spaces of lower dimensionality. In this chapter we first give a proof of Fubini's theorem in its original scope (Theorem 7–1 II). The classical form of the Fubini theorem will thus be available to students without the need to master the more elaborate preparation needed for later generalizations. Adequate preparation is contained in Chapter 5 as far as the end of Section 5–5, along with the necessary parts of Chapter 4. Subsequently we give two generalizations of the classical Fubini theorem. These generalizations are important tools in modern analysis. One of them, which we call the Fubini-Stone theorem (Theorem 7–2 I) treats the subject from the point of view of Chapter 6. This approach is really remarkably simple, and when coupled with the application of the ideas of Chapter 6 in Section 6–8, it yields the classical Fubini theorem for Euclidean spaces. The other (Theorem 7–6 II) proceeds according to the ideas of Chapter 5. As a necessary preliminary we develop a general theory of product-measures in Section 7–5.

In Section 7–4 the Fubini-Stone theorem is applied to the iteration of elementary integrals in $C_\infty(R^p)$ and $C_\infty(R^q)$, where functions on the space $R^{p+q}$ are concerned.

An approach to product-measures via the ideas of Chapter 6 is suggested by the material in Section 7–3, where we study functions of two variables which are products of functions of one variable. This material can be applied to the situation studied in Section 7–4. The results are of interest for a general class of measures in Euclidean spaces.

## 7–1 The Fubini theorem for Euclidean spaces

Suppose $p$ and $q$ are positive integers, and let $k = p + q$. We can think of $R^k$ as the product space $R^p \times R^q$. If we write points of $R^k$ as $(x, y)$, where $x \in R^p$ and $y \in R^q$, a function $f$: $R^k \to R^*$ yields a function

$$y \to f(x, y)$$

on $R^q$ to $R^*$ for each fixed value of $x$. If $f$ is summable with respect to Lebesgue measure in $R^k$ we shall say it is $L_k$-summable. We shall for our present purpose denote the integral by

$$\int_{R^k} f(x, y)\, d(x, y). \tag{1}$$

Likewise, if $\varphi$: $R^q \to R^*$ is $L_q$-summable, we denote the integral by

$$\int_{R^q} \varphi(y)\, dy.$$

We may omit the space symbols on the integral signs if clarity is not impaired or ambiguity introduced.

### THE MEASURE OF A SET IN $R^p \times R^q$

We begin our preparation for a proof of Fubini's theorem by considering what is essentially a special case of it. Once this has been disposed of, the proof of the general Fubini theorem proceeds by familiar methods.

We use $\mu_q$ for the Lebesgue measure function in $R^q$, and $\mu_q^*$ for Lebesgue outer measure. Likewise for $R^k$ and $R^p$.

Let $E$ be a set in $R^k = R^p \times R^q$. We write, for each $x$ in $R^p$,

$$E(x) = \{y: (x, y) \in E\}. \tag{2}$$

Thus $E(x) \subset R^q$. If $E = A \times B$, where $A \subset R^p$ and $B \subset R^q$ we observe that

$$E(x) = \begin{cases} B & \text{if } x \in A \\ \varnothing & \text{if } x \in R^p - A. \end{cases} \tag{3}$$

THEOREM 7–1 I. *If $E$ is any measurable set of finite measure in $R^k$, there is a set $G$ in $R^p$, with $\mu_p(G) = 0$, such that $E(x)$ is a measurable set with $\mu_q[E(x)]$ finite when $x$ is not in $G$. Moreover, the function $x \to \mu_q^*\{E(x)\}$ is summable, and*

$$\mu_k(E) = \int_{R^p} \mu_q^*\{E(x)\}\, dx. \tag{4}$$

*There is a corresponding state of affairs with the roles of $R^p$ and $R^q$ reversed.*

*Proof.* Suppose, to begin with, that $E$ is a bounded set. Then we can choose open intervals $A \subset R^p$, $B \subset R^q$ in such a way that $E \subset A \times B$, whence $E(x) \subset B$ for each $x$. Now, for each positive integer $i$ let $\{I_{ni}\}$ be a Lebesgue covering of $E$ such that $I_{ni} \subset A \times B$ and

$$\sum_n |I_{ni}| < \mu_k(E) + \frac{1}{i}. \tag{5}$$

Let $I_{ni} = A_{ni} \times B_{ni}$, where $A_{ni}$ and $B_{ni}$ are open intervals in $R^p$, $R^q$, respectively. For fixed $n$ and $i$ we define

(6) $$f_{ni}(x) = \begin{cases} \mu_q\{B_{ni}\} & \text{if } x \in A_{ni} \\ 0 & \text{if } x \in R^p - A_{ni}. \end{cases}$$

We observe that $A_{ni} \subset A$. Clearly, $f_{ni}$ is summable, and

(7) $$\int_{R^p} f_{ni}(x)\,dx = \int_A f_{ni}(x)\,dx = \mu_p(A_{ni})\mu_q(B_{ni}) = |I_{ni}|.$$

Next, we define $f_i : R^p \to R^*$ by

$$f_i(x) = \sum_n f_{ni}(x).$$

By (5), (7), and the monotone convergence theorem we see that $f_i$ is summable, and

(8) $$\int f_i(x)\,dx = \sum_n \int f_{ni}(x)\,dx < \mu_k(E) + \frac{1}{i}.$$

Now let $f(x) = \inf_i f_i(x)$. Then $f$ is summable, $f(x) = 0$ if $x \notin A$, and, since $i$ is arbitrary in (8),

(9) $$\int f(x)\,dx = \int_A f(x)\,dx \leq \mu_k(E).$$

Let $F = (A \times B) - E$. Proceeding just as we did with $E$, we arrive at a function $g : R^p \to R^*$ such that $g(x) = 0$ if $x$ is not in $A$, and

(10) $$\int_A g(x)\,dx \leq \mu_k(F).$$

If $x \in A$, $E(x)$ and $F(x)$ are disjoint sets whose union is $B$. Therefore,

(11) $$\mu_q(B) \leq \mu_q^*\{E(x)\} + \mu_q^*\{F(x)\} \qquad \text{if} \quad x \in A.$$

We shall prove that

(12) $$\mu_q^*\{E(x)\} \leq f(x), \qquad \mu_q^*\{F(x)\} \leq g(x).$$

It will be sufficient to consider the first inequality. It is clearly true if $x$ is not in $A$, so we assume $x \in A$. We may also assume $E(x) \neq \varnothing$, so suppose $y \in E(x)$. Choose a fixed $i$. Then $(x, y) \in I_{ni}$ for some $n$, so $x \in A_{ni}$, $y \in B_{ni}$. It is then clear $E(x)$ is contained in the union of a certain number of the sets $B_{ni}$, and that $x$ is in each of the corresponding sets $A_{ni}$. In view of (6) and of the definition of $f_i$, we see that $\mu_q^*\{E(x)\} \leq f_i(x)$; this being true for each $i$, we get (12).

Since $E$ is measurable, so is $F$. We can write

(13) $$\mu_k(E) + \mu_k(F) = \mu_k(A \times B) = \mu_p(A)\mu_q(B).$$

By adding (9) and (10) and using (13) we get

(14) $$\int_A \{f(x) + g(x) - \mu_q(B)\}\,dx \leq 0.$$

On the other hand, from (11) and (12) we see that

(15) $$\mu_q(B) \leq f(x) + g(x) \qquad \text{if} \quad x \in A,$$

so that the integrand in (14) is nonnegative. The conclusion is that the integrand is zero almost everywhere in $A$. That is, there is a set $G$ of measure zero contained in $A$ such that

(16) $$f(x) + g(x) = \mu_q(B) \qquad \text{if} \quad x \in A - G.$$

The inequality (14) is now an equality; using (13) we can write it as

$$\int_A f(x)\,dx + \int_A g(x)\,dx = \mu_k(E) + \mu_k(F).$$

From this we conclude that the inequalities in (9) and (10) are actually equalities. Likewise, from (11), (12), and (16) we see that

(17) $$\mu_q^*\{E(x)\} = f(x), \qquad \mu_q^*\{F(x)\} = g(x), \qquad \text{if} \quad x \in A - G.$$

These last equalities obviously hold if $x$ is not in $A$. We see, therefore, that the functions

$$x \to \mu_q^*\{E(x)\}, \qquad x \to \mu_q^*\{F(x)\}$$

are summable, because $f$ and $g$ are.

Finally, since $F(x) = B - E(x)$, the fact that

$$\mu_q^*\{E(x)\} + \mu_q^*\{F(x)\} = \mu_q(B)$$

if $x \in A - G$ implies that $E(x)$ is measurable when $x \in A - G$ (see Problem 3(*b*), Section 4–8). The measure is finite, of course, because $E(x) \subset B$. We also have (4), because we now know that the equality holds in (9). This finishes the proof for the case in which $E$ is bounded.

In the general case let $\{I_n\}$ be an expanding sequence of open intervals in $R^k$ such that $\bigcup_n I_n = R^k$. Let $E_n = E \cap I_n$. Then $E_n \subset E_{n+1}$, $E = \bigcup_n E_n$, and we have a similar situation with $E_n(x)$ and $E(x)$. We know that $\mu_k(E_n) \to \mu_k(E)$ (Theorem 4–4 III). Furthermore, $\mu_q^*\{E_n(x)\} \to \mu_q^*\{E(x)\}$ (see Problem 8, Section 4–8). From what has already been proved we then conclude, by the monotone convergence theorem, that the function $x \to \mu_q^*\{E(x)\}$ is summable and that (4) holds. There is then a set $G_0$ in $R^p$, of measure zero, such that $\mu_q^*[E(x)]$ is finite if $x$ is not in $G_0$. Let $G_n$ be the set (of measure zero) in $R^p$ such that $E_n(x)$ is not measurable if $x \in G_n$. Let $G = \bigcup_{i=0}^{\infty} G_i$. Then, since $E(x) = \bigcup_n E_n(x)$, $E(x)$ is measurable, with finite measure, if $x \in R^p - G$. This completes the proof.

We come now to the Fubini theorem. Here, $p$ and $q$ are positive integers, and $k = p + q$.

THEOREM 7–1 II. *Suppose that $f : R^k \to R^*$ is $L_k$-summable. Then there exists a set $F_1$ in $R^p$, of measure zero, and an $L_p$-summable function $f_1 : R^p \to R^*$ such that:*

(a) $$\int_{R^k} f(x, y)\,d(x, y) = \int_{R^p} f_1(x)\,dx;$$

(b) *the function $y \to f(x, y)$ is $L_q$-summable if $x \in R^p - F_1$;*

(c) $$f_1(x) = \int_{R^q} f(x, y)\,dy, \qquad \text{if} \quad x \in R^p - F_1.$$

*Similar assertions are valid with respect to a set $F_2$ of measure zero in $R^q$, a function $f_2 : R^q \to R^*$, and the function $x \to f(x, y)$ if $y$ is not in $F_2$.*

*Remark*. Combining (a) and (b) gives us the iterated integral representation of the integral of $f$:

$$\int_{R^k} f(x, y)\, d(x, y) = \int_{R^p} dx \int_{R^q} f(x, y)\, dy. \tag{18}$$

This is the succinct form of the algorithmic part of Fubini's theorem. The fuller statement of the theorem itself gives the precise assertion.

*Proof of the theorem*. Let $\mathscr{F}$ be the class of summable functions $f: R^k \to R^*$ such that the assertions in the theorem are true. We observe first of all that $f \in \mathscr{F}$ if $f$ is the characteristic function of a measurable set $E$ of finite measure in $R^k$. This is essentially the content of Theorem 7–1 I. As $F_1$ we take the $G$ of Theorem 7–1 I, and we take $f_1(x) = \mu_q^*\{E(x)\}$. When $x$ is not in $G$, $E(x)$ is measurable, with finite measure, so

$$f_1(x) = \mu_q\{E(x)\} = \int_{E(x)} 1 \cdot dy = \int_{R^q} f(x, y)\, dy.$$

Next, we observe that $\mathscr{F}$ is a linear class. We leave it for the reader to satisfy himself that if $f$ and $g$ are in $\mathscr{F}$, so are $f + g$ and $cf$. We are now assured that $\mathscr{F}$ contains all summable simple functions (finite linear combinations of characteristic functions of sets of finite measure). The next step is to show that any nonnegative summable function $f$ is in $\mathscr{F}$. To such a function corresponds a sequence $\{g_n\}$ of summable simple functions such that $g_n \nearrow f$. (For the meaning of $g_n \nearrow f$ and $g_n \searrow f$ see the subsection on monotone convergence in Section 6–1.) From this it is not hard to infer that $f \in \mathscr{F}$. We leave details to the reader. (See the suggestion given in the problem at the end of this section.) Finally, for an arbitrary summable $f$ we write $f = f^+ - f^-$ and use the fact that $\mathscr{F}$ is a linear class.

### PROBLEM

Supply details for the step about $g_n \nearrow f$, where $f \geq 0$ and $g_n \in \mathscr{F}$, in the proof of Theorem 7–1 II. [*Suggestion*. If $g_{n1}$ and $G_n$ correspond to $g_n$ as $f_1$ and $F_1$ correspond to $f$ in the statement of the theorem, consider how to modify the definition of $g_{n1}$ in a permissible way so as to insure that $\{g_{n1}\}$ is a nondecreasing sequence.]

## 7–2 The Fubini-Stone theorem

In this section we present a theorem about the iteration of integrals which arise from elementary integrals in the manner explained in Chapter 6. Since the theorem contains the classical Fubini theorem as a special case, and since the present form of the theorem is due to M. H. Stone [2], we call it the Fubini-Stone theorem.

### PRODUCT SPACES AND ITERATED INTEGRALS

To set the stage for the Fubini-Stone theorem we need three vector lattices of functions and three elementary integrals, appropriately related. For $i = 1, 2$ let $X_i$ be a nonempty set and let $\mathscr{F}_i$ be a vector lattice of functions on $X_i$ to $R$. Furthermore, let $I_i$ be an elementary integral on $\mathscr{F}_i$. Next, let $X_3 = X_1 \times X_2$, and let $\mathscr{F}_3$ be a vector lattice of functions on $X_3$ to $R$, with $I_3$ an elementary integral on $\mathscr{F}_3$. We are going to make some assumptions about the relation of $\mathscr{F}_3$ to $\mathscr{F}_1$ and $\mathscr{F}_2$, and about the relation of $I_3$ to $I_1$ and $I_2$. Briefly, what we assume is this: If $f \in \mathscr{F}_3$, $f$ is a function of the couple $(x_1, x_2)$. With $x_1$ fixed it is assumed to be a function of $x_2$ belonging to $\mathscr{F}_2$, such that if we apply $I_2$ to it we get a function of $x_1$ belonging to $\mathscr{F}_1$, and such that if we apply $I_1$ to this last function, the value we obtain is precisely $I_3(f)$. The substance of the theory to be developed is that this state of affairs is maintained to a significant extent if we start with $f \in \mathscr{L}_3$ (the class of $I_3$-summable functions) instead of with $f \in \mathscr{F}_3$. At the intermediate stages we now get elements of $\mathscr{L}_2$ and $\mathscr{L}_1$, respectively. There are some complications, however. An exceptional set of $x_1$-values must be allowed for; since this set has measure zero (in the measure determined by $I_1$), we are still able to realize the effect of $I_3$ on $f$ as equivalent to the successive applications of $I_2$ and then $I_1$.

## NOTATION

From a function $f: X_3 \to R^*$ we can construct, for each fixed $x_1 \in X_1$, the mapping $x_2 \to f(x_1, x_2)$. This function on $X_2$ to $R^*$ will be denoted by $f(x_1, \cdot)$. If this function happens to belong to $\mathscr{F}_2$, we can apply $I_2$ to it, thus obtaining a real number whose value depends on $x_1$. If this is the case for each $x_1$ in $X_1$, we shall denote the mapping $x_1 \to I_2[f(x_1, \cdot)]$ by $I_2[f(\cdot, \cdot)]$. For simplicity in printing we shall ordinarily omit the square brackets in these last notations.

We now define $\mathscr{F}_1 * \mathscr{F}_2$ to be the class of all $f: X_3 \to R$ such that $f(x_1, \cdot) \in \mathscr{F}_2$ for each $x_1 \in X_1$ and such that $I_2 f(\cdot, \cdot) \in \mathscr{F}_1$.

For each $i (i = 1, 2, 3)$ we obtain from $\mathscr{F}_i$ and $I_i$ a class $\mathscr{L}_i$ of summable functions $f: X_i \to R^*$, and a measure $\mu_i$ defined on a class of sets in $X_i$. Our principal concern here is with sets of measure zero (as in Section 6–4).

We define $\mathscr{L}_1 * \mathscr{L}_2$ to be the class of all $f: X_3 \to R^*$ such that there exists a set $E$ (depending on $f$) in $X_1$ of $\mu_1$-measure zero and an element $F \in \mathscr{L}_1$ satisfying the two conditions:

(a) $f(x_1, \cdot) \in \mathscr{L}_2$, if $x_1 \in X_1 - E$,

(b) $I_2 f(x_1, \cdot) = F(x_1)$, if $x_1 \in X_1 - E$.

For such an $f$ with corresponding $F$ we find it convenient to write $I_2 f(\cdot, \cdot) = F$. Since the definition does not fix the values of $F$ uniquely at points of $E$, $I_2 f(\cdot, \cdot)$ does not in this case have a unique meaning as an element of $\mathscr{L}_1$. Since the ambiguity involves only a set of $\mu_1$-measure zero, however, the numerical value $I_1[I_2 f(\cdot, \cdot)] = I_1(F)$ is unique. Here also we shall usually omit the square brackets.

## THE FUBINI-STONE THEOREM

We are now ready to state the Fubini-Stone theorem.

THEOREM 7–2 I. *Suppose that $\mathscr{F}_3 \subset \mathscr{F}_1 * \mathscr{F}_2$ and that $I_3(f) = I_1 I_2 f(\cdot, \cdot)$ for each $f \in \mathscr{F}_3$. Then $\mathscr{L}_3 \subset \mathscr{L}_1 * \mathscr{L}_2$ and $I_3(f) = I_1 I_2 f(\cdot, \cdot)$ for each $f \in \mathscr{L}_3$.*

*Proof.* The crucial tool in this proof is supplied by the following inequality (1), in which we use notation analogous to that already explained. The function $\mathbf{N}_i$ is determined by $I_i$ in the manner explained in Section 6–6. We use Theorem 6–6 I freely without explicit reference. *For any $f: X_3 \to R^*$,*

$$\mathbf{N}_1 \mathbf{N}_2 f(\cdot, \cdot) \leq \mathbf{N}_3(f). \tag{1}$$

In proving (1) we can assume $\mathbf{N}_3(f) < +\infty$. Therefore there exists an element $h \in \mathscr{F}_3^\circ$ such that $|f| \leq h$. Choose any such $h$. For convenience of notation let $g = |f|$. Choose a sequence $\{f_n\}$ from $\mathscr{F}_3$ in such a way that $f_n \nearrow h$. Then $I_3(f_n) \to I_3(h)$. We see that $f_n(x_1, \cdot) \nearrow h(x_1, \cdot)$, whence $h(x_1, \cdot) \in \mathscr{F}_2^\circ$. Moreover, $g(x_1, \cdot) \leq h(x_1, \cdot)$, so that $\mathbf{N}_2 g(x_1, \cdot) \leq I_2 h(x_1, \cdot)$. Also, $I_2 f_n(x_1, \cdot) \nearrow I_2 h(x_1, \cdot)$. From this we conclude that $I_2 h(\cdot, \cdot) \in \mathscr{F}_1^\circ$, and hence that $\mathbf{N}_1\mathbf{N}_2 g(\cdot, \cdot) \leq I_1 I_2 h(\cdot, \cdot)$, as well as that $I_1 I_2 f_n(\cdot, \cdot) \to I_1 I_2 h(\cdot, \cdot)$. But $I_3(f_n) = I_1 I_2 f_n(\cdot, \cdot)$. Thus we see that $I_1 I_2 h(\cdot, \cdot) = I_3(h)$ and $\mathbf{N}_1\mathbf{N}_2 g(\cdot, \cdot) \leq I_3(h)$. In view of the arbitrary choice of $h$ we infer that $\mathbf{N}_1\mathbf{N}_2 g(\cdot, \cdot) \leq \mathbf{N}_3(f)$. This is equivalent to (1), because $g = |f|$.

Now suppose $f \in \mathscr{L}_3$. By Theorem 6–4 VI there exists a sequence $\{f_n\}$ in $\mathscr{F}_3$ such that $\mathbf{N}_3(f_n - f) = I_3(|f_n - f|) < 2^{-n}$. Let $g_n = f_n - f$. We define $G : X_1 \to R^*$ by

$$G(x_1) = \sum_n \mathbf{N}_2 g_n(x_1, \cdot).$$

Then,

$$\mathbf{N}_1(G) \leq \sum_n \mathbf{N}_1\mathbf{N}_2 g_n(\cdot, \cdot) \leq \sum_n \mathbf{N}_3(g_n) < +\infty.$$

It follows that $G(x_1)$ is finite except when $x_1$ is in a certain set $E$ in $X_1$ of $\mu_1$-measure zero, and therefore that

$$\mathbf{N}_2 g_n(x_1, \cdot) = \mathbf{N}_2[f_n(x_1, \cdot) - f(x_1, \cdot)] \to 0$$

when $x_1$ is not in $E$. Since $f_n(x_1, \cdot) \in \mathscr{F}_2$, it follows from Corollary 6–6 IV that $f(x_1, \cdot) \in \mathscr{L}_2$ and hence also $g_n(x_1, \cdot) \in \mathscr{L}_2$ if $x_1 \in E^\sim$. We define a function $G_n : X_1 \to R^*$ by

$$G_n(x_1) = \begin{cases} I_2 g_n(x_1, \cdot) & \text{if } x_1 \in E^\sim \\ 0 & \text{if } x_1 \in E. \end{cases}$$

Since $|G_n(x_1)| \leq I_2(|g_n(x_1, \cdot)|) = \mathbf{N}_2 g_n(x_1, \cdot)$ if $x_1 \in E^\sim$, it is clear that

$$\mathbf{N}_1(G_n) \leq \mathbf{N}_1\mathbf{N}_2 g_n(\cdot, \cdot) \leq \mathbf{N}_3(g_n) < 2^{-n}. \tag{2}$$

If we define $F : X_1 \to R^*$ by

$$F(x_1) = \begin{cases} I_2 f(x_1, \cdot) & \text{if } x_1 \in E^\sim \\ 0 & \text{if } x_1 \in E, \end{cases}$$

we see that

$$G_n(x_1) = I_2 f_n(x_1, \cdot) - F(x_1) \tag{3}$$

except when $x_1 \in E$, and therefore that

$$\mathbf{N}_1(G_n) = \mathbf{N}_1[I_2 f_n(\cdot, \cdot) - F].$$

But $I_2 f_n(\cdot, \cdot) \in \mathscr{F}_1$. Therefore, by (2) and Theorem 6–6 IV, we conclude that $F \in \mathscr{L}_1$. This now gives us what is needed to conclude that $f \in \mathscr{L}_1 * \mathscr{L}_2$. Moreover, from (3) we infer that $G_n \in \mathscr{L}_1$ and that

$$I_1(G_n) = I_1 I_2 f_n(\cdot, \cdot) - I_1(F) = I_3(f_n) - I_1(F).$$

But $|I_1(G_n)| \leq I_1(|G_n|) = \mathbf{N}_1(G_n) \to 0$. Hence, $I_3(f_n) \to I_1(F)$. But, also, $I_3(f_n) \to I_3(f)$ because $I_3(|f_n - f|) \to 0$. Thus $I_3(f) = I_1(F) = I_1 I_2 f(\cdot, \cdot)$; this completes the proof.

## APPLICATION TO LEBESGUE INTEGRALS IN $R^k$

The basic theorem on iterated integrals, for the classical theory of Lebesgue integration of functions defined in Euclidean space, was first proved by G. Fubini. We can deduce it readily from Theorem 7–2 I by using Theorem 6–8 I.

It will now be more convenient to use a symbolism closer to the classical notation for integrals, using the $d$ of Leibniz. Let $p$ and $q$ be positive integers, and let

$$X_1 = R^p, \qquad X_2 = R^q, \qquad X_3 = R^{p+q} = X_1 \times X_2.$$

We denote points of $X_3$ by $(x_1, x_2)$, with $x_i \in X_i$, $i = 1, 2$. If $f : X_1 \to R^*$ is summable with respect to Lebesgue measure in $R^p$, we denote the Lebesgue integral of $f$ by $\int_{X_1} f(x_1)\, dx_1$. Likewise, in the case of a function defined on $X_2$. Similar notations are used for integrals over measurable subsets of $X_1$ or $X_2$. If $f : X_3 \to R^*$ is summable with respect to Lebesgue measure in $X_3$, we denote the integral by $\int_{X_3} f(x_1, x_2)\, d(x_1, x_2)$.

THEOREM 7–2 II. *If $f : X_3 \to R^*$ is summable with respect to Lebesgue measure in $X_3 = R^{p+q}$, there is a set $E \subset R^p$ of measure zero with respect to Lebesgue measure in $X_1 = R^p$, such that for each $x_1$ in $X_1 - E$ the mapping $x_2 \to f(x_1, x_2)$ is summable with respect to Lebesgue measure in $X_2 = R^q$, the mapping*

$$x_1 \to \int_{X_2} f(x_1, x_2)\, dx_2$$

*is summable over $X_1 - E$ with respect to Lebesgue measure in $R^p$, and*

$$\int_{X_3} f(x_1, x_2)\, d(x_1, x_2) = \int_{X_1 - E} \left\{ \int_{X_2} f(x_1, x_2)\, dx_2 \right\} dx_1. \tag{4}$$

*Proof.* Let $\mathscr{F}_i = C_\infty(X_i)$, and for $f \in \mathscr{F}_i$ let $I_i(f) = \int_{F_i} f(x_i)\, dx_i$, where $F_i$ is any compact interval in $X_i$ such that $\{x_i : f(x_i) \neq 0\} \subset F_i$. The Lebesgue integral may be thought of as a Riemann integral, since the two methods of integration agree in this case. It is easily verified that the value of $I_i(f)$ is independent of $F_i$. Now suppose that $f \in \mathscr{F}_3$. Let $F_1$ and $F_2$ be compact intervals, in $X_1$ and $X_2$, respectively, such that $f(x_1, x_2) = 0$ at all points not in $F_1 \times F_2$. Because $f$ is continuous we know from classical calculus that

$$\int_{F_1 \times F_2} f(x_1, x_2)\, d(x_1, x_2) = \int_{F_1} \left\{ \int_{F_2} f(x_1, x_2)\, dx_2 \right\} dx_1.$$

Moreover, the mapping $x_2 \to f(x_1, x_2)$ belongs to $\mathscr{F}_2$ for each $x_1$, and the mapping

$$x_1 \to \int_{F_2} f(x_1, x_2)\, dx_2$$

belongs to $\mathscr{F}_1$. Hence Theorem 7–2 I is applicable. Its application here yields precisely the theorem we have under consideration, because of Theorem 6–8 I.

*Comment.* Theorem 7–2 II is essentially the same as Theorem 7–1 II, but the method of proof is entirely different.

## PROBLEMS

1. With the notation used in Theorem 7–2 I, suppose that $f : X_3 \to R^*$ is measurable (with respect to the elementary integral $I_3$). Let the assumptions of Theorem 7–2 I hold. Suppose further that there exists a sequence $\{f_n\}$ of functions $f_n : X_3 \to R$ such that $0 \le f_n, f_n \nearrow |f|$, and $f_n \in \mathscr{L}_3$.

(For circumstances under which such a sequence will exist see Problem 4, Section 6–5, and Problem 5, Section 6–7.) Suppose that there exists a set $E \subset X_1$, with $\mu_1(E) = 0$, and a function $F \in \mathscr{L}_1$ such that $|f(x_1, \cdot)| \in \mathscr{L}_2$ and $I_2|f(x_1, \cdot)| = F(x_1)$ if $x_1 \in X_1 - E$, so that $I_1I_2|f(\cdot, \cdot)| = I_1(F)$ is well-defined. Prove that $f \in \mathscr{L}_3$, and hence that $I_3(f) = I_1I_2f(\cdot, \cdot)$.

2. In the notation of Theorem 7–2 II, suppose that $f : R^{p+q} \to R^*$ is $L$-measurable and that one of the following iterated Lebesgue integrals exists:

$$\int_{R^p}\left\{\int_{R^q}|f(x_1, x_2)|\, dx_2\right\} dx_1, \qquad \int_{R^q}\left\{\int_{R^p}|f(x_1, x_2)|\, dx_1\right\} dx_2.$$

Prove that $f$ is $L$-summable over $R^{p+q}$. This may be demonstrated in the spirit of Chapter 5 by using Theorem 7–1 II, or in the spirit of Chapter 6 by using Theorem 7–2 II.

3. Suppose that $f : R^k \to R^*$ and $g : R^k \to R^*$ are $L$-summable. For given $x \in R^k$ define $h_x : R^k \to R^*$ by $h_x(y) = f(y)g(x - y)$. Prove that three exists a set $E$ of $L$-measure zero in $R^k$ and an $L$-summable function $F : R^k \to R^*$ such that $h_x$ is $L$-summable and $F(x) = \int h_x\, d\mu$ when $x$ is not in $E$. Show, moreover, that

$$\int |F|\, d\mu \leq \left(\int |f|\, d\mu\right)\left(\int |g|\, d\mu\right),$$

where integration is over $R^k$ and $\mu$ is Lebesgue measure. The function $F$ is called the *convolution product* of $f$ and $g$, and denoted by $f * g$. Show further that $f * g$ is equivalent to $g * f$. [*Suggestions.* Show first, by methods of Chapter 5, that the mappings $(x, y) \to f(y)$ and $(x, y) \to g(x - y)$ are $L$-measurable as functions on $R^k \times R^k$ to $R^*$. This requires knowing that $E \times R^k$ is $L$-measurable in $R^k \times R^k$ if $E$ is $L$-measurable in $R^k$. It is also necessary to know, for such an $E$, that the set $\{(x, y) : x - y \in E\}$ is $L$-measurable. This can be dealt with by using a linear transformation in $R^k \times R^k$. Next, use Problem 2 to show that the mapping $(x, y) \to f(y)g(x - y)$ is $L$-summable. Here it will be necessary to show that

$$\int_{R^k} |g(x - y)|\, dx = \int_{R^k} |g(x)|\, dx$$

(using integration notation as in Section 7–1). This can be carried back to the invariance of $L$-measure in $R^k$ under translation, by using a regular approximating sequence of simple functions converging to $|g|$.]

4. A standard "integration by parts" formula reads as follows:

$$\int_a^b F(x)g(x)\, dx = F(b)G(b) - \int_a^b f(x)G(x)\, dx,$$

where $F$ and $G$ are defined when $x \in R$ and $a \leq x \leq b$ by the formulas

$$F(x) = \int_a^x f(t)\, dt, \qquad G(x) = \int_a^x g(t)\, dt.$$

Prove this, under the following assumptions, where the integrals are with respect to Lebesgue measure in $R$. Let $a, b$ be members of $R^*$ such that $a < b$. Suppose $A = \{x : x \in R, a \leq x \leq b\}$, and let $f, g$ be measurable functions on $R$ to $R^*$ which are summable over $A$. [*Suggestions.* The proof of this result can be based on Fubini's theorem. See Theorem 9–8 IX for a wholly different approach and method. Let $A(x) = \{y : y \in R, a \leq y \leq x\}$ if $x \in A$, and $A(x) = \varnothing$ otherwise. Let $C(x) = A(x) - \{x\}$, and let $B(y) = \{x : x \in R, y < x \leq b\}$ if $y \in R$ and $a \leq y < b$, $B(y) = \varnothing$ otherwise. Let $E$ be a set in $R \times R$ defined as follows: $E = \{(x, y) : x, y \in A \text{ and } y < x\}$. Observe that the characteristic function of $E$ can be expressed in the two ways

$$\chi_E(x, y) = \chi_A(y)\chi_{B(y)}(x) = \chi_A(x)\chi_{C(x)}(y).$$

Show that the function $(x, y) \to g(x)f(y)\chi_E(x, y)$ is summable over $R \times R$, and from Fubini's theorem deduce that

$$\int_A \left\{g(x) \int_{C(x)} f(y)\, dy\right\} dx = \int_A \left\{f(y) \int_{B(y)} g(x)\, dx\right\} dy.$$

Then finish the proof.]

## 7–3 Products of functions of one variable

We continue with the notation used in Section 7–2. For convenience we introduce the following notation: If $f : X_1 \to R^*$ and $g : X_2 \to R^*$ are given, write $h = f \odot g$ for the function $h : X_3 \to R^*$ defined by $h(x_1, x_2) = f(x_1)g(x_2)$. (Recall that 0 times $\pm\infty$ is 0, by definition.)

Throughout this section we make the following hypotheses:

$$H_1 : \mathscr{F}_3 \subset \mathscr{F}_1 * \mathscr{F}_2 \text{ and } I_3 f = I_1 I_2 f(\cdot, \cdot) \text{ if } f \in \mathscr{F}_3;$$

$$H_2 : f \odot g \in \mathscr{F}_3 \text{ if } f \in \mathscr{F}_1 \text{ and } g \in \mathscr{F}_2.$$

The hypothesis $H_1$ was made in Theorem 7–2 I. As a consequence of $H_1$ and $H_2$ we observe that $I_3(f \odot g) = I_1(f)I_2(g)$, because $I_2 h(x_1, \cdot) = f(x_1)I_2(g)$ if $h = f \odot g$.

LEMMA 7–3 I. *Suppose $H_1$ and $H_2$ are satisfied. Then, if $w = u \odot v$, where $u \in \mathscr{F}_1^\circ$, $v \in \mathscr{F}_1^\circ$, $u \geq 0$, and $v \geq 0$, we have $w \in \mathscr{F}_3^\circ$ and*

(1) $$I_3(w) = I_1(u)I_2(v).$$

*Proof.* Suppose $u_n \nearrow u$, $v_n \nearrow v$, where $u_n \in \mathscr{F}_1$, $v_n \in \mathscr{F}_2$. We may assume $u_n \geq 0$, for otherwise we replace $u_n$ by $0 \vee u_n$; likewise for $v_n$. Let $w_n = u_n \odot v_n$. Then $w_n \nearrow w$, and so $w \in \mathscr{F}_3^\circ$, by $H_2$. Since $I_3(w_n) = I_1(u_n)I_2(v_n)$, we obtain (1).

LEMMA 7–3 II. *Suppose $H_1$ and $H_2$ are satisfied. Suppose $f : X_1 \to R$ and $g : X_2 \to R$ (finite values!) are given, with $f \geq 0$, $g \geq 0$, and with $\mathbf{N}_1(f)$ and $\mathbf{N}_2(g)$ finite. Let $h = f \odot g$. Then*

(2) $$\mathbf{N}_3(h) = \mathbf{N}_1(f)\mathbf{N}_2(g).$$

*Proof.* Because of the finiteness assumptions we see that $\mathbf{N}_1\mathbf{N}_2\, h(\cdot, \cdot) = \mathbf{N}_1(f)\mathbf{N}_2(g)$. Therefore, in view of (1) in Section 7–2, we know that $\mathbf{N}_1(f)\mathbf{N}_2(g) \leq \mathbf{N}_3(h)$. Let $u$ and $v$ be arbitrary elements of $\mathscr{F}_1^\circ$ and $\mathscr{F}_2^\circ$, respectively, such that $f \leq u$, $g \leq v$. Then $w = u \odot v \in \mathscr{F}_3^\circ$ and $I_3(w) = I_1(u)I_2(v)$, by Lemma 7–3 I. Also, $h \leq w$, and so $\mathbf{N}_3(h) \leq I_3(w) = I_1(u)I_2(v)$. From this we conclude $\mathbf{N}_3(h) \leq \mathbf{N}_1(f)\mathbf{N}_2(g)$, because $I_1(u)$ can be as close to $\mathbf{N}_1(f)$ as we please, and likewise for $I_2(v)$ and $\mathbf{N}_2(g)$. Thus we obtain (2).

Let $\mu_i$ be the measure in $X_i$ determined by $I_i$, and let $\mathscr{L}_i$ be the class of summable functions on $X_i$, as determined by $I_i$. If $A \subset X_i$, we shall call $\mathbf{N}_i(\chi_A)$ the *outer measure* of $A$ (see (5) in Section 6–7). We recall that $A$ is measurable if $\chi_A$ is measurable, and that $A$ then has finite measure $\mu_i(A) = \mathbf{N}_i(\chi_A) = I_i(\chi_A)$ if and only if $\chi_A \in \mathscr{L}_i$.

THEOREM 7–3 III. *Suppose $H_1$ and $H_2$ are satisfied. Suppose $A \subset X_1$, $B \subset X_2$. Let $\mu_1(A) = 0$, and suppose that $B$ has finite outer measure. Then $\mu_3(A \times B) = 0$.*

*Proof.* If $E = A \times B$, we see that $\chi_E = \chi_A \odot \chi_B$. We can then use (2) to deduce that $\mathbf{N}_3(\chi_E) = 0$. This implies that $E$ is a set of measure zero (Theorem 6–6 I(*f*)).

Before stating the next theorem we recall the notation $\mathscr{M}_i$ for the class of measurable functions on $X_i$ determined by $I_i$. We also recall that in Section 6–7 the assumption that the constant function 1 is measurable played an important part in linking the theory of measurability in Chapter 6 with that in Chapter 5.

THEOREM 7–3 IV. *Suppose $H_1$ and $H_2$ are satisfied. Then* (a): *if $f \in \mathscr{L}_1$, $f_2 \in \mathscr{L}_2$, and the values of $f$ and $g$ are all finite, the function $h = f \odot g$ is in $\mathscr{L}_3$ and*

$$I_3(h) = I_1(f)I_2(g). \tag{3}$$

(b) *If we assume in addition that $1 \in \mathscr{M}_1$ and $1 \in \mathscr{M}_2$, then the conclusions in* (a) *are valid without the restriction to finite values for $f$ and $g$.*

*Proof of* (a). By Theorem 6–4 VI there exist sequences $\{f_n\}$, $\{g_n\}$ in $\mathscr{F}_1$ and $\mathscr{F}_2$, respectively, such that

$$\mathbf{N}_1(f_n - f) = I_1(|f_n - f|) \to 0$$

and

$$\mathbf{N}_2(g_n - g) = I_2(|g_n - g|) \to 0.$$

Let $h_n = f_n \odot g_n$. Since

$$|h_n(x_1, x_2) - h(x_1, x_2)| \le |f_n(x_1)|\,|g_n(x_2) - g(x_2)| + |f_n(x_1) - f(x_1)|\,|g(x_2)|,$$

we can apply $\mathbf{N}_3$ and use (2) to obtain

$$\mathbf{N}_3(h_n - h) \le \mathbf{N}_1(f_n)\mathbf{N}_2(g_n - g) + \mathbf{N}_1(f_n - f)\mathbf{N}_2(g),$$

whence $\mathbf{N}_3(h_n - h) \to 0$. Since $|h| \le |h - h_n| + |h_n|$, it follows that $\mathbf{N}_3(h) < +\infty$. We can then infer from Corollary 6–6 IV that $h \in \mathscr{L}_3$. Then $I_3(h_n) \to I_3(h)$, because

$$|I_3(h_n - h)| \le I_3(|h_n - h|) = \mathbf{N}_3(h_n - h).$$

But $I_3(h_n) = I_1(f_n)I_2(g_n) \to I_1(f)I_2(g)$. Thus we obtain (3). This finishes case (a).

*Proof of* (b). Let $A_n = \left\{x_1 : |f(x_1)| > \dfrac{1}{n}\right\}$, $n = 1, 2, \ldots, A_0 = \{x_1 : |f(x_1)| > 0\}$. Define $B_n$ and $B_0$ analogously in relation to $g$. All of these sets are measurable, by Theorem 6–7 II (here we use $1 \in \mathscr{M}_i$). Observe that $A_0 = \bigcup_n A_n$. The characteristic function of $A_n$ is less than or equal to $n\,|f|$. Hence $\mu_1(A_n)$ is finite. Likewise $\mu_2(B_n) < +\infty$.

Now, let $S = \{x_1 : |f(x_1)| = +\infty\}$, $T = \{x_2 : |g(x_2)| = +\infty\}$. Define

$$F(x_1) = \begin{cases} f(x_1) & \text{if } x_1 \in S^{\sim} \\ 0 & \text{if } x_1 \in S, \end{cases}$$

and define $G$ analogously in relation to $g$ and $T$. Since $f$ and $g$ are summable, we know that $F(x_1) = f(x_1)$ a.e., $I_1(F) = I_1(f)$, and likewise for $G$ and $g$. Let $H = F \odot G$. By (a) we know that $H \in \mathscr{L}_3$ and

$$I_3(H) = I_1(F)I_2(G) = I_1(f)I_2(g).$$

Hence, all that remains to prove is that the set $U = \{(x_1, x_2) : h(x_1, x_2) \ne H(x_1, x_2)\}$ is such that $\mu_3(U) = 0$.

Now, it is easy to see that

$$U = (S \times B_0) \cup (A_0 \times T).$$

But

$$S \times B_0 = \bigcup_n (S \times B_n).$$

Now, $\mu_1(S) = 0$ and $\mu_2(B_n) < +\infty$, so that $\mu_3(S \times B_n) = 0$, by Theorem 7–3 III. Hence, $\mu_3(S \times B_0) = 0$. By a symmetrical argument, $\mu_3(A_0 \times T) = 0$, and hence $\mu_3(U) = 0$. This completes the proof.

THEOREM 7–3 V. *Suppose $H_1$ and $H_2$ are satisfied. Suppose $A$ and $B$ are measurable sets in $X_1$ and $X_2$ respectively, with $\mu_1(A)$ and $\mu_2(B)$ finite. Then $A \times B$ is $\mu_3$-measurable and*

(4) $$\mu_3(A \times B) = \mu_1(A)\mu_2(B).$$

*If we further assume that the measures $\mu_1$ and $\mu_2$ are $\sigma$-finite, then $A \times B$ is $\mu_3$-measurable whenever $A$ is $\mu_1$-measurable and $B$ is $\mu_2$-measurable; moreover,* (4) *is still true.*

*Proof.* The first assertion is an immediate consequence of Theorem 7–3 IV, applied to the product of the characteristic functions of $A$ and $B$. For the second assertion, we use the $\sigma$-finiteness and familiar procedures to write

$$A = \bigcup_n A_n,$$

where $\{A_n\}$ is a disjoint sequence of measurable sets of finite measure. Similarly for $B$. Then

$$A \times B = \bigcup_{m,n} (A_m \times B_n),$$

and the result follows easily from what has already been proved.

## 7–4 Iterated integrals and products of Euclidean spaces

Let $p$ and $q$ be positive integers, and let $X = R^p$, $Y = R^q$; then $X \times Y = R^{p+q}$. Let $I$ and $J$ be elementary integrals on $C_\infty(X)$ and $C_\infty(Y)$, respectively. If $f: X \times Y \to R^*$ is a function such that for a fixed $x$ the mapping $y \to f(x, y)$ belongs to $C_\infty(Y)$, the $J$-integral of this function will now be denoted by $J_y f(x, y)$. If this situation occurs for each $x$, and if the mapping $x \to J_y f(x, y)$ belongs to $C_\infty(X)$, the $I$-integral of this function will be denoted by $I_x J_y f(x, y)$. For our present purpose this notation is more convenient than that which was used in connection with Theorem 7–2 I. We shall have need as well for the notations $I_x f(x, y)$, $J_y I_x f(x, y)$, whose meanings will now be apparent. We may still wish to denote functions, as distinct from values of functions, by putting a dot in place of $x$ or $y$. Thus, $J_y f(\cdot, y)$ denotes the function which maps $x$ into $J_y f(x, y)$.

THEOREM 7–4 I. *Let $I$ and $J$ be as specified above. If $f \in C_\infty(X \times Y)$, then $J_y f(\cdot, y) \in C_\infty(X)$, $I_x f(x, \cdot) \in C_\infty(Y)$, and*

(1) $$I_x J_y f(x, y) = J_y I_x f(x, y).$$

*If we define*

(2) $$K(f) = I_x J_y f(x, y),$$

*then $K$ is an elementary integral on $C_\infty(X \times Y)$. Hence the Stone-Fubini theorem applies with $I$, $J$, $K$ in place of $I_1$, $I_2$, $I_3$, and also with $J$, $I$, $K$ in place of $I_1$, $I_2$, $I_3$.*

*Proof.* If $f \in C_\infty(X, Y)$, it is evident that $f(x, \cdot) \in C_\infty(Y)$ and $f(\cdot, y) \in C_\infty(X)$, for we can choose compact intervals $E$, $F$ in $X$, $Y$, respectively in such a way that $f(x, y) = 0$ if $(x, y)$ is not in $E \times F$. With $E$ and $F$ thus chosen, there exist constants $M_1$, $M_2$ such that $|I(g)| \leq M_1 \max |g(x)|$ if $g \in C_\infty(X)$ and $\{x : g(x) \neq 0\} \subset E$, while $|J(h)| \leq M_2 \max |h(y)|$ if $h \in C_\infty(Y)$ and $\{y : h(y) \neq 0\} \subset F$ (see Theorem 6–9 I). Now suppose $\epsilon > 0$. With the aid of the Stone-Weierstrass theorem (Theorem 3–15 VI) it can be proved that there exists a function $w \in C_\infty(X \times Y)$ of the form

$$w(x, y) = \sum_{i=1}^{n} u_i(x)v_i(y), \qquad u_i \in C_\infty(X),\ v_i \in C_\infty(Y), \tag{3}$$

such that

$$|f(x, y) - w(x, y)| < \epsilon \tag{4}$$

for every $(x, y) \in X \times Y$, and moreover such that, $u_i(x) = 0$ for each $i$, if $x$ is not in $E$, and $v_i(y) = 0$ for each $i$ if $y$ is not in $F$. We shall continue now with the rest of the argument; later we shall give details about obtaining the $u_i$'s and the $v_i$'s.

From (4) it is clear that

$$|J_y f(x, y) - J_y w(x, y)| \leq M_2 \epsilon. \tag{5}$$

But

$$J_y w(x, y) = \sum_{i=1}^{n} u_i(x) J(v_i). \tag{6}$$

This function of $x$ is continuous, and its value is zero if $x$ is not in $E$. Since $\epsilon$ is arbitrary, it follows from (5) and the facts about uniform approximation by continuous functions (Theorem 3–6 II in particular) that $J_y f(\cdot, y) \in C_\infty(X)$. Moreover, $J_y f(x, y) = 0$ if $x$ is not in $E$. We can then continue to the conclusion that

$$|I_x J_y f(x, y) - I_x J_y w(x, y)| \leq M_1 M_2 \epsilon. \tag{7}$$

A similar reasoning shows that $I_x f(x, \cdot) \in C_\infty(Y)$ and

$$|J_y I_x f(x, y) - J_y I_x w(x, y)| \leq M_2 M_1 \epsilon. \tag{8}$$

But we observe that

$$I_x J_y w(x, y) = \sum_{i=1}^{n} I(u_i) J(v_i) = J_y I_x w(x, y).$$

Therefore, from (7) and (8) we see that

$$|I_x J_y f(x, y) - J_y I_x f(x, y)| \leq 2 M_1 M_2 \epsilon. \tag{9}$$

From this we obtain (1).

The definition of $K$ in (2) shows that it is a nonnegative linear functional on $C_\infty(X \times Y)$. It is then an elementary integral, by Theorem 6–9 I.

We still have to explain about (3) and (4). We observe that $f(x, y) = 0$ if $(x, y)$ is outside $E \times F$ or on the boundary of $E \times F$. We may therefore choose compact intervals $E_1$, $F_1$ with $E_1 \subset E$, $F_1 \subset F$, in such a way that

$$|f(x, y)| \leq \frac{\epsilon}{6} \quad \text{if} \quad (x, y) \in (E \times F) - (E_1 \times F_1). \tag{10}$$

We can construct a continuous function $\varphi : X \to R$ in such a way that $\varphi(x) = 1$ if $x \in E_1$, $\varphi(x) = 0$ if $x$ is not in $E$, and $0 \leq \varphi(x) \leq 1$ if $x \in E - E_1$. Let $\psi : Y \to R$ be constructed in exactly the same way with reference to $F_1$ and $F$. Now consider the algebra $C(E \times F)$ of all continuous functions on $E \times F$ to $R$, and the subalgebra of $C(E \times F)$ composed of all finite linear combinations of functions of the form $U(x)V(y)$, where $U \in C(E)$ and $V \in C(F)$. This subalgebra contains all constant functions on $E \times F$ to $R$, and it evidently separates points of $E \times F$, so that the subalgebra is dense in $C(E \times F)$ in the sense of the Stone-Weierstrass theorem. We may therefore choose $U_i \in C(E)$, $V_i \in C(F)$ $(i = 1, \ldots, n)$, so that

$$|f(x, y) - \sum_{i=1}^{n} U_i(x)V_i(y)| < \frac{\epsilon}{6} \tag{11}$$

if $(x, y) \in E \times F$. Now define

$$u_i(x) = \begin{cases} \varphi(x)U_i(x) & \text{if } x \in E, \\ 0 & \text{if } x \in E^{\sim}, \end{cases} \qquad v_i(y) = \begin{cases} \psi(y)V_i(y) & \text{if } y \in F, \\ 0 & \text{if } y \in F^{\sim}, \end{cases}$$

and define $w$ by (3). It is evident from (11) and the definitions of $\varphi$ and $\psi$ that

$$|f(x, y) - w(x, y)| < \frac{\epsilon}{6} \quad \text{if } (x, y) \in (E_1 \times F_1) \cup [(X \times Y) - (E \times F)]. \tag{12}$$

If $(x, y) \in (E \times F) - (E_1 \times F_1)$, we see by (10) and (11) that

$$|\sum_i U_i(x)V_i(y)| < \frac{\epsilon}{6} + |f(x, y)| \leq \frac{\epsilon}{3}. \tag{13}$$

Hence, using (11) and (13), we see that $(x, y) \in (E \times F) - (E_1 \times F_1)$ implies

$$|f(x, y) - w(x, y)| < \frac{\epsilon}{6} + \sum_i U_i(x)V_i(y)[1 - \varphi(x)\psi(y)]| < \frac{\epsilon}{6} + \frac{2\epsilon}{3} < \epsilon.$$

This result, along with (12), shows that (4) is satisfied. The composition of $w$ is as required, and so the proof is complete.

It may be remarked that this proof yields, as a special case, the fact that if $f : R^2 \to R$ is in $C_\infty(R^2)$ and if $f(x, y) = 0$ when $x$ is not in $[a, b]$ or $y$ is not in $[\alpha, \beta]$, then the Riemann integrals

$$\int_\alpha^\beta f(x, y)\, dy, \quad \int_a^b f(x, y)\, dx$$

are continuous in $x$ and $y$, respectively, and

$$\int_a^b dx \int_\alpha^\beta f(x, y)\, dy = \int_\alpha^\beta dy \int_a^b f(x, y)\, dx.$$

The method of proof can be adapted also to the case when $f$ is any continuous real function defined on the rectangle $[a, b] \times [\alpha, \beta]$. Notice that there is no reference to uniform continuity. The usual arguments of classical analysis in this situation are completely replaced by the use of the Stone-Weierstrass Theorem.

## APPLICABILITY OF SECTION 7–3

In the situation of Theorem 7–4 I we know from Theorem 6–10 IV that each of the elementary integrals leads to a measure which is the completion of a regular Borel measure.

Let $\mu$, $\nu$, $\lambda$ be the measures induced by $I$, $J$, $K$, respectively. The results of Section 7–3 are applicable here (with $I$, $J$, $K$ in place of $I_1$, $I_2$, $I_3$), for the hypotheses $H_1$, $H_2$ of Section 7–3 are satisfied, with $\mathscr{F}_1 = C_\infty(X)$, $\mathscr{F}_2 = C_\infty(Y)$, $\mathscr{F}_3 = C_\infty(X \times Y)$. Moreover, the measures $\mu$, $\nu$ are $\sigma$-finite, because of the nature of Euclidean space and the fact that compact sets are of finite measure. Hence, if $A \subset X$, $B \subset Y$, with $A$ $\mu$-measurable and $B$ $\nu$-measurable, the Cartesian product $A \times B$ is $\lambda$-measurable, and $\lambda(A \times B) = \mu(A)\nu(B)$. This is true, in particular, when $\mu$, $\nu$, and $\lambda$ are Lebesgue measures in $R^p$, $R^q$, and $R^{p+q}$, respectively.

It can occur that $A \times B$ is measurable, even though one of the sets $A$, $B$ is not measurable. For instance, if $A$ is measurable, with $\mu(A) = 0$, while $B$ is not $\nu$-measurable, but has finite outer measure (in the sense of Section 6–7), then $A \times B$ is measurable, with $\lambda(A \times B) = 0$ (Theorem 7–3 III). We know that such a $B$ exists if $\nu$ is Lebesgue measure in $R^q$.

### PRODUCT-MEASURE

In the situation of Theorem 7–4 I the measure $\lambda$ is determined in a definite manner by $\mu$ and $\nu$. It is common practice to say that $\lambda$ is the *product-measure* determined by $\mu$ and $\nu$, and to write $\lambda = \mu \times \nu$. From this point of view, if $\mu_p$ is Lebesgue measure in $R^p$, we have $\mu_{p+q} = \mu_p \times \mu_q$. There are other ways of approaching the subject of product-measure, with different definitions, not all of which are equivalent to the above, even when applied to the very $\mu$, $\nu$ we are discussing here. In Section 7–5 we present an alternative approach to product-measures as a basis for a different study of Fubini's theorem. Some comments will be made there about comparison with the product-measure $\mu \times \nu$ as we have defined it here.

## 7–5 Abstract theory of product-measures

In Section 7–4 we defined the product of two measures which are induced by elementary integrals in $C_\infty(R^p)$ and $C_\infty(R^q)$, respectively. This product-measure is the measure in $R^{p+q}$ induced by the elementary integral which is the iteration of the two given integrals.

In this section we approach the subject of product-measure from a set-theoretic standpoint. Integration will be in the sense of Chapter 5.

Let $X_1$, $X_2$ be nonempty sets, and let $\mathbf{S}_i$ be a $\sigma$-ring of subsets of $X_i$ $(i = 1, 2)$. We denote by $\mathbf{S}_1 \times \mathbf{S}_2$ the $\sigma$-ring in $X_1 \times X_2$ generated by all sets of the form $E_1 \times E_2$, where $E_i \in \mathbf{S}_i$.

THEOREM 7–5 I. *If $E \subset X_1 \times X_2$ and $y_i \in X_i$, let*

$$E(y_1) = \{x_2 \in X_2 : (y_1, x_2) \in E\},$$
$$E(y_2) = \{x_1 \in X_1 : (x_1, y_2) \in E\}.$$

*Then $E \in \mathbf{S}_1 \times \mathbf{S}_2$ implies $E(y_1) \in \mathbf{S}_2$ and $E(y_2) \in \mathbf{S}_1$ for every choice of $y_1$, $y_2$.*

*Proof.* The implication is clearly valid if $E$ is of the form $E_1 \times E_2$, where $E_i \in \mathbf{S}_i$. It is easy to check that, if we consider the class of all subsets $E$ of $X \times Y$ such that we always have $E(y_1) \in \mathbf{S}_2$ and $E(y_2) \in \mathbf{S}_1$, this class is a $\sigma$-ring. Hence, it must contain $\mathbf{S}_1 \times \mathbf{S}_2$, and our proof is finished.

THEOREM 7–5 II. *Suppose $f : X_1 \times X_2 \to R^*$ is measurable with respect to $\mathbf{S}_1 \times \mathbf{S}_2$. Then $f(\cdot, x_2)$ is measurable with respect to $\mathbf{S}_1$ for each fixed $x_2$, and $f(x_1, \cdot)$ is measurable with respect to $\mathbf{S}_2$ for each fixed $x_1$.*

*Proof.* Let $G$ be an open set in $R^*$, and let $E = \{(x_1, x_2) : f(x_1, x_2) \in G\}$. Then it is clear that $E(x_2) = \{x_1 : f(x_1, x_2) \in G\}$. If $X_i \in \mathbf{S}_i$ for each $i$, the fact that $f(\cdot, x_2)$ is measurable now follows at once from Theorems 5–1 I and 7–5 I. In the general case we have to consider the sets where $f$ and $f(\cdot, x_2)$ are different from zero, and their intersections with $E$ and $E(x_2)$, respectively. Again we get what is needed from Theorem 7–5 I. The argument for $f(x_1, \cdot)$ is the same, of course. We leave the details to the reader.

Now, suppose that we have a measure $\mu_i$ defined on $\mathbf{S}_i$, $i = 1, 2$. We wish to define a measure $\mu$ on $\mathbf{S}_1 \times \mathbf{S}_2$ with the property that $\mu(E_1 \times E_2) = \mu_1(E_1)\mu_2(E_2)$ if $E_i \in \mathbf{S}_i$. In order to be able to do this we shall assume that each of the measure spaces $(X_i, \mathbf{S}_i, \mu_i)$ is $\sigma$-finite.

The motivation for the procedure which we shall use can be explained in this way: If the measure $\mu$ exists, and if Fubini's theorem turns out to be true, then for sets $E$ of finite measure in $X \times Y$, $\mu(E)$ should be expressible as an iterated integral of $\chi_E$. For integrals which involve functions of two variables it is sometimes convenient to use a notation which displays the variables; the "variable of integration" will usually be made to appear twice, once in the functional symbol and once in connection with the measure. Thus, for fixed $x_1$, the $\mu_2$-integral of $f(x_1, x_2)$ over a set $A$, where $A \in \mathbf{S}_2$, will be denoted by

$$\int_A f(x_1, x_2)\mu_2(dx_2).$$

If $E \in \mathbf{S}_1 \times \mathbf{S}_2$ we have

$$\chi_E(x_1, x_2) = \begin{cases} 1 & \text{if } x_2 \in E(x_1) \\ 0 & \text{otherwise.} \end{cases}$$

Hence, for a set $E$ of finite measure we expect to have

$$\mu(E) = \int_{X_1}\left[\int_{E(x_1)} 1 \cdot \mu_2(dx_2)\right]\mu_1(dx_1),$$

or

$$\mu(E) = \int_{X_1} \mu_2[E(x_1)]\mu_1(dx_1). \tag{1}$$

We expect also a corresponding formula with indices 1, 2 reversed.

Our actual procedure, then, is to use (1) as a basis for defining the product-measure $\mu$. With each $E \in \mathbf{S}_1 \times \mathbf{S}_2$ we associate two functions $f$, $g$, defined as follows:

$$\begin{cases} f : X_1 \to R^* \text{ is defined by } f(x_1) = \mu_2[E(x_1)] \\ g : X_2 \to R^* \text{ is defined by } g(x_2) = \mu_1[E(x_2)]. \end{cases} \tag{2}$$

Theorem 7–5 I shows that $E(x_1) \in \mathbf{S}_2$ and $E(x_2) \in \mathbf{S}_1$, so that we can indeed define $f$ and $g$. It is not *a priori* evident that $f$ and $g$ are measurable, but we have the following important theorem which enables us to proceed:

THEOREM 7–5 III. *Suppose that the measure spaces* $(X_i, \mathbf{S}_i, \mu_i)$ $(i = 1, 2)$ *are both $\sigma$-finite. Then, for each $E$ in $\mathbf{S}_1 \times \mathbf{S}_2$ the functions $f$, $g$ defined by* (2) *are measurable (with respect to $\mathbf{S}_1$ and $\mathbf{S}_2$, respectively). If either of the functions $f$, $g$ is summable, so is the other, and*

$$\int_{X_1} f\, d\mu_1 = \int_{X_2} g\, d\mu_2. \tag{3}$$

*Proof.* Let $\mathscr{D}$ be the class of all sets $E$ of the form $A \times B$, where $A \in \mathbf{S}_1$, $B \in \mathbf{S}_2$, $\mu_1(A) < +\infty$, and $\mu_2(B) < +\infty$. Let $\mathscr{E}$ be the class of all sets $E$ which can be expressed as finite unions of pairwise disjoint members of $\mathscr{D}$. Let $\mathscr{K}$ be the class of all sets $E$ in $\mathbf{S}_1 \times \mathbf{S}_2$ for which the assertions about $f$ and $g$ in the theorem are true.

We divide the proof of the theorem into a number of steps.

*Step 1.* $\mathscr{D} \subset \mathscr{K}$. If $E = A \times B \in \mathscr{D}$, it is easy to see that

$$f(x_1) = \begin{cases} 0 & \text{if } x_1 \notin A \\ \mu_2(B) & \text{if } x_1 \in A. \end{cases}$$

Thus $f$ is summable, and $\int_{x_1} f\, d\mu_1 = \mu_1(A)\mu_2(B)$. We leave the rest of Step 1 to the reader.

*Step 2.* If $E = \bigcup_n E_n$, where the $E_n$'s are disjoint and each $E_n$ is in $\mathscr{K}$, then $E \in \mathscr{K}$. In particular, $\mathscr{E} \subset \mathscr{K}$. To prove this, let $f$ and $f_n$ be related to $E$ and $E_n$, respectively, as in (2); likewise for $g$ and $g_n$. For arbitrary $x_1$ we see that $\{E_n(x_1)\}$ is a disjoint sequence and $E(x_1) = \bigcup_n E_n(x_1)$, whence $f(x_1) = \sum_n f_n(x_1)$. Therefore, $f$ is measurable; likewise for $g$. If one of the functions $f, g$ (say $f$) is summable, we deduce from $0 \leq f_n \leq f$ that $f_n$ is summable. Since $f_1 + \cdots + f_n \nearrow f$, $g_1 + \cdots + g_n \nearrow g$, and

$$\int_{X_1} (f_1 + \cdots + f_n)\, d\mu_1 = \int_{X_2} (g_1 + \cdots + g_n)\, d\mu_2,$$

it follows by the monotone convergence theorem that $g$ is summable and that $\int f\, d\mu_1 = \int g\, d\mu_2$. Thus $E \in \mathscr{K}$.

*Step 3.* $\mathscr{E}$ is a ring. Suppose that $D_1 = A_1 \times B_1$ and $D_2 = A_2 \times B_2$ are members of $\mathscr{D}$. We observe that $D_1 \cap D_2$ and $D_1 - D_2$ are in $\mathscr{E}$, because

(4) $$D_1 \cap D_2 = (A_1 \cap A_2) \times (B_1 \cap B_2),$$

(5) $$D_1 - D_2 = [(A_1 \cap A_2) \times (B_1 - B_2)] \cup [(A_1 - A_2) \times B_1].$$

Now, consider two members of $\mathscr{E}$, say $E = E_1 \cup \cdots \cup E_m$, $F = F_1 \cup \cdots \cup F_n$, where $E_1, \ldots, E_m$ are disjoint members of $\mathscr{D}$ and $F_1, \ldots, F_n$ are also disjoint members of $\mathscr{D}$. Then $E \cap F$ is the union of the sets $E_i \cap F_j$ ($i = 1, \ldots, m, j = 1, \ldots, n$), which belong to $\mathscr{D}$ (by (4)) and are disjoint. Hence, $E \cap F \in \mathscr{E}$. Thus we see that $\mathscr{E}$ is closed under the formation of finite intersections. An easy calculation shows that

$$E - F = \bigcup_{1=i}^{m} \bigcap_{j=1}^{n} (E_i - F_j),$$

and from this, in view of (5) and what has just been said, we see that $E - F \in \mathscr{E}$, for it is a finite disjoint union of members of $\mathscr{E}$. Finally, $\mathscr{E}$ is closed under finite unions, for the identity

$$E \cup F = (E - F) \cup (F - E) \cup (E \cap F)$$

shows that $E \cup F \in \mathscr{E}$ if $E$ and $F$ are in $\mathscr{E}$ (for it is a union of three disjoint members of $\mathscr{E}$). Thus $\mathscr{E}$ is a ring.

*Step 4.* Every element of $\mathbf{S}_1 \times \mathbf{S}_2$ is contained in a countable union of disjoint members of $\mathscr{E}$ (and hence, in fact, in a countable union of disjoint members of $\mathscr{D}$). To prove this we observe, in the first place, that if $E \in \mathbf{S}_1 \times \mathbf{S}_2$, there exist sequences $\{A_n\}$, $\{B_n\}$ from $\mathbf{S}_1$ and

$\mathbf{S}_2$, respectively, such that $E \subset \bigcup_n (A_n \times B_n)$ (see Problem 9, Section 4–2). By the $\sigma$-finiteness of $\mathbf{S}_1$ and $\mathbf{S}_2$ there exist sets $A_{ni}$ and $B_{nj}$, of finite measure, in $\mathbf{S}_1$ and $\mathbf{S}_2$, respectively, such that

$$A_n \subset \bigcup_i A_{ni}, \qquad B_n \subset \bigcup_j B_{nj}.$$

Then

$$A_n \times B_n \subset \bigcup_{i,j} (A_{ni} \times B_{nj}).$$

We see, therefore, that there exists a sequence $\{D_n\}$ in $\mathscr{D}$ such that $E \subset \bigcup_n D_n$. If we define $E_1 = D_1$, $E_n = D_n - (D_1 \cup \cdots \cup D_n)$ if $n > 1$, then $\{E_n\}$ is a disjoint sequence from $\mathscr{E}$, and $E \subset \bigcup_n E_n$.

Before continuing to the next steps in the argument we make some further definitions. Let $F_0$ be an arbitrary fixed member of $\mathscr{E}$, and let $\mathscr{E}_0$ be the class of all sets of the form $E \cap F_0$, where $E \in \mathscr{E}$. Let $\mathscr{K}_0$ be the class of all members of $\mathscr{K}$ which are contained in $F_0$. We recall the notation $\sigma(\mathscr{E})$ for the $\sigma$-ring generated by $\mathscr{E}$.

*Step 5.* $\sigma(\mathscr{E}) = \sigma(\mathscr{D}) = \mathbf{S}_1 \times \mathbf{S}_2$. It is evident that $\sigma(\mathscr{E}) = \sigma(\mathscr{D})$, because $\mathscr{D} \subset \mathscr{E} \subset \sigma(\mathscr{D})$. Obviously, $\sigma(\mathscr{D}) \subset \mathbf{S}_1 \times \mathbf{S}_2$. Hence, to finish the argument, we wish to show that $\mathbf{S}_1 \times \mathbf{S}_2 \subset \sigma(\mathscr{D})$; for this it suffices to show that $E \in \sigma(\mathscr{D})$ if $E = A \times B$, where $A \in \mathbf{S}_1$, $B \in \mathbf{S}_2$. Using the $\sigma$-finiteness of the measure space, we write

$$A \subset \bigcup_n A_n, \qquad B \subset \bigcup_n B_n,$$

where $A_n \in \mathbf{S}_1$, $B_n \in \mathbf{S}_2$, and the measures of $A_n$ and $B_n$ are finite. Then

$$E \subset \bigcup_{m,n} (A_m \times B_n), \qquad E = \bigcup_{m,n} [E \cap (A_m \times B_n)].$$

But

$$E \cap (A_m \times B_n) = (A \cap A_m) \times (B \cap B_n) \in \mathscr{D},$$

and so we see that $E \in \sigma(\mathscr{D})$.

*Step 6.* $\mathscr{E}_0$ is a ring and $\sigma(\mathscr{E}_0)$ is the class of all members of $\mathbf{S}_1 \times \mathbf{S}_2$ which are contained in $F_0$. Since $\mathscr{E}$ is a ring, and since $\mathscr{E}_0$ is the class of all members of $\mathscr{E}$ contained in $F_0$, it is clear that $\mathscr{E}_0$ is a ring. The second part of the assertion follows from Theorem 4–2 II and Step 5.

*Step 7.* $\mathscr{K}_0$ is a monotone family (see Section 4–2). First we suppose that $\{E_n\}$ is a sequence of members of $\mathscr{K}_0$ such that $E_{n+1} \subset E_n$. Let $E = \bigcap_n E_n$. For each $x_1$ we see that $E_{n+1}(x_1) \subset E_n(x_1)$ and $E(x_1) = \bigcap_n E_n(x_1)$. Now, $F_0$ is contained in a set $A \times B$, where $A$ and $B$ are sets of finite measure in $\mathbf{S}_1$ and $\mathbf{S}_2$, respectively. Since $E_n$ is contained in $F_0$, we see that $E_n(x_1) \subset B$ if $x_1 \in A$, while $E_n(x_1) = \varnothing$ if $x_1 \notin A$. Therefore,

$$f_n(x_1) = \mu_2[E_n(x_1)] \begin{cases} = 0 & \text{if } x_1 \notin A \\ \leq \mu_2(B) & \text{if } x_1 \in A. \end{cases}$$

The situation for $g_n(x_2) = \mu_1[E_n(x_2)]$ is analogous. We see from these remarks that $f_n$ and $g_n$, being in $\mathscr{K}$, are measurable, and therefore summable. We can apply Theorem 4–4 IV to infer that $\mu_2[E_n(x_1)] \to \mu_2[E(x_1)]$, that is, that $f_n(x_1) \to f(x_1)$; likewise for $g_n$ and $g$. Therefore, by the monotone convergence theorem, $f$ and $g$ are summable; since the integrals of $f_n$ and $g_n$ are equal, so are those of $f$ and $g$. Therefore $E \in \mathscr{K}_0$.

If $E_n \in \mathscr{K}_0$, $E_n \subset E_{n+1}$, and $E = \bigcup_n E_n$, we use the monotone convergence theorem to deduce that $E \in \mathscr{K}_0$. In this part of the argument the fact that $E_n \subset F_0$ is not indispensable. We leave details to the reader. This finishes the proof that $\mathscr{K}_0$ is a monotone class.

*Step 8.* It follows from Step 2 ($\mathscr{E} \subset \mathscr{K}$) that $\mathscr{E}_0 \subset \mathscr{K}_0$. It follows from Step 7 that $\mathscr{K}_0$ contains the monotone family generated by $\mathscr{E}_0$. Thus, in view of Step 6 and Theorem 4–2 I, $\mathscr{K}_0$ contains all members of $\mathbf{S}_1 \times \mathbf{S}_2$ which are contained in $F_0$.

*Step 9.* Suppose $E \in \mathbf{S}_1 \times \mathbf{S}_2$. Now, use Step 4 to write $E \subset \bigcup_n E_n$; hence, $E = \bigcup_n (E \cap E_n)$, where $\{E_n\}$ is a sequence of disjoint members of $\mathscr{E}$. Applying Step 8, with $E_n$ in place of $F_0$, we see that $E \cap E_n \in \mathscr{K}$. Finally, by Step 2, $E \in \mathscr{K}$. This completes the proof of Theorem 7–5 III.

We can now proceed to the definition of a measure on $\mathbf{S}_1 \times \mathbf{S}_2$. If $E \in \mathbf{S}_1 \times \mathbf{S}_2$, we define

$$\mu(E) = \begin{cases} \int_{X_1} f \, d\mu, & \text{if } f \text{ is summable,} \\ +\infty & \text{if } f \text{ is not summable,} \end{cases} \tag{6}$$

where $f$ is defined in (2) (preceding Theorem 7–5 III). By Theorem 7–5 III we can substitute

$$\int_{X_2} g \, d\mu_2 \text{ for } \int_{X_1} f \, d\mu_1.$$

THEOREM 7–5 IV. *Let $(X_i, \mathbf{S}_i, \mu_i)$ $(i = 1, 2)$ be $\sigma$-finite measure spaces. The function $\mu : \mathbf{S}_1 \times \mathbf{S}_2 \to R^*$ defined in (6) is a $\sigma$-finite measure on $\mathbf{S}_1 \times \mathbf{S}_2$.*

*Proof.* Obviously, $\mu(\varnothing) = 0$, since $f = 0$ if $E = \varnothing$. Let $E = \bigcup_n E_n$ be a countable disjoint union of elements of $\mathbf{S}_1 \times \mathbf{S}_2$. Then $E(x_1) = \bigcup_n E_n(x_1)$ and $f(x_1) = \sum_n f_n(x_1)$ for each $x_1$. If $f$ is summable, each $f_n$ is summable and we can use the monotone convergence theorem to infer that $\mu(E) = \Sigma\, \mu(E_n)$. If $f$ is not summable, there are two possibilities: either each $f_n$ is summable, but $\sum_n \int_{X_1} f_n \, d\mu_1 = +\infty$, in which case $\sum_n \mu(E_n) = +\infty$; or some $f_n$ is not summable, in which case $\mu(E_n) = +\infty$. In either case $\sum_n \mu(E_n) = \mu(E) = +\infty$.

To see that $\mu$ is a $\sigma$-finite measure we observe that $\mu(E)$ is finite if $E$ is in $\mathscr{D}$ or $\mathscr{E}$ (see Step 1 of the proof of Theorem 7–5 III). Then we use the fact stated in Step 4 of the proof just referred to.

THEOREM 7–5 V. *Under the conditions in the preceding theorem, $\mu(E) = 0$ if and only if $\mu_2[E(x_1)] = 0$ a.e. in $X_1$ (or, also, if and only if $\mu_1[E(x_2)] = 0$ a.e. in $X_2$.*

*Proof.* See Theorem 5–4 VII.

The measure $\mu$ defined in (6) is derived in a definite way from $\mu_1$ and $\mu_2$. In the context of this section of the book we shall write $\mu = \mu_1 \times \mu_2$. This definition of product-measure is different from the one in Section 7–4, and not always equivalent to it, even when both definitions are applicable. In Section 7–4 the measures $\mu$, $\nu$ and the product measure $\lambda$ were all complete measures. In the present section, $\mu_1 \times \mu_2$ need not be a complete measure, even if $\mu_1$ and $\mu_2$ are complete. We shall exhibit an example of this possibility in the discussion which follows.

## THE PRODUCT OF TWO LEBESGUE MEASURES

Let us now denote by $\mathbf{S}_p$ the class of all Lebesgue-measurable subsets of $R^p$, and let $\mu_p$ denote the Lebesgue measure function on $\mathbf{S}_p$. We shall discuss the product-measure $\mu_p \times \mu_q$, where $p$ and $q$ are any two positive integers. We know that $\mathbf{S}_p \times \mathbf{S}_q$ is a $\sigma$-ring of sets in $R^p \times R^q = R^{p+q}$, and that $\mu_p \times \mu_q$ is a measure on $\mathbf{S}_p \times \mathbf{S}_q$. The measure $\mu_p \times \mu_q$ is not complete. We can see that this is so as follows: Suppose $A \in \mathbf{S}_p$ and $\mu_p(A) = 0$, but $A \neq \varnothing$. Let $B$ be a compact interval in $\mathbf{S}_q$, and let $B_1$ be a subset of $B$ which is not in $\mathbf{S}_q$ (see Section 4–8). Then $E_1 = A \times B_1$ is a nonempty subset of $E = A \times B$, but $E_1$ is not in $\mathbf{S}_p \times \mathbf{S}_q$, because $E_1(x_1) = B_1$ if $x_1 \in A$, and $E_1 \in \mathbf{S}_p \times \mathbf{S}_q$ would imply $B_1 \in \mathbf{S}_q$, by Theorem 7–5 I. But the product-measure of $E$ is $\mu_p(A)\mu_q(B) = 0$; therefore the measure $\mu_p \times \mu_q$ is not complete.

Since we know that $\mu_{p+q}$ is a complete measure, it is clear that, with the present definition of the product of two measures, $\mu_{p+q} \neq \mu_p \times \mu_q$. This is in contrast to the situation in Section 7–4, where we used a different definition of product-measure. The relation between $\mu_{p+q}$ and $\mu_p \times \mu_q$ in the present situation is explained in the following theorem.

THEOREM 7–5 VI. *With the notations here established $\mu_{p+q}$ is the completion of $\mu_p \times \mu_q$.*

*Proof.* For convenience let us write $\mathbf{S} = \mathbf{S}_p \times \mathbf{S}_q$, $\mu = \mu_p \times \mu_q$. We wish to show that $\bar{\mathbf{S}} = \mathbf{S}_{p+q}$ and $\bar{\mu} = \mu_{p+q}$. Now, it was shown in Section 7–4, as an application of Theorem 7–3 V, that if $A \in \mathbf{S}_p$ and $B \in \mathbf{S}_q$, with $\mu_p(A) < +\infty$, $\mu_q(B) < +\infty$, then $A \times B \in \mathbf{S}_{p+q}$ and $\mu_{p+q}(A \times B) = \mu_p(A)\mu_q(B)$. With the notation $\mathscr{D}$ introduced in the proof of Theorem 7–5 III, this means that $\mathscr{D} \subset \mathbf{S}_{p+q}$ and that $\mu$ and $\mu_{p+q}$ agree on $\mathscr{D}$. From this we see, since $\mathbf{S}_{p+q}$ is a $\sigma$-ring, that $\mathbf{S} \subset \mathbf{S}_{p+q}$. Moreover, it can be proved (see Problem 3 at the end of this section) that $\mu$ and $\mu_{p+q}$ agree on $\mathbf{S}$. Since $\mu_{p+q}$ is complete, it then follows, by the remarks following the proof of Theorem 4–11 I, that $\bar{\mathbf{S}} \subset \mathbf{S}_{p+q}$ and that $\bar{\mu}$ and $\mu_{p+q}$ agree on $\mathbf{S}$.

All that now remains is to prove that $\mathbf{S}_{p+q} \subset \bar{\mathbf{S}}$. For this we assert, in the first place, that every Borel set in $R^{p+q}$ belongs to $\mathbf{S}$. Any open interval in $R^{p+q}$ clearly belongs to $\mathbf{S}$, for it is the product of an open interval in $R^p$ and an open interval in $R^q$. Since $R^{p+q}$ has a countable basis of neighborhoods consisting of open intervals, every open set is in $\mathbf{S}$, and hence every Borel set is in $\mathbf{S}$. Next, every element of $\mathbf{S}_{p+q}$ is a disjoint union of a Borel set and a set of measure zero (Theorem 4–8 II), and the set of measure zero is a subset of a Borel set of measure zero (Theorem 4–8 I). From this it is clear (in view of the method of completing a measure) that $\mathbf{S}_{p+q} \subset \bar{\mathbf{S}}$. We have therefore completed the proof.

## PROBLEMS

1. Work out the proof of Theorem 7–5 II in all details for the general case, when $X_i$ need not belong to $\mathbf{S}_i$.
2. Finish the arguments in Steps 1 and 7 of the proof of Theorem 7–5 III.
3. With respect to the measure $\mu$ defined in (6), prove the following: If $\lambda$ is any measure on $\mathbf{S}_1 \times \mathbf{S}_2$ such that $\lambda(E) = \mu(E)$ if $E \in \mathscr{D}$, then $\lambda = \mu$. [*Hint.* For any fixed $F_0$ in $\mathscr{E}$, defined $\mathscr{E}_0$ as in the proof of Theorem 7–5 III, and consider the class $\mathscr{M}$ of all $E$ which are contained in $F_0$ and such that $\lambda(E) = \mu(E)$. Show that $\mathscr{M}$ is a monotone family.]

## 7–6 The abstract Fubini theorem

In this section we deal with Fubini's theorem from the point of view of the theory of integration developed in Chapter 5. We build upon the work of Section 7–5. The essential key is furnished by Theorems 7–5 III and 7–5 IV. The main difficulty of the whole business is in the proof of Theorem 7–5 III.

As in Section 7–5, let $(X_1, \mathbf{S}_1, \mu_1)$ and $(X_2, \mathbf{S}_2, \mu_2)$ be measure spaces; we assume that they are $\sigma$-finite. This will be taken for granted without explicit restatement in the theorems of this section. Let $\mu$ be the measure defined on $\mathbf{S}_1 \times \mathbf{S}_2$ as in (6), Section 7–5. In this general setting there is a counterpart of the theorem originally given by Fubini as a proposition about Lebesgue integrals in multidimensional spaces.

THEROEM 7–6 I. *Suppose $f : X_1 \times X_2 \to R^*$ is $\mu$-summable. Then there exists a function $f_1 : X_1 \to R^*$ which is $\mu_1$-summable and a set $F \subset X_1$, $\mu_1$-measurable and with $\mu_1(F) = 0$, such that*

(a)
$$\int_{X_1 \times X_2} f \, d\mu = \int_{X_1} f_1 \, d\mu_1,$$

(b)
$$f(x_1, \cdot) : X_2 \to R^* \text{ is } \mu_2\text{-summable if } x_1 \in X_1 - F,$$

(c)
$$f_1(x_1) = \int_{X_2} f(x_1, x_2) \mu_2(dx_2)$$

*if $x_1 \in X_1 - F$.*

*A symmetrical assertion is true with the roles of $X_1$ and $X_2$ exchanged.*

*Comment.* In view of (b) and (c), it is customary to write (a) in one of the forms

(1)
$$\int_{X_1 \times X_2} f \, d\mu = \int_{X_1} \left[ \int_{X_2} f(x_1, x_2) \mu_2(dx_2) \right] \mu_1(dx_1),$$

(2)
$$\int_{X_1 \times X_2} f \, d\mu = \int_{X_1} \mu_1(dx_1) \int_{X_2} f(x_1, x_2) \mu_2(dx_2),$$

(3)
$$\int_{X_1 \times X_2} f \, d\mu = \int_{X_1} d\mu_1 \int_{X_2} f \, d\mu_2.$$

*Proof.* Let $\mathscr{F}$ be the class of $\mu$-summable functions $f$ to which there correspond $f_1$ and $F$ with the asserted properties. We prove in four steps that $\mathscr{F}$ includes all $\mu$-summable functions.

*Step 1.* We prove that $\mathscr{F}$ is a linear class. Suppose $f$ and $g$ are in $\mathscr{F}$. Then we have $f_1$, $F$ in relation to $f$, and $g_1$, $G$ in relation to $g$ in the manner asserted in the theorem. It is easy to verify that $f_1 + g_1$ and $F \cup G$ meet the requirements in relation to $f + g$, so that $f + g \in \mathscr{F}$. The proof that $cf \in \mathscr{F}$ if $c$ is real is similar.

*Step 2.* We prove that, if $E$ is a set of finite measure in $\mathbf{S}_1 \times \mathbf{S}_2$, then $\chi_E \in \mathscr{F}$, and hence, by Step 1, $\mathscr{F}$ contains all finite linear combinations of such characteristic functions. For the case $f = \chi_E$ we take $f_1(x_1) = \mu_2[E(x_1)]$ and $F = \{x_1 : f_1(x_1) = +\infty\}$. We know by Theorem 7–5 III that $f_1$ is $\mu_1$-measurable; it is $\mu_1$-summable because we specified that $\mu(E)$ be finite (see (6) in Section 7–5). It follows that $\mu(F) = 0$ for the set $F$ as defined. In this case (a) is true from the definition of $\mu(E)$, while (b) and (c) are true because $\chi_E(x_1, \cdot)$ is the characteristic function of $E(x_1)$.

*Step 3.* Suppose $f_n$ and $f$ are $\mu$-summable functions such that $f_n \in \mathscr{F}$ and $f_n \nearrow f$. Then we can infer that $f \in \mathscr{F}$. Here, we let $g_n : X_1 \to R^*$ and $F_n \subset X_1$ stand in relation to $f_n$ in the manner asserted in the theorem ($g_n$ to $f_n$ as $f_1$ is to $f$ in the theorem). We shall explain how to get a suitable $g : X_1 \to R^*$ and $F \subset X_1$ to correspond to the limit function $f$. We begin by redefining $g_n$ on $\bigcup_n F_n$, by putting $g_n(x_1) = 0$ if $x_1 \in \bigcup_n F_n$. Since $\mu_1\left(\bigcup_n F_n\right) = 0$, this does not affect the measurability of $g_n$ or the value of the integral of $g_n$. This change permits us to assert that $\{g_n(x_1)\}$ is a nondecreasing sequence for *every* $x_1$, for we know this to be true when $x_1 \in X_1 - \bigcup_n F_n$ from the relation

$$g_n(x_1) = \int_{X_2} f_n(x_1, x_2)\mu_2(dx_2), \qquad x_1 \in X_1 - \bigcup_n F_n, \tag{4}$$

which is valid after the modification of $g_n$. Thus $g_n$ converges pointwise to a limit function $g$. Now

$$\int_{X_1} g_n \, d\mu_1 = \int_{X_1 \times X_2} f_n \, d\mu \leq \int_{X_1 \times X_2} f \, d\mu < +\infty.$$

Therefore, by Theorem 5–5 I, $g$ is $\mu_1$-summable and $\int_{X_1} g_n \, d\mu_1 \to \int_{X_1} g \, d\mu_1$. At the same time, we see that the integral of $g$ over $X_1$ is equal to the integral of $f$ over $X_1 \times X_2$. Let $G = \{x_1 : g(x_1) = +\infty\}$. We know that $\mu_1(G) = 0$. Let $F = G \cup \bigcup_n F_n$. Then $\mu_1(F) = 0$. If $x_1 \in X - F$, the integrals in (4) have a finite upper bound; from this we infer (by the monotone convergence theorem) that $f(x_1, \cdot)$ is $\mu_2$-summable and

$$g(x_1) = \int_{X_2} f(x_1, x_2)\mu_2(dx_2), \qquad x_1 \in X_1 - F.$$

This completes the proof that $f \in \mathscr{F}$.

*Step 4.* Suppose $f : X_1 \times X_2 \to R^*$ is $\mu$-summable. Write $f = f^+ - f^-$. By Step 1 we see that it suffices to prove $f \in \mathscr{F}$ on the assumption that $f \geq 0$. But for such an $f$ we can write $f_n \nearrow f$, where each $f_n$ is a finite linear combination of characteristic functions of sets of finite measure (and $f_n \geq 0$ as well). By Steps 2 and 3 we know that $f_n \in \mathscr{F}$ and therefore $f \in \mathscr{F}$.

The situation is plainly symmetrical as regards the roles of $X_1$, $\mu_1$ and $X_2$, $\mu_2$. This is guaranteed by (3) in Theorem 7–5 III. Thus the proof of the theorem is completed.

Theorem 7–6 I is not quite a true generalization of Fubini's theorem, for it does not reduce to the original theorem of Fubini when we take $\mu_1$ and $\mu_2$ to be Lebesgue measures in two Euclidean spaces, say $R^p$ and $R^q$. This is because of the fact, explained in Section 7–5, that for this special case $\mu_1 \times \mu_2$ is not Lebesgue measure in $R^{p+q}$. In view of Theorem 7–5 VI, we should then look for a modification of Theorem 7–6 I in which we start with a function $f$ which is $\bar{\mu}$-summable, where $\bar{\mu}$ is the completion of $\mu$. There is indeed such a modified theorem, which contains as a special case the Fubini theorem for Euclidean spaces and Lebesgue measures.

THEOREM 7–6 II. *Suppose that $\mu_1$ and $\mu_2$ are complete measures. Let $\mu = \mu_1 \times \mu_2$ be defined by* (6) *in Section* 7–5, *and let $\bar{\mu}$ be the completion of $\mu$. Suppose that $f : X_1 \times X_2 \to R^*$ is $\bar{\mu}$-summable (instead of $\mu$-summable, as assumed in Theorem* 7–6 I). *Then all the conclusions of Theorem* 7–6 I *remain valid, with $\bar{\mu}$ instead of $\mu$ in* (a).

*Proof.* The key ideas are set forth in Section 5–9. From $f$ we construct a function $g$ which is summable with respect to $\mu$ and such that

$$(4) \qquad \int_{X_1 \times X_2} g \, d\mu = \int_{X_1 \times X_2} f \, d\bar{\mu}.$$

We moreover arrange that, if $E = \{x : f(x) \neq g(x)\}$, then $\bar{\mu}(E) = 0$. We now apply Theorem 7–6 I to $g$, obtaining a function $g_1 : X_1 \to R^*$ and a set $G \subset X_1$ which are related to $g$ as $f_1$ and $F$ are to $f$ in Theorem 7–6 I. As we shall see, $g_1$ will serve as the $f_1$ we need. We must find a suitable set $F$. Now, $E$ is contained in some set $H$, where $H \in \mathbf{S}_1 \times \mathbf{S}_2$ and $\mu(H) = 0$. Therefore, by Theorem 7–5 V, $\mu_2[H(x_1)] = 0$ except when $x_1$ is in a certain set, say $G_0$, for which $\mu_1(G_0) = 0$. Let $F = G_0 \cup G$. Now, for a fixed $x_1$ in $X_1 - F$, $g(x_1, \cdot)$ is $\mu_2$-summable and

$$(5) \qquad g_1(x_1) = \int_{X_2} g(x_1, x_2)\mu_2(dx_2).$$

For such an $x_1$, the set of $x_2$-values for which $f(x_1, x_2) \neq g(x_1, x_2)$ is $E(x_1)$, which is contained in $H(x_1)$, whose $\mu_2$-measure is zero. Since $\mu_2$ is a complete measure, $\mu_2[E(x_1)] = 0$. Moreover, since $g(x_1, x_2) = 0$ if $x_2 \in E(x_1)$, we can infer that $f(x_1, \cdot)$ is $\mu_2$-measurable, and hence also that it is $\mu_2$-summable and that we can replace $g$ by $f$ in (5)—all this if $x_1 \in X_1 - F$. Since $\int_{X_1} g_1 \, d\mu_1 = \int_{X_1 \times X_1} g \, d\mu$, we see from (4) that we have proved what is needed as regards $g_1$ and $F$ in relation to $f$. The same kind of argument applies with the roles of $X_1$ and $X_2$ exchanged.

## SUGGESTED READING FOR CHAPTER 7

References emphasizing Lebesgue measure in Euclidean spaces:

BURKILL [1], pp. 61–64.
CARATHEODORY [1], pp. 621–641.
GOFFMAN [1], Chapter 20.
GRAVES [1], pp. 215–220.
HOBSON [1], Vol. I, pp. 626–632.
KESTELMAN [1], Chapter 8.
NATANSON [1], Vol. II, pp. 85–93.
THIELMAN [1], pp. 174–180.
DE LA VALLÉE-POUSSIN [1], pp. 54–58.
WILLIAMSON [1], pp. 63–65.

References using a more abstract approach, in the spirit of Chapter 5:

HAHN and ROSENTHAL [1], pp. 238–245.
HALMOS [1], Chapter 7.
KOLMOGOROV and FOMIN [1], pp. 78–90.
MUNROE [1], pp. 199–210.
SAKS [1], pp. 76–88.

References using the Daniell integral:

AUMANN [1], pp. 403–405.
LOOMIS [1], pp. 44–46.
MCSHANE [1], pp. 136–150.
MCSHANE and BOTTS [1], Section 6 of Chapter 5.
ZAANEN [1], Chapter 5.

CHAPTER EIGHT

# The Theory of Signed Measures

## 8–0 Introduction

Suppose $(X, \mathbf{S}, \mu)$ is a measure space, and suppose $f \in \mathscr{L}(\mu)$ (notation of Section 5–4). For $E \in \mathbf{S}$ let

$$(1) \qquad m(E) = \int_E f\, d\mu, \qquad \nu(E) = \int_E |f|\, d\mu.$$

We know (Theorem 5–5 II) that $m$ and $\nu$ are countably additive on $\mathbf{S}$. Since $\nu$ has non-negative values, it is a measure on $\mathbf{S}$. In this case both $m$ and $\nu$ have all their values finite. The set function $m$ is an example of what we shall call a *signed measure* (general definition in Section 8–1); here $m(E)$ may be negative.

The purpose of this chapter is to investigate the nature of signed measures in general. There are three aspects of this investigation. In the first place, it turns out that every signed measure can be expressed as the difference of two measures. In the case of the $m$ defined in (1), we can write $m = m^+ - m^-$, where

$$m^+(E) = \int_E f^+\, d\mu, \qquad m^-(E) = \int_E f^-\, d\mu.$$

The measure $\nu$ in (1) is then seen to be expressible as $\nu = m^+ + m^-$. But, in the case of an arbitrary signed measure, we have no given basic measure $\mu$ and no given function $f$ associated with the signed measure; we must then find a way to express $m^+$ and $m^-$ directly from $m$, without the intervention of $\mu$ and $f$. These matters are considered in Section 8–1.

The second aspect of our study has to do with determining when a signed measure is expressible as an integral, as is the case with $m$ in (1). Here, the essential concept is absolute continuity (Section 8–2) and the main result is the Radon-Nikodym theorem (Section 8–3). In Section 8–4 we have one of the important applications of the Radon-Nikodym theorem in the proof of Theorem 8–4 I.

The third stage in our study comes in Section 8–5; there, under rather general conditions, it is shown that any signed measure is the sum of an absolutely continuous signed measure and a signed measure of a quite different sort. Here, a basic measure function is assumed to be present. The absolutely continuous part of the signed measure is expressible as an integral. The other part, called a *singular* signed measure, takes all its nonzero values on a certain set of measure zero.

These developments all occur in the framework of the theory of measure and integration, as developed in Chapters 4 and 5. But one may also make an analogous investigation in which the basic point of view is supplied by Chapter 6. Corresponding to the idea of expressing a signed measure as the difference of two measures, there is the idea of expressing a linear functional (suitably restricted) as the difference of two nonnegative linear functionals. Corresponding to the central idea in the Radon-Nikodym theorem there is the idea of trying to express one integral in terms of another integral, when both integrals originate from elementary integrals over the same basic vector lattice of functions. These matters are explored in Section 8–6. The counterpart of the Radon-Nikodym theorem is Theorem 8–6 IV.

In Section 8–7 we have a decomposition for linear functionals on a vector lattice. Every continuous linear functional on $C_\infty(R^k)$ is expressible as a difference of positive linear functionals, which are elementary integrals. From this result, in conjunction with the results of Section 6–9, 6–10, we are able to prove the Riesz representation theorem for continuous linear functionals on $C_\infty(R^k)$ (Theorem 8–7 IV).

## 8–1 Signed measures

Let $\mathbf{S}$ be a $\sigma$-ring composed of subsets of a basic set $X$, and let $\mu : \mathbf{S} \to R^*$ be a function such that

(i) $\mu(\varnothing) = 0$,

(ii) at most one of the values $-\infty$, $+\infty$ is in the range of $\mu$,

(iii) $\mu$ is countably additive.

Then we call $\mu$ a *signed measure*.

A few comments on (ii) and (iii) are needed. We impose condition (ii) in order to be able to give a clear meaning to (iii). Addition in $R^*$ is associative, so long as both $+\infty$ and $-\infty$ do not enter as summands. When we say that $\mu$ is countably additive, we mean that, given any countable disjoint family $\{E_n\}$ in $\mathbf{S}$, with $E = \bigcup_n E_n$, the sums $\sum_{i=1}^{n} \mu(E_i)$ approach a definite limit $\sum_{i=1}^{\infty} \mu(E_i)$ in $R^*$, and

$$\mu(E) = \sum_{i=1}^{\infty} \mu(E_i).$$

It is clear that a signed measure $\mu$ is a measure if $\mu(E) \geq 0$ for each $E$.

A signed measure is not necessarily monotone in the sense of Section 4–3.

The signed measure $\mu$ is called $\sigma$-finite if each element of $\mathbf{S}$ is expressible as a countable union of sets $E_1, E_2, \ldots$ such that $\mu(E_n)$ is finite for each $n$.

In the following theorem we catalogue some facts for future reference. We note, in particular, that the assertions in Theorems 4–4 III, IV remain valid for signed measures.

THEOREM 8–1 I. *Let $\mu$ be a signed measure on* $\mathbf{S}$.

(a) *If $A$, $B$ are in* $\mathbf{S}$, *with $A \subset B$ and $\mu(A)$ infinite, then $\mu(A) = \mu(B)$.*

(b) *If $\{E_n\}$ is a sequence in* $\mathbf{S}$ *such that $E_n \subset E_{n+1}$, then $\mu(E_n) \to \mu\left(\bigcup_i E_i\right)$.*

(c) *If* $\{E_n\}$ *is a sequence in* $\mathbf{S}$ *such that* $E_{n+1} \subset E_n$, *and if* $\mu(E_n)$ *is finite for some* $n$, *then* $\mu(E_n) \to \mu\left(\bigcap_i E_i\right)$.

*Proof of* (a). If $A \subset B$, we have

$$\mu(B) = \mu(A) + \mu(B - A).$$

Since only one of the values $-\infty$, $+\infty$ can be involved, we see that $\mu(B)$ must be the same infinity as $\mu(A)$.

*Proof of* (b) *and* (c). The argument for (b) is exactly as in the proof of Theorem 4–4 III. The argument for (c) is almost the same as in the proof of Theorem 4–4 IV. The only difference is in connection with the matter of finiteness of $\mu(E_n)$ and $\mu\left(\bigcap_n E_n\right)$. It follows from (a) that $\mu(F)$ is finite if $F \in \mathbf{S}$, $F \subset E_m$, and $\mu(E_m)$ is finite. This argument takes the place of the appeal to the monotone character of the measure in the proof of Theorem 4–4 IV.

## THE TOTAL VARIATION

If $E \in \mathbf{S}$, by a *mesh* in $E$ we shall mean a finite disjoint family $E_1, \ldots, E_n$ of sets, with $E_i \in \mathbf{S}$ and $E_i \subset E$ for each $i$. Now, if $\mu$ is a signed measure on $\mathbf{S}$, we define a nonnegative function $V_\mu : \mathbf{S} \to R^*$ as follows

$$V_\mu(E) = \sup \sum_i |\mu(E_i)|, \tag{1}$$

where the supremum is taken over all possible meshes $\{E_i\}$ in $E$. We call $V_\mu(E)$ the *total variation* of $\mu$ on $E$. The function $V_\mu$ is called the total variation of $\mu$.

THEOREM 8–1 II. *The total variation* $V_\mu$ *of the signed measure* $\mu$ *is a measure on* $\mathbf{S}$.

*Proof.* It is obvious that $V_\mu(\varnothing) = 0$. Let $\{E_n\}$ be a countable disjoint family in $\mathbf{S}$, with $E = \bigcup_n E_n$. Let $\{A_i\}$ be a mesh in $E$, and let $A_{in} = A_i \cap E_n$. Then $\{A_{in}\}$ (with $n$ fixed) is a mesh in $E_n$, and

$$A_i = \bigcup_n A_{in}, \qquad \mu(A_i) = \sum_n \mu(A_{in}).$$

We see that

$$\sum_i |\mu(A_i)| \le \sum_n \sum_i |\mu(A_{in})| \le \sum_n V_\mu(E_n),$$

whence

$$V_\mu(E) \le \sum_n V_\mu(E_n). \tag{2}$$

We wish now to prove the reverse of inequality (2); for this purpose we may assume that $V_\mu(E)$ is finite. Since it is easily seen from the definition that $V_\mu$ is a monotone set function, this means that $V_\mu(E_n)$ also is finite. Suppose $\epsilon > 0$. Choose a mesh $\{E_{in}\}$ ($n$ fixed) in $E_n$ so that

$$\sum_i |\mu(E_{in})| > V_\mu(E_n) - \frac{\epsilon}{2^n}.$$

For an arbitrary $N$ the meshes $\{E_{i1}\}, \ldots, \{E_{iN}\}$ can be pooled to form a mesh in $E$. Then

$$\sum_{n=1}^{N} V_\mu(E_n) < \sum_{n=1}^{N} \left\{ \sum_i |\mu(E_{in})| + \frac{\epsilon}{2^n} \right\} \leq V_\mu(E) + \epsilon.$$

Since $N$ and $\epsilon$ are arbitrary, we obtain the reverse of (2). Therefore $V_\mu$ is a measure.

## THE UPPER AND LOWER VARIATIONS

We now define two more set functions which will turn out to be measures associated with $\mu$. Regardless of the sign of $\mu(E)$, there may be subsets $A$ of $E$ in $\mathbf{S}$ such that $\mu(A)$ is positive. There certainly are such subsets for which $\mu(A) = 0$ (namely $A = \varnothing$). We define

(3) $$\mu^+(E) = \sup\{\mu(A) : A \in \mathbf{S},\ A \subset E\}.$$

Then certainly $\mu^+(E) \geq 0$. We also define

(4) $$\mu^-(E) = -\inf\{\mu(A) : A \in \mathbf{S},\ A \subset E\}.$$

Since $-\mu$ is also a signed measure, we can apply these definitions to it. We see that

(5) $$\mu^- = (-\mu)^+.$$

The functions $\mu^+$, $\mu^-$ are called the *upper* and *lower variations*, respectively, of $\mu$.

THEOREM 8–1 III. *Let $\mu$ be a signed measure. Then $\mu^+$ and $\mu^-$ are measures. If $\mu^+(E) = +\infty$ for a given $E$, then $\mu(E) = +\infty$ also. If $\mu^-(E) = +\infty$, then $\mu(E) = -\infty$. Therefore one of the two functions $\mu^+$, $\mu^-$ has no infinite values. The following relations are valid*

(6) $$\mu = \mu^+ - \mu^-,$$

(7) $$V_\mu = \mu^+ + \mu^-.$$

*Proof.* We first prove that $\mu^+$ is a measure. From (5) we can then conclude that $\mu^-$ is a measure. The treatment of $\mu^+$ is rather like the proof of Theorem 8–1 II. If $\{E_n\}$ is a countable disjoint family in $\mathbf{S}$, with $E = \bigcup_n E_n$, and if $A \in \mathbf{S}$, $A \subset E$, then $A = \bigcup_n (A \cap E_n)$, so that

$$\mu(A) = \sum_n \mu(A \cap E_n) \leq \sum_n \mu^+(E_n),$$

whence

(8) $$\mu^+(E) \leq \sum_n \mu^+(E_n).$$

In proving the reverse of the inequality (8) we may assume that $\mu^+(E)$ is finite. Then $\mu^+(E_n)$ also is finite, for it is easy to see that $\mu^+$ is monotone. Suppose $\epsilon > 0$ and choose $A_n \in \mathbf{S}$, $A_n \subset E_n$ so that $\mu(A_n) > \mu^+(E_n) - \dfrac{\epsilon}{2^n}$. Then $A = \bigcup_n A_n$ is in $\mathbf{S}$ and contained in $E$, so that $\mu(A) \leq \mu^+(E)$. But

$$\sum_n \mu^+(E_n) < \sum_n \left[\mu(A_n) + \frac{\epsilon}{2^n}\right] = \mu(A) + \epsilon \leq \mu^+(E) + \epsilon,$$

whence we get the reverse of (8).

Now, let us assume that $\mu^+(E) = +\infty$, and show that $\mu(E) = +\infty$. By Theorem 8–1 I (a) it will suffice to obtain a subset $F$ of $E$ for which $\mu(F) = +\infty$. In the following discussion all the sets will either be chosen from **S** or will of necessity be in **S**. There exists a set $E_1 \subset E$ with $\mu(E_1) > 1$. Since

$$+\infty = \mu^+(E) = \mu^+(E_1) + \mu^+(E - E_1),$$

the value of $\mu^+$ is $+\infty$ for at least one of the sets $E_1$, $E - E_1$. Let $F_1$ denote one of these two sets for which $\mu^+(F_1) = +\infty$. Writing $F_0 = E$, we proceed by induction to obtain sequences $\{E_n\}$, $\{F_n\}$ such that $E_n \subset F_{n-1}$, $\mu(E_n) > n$, and $F_n$ is either $E_n$ or $F_{n-1} - E_n$, the choice being such as to insure that $\mu^+(F_n) = +\infty$. We observe that $F_{n+1} \subset F_n$. Hence, if $m < n$ and we have both $F_m = F_{m-1} - E_m$ and $F_n = F_{n-1} - E_n$, then $E_n \cap E_m = \varnothing$. There are now two possibilities to consider. It may be that $F_n = F_{n-1} - E_n$ for an infinite number of values of $n$, say $n_1 < n_2 < \cdots$. In this case let $F = \bigcup_n E_{n_i}$. Then we have a disjoint union, so

$$\mu(F) = \sum_i \mu(E_{n_i}) \geq \sum_i n_i = +\infty.$$

Or it may be that $F_n = E_n$ for all but a finite number of values of $n$. In this case, if $\mu(F_n) = +\infty$ for some $n$, we have what we are after. Otherwise we have $n < \mu(F_n) < +\infty$ for all sufficiently large $n$, and we can use Theorem 8–1 I (c) to conclude that $\mu\left(\bigcap_n F_n\right) = +\infty$. This finishes the proof that $\mu(E) = +\infty$ if $\mu^+(E) = +\infty$. It follows from (5) that $\mu^-(E) = +\infty$ implies $\mu(E) = -\infty$.

Next, we wish to prove (6). From the definitions it is apparent that $-\mu^-(E) \leq \mu(E) \leq \mu^+(E)$. From these inequalities and the fact that only one of $\mu^+(E)$, $\mu^-(E)$ can be infinite it follows that $\mu(E) = \mu^+(E) - \mu^-(E)$ if $\mu(E)$ is infinite. We now assume that $\mu(E)$ is finite; by Theorem 8–1 I (a) $\mu(A)$ is finite for every $A$ contained in $E$ (and belonging to **S**). If $A \subset E$, $E - A \subset E$ also, and

(9) $$-\mu^-(E) \leq \mu(E - A) \leq \mu^+(E).$$

Now,

(10) $$\mu(A) = \mu(E) - \mu(E - A).$$

From (9) and (10) we see that

$$\mu(A) \leq \mu(E) + \mu^-(E),$$

whence

(11) $$\mu^+(E) \leq \mu(E) + \mu^-(E).$$

In a similar way we obtain the result

(12) $$-\mu^-(E) \geq \mu(E) - \mu^+(E).$$

Since $\mu(E)$ is finite, we know that $\mu^+(E)$ and $\mu^-(E)$ are finite. Hence, (11) and (12) together imply that $\mu(E) = \mu^+(E) - \mu^-(E)$. Thus (6) is proved.

Finally, we wish to prove (7). Let $E$ be given. Choose any $c$ in $R^*$ such that $c < V_\mu(E)$. Choose a mesh $\{E_i\}$ in $E$ such that $c < \sum_i |\mu(E_i)|$. Let $F$ be the union of the $E_i$'s for which $\mu(E_i) \geq 0$, and let $G$ be the union of the $E_i$'s for which $\mu(E_i) < 0$. Then $\mu(F) \leq \mu^+(E)$, $\mu(G) \geq -\mu^-(E)$, and so

$$c < \mu(F) - \mu(G) \leq \mu^+(E) + \mu^-(E),$$

whence

(13) $$V_\mu(E) \leq \mu^+(E) + \mu^-(E).$$

In proving the reverse of this inequality we may assume that $V_\mu(E)$ is finite. Since a single subset $A$ of $E$ (in **S**) is a mesh in $E$, we see that $|\mu(A)| \leq V_\mu(E)$ for any such $A$. Therefore $\mu^+(E)$ and $\mu^-(E)$ are finite. If $A \subset E$,

$$2\mu(A) = \mu(A) + \mu(E) - \mu(E - A),$$

$$2\mu(A) \leq \mu(E) + |\mu(A)| + |\mu(E - A)|$$

$$\leq \mu(E) + V_\mu(E),$$

whence $2\mu^+(E) \leq \mu(E) + V_\mu(E)$. Using (6), we see that

$$\mu^+(E) + \mu^-(E) \leq V_\mu(E).$$

In view of (13), we have the proof of (7).

### THE REPRESENTATION $\mu = \mu^+ - \mu^-$ OF THE SIGNED MEASURE $\mu$

The representation $\mu = \mu^+ - \mu^-$ of the signed measure $\mu$ is called the *Jordan decomposition* of $\mu$. We observe that $\mu = \mu^+$ and $\mu^- = 0$ if $\mu$ is a measure. The name Jordan here is that of Camille Jordan (1838–1922). Actually, the idea of decomposing a signed measure into its upper and lower variations is ascribed to Lebesgue and not to Jordan. However, Jordan had made the decomposition of a real function of bounded variation as the difference of two nonnegative monotone functions (see Theorem 9–4 II), and this is a natural precursor of the decomposition theorem for signed measures.

If $(X, \mathbf{S}, \mu)$ is a measure space, if $f : X \to R^*$ is summable with respect to $\mu$, and if we define

$$m(E) = \int_E f \, d\mu, \tag{14}$$

the functions $m^+$, $m^-$ turn out to be

$$m^+(E) = \int_E f^+ \, d\mu, \qquad m^-(E) = \int_E f^- \, d\mu.$$

Then the total variation is given by

$$V_m(E) = \int_E |f| \, d\mu.$$

Verification of these assertions is left as an exercise for the reader. See Problem 4.

### HAHN DECOMPOSITIONS OF $X$

If we consider the signed measure $m$ defined by (14), we see that the following decomposition of the space $X$ suggests itself. Let

$$A = \{x : f(x) \geq 0\}, \qquad B = \{x : f(x) < 0\}. \tag{15}$$

Suppose now that $E \in \mathbf{S}$. Then $E \cap A$ and $E \cap B$ are in **S** (see Problem 10, Section 5–1). Since $f^-(x) = 0$ if $x \in A$ and $f^+(x) = 0$ if $x \in B$, we see that $m(E \cap A) = m^+(E \cap A) \geq 0$ and $m(E \cap B) = -m^-(E \cap B) \leq 0$. These considerations motivate the following definition. The concept to be defined is named after Hans Hahn (1879–1934) because of his general theorem on this subject.

Suppose now that $\mu$ is any signed measure on **S**. Suppose also that there exist sets $A$, $B$ such that

(i) $A \cap B = \varnothing$, $A \cup B = X$,

(ii) if $E \in \mathbf{S}$, then $E \cap A$ and $E \cap B$ are in **S** and $\mu(E \cap A) \geq 0$, $\mu(E \cap B) \leq 0$.

Then we say that the expression of $X$ as $X = A \cup B$ is *a Hahn decomposition of X relative to* $\mu$. (The first mentioned set in the pair $A$, $B$ is the one for which $\mu(E \cap A) \geq 0$.)

There is a relationship between a Hahn decomposition of $X$ relative to $\mu$ and the Jordan decomposition of $\mu$. If $X = A \cup B$ is a Hahn decomposition of $X$, then

$$\mu^+(E) = \mu(E \cap A), \qquad \mu^-(E) = -\mu(E \cap B) \tag{16}$$

for each $E$ in **S**. To prove this, suppose that $F \in \mathbf{S}$ and $F \subset E \cap A$. Then $F = F \cap A$, so $\mu(F) \geq 0$. But then, by the definition of $\mu^-$, we see that $-\mu^-(E \cap A) \geq 0$. Since $\mu^-$ is nonnegative, we conclude that $\mu^-(E \cap A) = 0$. In a similar manner we see that $\mu^+(E \cap B) = 0$. Now $E = (E \cap A) \cup (E \cap B)$, whence $\mu^+(E) = \mu^+(E \cap A)$. But $\mu(E \cap A) = \mu^+(E \cap A) - \mu^-(E \cap A) = \mu^+(E \cap A)$, so we obtain the first formula in (16). The other formula is obtained by a similar argument.

We call attention to the fact that if $X = A \cup B$ is a Hahn decomposition of $X$ relative to $\mu$, and if $A \in \mathbf{S}$, then

$$\mu^-(A) = 0. \tag{17}$$

Likewise, if $B \in \mathbf{S}$ (even though $A$ is perhaps not in **S**), we have

$$\mu^+(B) = 0. \tag{18}$$

A Hahn decomposition may not be unique. For instance, in the case of (15), in connection with the signed measure $m$ defined by (14), we could shift the set $\{x : f(x) = 0\}$ from $A$ to $B$ and still have a Hahn decomposition. With $A$ and $B$ as given in (15), $B \in \mathbf{S}$, but $A$ is not in **S** unless $X$ is in **S**.

THEOREM 8–1 IV. *Let $\mu$ be a signed measure. If $+\infty$ is not in the range of $\mu$, there exists a Hahn decomposition of the space X relative to $\mu$, say $X = A \cup B$, such that $A \in$* **S**. *If $-\infty$ is not in the range of $\mu$, we can claim the existence of a Hahn decomposition with $B \in$* **S**, *but if neither $+\infty$ nor $-\infty$ is in the range of $\mu$, these two Hahn decompositions may be different. If $X \in$* **S**, *there is a Hahn decomposition such that both A and B are in* **S**.

*Proof.* If $X = A \cup B$ is a Hahn decomposition relative to $\mu$, $X = B \cup A$ is a Hahn decomposition relative to the signed measure $-\mu$. It will therefore be sufficient to give the proof on the assumption that $+\infty$ is not in the range of $\mu$.

If $X \in \mathbf{S}$ the proof is quite easy. Since $\mu(X) = +\infty$ is ruled out, $\mu^+(X)$ must be finite, by Theorem 8–1 III. Choose $A_n$ in **S** so that $\mu(A_n) > \mu^+(X) - 1/2^n$. Then $\mu(A_n)$ is finite. Using the Jordan decomposition of $\mu$, we see that

$$\mu^-(A_n) = \mu^+(A_n) - \mu(A_n) \leq \mu^+(X) - \mu(A_n),$$

so that

$$\mu^-(A_n) < \frac{1}{2^n}. \tag{19}$$

If $E \in \mathbf{S}$ and $E \subset X - A_n$, we have

$$\mu(E) + \mu(A_n) = \mu(E \cup A_n) \leq \mu^+(X),$$

so that $\mu(E) \leq \mu^+(X) - \mu(A_n)$, whence

$$\mu^+(X - A_n) \leq \frac{1}{2^n}\cdot \tag{20}$$

Now, let

$$A = \bigcap_{k=1}^{\infty} \bigcup_{n \geq k} A_n, \qquad X - A = \bigcup_{k=1}^{\infty} \bigcap_{n \geq k} (X - A_n).$$

Then, with the aid of (19) we see that

$$\mu^-(A) \leq \mu^-\left(\bigcup_{n \geq k} A_n\right) \leq \sum_{n=k}^{\infty} \mu^-(A_n) < \frac{1}{2^{k-1}},$$

whence $\mu^-(A) = 0$. The set $X - A$ is the union of the expanding sequence of sets whose $k$th member is $\bigcap_{n \geq k} (X - A_n)$. Therefore,

$$\mu^+\left(\bigcap_{n \geq k} (X - A_n)\right) \rightarrow \mu^+(X - A).$$

From (20) we then conclude that $\mu^+(X - A) = 0$.

Now, suppose that $E \in \mathbf{S}$. Then $E \cap A \subset A$, so $0 \leq \mu^-(E \cap A) \leq \mu^-(A) = 0$; it follows that $\mu(E \cap A) = \mu^+(E \cap A) \geq 0$. A similar argument shows that $\mu(E \cap B) \leq 0$ if $B = X - A$. Hence, we have a Hahn decomposition of $X$ relative to $\mu$.

When $X$ is not in $\mathbf{S}$ we must give a different proof. Let $\mathscr{P}$ be the class of sets $P \in \mathbf{S}$ such that $\mu^-(P) = 0$. This is a $\sigma$-ring. Let $p = \sup \{\mu^+(P) : P \in \mathscr{P}\}$. If we choose $P_n \in \mathscr{P}$ so that $\mu^+(P_n) \rightarrow p$, and let $A = \bigcup_n P_n$, then $A \in \mathscr{P}$, $P_n \subset A$, so $\mu^+(P_n) \leq \mu^+(A) \leq p$, whence $\mu^+(A) = p$. Our hypothesis that $+\infty$ is not in the range of $\mu$ insures that $p$ is finite.

Now, let $B = X - A$. We wish to show that $X = A \cup B$ is a Hahn decomposition of $X$. Suppose $E \in \mathbf{S}$. Since $A \in \mathbf{S}$, $E \cap A$ and $E \cap B = E - A$ are in $\mathbf{S}$. We have $E \cap A \subset A$, whence $0 \leq \mu^-(E \cap A) \leq \mu^-(A) = 0$. Thus $\mu(E \cap A) = \mu^+(E \cap A) \geq 0$. To show that $\mu(E \cap B) \leq 0$, it will suffice to show that $\mu^+(E \cap B) = 0$. Let $\mathbf{S}_1$ be the $\sigma$-ring composed of all members of $\mathbf{S}$ which are contained in $E$, and let $\mu_1$ be the restriction of $\mu$ to $\mathbf{S}_1$. Then $\mu_1^+$ is the restriction of $\mu^+$ to $\mathbf{S}_1$, and likewise for $\mu_1^-$, $\mu^-$. By the earlier part of the proof there exists a Hahn decomposition of $E$ with respect to $\mu_1$, say $E = A_1 \cup B_1$; here $A_1$ and $B_1$ are in $\mathbf{S}$, and $\mu^+(B_1) = 0$, $\mu^-(A_1) = 0$. Now, we can write

$$E \cap B = (E \cap B \cap A_1) \cup (E \cap B \cap B_1).$$

It follows from this that $\mu^+(E \cap B) = \mu^+(E \cap B \cap A_1)$, because $0 \leq \mu^+(E \cap B \cap B_1) \leq \mu^+(B_1) = 0$. Now, suppose that $\mu^+(E \cap B \cap A_1) > 0$. This implies the existence of a set $F$ such that $F \subset E \cap B \cap A_1$ and $\mu(F) > 0$. But then $F \cap A = \varnothing$, and also $\mu^-(F) = 0$ (the latter because $\mu^-(A_1) = 0$). Hence, $F \in \mathscr{P}$, so that $A \cup F \in \mathscr{P}$ and $\mu^+(A \cup F) = \mu^+(A) + \mu^+(F) > p$, contrary to the definition of $p$. We must therefore conclude that $\mu^+(E \cap B) = 0$; this completes the proof.

It is possible to give a different proof of the Hahn decomposition theorem, without prior knowledge of the Jordan decomposition, and dealing directly from the outset with the case in which $X$ need not be in $\mathbf{S}$. See Halmos [1].

**PROBLEMS**

1. Suppose $\mu$ is a signed measure, and that $E = \bigcup_n E_n$, $E_n \in \mathbf{S}$, with the $E_n$'s disjoint and $\mu(E)$ finite. Show that the series $\sum_n \mu(E_n)$ is absolutely convergent. [*Hint.* Separate the $E_n$'s into two classes according to the sign of $\mu(E_n)$.]

2. In the definition of a signed measure, suppose the condition of countable additivity is replaced by the condition that $\mu$ be finitely additive. Defining $V_\mu$, $\mu^+$ and $\mu^-$ as before, show that they are finitely additive. Show also that we still get the Jordan decomposition of $\mu$, as well as the formula (7), provided that we assume all values of $\mu$ are finite.

3. If $\mu$ and $\nu$ are two signed measures on $\mathbf{S}$, both with finite values, let $\mu \leq \nu$ mean that $\mu(E) \leq \nu(E)$ for every $E$ in $\mathbf{S}$. In this way we partially order the class of all finite signed measures on $\mathbf{S}$. The zero measure is in this class. Show that $\mu^+$ is the least upper bound of $\mu$ and 0 in this partial ordering. We write $\mu^+ = \sup(\mu, 0)$. Show also that $\mu^- = -\inf(\mu, 0)$. Show generally that

$$\sup(\mu, \nu) = \mu + \sup(\mu - \nu, 0)$$

and

$$\sup(\mu, \nu) + \inf(\mu, \nu) = \mu + \nu.$$

This class of finite measures is a vector lattice.

4. If $(X, \mathbf{S}, \mu)$ is a measure space and $f \in \mathscr{L}(\mu)$, define $m : \mathbf{S} \to R$ by $m(E) = \int_E f\,d\mu$. Show that $m^+(E) = \int_E f^+\,d\mu$. [*Suggestion.* Define $\nu(E) = \int_E f^+\,d\mu$ and prove $\nu(E) \leq m^+(E)$ and $m^+(E) \leq \nu(E)$ separately.]

5. Suppose that $\mu$ is a signed measure such that $\mu(E)$ is always finite. Show that the values of $\mu$ are bounded.

6. A signed measure $\mu$ is said to be *of bounded variation* when the function $V_\mu$ is bounded. Show that this is the case if and only if all the values of $\mu$ are finite.

7. Let $\nu_1$ and $\nu_2$ be finite regular Borel measures on $R^k$ (see Section 6–10). Let $\nu = \nu_1 - \nu_2$ and let $\nu = \nu^+ - \nu^-$ be the Jordan decomposition of $\nu$. Prove that $\nu^+$ and $\nu^-$ are finite regular Borel measures. [*Suggestions.* (1) Show that to each Borel set $E$ and each $\epsilon > 0$ correspond a compact set $A$ and an open set $U$ with $A \subset E \subset U$, such that $|\nu(E) - \nu(F)| < \epsilon$ if $F$ is any Borel set such that $A \subset F \subset U$. For this let $A = A_1 \cup A_2$ and $U = U_1 \cap U_2$, where $A_i$ and $U_i$ are suitably chosen in relation to $\nu_i$. See Problem 2, Section 6–10. (2) With $A$ and $U$ chosen as in (1) show that $|\nu(G)| < 2\epsilon$ if $G$ is a Borel set contained in $U - A$. For this let $F = E - G$, $H = E \cup (G - E)$, so that $A \subset F \subset U$, $A \subset H \subset U$, and $G = (H - E) \cup (E - F)$. (3) From (2) show that $\nu^+(U - A) \leq 2\epsilon$ and hence that $\nu^+(U) \leq \nu^+(E) + 2\epsilon$. Go on to discuss $\nu^-$.]

## 8–2 Absolute continuity

Let $(X, \mathbf{S}, \mu)$ be a measure space, and let $\nu$ be a signed measure on $\mathbf{S}$. We shall say that $\nu$ is *absolutely continuous with respect to* $\mu$ if $\nu(E) = 0$ whenever $\mu(E) = 0$. An example of this situation is furnished by taking any $f \in \mathscr{L}(\mu)$ and defining $m(E) = \int_E f\,d\mu$. Then $m$ is absolutely continuous with respect to $\mu$. Under certain conditions on $X$ and $\mu$ (as we shall see in Section 8–3) all signed measures absolutely continuous with respect to $\mu$ are obtained in this way.

We denote by $AC[\mu]$ the class of signed measures on $\mathbf{S}$ which are absolutely continuous with respect to $\mu$.

THEOREM 8–2 I. *Each of the following three assertions implies the truth of the other two:*
(a) $\nu^+$ *and* $\nu^-$ *are in* $AC[\mu]$.
(b) $V_\nu$ *is in* $AC[\mu]$.
(c) $\nu$ *is in* $AC[\mu]$.

*Proof.* It is very easy to see that (a) implies (b) and (b) implies (c). All that remains is to prove that (c) implies (a). Let $X = A \cup B$ be a Hahn decomposition of $X$ relative to $\nu$, and suppose that $\mu(E) = 0$. Then $\mu(E \cap A) = \mu(E \cap B) = 0$, whence $\nu(E \cap A) = \nu(E \cap B) = 0$, by the hypothesis (c). But then (see (16) in Section 8–2) $\nu^+(E) = \nu(E \cap A) = 0$ and $\nu^-(E) = \nu(E \cap B) = 0$. Thus (a) is true.

The following theorem is sometimes useful.

THEOREM 8–2 II. *Let* $(X, \mathbf{S}, \mu)$ *be a measure space and suppose that* $\nu$ *is a signed measure on* $\mathbf{S}$. *(a) In order that* $\nu$ *be in* $AC[\mu]$ *it is sufficient that to each* $\epsilon > 0$ *correspond a* $\delta > 0$ *such that* $|\nu(E)| < \epsilon$ *whenever* $\mu(E) < \delta$. (b) *If* $\nu(E)$ *is finite whenever* $\mu(E)$ *is finite, the condition on* $\nu$ *in* (*a*) *is also necessary when* $\nu \in AC[\mu]$.

*Proof of* (a). This is easy. We omit the argument.

*Proof of* (b). We assume $\nu \in AC[\mu]$; hence, by the preceding theorem, $V_\nu \in AC[\mu]$. Since $V_\nu$ is a measure, and therefore monotone, we may argue exactly as in the proof of Theorem 5–5 III, with $V_\nu$ in the place of $m$. We need to know that $V_\nu(G_n)$ is finite, but this is assured, because $\mu(G_n)$ is finite, hence so is $\nu(G_n)$, and hence $\nu^+(G_n)$ and $\nu^-(G_n)$ are finite (see Theorem 8–1 III).

In Section 8–3 we shall need the following result.

LEMMA 8–2 III. *Let* $(X, \mathbf{S}, \mu)$ *be a measure space with* $X \in \mathbf{S}$ *and* $\mu(X)$ *finite. Let* $m$ *be a measure on* $\mathbf{S}$ *which is such that* $m \in AC[\mu]$ *and* $m(X) > 0$. *Then there exists* $\epsilon > 0$ *and* $A \in \mathbf{S}$ *such that* $\mu(A) > 0$ *and* $\epsilon\mu(E \cap A) \leq m(E \cap A)$ *for each* $E$ *in* $\mathbf{S}$.

*Proof.* The assertion can be restated in a manner which makes it easier to see how to undertake the proof. For any fixed $\epsilon > 0$ let $\nu = m - \epsilon\mu$. Then $\nu$ is a signed measure. The condition $\epsilon\mu(E \cap A) \leq m(E \cap A)$ for every $E$ in $\mathbf{S}$ is equivalent to $\nu^-(A) = 0$, and is satisfied if $X = A \cup B$ is a Hahn decomposition of $X$ relative to $\nu$. Since $X \in \mathbf{S}$, such a decomposition will be available, with both $A$ and $B$ in $\mathbf{S}$. The problem then is to choose $\epsilon$ in such a way that we can obtain a decomposition for which $\mu(A) > 0$.

Take $\epsilon_n = 1/n$, $n = 1, 2, \cdots$, and let $X = A_n \cup B_n$ be a Hahn decomposition of $X$ relative to $\nu_n$, $(\nu_n = m - \epsilon_n\mu)$ with $A_n$ and $B_n$ in $\mathbf{S}$. Let

$$G = \bigcup_n A_n, \qquad H = \bigcap_n B_n.$$

Observe that $G = X - H$. Now, $H \subset B_n$; therefore, by (16) in Section 8–1, $\nu_n(H) = -\nu_n^-(H) \leq 0$, whence $0 \leq m(H) \leq \epsilon_n\mu(H)$. Since $\mu(H)$ is finite, this implies $m(H) = 0$. Therefore, $m(G) = m(X) > 0$. By the absolute continuity of $m$ it follows that $\mu(G) > 0$, and hence certainly that $\mu(A_n) > 0$, for some $n$. This is what we want. We take $\epsilon = \epsilon_n$, $A = A_n$, and the lemma is proved.

### PROBLEMS

1. Prove (a) in Theorem 8–2 II.
2. Let $\mu$ be Lebesgue measure in $R^k$. Let $\nu$ be a signed measure on the $L$-measurable sets in $R^k$, and suppose that $\nu \in AC[\mu]$. Let $A$ be any set in $R^k$, let $E_1, E_2$ be two $L$-measurable kernels of $A$, and let $F_1, F_2$ be two $L$-measurable covers of $A$. Prove that $\nu(E_1) = \nu(E_2) = \nu(F_1) = \nu(F_2)$.

## 8–3 The Radon-Nikodym theorem

We come directly to the principal result of this section:

THEOREM 8–3 I. *(The Radon-Nikodym theorem.) Let $(X, \mathbf{S}, \mu)$ be a $\sigma$-finite measure space such that $X \in \mathbf{S}$. Let $\nu$ be a signed measure on $\mathbf{S}$ such that the values of $\nu$ are finite and $\nu \in AC[\mu]$. Then there exists a $\mu$-summable function $f : X \to R$ such that*

(1) $$\nu(E) = \int_E f\,d\mu$$

*for each $E$ in $\mathbf{S}$. Any two such functions $f$ are $\mu$-equivalent; that is, the set where they differ in value has $\mu$-measure zero.*

The naming of the theorem is in recognition of J. Radon's treatment of the case in which $X = R^k$ and $\mu$ is Lebesgue measure (in Radon [1]), and O. Nikodym's treatment of the general abstract case (in Nikodym [1]).

*Proof of the theorem.* The last assertion, about the extent to which $f$ is unique, is easily seen from results in Section 5–4. We leave this to the reader. The problem is then to show the existence of a suitable function $f$. We proceed by steps.

*Step 1.* To begin with, let us work under the additional assumptions that $\mu(X)$ is finite and that $\nu$ is not merely a signed measure, but a measure. Let $\mathscr{F}$ be the class of all $\mu$-summable $f : X \to R^*$ such that $f \geq 0$ and $\int_E f\,d\mu \leq \nu(E)$ for each $E$ in $\mathbf{S}$. The zero function is certainly in $\mathscr{F}$. Since $\nu(X)$ is finite, the supremum

(2) $$c = \sup_{f \in \mathscr{F}} \int_X f\,d\mu$$

is finite. We shall show that there is a function $f : X \to R$ in $\mathscr{F}$ whose integral over $X$ is equal to $c$, and that for this $f$ we have (1).

Suppose $f_n \in \mathscr{F}$ and $\int_X f_n\,d\mu \to c$. Let $g_n = f_1 \vee \cdots \vee f_n$. Clearly, $g_n \geq 0$ and $g_n$ is $\mu$-summable. We wish to show that $g_n \in \mathscr{F}$. If $E \in \mathbf{S}$, let

$$E_1 = \{x : g_n(x) = f_1(x)\} \cap E,$$
$$E_2 = \{x : g_n(x) = f_2(x)\} \cap (E - E_1),$$
$$\cdots$$
$$E_n = \{x : g_n(x) = f_n(x)\} \cap (E - E_1 - \cdots - E_{n-1}).$$

Then $E = E_1 \cup \cdots \cup E_n$, the $E_i$'s are disjoint and in $\mathbf{S}$, and $g_n(x) = f_i(x)$ on $E_i$. Then

$$\int_E g_n \, d\mu = \sum_i \int_{E_i} f_i \, d\mu \leq \sum_i \nu(E_i) = \nu(E).$$

Therefore $g_n \in \mathscr{F}$. Now, let $g = \sup_n f_n$. Clearly, $g_n \nearrow g$. Since $\int_X g_n \, d\mu \leq \nu(X)$, we see that $g$ is $\mu$-summable. It then follows that $\int_E g_n \, d\mu \to \int_E g \, d\mu$ and that $g \in \mathscr{F}$. Since $f_n \leq g_n$, we see that $c = \int_X g \, d\mu$. We define

$$f(x) = \begin{cases} g(x) & \text{if } g(x) < +\infty \\ 0 & \text{if } g(x) = +\infty. \end{cases}$$

Then $f(x) = g(x)$ a.e. (with respect to $\mu$), so that $f$ is $\mu$-summable and yields the same integral as $g$ over any $E$ in $\mathbf{S}$.

Now, let $m : \mathbf{S} \to R$ be defined by

$$m(E) = \nu(E) - \int_E f \, d\mu, \qquad E \in \mathbf{S}.$$

Evidently $m$ is a measure; moreover, $m \in AC[\mu]$. If $m(X) = 0$, $m$ is identically zero, and we have (1). We shall show that $m(X) > 0$ leads to a contradiction. Here we use Lemma 8–2 III. Choosing $\epsilon$ and $A$ as in that lemma, we let $h = f + \epsilon\chi_A$. Since

$$\int_X h \, d\mu = \int_X f \, d\mu + \epsilon\mu(A) > c,$$

the contradiction will come if we show that $h \in \mathscr{F}$. Now, for any $E$,

$$\int_E h \, d\mu = \int_E f \, d\mu + \epsilon\mu(E \cap A) \leq \int_E f \, d\mu + m(E \cap A),$$

$$\begin{aligned} \int_E h \, d\mu &\leq \int_E f \, d\mu + \nu(E \cap A) - \int_{E \cap A} f \, d\mu \\ &= \int_{E-A} f \, d\mu + \nu(E \cap A) \\ &\leq \nu(E - A) + \nu(E \cap A) = \nu(E). \end{aligned}$$

Therefore, $h \in \mathscr{F}$, and this part of the proof is complete.

*Step 2.* We now drop the assumption that $\mu(X)$ is finite, but retain the assumption that $\nu$ is a measure. With the assumption of $\sigma$-finiteness, as in the theorem, we can write $X = \bigcup_n X_n$, where $\{X_n\}$ is a countable disjoint union of members of $\mathbf{S}$ such that $\mu(X_n) < +\infty$. If $\mathbf{S}_n$ is the $\sigma$-ring of all elements of $\mathbf{S}$ which are subsets of $X_n$, we can use Step 1 to infer that there is a $\mu$-summable nonnegative function $f_n : X_n \to R$ such that

$$\nu(E) = \int_E f_n \, d\mu \qquad \text{if } E \in \mathbf{S}_n. \tag{3}$$

We define $f : X \to R$ by setting $f(x) = f_n(x)$ if $x \in X_n$. It must then be shown that $f$ is $\mu$-summable and that (1) holds if $E \in \mathbf{S}$. We leave the details of this to the reader as an exercise.

*Step 3.* We can now treat the theorem in its general form. We use the Jordan decomposition of $\nu$; since $\nu^+$ and $\nu^-$ are also in $AC[\mu]$ (Theorem 8–3 I), we can apply Step 2 to $\nu^+$ and $\nu^-$. We then assemble the results and we have what is required.

### AN ALTERNATIVE PROOF

There is an interesting and entirely different way of dealing with the first step in the proof of Theorem 8–3 I. Here, the central idea is to make use of the inner-product representation of continuous linear functionals on a Hilbert space (Theorem 3–14 V) and the fact that $L^2(m)$ is a Hilbert space when $(X, \mathbf{S}, m)$ is a measure space.

Our assumptions are: $\mu$ and $\nu$ are measures on $\mathbf{S}$, $\mu(X)$ and $\nu(X)$ are finite, and $\nu \in AC[\mu]$. Let $m = \mu + \nu$. Then $m$ is also a measure on $\mathbf{S}$. Any bounded measurable function is summable (with respect to each measure). From the fact that $\nu(E) \leq m(E)$ for each $E$ we see, first for nonnegative functions and then in general, that $\mathcal{L}(m) \subset \mathcal{L}(\nu)$ and that $\int |f|\, d\nu \leq \int |f|\, dm$ if $f \in \mathcal{L}(m)$. Likewise with $\mu$ in place of $\nu$.

Now, suppose $f \in \mathcal{L}^2(m)$. Writing $f = f \cdot 1$, we see by Theorem 5–8 I that $f \in \mathcal{L}(m)$ and that

$$\left|\int f\, d\nu\right| \leq \int |f|\, dm \leq \left(\int |f|^2\, dm\right)^{1/2}\left(\int 1 \cdot dm\right)^{1/2}. \tag{4}$$

Since $m(E) = 0$ implies $\nu(E) = 0$, we see that, in the definition

$$\varphi([f]) = \int f\, d\nu, \tag{5}$$

$\varphi([f])$ depends only on the equivalence class $[f]$ (equivalence with respect to $\nu$) and not on the particular representative of this class; hence, by (4), $\varphi$ is a continuous linear functional on $L^2(m)$. By Theorem 3–14 V and the definition of the inner product in $L^2(m)$ we now see that there exists a function $g \in \mathcal{L}^2(m)$ such that

$$\int f\, d\nu = \int fg\, dm \tag{6}$$

for each $f$ in $\mathcal{L}^2(m)$.

If $E = \{x : g(x) < 0\}$ and $f = \chi_E$, we see from (6) that $\nu(E) \leq 0$, whence $\nu(E) = 0$, $\int_E g\, dm = 0$, and therefore $m(E) = 0$. Therefore, without affecting (6), we can redefine $g$ so that $g(x) \geq 0$ for every $x$. We do this.

Now, suppose that $f \geq 0$ and that $f$ is measurable. Let $f_n(x) = n \wedge f(x)$. Then $f_n \nearrow f$, $f_n g \nearrow fg$, and $f_n \in \mathcal{L}^2(m)$. Applying (6) to $f_n$ and using the monotone convergence theorem, we see that $f \in \mathcal{L}(\nu)$ if and only if $fg \in \mathcal{L}(m)$ and that (6) holds for $f$ in this case. By induction then, from $f \geq 0$ and $f \in \mathcal{L}(\nu)$ we infer that $fg^n \in \mathcal{L}(m)$ for $n = 1, 2, \ldots$ and

$$\int fg^{n-1}\, d\nu = \int fg^n\, dm = \int fg^n\, d\mu + \int fg^n\, d\nu.$$

Furthermore,

$$\int f\, d\nu = \int fg\, d\mu + \cdots + \int fg^n\, d\mu + \int fg^n\, d\nu. \tag{7}$$

Putting $f = \chi_G$, where $G = \{x : g(x) \geq 1\}$, we see that $\nu(G) \geq n\mu(G)$, whence $\mu(G) = 0$. By absolute continuity, $\nu(G) = 0$ as well. If $x \in X - G$ and $f(x)$ is finite, $f(x)\, g^n(x) \searrow 0$. Since $f(x)$ is finite except perhaps on a set of $\nu$-measure zero, we conclude that $\int fg^n\, d\nu \to 0$ in (7).

Now, let us define

$$f_0(x) = \begin{cases} \dfrac{g(x)}{1 - g(x)} & \text{if} \quad g(x) < 1 \\ 0 & \text{if} \quad g(x) \geq 1. \end{cases}$$

Then, with $f$ and $G$ as in the preceding paragaraph,

$$f(x)[g(x) + \cdots + g^n(x)] \nearrow f(x)f_0(x)$$

if $x \in X - G$, so we see from (7) that $ff_0 \in \mathscr{L}(\mu)$ and

$$\int f\,d\nu = \int ff_0\,d\mu \tag{8}$$

if $f \geq 0$ and $f \in \mathscr{L}(\nu)$. We can take $f = 1$. This shows that $f_0 \in \mathscr{L}(\mu)$. Then, evidently, if $E \in \mathbf{S}$ we have $\nu(E) = \int_E f_0\,d\mu$. Thus we have finished our alternative proof of Step 1 in the proof of Theorem 8–3 I.

### PROBLEMS

1. Prove the assertion in the last sentence of Theorem 8–3 I.
2. Finish the argument in the last part of Step 2 in the proof of Theorem 8 3 I.
3. Let $\mu$ and $\nu$ be as in Theorem 8–3 I, except that $\nu$ is assumed to be $\sigma$-finite instead of finite. Show that there exists a $\mu$-measurable function $f : X \to R$ such that $f$ is $\mu$-summable over every set $E$ such that $\nu(E)$ is finite, and such that (1) holds for such sets $E$. Moreover, one of the two functions $f^+$, $f^-$ will be $\mu$-summable over $X$. What about uniqueness of $f$?
4. In connection with (8), show that $f \in \mathscr{L}(\nu)$ if and only if $ff_0 \in \mathscr{L}(\mu)$, and that (8) then holds.
5. Assume that $v : R \to R$ is strictly increasing, with a continuous derivative $v'$. Let $\nu$ be the Lebesgue-Stieltjes measure generated by $v$ (as in Section 4–10). Let $\mu$ be Lebesgue measure. (a) Show that $\int_R g\,d\nu = \int_R gv'\,d\mu$ for all $g : R \to R^*$ such that $g$ is $\nu$-summable. (b) Suppose $E = v(R)$ and define $f : E \to R^*$ by $f(x) = g(v^{-1}(x))$. Show that $\int_E f\,d\mu = \int_R gv'\,d\mu$ for $g$ as in (a).

## 8–4 Continuous linear functionals on $L^p(\mu)$

We work with $L^p(\mu)$ as defined in Section 5–8. Suppose $p \geq 1$. We define $p'$, depending on $p$, as follows:

$$p' = \begin{cases} \dfrac{p}{p-1} & \text{if} \quad 1 < p < \infty \\ \infty & \text{if} \quad p = 1 \\ 1 & \text{if} \quad p = \infty. \end{cases}$$

For simplicity in notation we shall write

$$\|f\|_p = \left(\int |f|^p\,d\mu\right)^{1/p}$$

when $1 \leq p < \infty$ and $f \in \mathscr{L}^p(\mu)$, and

$$\|f\|_\infty = \sup{}^\circ |f(x)|$$

when $f \in \mathscr{L}^\infty(\mu)$. Also, we shall frequently ignore the notational distinction between $f$ and $[f]$. Observe that $\|f\|_p$ is equal to the norm of $[f]$ in $L^p(\mu)$.

If $g$ is a fixed element of $\mathscr{L}^{p'}(\mu)$ and $f$ is a variable element of $\mathscr{L}^p(\mu)$, the product $fg$ is in $\mathscr{L}(\mu)$, and

$$\Phi([f]) = \int fg \, d\mu \tag{1}$$

defines a continuous linear functional on $L^p(\mu)$. This functional is continuous, for

$$|\Phi([f])| \leq \|f\|_p \, \|g\|_{p'}. \tag{2}$$

When $1 < p < \infty$, we obtain (2) from Theorem 5–8 I. The cases $p = 1, p = \infty$ are simpler, and we leave verification of (2) to the reader in these cases.

In this section we shall show, with some restriction on the measure space $(X, \mathbf{S}, \mu)$, that every continuous linear functional $\Phi$ on $L^p(\mu)$ can be represented in the form (1), provided that $1 \leq p < \infty$.

THEOREM 8–4 I. *Suppose that* $1 \leq p < \infty$. *Suppose that* $X \in \mathbf{S}$, *and let the measure space* $(X, \mathbf{S}, \mu)$ *be σ-finite. Then to each continuous linear functional* $\Phi$ *on* $L^p(\mu)$ *corresponds a unique element* $[g]$ *of* $L^{p'}(\mu)$, *with representative* $g \in \mathscr{L}^{p'}(\mu)$, *such that* $\Phi$ *is given by* (1) *and the norm of* $\Phi$ *is*

$$\|\Phi\| = \|g\|_{p'}. \tag{3}$$

*Comments on the theorem.* We already know the theorem for the case $p = 2$, from Theorem 3–14 V, because $L^2(\mu)$ is a Hilbert space. In this case there is no restriction on the measure space. The theorem is not true for the case $p = \infty$, even in the simple case when $X$ is a set of finite Lebesgue measure in $R$ and $\mu$ is Lebesgue measure in $R$. If $1 < p < \infty$, the restriction placed on $(X, \mathbf{S}, \mu)$ is unnecessary. If $p = 1$, some restriction is necessary. Under the given restrictions, which are satisfied in most of the cases of common interest, the proof is essentially the same for $p = 1$ as for $p > 1$. A proof for the case $1 < p < \infty$, without restriction on $(X, \mathbf{S}, \mu)$, is indicated in a problem. A proof under weaker restrictions can be given for the case $p = 1$; see Zaanen [1], pp. 199–200.

*The uniqueness of* $[g]$. If $g_1$ and $g_2$ are two functions $g$ in $\mathscr{L}^{p'}(\mu)$ such that (1) holds for all $f$, then $g_1(x) = g_2(x)$ a.e., so that $[g_1] = [g_2]$. For, we can replace $f$ by $\chi_E$, where $E$ is any measure set of finite measure. Therefore $\int_E (g_1 - g_2) \, d\mu = 0$, whence $g_1(x) = g_2(x)$ a.e. on $E$. Now, the set $E$ on which $|g_1 - g_2|$ is positive is expressible as a countable union $\{E_n\}$ of sets of finite measure; by the foregoing we must have $\mu(E_n) = 0$ for each $n$, and hence $\mu(E) = 0$. This argument is valid even when $(X, \mathbf{S}, \mu)$ is not σ-finite, provided that $p > 1$, because of Theorem 5–4 II.

*Proof of the theorem when* $X \in \mathbf{S}$ *and* $\mu(X) < +\infty$.

For this special case, suppose $\Phi$ is given. If $E \in \mathbf{S}$, $\chi_E \in \mathscr{L}^p(\mu)$; let $\nu : \mathbf{S} \to R$ be defined by

$$\nu(E) = \Phi(\chi_E). \tag{4}$$

Observe that $\|\chi_E\|_p = \{\mu(E)\}^{1/p}$. Therefore

$$|\nu(E)| \leq \|\Phi\| \, \{\mu(E)\}^{1/p}. \tag{5}$$

If $G = E \cup F$, where $E$ and $F$ are disjoint members of $\mathbf{S}$, $\chi_G = \chi_E + \chi_F$. Since $\Phi$ is linear, we then see that $\nu(E \cup F) = \nu(G)$. Thus $\nu$ is finitely additive. We shall prove that it is countably additive. Suppose that $\{E_n\}$ is a countable disjoint family from $\mathbf{S}$. Let

$$E = \bigcup_{n=1}^{\infty} E_n, \qquad F_n = \bigcup_{i=1}^{n} E_i, \qquad G_n = E - F_n.$$

Then $\nu(E) = \nu(F_n) + \nu(G_n) = \sum_{i=1}^{n} \nu(E_i) + \nu(G_n)$. But $\mu(G_n) \to 0$, because $\mu$ is countably additive. Hence, $\nu(G_n) \to 0$, by (5). Therefore $\nu$ is countably additive, and is a signed measure. It is absolutely continuous with respect to $\mu$, because of (5). We can therefore use Theorem 8–3 I to assert the existence of a function $g \in \mathscr{L}(\mu)$ such that

$$\nu(E) = \int_E g \, d\mu \tag{6}$$

for each $E$. From (6) and (4) it follows at once that $\Phi([f])$ is represented as in (1) whenever $f$ is any simple function. For, if

$$f = \sum_i c_i \chi_{E_i},$$

where the $E_i$'s form a finite disjoint family,

$$\Phi([f]) = \sum_i c_i \nu(E_i) = \sum_i c_i \int_{E_i} g \, d\mu = \int fg \, d\mu.$$

Now, suppose that $f$ is any bounded measurable function. By Theorem 5–8 II there exists a sequence $\{f_n\}$ of simple functions such that $|f_n(x)| \le |f(x)|$ for each $x$ and $\|f_n - f\|_p \to 0$. By passing to a subsequence and then denoting the subsequence itself by $\{f_n\}$, we may assume that $f_n(x) \to f(x)$ a.e. Then $\Phi([f_n]) \to \Phi([f])$ because $\Phi$ is continuous, and $\int f_n g \, d\mu \to \int fg \, d\mu$, by the theorem on dominated convergence. Hence, (1) holds for this $f$. Moreover, the inequality

$$|\Phi([f])| \le \|\Phi\| \, \|f\|_p \tag{7}$$

holds for any $f \in \mathscr{L}^p(\mu)$, and so certainly for the $f$ here considered. We can now apply Theorem 5 8 III to conclude that $g \in \mathscr{L}^{p'}(\mu)$, with

$$\|g\|_{p'} \le \|\Phi\|. \tag{8}$$

Now, suppose that $f$ is any element of $\mathscr{L}^p(\mu)$. We use Theorem 5–8 II again to obtain a sequence $\{f_n\}$ of simple functions such that $\|f_n - f\|_p \to 0$. Then

$$\int f_n g \, d\mu = \Phi([f_n]) \to \Phi([f]).$$

But also

$$\left| \int f_n g \, d\mu - \int fg \, d\mu \right| \le \int |f_n - f| \, |g| \, d\mu \le \|f_n - f\|_p \, \|g\|_{p'},$$

so that $\int f_n g \, d\mu \to \int fg \, d\mu$. Therefore (1) holds in the general case. The fact that (3) holds is now evident from (2) and (8).

*Proof in case $X \in \mathbf{S}$ and $(X, \mathbf{S}, \mu)$ is $\sigma$-finite.* The technique here is to represent $X$ as a countable union $\bigcup_n E_n$ of sets of finite measure, and to define the required $g$ suitably by considering $F_n = E_1 \cup \cdots \cup E_n$ and using what has already been proved. Suppose $X_1$ is a fixed element of $\mathbf{S}$ of finite measure. If $\mathbf{S}_1$ is the class of elements of $\mathbf{S}$ contained in $X_1$ and $\mu_1$ is the restriction of $\mu$ to $\mathbf{S}_1$, we can identify $\mathscr{L}^p(\mu_1)$ with the class of those elements of $\mathscr{L}^p(\mu)$ which have zero values at all points of $X - X_1$. If $\Phi$ is a given continuous linear functional on $L^p(\mu)$, let $\Phi_1$ be its restriction to $L^p(\mu_1)$. It is clear that $\|\Phi_1\| \le \|\Phi\|$. By what has been proved we know that there exists a $g$ in $\mathscr{L}^{p'}(\mu_1)$ such that

$$\Phi([f]) = \int_{X_1} fg \, d\mu \quad \text{and} \quad \|g\|_{p'} = \|\Phi_1\| \le \|\Phi\|.$$

Now, let us do this with $X_1$ successively equal to $F_1, F_2, \ldots$, and let the $g$ corresponding to $\Phi_1$ for the case $X_1 = F_n$ be denoted by $g_n$. We know that $g_n \in \mathscr{L}^{p'}(\mu)$ and $g_n(x) = 0$ if $x \in X - F_n$. Moreover,

(9) $$\|g_n\|_{p'} \leq \|\Phi\|.$$

If $f \in \mathscr{L}^p(\mu)$ and $f(x) = 0$ when $x \in X - F_n$, we know that

(10) $$\Phi([f]) = \int f g_n \, d\mu = \int f g_{n+1} \, d\mu.$$

From this we see that $g_n(x) = g_{n+1}(x)$ a.e. on $F_n$ (for we can replace $f$ by $\chi_E$, where $E$ is any measurable subset of $F_n$).

We define

$$g(x) = \begin{cases} g_1(x) & \text{if } x \in F_1 \\ g_{n+1}(x) & \text{if } x \in F_{n+1} - F_n. \end{cases}$$

Then

(11) $$g(x) = g_n(x) \text{ a.e. on } F_n.$$

It can be seen that $g \in \mathscr{L}^{p'}(\mu)$ and

(12) $$\|g\|_{p'} \leq \|\Phi\|.$$

This is clear from (9) if $p' = \infty$. For the case $p' < \infty$ we obtain (12) by using (9) and Fatou's lemma, as applied to $|g|^{p'} \chi_{F_n}$. If $f \in \mathscr{L}^p(\mu)$ and $f_n = f\chi_{F_n}$, we know by (10) and (11) that

$$\Phi([f_n]) = \int f_n g \, d\mu.$$

Since $\|f_n - f\|_p \to 0$, we conclude as in the earlier proof that (1) holds in this case. As before (3) follows from (2) and (12). The uniqueness of $[g]$ has already been discussed.

## PROBLEM

Prove Theorem 8–4 I for the case $1 < p < \infty$ when the measure space $(X, \mathbf{S}, \mu)$ is arbitrary. [*Suggestion.* With $\Phi$ given, to each set $E$ of finite measure corresponds a function $h \in \mathscr{L}^{p'}(\mu)$ such that $h(x) = 0$ if $x \in X - E$ and such that

$$\Phi([f]) = \int fh \, d\mu, \qquad \|h\|_{p'} \leq \|\Phi\|$$

if $f \in \mathscr{L}^p(\mu)$ and $f(x) = 0$ when $x \in X - E$. Envisage the class of all such $E$'s and the corresponding $h$'s, and let $M = \sup \|h\|_{p'}$ as $E$ varies. Show that it is possible to arrange a sequence $\{E_n\}$ such that $E_n \subset E_{n+1}$ and $\|h_n\|_{p'} \to M$. Moreover, $h_n(x) = h_m(x)$ a.e. on $E_m$ if $m < n$. Then show that $\{h_n\}$ converges in mean (of order $p'$) to a function $g$ such that $g(x) = 0$ a.e. in $X - \bigcup_n E_n$, and $\|g\|_{p'} = M$. Finally, for given $f \in \mathscr{L}^p(\mu)$, use the fact that $\{x : f(x) \neq 0\}$ is expressible as a countable union of sets of finite measure, and show that (1) holds.]

## 8–5 The Lebesgue decomposition of a signed measure

Consider a measure space $(X, \mathbf{S}, \mu)$ such that $X \in \mathbf{S}$. Let $\nu$ be a signed measure on $\mathbf{S}$, and suppose there is a decomposition $X = A \cup B$, where $A$ and $B$ are disjoint members of $\mathbf{S}$ such that $\mu(A) = 0$ and $\nu(E \cap B) = 0$ for every $E$ in $\mathbf{S}$. Then we say that $\nu$ is *singular with respect to* $\mu$, and we write $\nu \perp \mu$.

Since $E = (E \cap A) \cup (E \cap B)$ in the above situation, we see that

$$\mu(E) = \mu(E \cap B), \qquad \nu(E) = \nu(E \cap A). \tag{1}$$

If $\nu \perp \mu$ and $\nu$ is not identically zero, it certainly is not absolutely continuous with respect to $\mu$. For, suppose $E$ is such that $\nu(E) \neq 0$. Then $\mu(E \cap A) = 0$, but $\nu(E \cap A) \neq 0$. To put the matter another way: If $\nu \perp \mu$ and $\nu \in AC[\mu]$, then $\nu = 0$.

It is easy to see that $\nu \perp \mu$ implies $V_\nu \perp \mu$, and hence also $\nu^+ \perp \mu$, $\nu^- \perp \mu$. Conversely, if $\nu^+ \perp \mu$ and $\nu^- \perp \mu$, then $\nu \perp \mu$. This is a special case of a more general proposition (see Problem 2).

The following theorem is called the Lebesgue decomposition theorem. It is related to the result stated in Problem 2, Section 9–8.

THEOREM 8–5 I. *Let $(X, \mathbf{S}, \mu)$ be a $\sigma$-finite measure space with $X \in \mathbf{S}$. Let $\nu$ be a $\sigma$-finite signed measure on $\mathbf{S}$. Then $\nu$ can be expressed as a sum $\nu = \nu_1 + \nu_2$, where $\nu_1$ and $\nu_2$ are $\sigma$-finite signed measures on $\mathbf{S}$ such that $\nu_1 \in AC[\mu]$ and $\nu_2 \perp \mu$.*

*Proof. Step 1.* Suppose, to begin with, that $\nu$ is a measure (that is, that its values are nonnegative) and that $\mu(X)$ and $\nu(X)$ are finite. Then $\mu + \nu$ is a measure, and $\nu \in AC[\mu + \nu]$. By the Radon-Nikodym theorem there exists a function $f : X \to R$, summable with respect to $\mu + \nu$, with

$$\nu(E) = \int_E f \, d(\mu + \nu)$$

for every $E$. The proof of the cited theorem shows that we can take $f \geq 0$. The function $f$ is also summable with respect to $\mu$ and $\nu$ separately, and we can write

$$\nu(E) = \int_E f \, d\mu + \int_E f \, d\nu. \tag{2}$$

Now, let $A = A_1 \cup A_2$, where

$$A_1 = \{x : f(x) = 1\}, \qquad A_2 = \{x : f(x) > 1\},$$

and let $B = \{x : f(x) < 1\}$. Then

$$A_2 = \bigcup_n E_n, \qquad \text{where} \quad E_n = \left\{x : f(x) \geq 1 + \frac{1}{n}\right\}.$$

From (2) we see that

$$\nu(E_n) \geq \left(1 + \frac{1}{n}\right)[\mu(E_n) + \nu(E_n)],$$

whence it follows that $\mu(E_n) + \nu(E_n) = 0$. Therefore $\mu(A_2) + \nu(A_2) = 0$, so that $\mu(A_2) = \nu(A_2) = 0$. Putting $E = A_1$ in (2), we see that $\nu(A_1) = \mu(A_1) + \nu(A_1)$, so that $\mu(A_1) = 0$.

We now define $\nu_1$ and $\nu_2$ for arbitrary $E$ by

$$\nu_1(E) = \nu(E \cap B), \qquad \nu_2(E) = \nu(E \cap A). \tag{3}$$

We observe that $A \cup B = X$, $A \cap B = \varnothing$, $\mu(A) = 0$. Clearly, $\nu_1$ and $\nu_2$ are measures on $\mathbf{S}$, $\nu = \nu_1 + \nu_2$, and $\nu_2(E \cap B) = 0$ for every $E$, so that $\nu_2 \perp \mu$. To prove that $\nu_1 \in AC[\mu]$, suppose that $\mu(E) = 0$. Then $\mu(E \cap B) = 0$, so that from (2) we obtain

$$\nu(E \cap B) = \int_{E \cap B} f \, d\nu.$$

We can write this in the form

$$\int_{E\cap B}(1-f)\,d\nu=0.$$

Since $1-f(x)>0$ when $x\in B$, it follows that $\nu(E\cap B)=0$; that is, $\nu_1(E)=0$. Hence, $\nu_1\in AC[\mu]$. This finishes Step 1.

We observe that the sought for decomposition is determined as soon as we find a decomposition of $X$ into disjoint measurable sets $A$, $B$ such that $\mu(A)=0$ and such that $\nu(E\cap B)=0$ whenever $\mu(E)=0$. Then $\nu_1$ and $\nu_2$ are determined by (3). This observation will be used in the next two steps of the proof.

*Step 2.* Now we pass to the general $\sigma$-finite situation, but we continue to assume that $\nu$ is a measure. There exists an expression of $X$ as a countable disjoint union $\bigcup_n E_n$ such that $\mu(E_n)$ and $\nu(E_n)$ are both finite. By Step 1 there exists a decomposition $E_n=A_n\cup B_n$ such that $A_n\cap B_n=\varnothing$, $\mu(A_n)=0$, and such that $\nu(E\cap B_n)=0$ if $\mu(E\cap B_n)=0$. Let $A=\bigcup_n A_n$, $B=X-A$. Then $\mu(A)=0$. Suppose now that $\mu(E)=0$. Then $\mu(E\cap B_n)=0$, so $\nu(E\cap B_n)=0$. Since the $E_n$'s are disjoint, we see that $B=\bigcup_n B_n$, whence $E\cap B=\bigcup_n(E\cap B_n)$, and therefore $\nu(E\cap B)=0$. This shows that we have what is needed to obtain the decomposition $\nu=\nu_1+\nu_2$ in this case. We observe that the $\nu_1$ and $\nu_2$ defined by (3) will be $\sigma$-finite, because $\nu$ is $\sigma$-finite (see Theorem 8–1 I(a), which assures that $\nu(F)$ is finite if $F\subset E$ and $\nu(E)$ is finite).

*Step 3.* Now consider the general case of the theorem. Let $\nu=\nu^+-\nu^-$ be the Jordan decomposition of $\nu$. By Step 2 there are two sets of measure zero, $A_1$ and $A_2$, such that, if $B_i=X-A_i$ $(i=1,2)$, then $\nu^+(E\cap B_1)=0$ whenever $\mu(E)=0$, and $\nu^-(E\cap B_2)=0$ whenever $\mu(E)=0$. Let $A=A_1\cup A_2$, $B=X-A=B_1\cap B_2$. Suppose $\mu(E)=0$. Then $\nu(E\cap B)=\nu^+(E\cap B_1\cap B_2)-\nu^-(E\cap B_1\cap B_2)=0$, because $\mu(E\cap B_2)=\mu(E\cap B_1)=0$. Since $\mu(A)=0$, we have what is necessary in this case.

*Step 4.* It remains to discuss the uniqueness of the decomposition $\nu=\nu_1+\nu_2$. Let $\nu=\nu_3+\nu_4$ be a second decomposition of the same kind. Because of the $\sigma$-finiteness it clearly suffices to prove that $\nu_1(E)=\nu_3(E)$ and $\nu_2(E)=\nu_4(E)$ for every set $E$ such that $\mu(E)$ and $\nu(E)$ are finite. The property of being singular or absolutely continuous with respect to $\mu$ is retained when we restrict $\mu$ and $\nu$ to a $\sigma$-ring consisting of all members of $\mathbf{S}$ contained in a fixed measurable set. Hence, we may as well assume that all the values of $\mu$ and $\nu$ are finite. But in this case we can write $\nu_1-\nu_3=\nu_4-\nu_2$. Here, $(\nu_1-\nu_3)\in AC[\mu]$ and $(\nu_4-\nu_2)\perp\mu$ (see Problem 2). But then $\nu_1-\nu_3=\nu_4-\nu_2=0$, by the remarks following (1). This completes the proof.

**PROBLEMS**

1. Suppose $\nu\perp\mu$. Show that $V_\nu\perp\mu$.
2. Suppose $\nu_1$ and $\nu_2$ are signed measures such that $\nu_1\perp\mu$ and $\nu_2\perp\mu$. Suppose they are such that if both $\nu_1$ and $\nu_2$ have infinite values, then these values are of the same sign. Then $\nu=\nu_1+\nu_2$ is a signed measure. Show that $\nu\perp\mu$. In particular, if $\nu$ is any signed measure, and $\nu^+\perp\mu$ and $\nu^-\perp\mu$, then $\nu\perp\mu$.

## 8–6 Alternative approach via elementary integrals

In the theory of integration developed in Chapter 6 the elementary integral $I$ plays the basic role, and the measure $\mu$ which it induces does not enter the scene until comparatively late. It is therefore natural to inquire whether there is not something in this theory which is comparable to the Radon-Nikodym theorem. Of course, we could consider two elementary integrals $I_1$, $I_2$ and the measures $\mu_1$, $\mu_2$ which they induce. If it should then turn out that $\mu_2$ is absolutely continuous with respect to $\mu_1$, we could make use of the theory in earlier sections of the present chapter. What we seek, however, is a theory which shows a connection between the integration theories based on $I_1$ and $I_2$ without major intervention of the corresponding measures (or at least by methods more characteristic of Chapter 6 than of Chapter 5). Such a connection can be shown to exist if $I_2(f) \leq I_1(f)$ for each $f$ such that $f \geq 0$ in the basic vector lattice $\mathscr{F}$ on which the two elementary integrals are defined.

We therefore begin as in Section 6–1 with the basic space $X$, the vector lattice $\mathscr{F}$ of functions $f: X \to R$, and two elementary integrals $I_1, I_2$. If $I_2(f) \leq I_1(f)$ when $f \in \mathscr{F}$ and $f \geq 0$, we indicate this by writing $I_2 \leq I_1$. With $I_i$ there is associated as in Chapter 6 the class $\mathscr{L}_i$ of summable functions, the class $\mathscr{M}_i$ of measurable functions, and the induced measure $\mu_i$ on the $\sigma$-ring $\mathbf{S}_i$ of measurable sets. We also have the norm $\mathbf{N}_i$ and the class $\mathscr{T}_i$ of functions $f: X \to R^*$ such that $\mathbf{N}_i(f) < +\infty$ (see Section 6–6). From this situation we obtain Theorem 8–6 II as the major result. First, however, we must lay the ground work.

THEOREM 8–6 I. *Suppose that $I_2 \leq I_1$ as heretofore explained. Then:*
(a) $\mathbf{N}_2(f) \leq \mathbf{N}_1(f)$ *for every* $f$; (b) $\mathscr{T}_1 \subset \mathscr{T}_2$; (c) $\mathscr{L}_1 \subset \mathscr{L}_2$; (d) $I_2(f) \leq I_1(f)$ *if* $f \in \mathscr{L}_1$ *and* $f \geq 0$; (e) $\mathscr{M}_1 \subset \mathscr{M}_2$; (f) $\mathbf{S}_1 \subset \mathbf{S}_2$, *and* $\mu_2(E) \leq \mu_1(E)$ *if* $E \in \mathbf{S}_1$.

*Proof of* (a) *and* (b). It is clear that $I_2(h) \leq I_1(h)$ if $h \in \mathscr{F}^\circ$ and $h \geq 0$; (a) is an immediate consequence, and (b) follows from (a).

*Proof of* (c) *and* (d). Suppose $f \in \mathscr{L}_1$. Then $\mathbf{N}_2(f) \leq \mathbf{N}_1(f) = I_1(|f|) < +\infty$, so $f \in \mathscr{T}_2$. There exists a sequence $\{f_n\}$ in $\mathscr{F}$ with $\mathbf{N}_1(f_n - f) = I_1(|f_n - f|) \to 0$ (Theorem 6–4 VI). Then $\mathbf{N}_2(f_n - f) \to 0$. Since $f_n \in \mathscr{L}_2$, it follows by Theorem 6–6 IV that $f \in \mathscr{L}_2$. If $f \geq 0$, $I_2(f) = \mathbf{N}_2(f) \leq \mathbf{N}_1(f) = I_1(f)$.

*Proof of* (e). Suppose $f \in \mathscr{M}_1$. Then $g \vee (f \wedge h) \subset \mathscr{L}_1$ if $g, h \in \mathscr{F}$ (see Problem 3 (b), Section 6–5). Hence, $g \vee (f \wedge h) \in \mathscr{L}_2$ under these conditions (by (c)). Now suppose $g \leq 0 \leq h$, $g, h \in \mathscr{L}_2$. Choose $g_n, h_n \in \mathscr{F}$ so that $I_2(|g_n - g|) \to 0$, $I_2(|h_n - h|) \to 0$. Let $F_n = g_n \vee (f \wedge h_n)$, $F = g \vee (f \wedge h)$. We know that $F_n \in \mathscr{L}_2$, by what has been said. But $\mathbf{N}_2(F_n - F) \to 0$, because $\mathbf{N}_2(g_n - g) \to 0$ and $\mathbf{N}_2(h_n - h) \to 0$ (see Problem 2 (b), Section 6–6). From $|F_n| \leq |F_n - F_m| + |F_m|$ and $|F| \leq |F - F_n| + |F_n|$ it is easy to see that $\mathbf{N}_2(F) < +\infty$. Hence we can use Theorem 6–6 IV to conclude that $F \in \mathscr{L}_2$. This implies that $f \in \mathscr{M}_2$.

*Proof of* (f). This follows from (e) and (d).

For the next theorem we wish to apply Theorem 6–7 II to $\mathscr{M}_1$, so we need to know that $1 \in \mathscr{M}_1$. One way to insure this is to impose Stone's axiom on the vector lattice $\mathscr{F}$ (see (3) in Section 6–7 and Theorem 6–7 IV (c)). We shall also need to know (a) that $\mathscr{L}_1$ contains a function $f_0$ such that $0 < f_0(x) \leq 1$ for every $x$, and (b) that the measure spaces $(X, \mathbf{S}, \mu_i)$ are $\sigma$-finite for $i = 1, 2$. Since $1 \in \mathscr{M}_1$ implies $1 \in \mathscr{M}_2$, we can get all that we need by assuming that $\mathscr{F}$ contains a sequence $\{f_n\}$ such that $\sum_n |f_n(x)| = +\infty$ for each $x$, along with the assumption that $1 \in \mathscr{M}_1$. See Problem 5, Section 6–7.

In the proof of Theorem 8–6 II we shall make use of the Hilbert space $L_1^2$, formed from the class $\mathscr{L}_1^2$ of all functions $f: X \to R^*$ which are in $\mathscr{M}_1$ and such that $|f|^2 \in \mathscr{L}_1$. The $L^p$ spaces were discussed in Section 5–8 from the point of view of the theory of integration in Chapter 5, and in Section 6–11 from the point of view of Chapter 6. We shall have occasion to speak about continuity and convergence in the sense of the metric topology of $L_1^2$. To avoid awkward difficulties with additional notation we shall in certain places ignore the distinction between an element of $\mathscr{L}_1^2$ and the element of $L_1^2$ which it represents.

THEOREM 8–6 II. *Let $I_1$ and $I_2$ be elementary integrals on $\mathscr{F}$ such that $I_2 \leq I_1$. Suppose that $1 \in \mathscr{M}_1$, and that $\mathscr{F}$ contains a sequence $\{f_n\}$ such that $\sum_n |f_n(x)| = +\infty$ for each $x$. Then there exists a function $\varphi : X \to R$ such that:* (a) $\varphi \in \mathscr{M}_1$; (b) $0 \leq \varphi(x) \leq 1$ *for each* $x$; (c) $f \in \mathscr{L}_2$ *if and only if* $\varphi f \in \mathscr{L}_1$; (d) $I_2(f) = I_1(\varphi f)$ *if* $f \in \mathscr{L}_2$; (e) $\mu_2(\{x : \varphi(x) = 0\}) = 0$.

*Proof.* Suppose $f, g \in \mathscr{L}_1^2$. Then $fg \in \mathscr{L}_1$ and

(1) $$I_1(|fg|) \leq [I_1(|f|^2)]^{1/2} [I_1(|g|^2)]^{1/2}$$

(see Theorem 5–8 I). Then also $fg \in \mathscr{L}_2$ and $|I_2(fg)| \leq I_2(|fg|) \leq I_1(|fg|)$. We see from these inequalities that $I_2(fg)$ defines a continuous bilinear functional of $f$ and $g$ on $L_1^2 \times L_1^2$. Hence, there is a continuous linear function $T : L_1^2 \to L_1^2$ such that

(2) $$I_2(fg) = I_1(fT(g)).$$

(Here we are ignoring the distinction between elements of $\mathscr{L}_1^2$ and elements of $L_1^2$, for notational convenience.) For the existence of $T$ in this situation see Problem 6, Section 3–14.

Now, suppose that $f \in \mathscr{L}_1^2$, $h \in \mathscr{M}_1$, and let $h$ be bounded, say $|h(x)| \leq c < +\infty$. The product $hf$ is in $\mathscr{M}_1$ (see Theorem 6–7 II and Theorem 5–1 VI). Also, $|hf|^2 \leq c^2 |f|^2$, and so $hf \in \mathscr{L}_1^2$. Applying (2) in two different ways, we see that

(3) $$I_1(fhT(g)) = I_2(fhg) = I_1(fT(gh)).$$

Since $f$ is arbitrary and $I_1(fg)$ defines the inner product of $f$ and $g$ in $L_1^2$, we conclude from (3) that $hT(g)$ and $T(gh)$ represent the same element of $L_1^2$, that is, that as functions they differ in value on a set of $\mu_1$-measure zero.

Now, let $f_0 \in \mathscr{L}_1$ be such that $0 < f_0(x) \leq 1$ for each $x$ (see the remarks preceding the theorem). Let $h_0(x) = \sqrt{f_0(x)}$. It is easily proved that $h_0 \in \mathscr{M}_1$, so $h_0 \in \mathscr{L}_1^2$. Suppose $g \in \mathscr{L}_1^2$ and let $g_n = (-n) \vee (g \wedge n)$. Then $g_n \in \mathscr{M}_1$, $|g_n| \leq n$, $|g_n| \leq |g|$, so $g_n$ is bounded and $g_n \in \mathscr{L}_1^2$. From preceding results we know that

(4) $$h_0 T(g_n) = T(g_n h_0) = g_n T(h_0),$$

where equality in (4) is that between elements of $L_1^2$. Now, $g_n(x) \to g(x)$ when $g(x)$ is finite. Since $|g_n - g|^2 \leq 4|g|^2$, it is then clear that $I_1(|g_n - g|^2) \to 0$. This implies that $T(g_n) \to T(g)$ (convergence in $L_1^2$), and hence that $h_0 T(g_n) \to h_0 T(g)$ (because $h_0$ is bounded). We wish to conclude that $gT(h_0) \in L_1^2$ and that $gT(h_0) = h_0 T(g)$. We cannot argue directly that $g_n T(h_0)$ converges to $gT(h_0)$ in the $L_1^2$ metric, but we know from (4) that $g_n T(h_0) \to h_0 T(g)$. However, when a sequence converges in mean (of order two in this case), a subsequence converges pointwise almost everywhere to the function which is the limit in mean. In this way we can see that $gT(h_0)$ differs from $h_0 T(g)$ on a set of $\mu_1$-measure zero. Therefore,

(5) $$h_0 T(g) = gT(h_0) \quad \text{in } L_1^2 \text{ if } g \in \mathscr{L}_1^2.$$

Let $h_1 \in \mathscr{F}_1^2$ be a representative of the element $T(h_0)$ of $L_1^2$, and define $\varphi_0$ by

(6) $$\varphi_0(x) = \frac{h_1(x)}{h_0(x)}.$$

Since $h_0(x) > 0$ for each $x$, it is easy to see by methods of Chapter 5 that $\varphi_0 \in \mathscr{M}_1$.

Now, suppose $f \in \mathscr{L}_1$. Let $E = \{x : f(x) \geq 0\}$, $F = \{x : f(x) < 0\}$. Let $g = |f|^{1/2}$ and define

$$h(x) = \begin{cases} g(x) & \text{if } x \in E \\ -g(x) & \text{if } x \in F. \end{cases}$$

That is, $h = g\chi_E - g\chi_F$. We see that $g \in \mathscr{L}_1^2$ and also $h \in \mathscr{L}_1^2$. Moreover, $gh = f$. From (5) and (6) we see that $T(g) = g\varphi_0$. Hence $hT(g) = hg\varphi_0 = \varphi_0 f$. Using (2), we see that $I_2(gh) = I_1(hT(g)) = I_1(\varphi_0 f)$. Thus we have the result:

(7) $$I_2(f) = I_1(\varphi_0 f)$$

if $f \in \mathscr{L}_1$.

Now, suppose $f \in \mathscr{L}_1$ and $f \geq 0$. Then $0 \leq I_2(f) \leq I_1(f)$. From this and (7) we infer that

(8) $$0 \leq I_1(\varphi_0 f)$$

and

(9) $$0 \leq I_1(f - \varphi_0 f) = I_1[(1 - \varphi_0)f].$$

From these inequalities we can deduce that $0 \leq \varphi_0(x) \leq 1$ except on a set of $\mu_1$-measure zero. We use the fact that the measure $\mu_1$ is $\sigma$-finite. If the set $\{x : \varphi(x) < 0\}$ has positive measure, then for some $c < 0$ the set $\{x : \varphi(x) < c\}$ contains a set $E$ in $\mathbf{S}_1$ with $0 < \mu_1(E) < +\infty$. If we put $f = \chi_E$, then $\varphi_0 f \leq c\chi_E$, whence $I_1(\varphi_0 f) \leq c\mu_1(E) < 0$, in contradiction to (8). Likewise from (9) we conclude that the set $\{x : 1 < \varphi_0(x)\}$ has $\mu_1$-measure zero.

It now follows that if we define $\varphi$ so that $\varphi(x) = \varphi_0(x)$ if $0 \leq \varphi_0(x) \leq 1$, and $\varphi(x) = 0$ otherwise, then $\varphi \in \mathscr{M}_1$ and we can replace $\varphi_0$ by $\varphi$ in (7).

Suppose that $f \in \mathscr{L}_2$. Choose $f_n \in \mathscr{F}$ so that $I_2(|f_n - f|) < 1/n$, and choose $h_n \in \mathscr{F}^\circ$ so that $|f_n - f| \leq h_n$, $I_2(h_n) < 2/n$. By using (7) with $f \in \mathscr{F}$ it is easy to verify that $\varphi h_n \in \mathscr{L}_1$ and $I_1(\varphi h_n) = I_2(\varphi h_n) = I_2(h_n)$. Then, since $|\varphi f_n - \varphi f| \leq \varphi h_n$, we see that

$$\mathbf{N}_1(\varphi f_n - \varphi f) \leq \mathbf{N}_1(\varphi h_n) = I_1(\varphi h_n) = I_2(h_n) < \frac{2}{n}.$$

Using Theorem 6–6 IV, we conclude that $\varphi f \in \mathscr{L}_1$. Moreover,

$$|I_1(\varphi f) - I_2(f_n)| = |I_1(\varphi f) - I_1(\varphi f_n)| \leq I_1(|\varphi f - \varphi f_n|) \leq I_1(\varphi h_n) = I_2(h_n) < \frac{2}{n},$$

and so

$$|I_1(\varphi f) - I_2(f)| < \frac{2}{n} + I_2(|f_n - f|) < \frac{3}{n},$$

whence $I_1(\varphi f) = I_2(f)$.

We have now proved all of the theorem except (e) and the assertion that $f \in \mathscr{L}_2$ if $\varphi f \in \mathscr{L}_1$. We turn to (e). We make use of the fact that the measure $\mu_2$ is $\sigma$-finite. Let $E$ be the intersection of $\{x : \varphi(x) = 0\}$ with a set of finite $\mu_2$-measure. Then $\chi_E \in \mathscr{L}_2$, so $I_2(\chi_E) = I_1(\varphi\chi_E)$. But $\varphi\chi_E = 0$, and thus $\mu_2(E) = I_2(\chi_E) = 0$. It follows that the set on which $\varphi(x) = 0$ has $\mu_2$-measure zero.

Now suppose that $f$ is a function such that $\varphi f \in \mathscr{L}_1$. Then $(\varphi f)^+$ and $(\varphi f)^-$ are in $\mathscr{L}_1$. But $(\varphi f)^+ = \varphi f^+$ and $(\varphi f)^- = \varphi f^-$. If $\varphi f \in \mathscr{L}_1$ and $f \geq 0$ together imply $f \in \mathscr{L}_2$, we see from the above that we shall have the same implication without the restriction $f \geq 0$. We therefore deal with the case $\varphi f \in \mathscr{L}_1, f \geq 0$. Let $E = \{x : \varphi(x) = 0\}$. Define $g(x) = f(x)$ if $x \in X - E$, $g(x) = 0$ if $x \in E$. Define

$$g_n = \frac{n\varphi f}{n\varphi + 1}.$$

We have the following facts: $g_n \nearrow g$, $0 \leq g_n \leq n\varphi f$, $g_n \leq g \leq f$, whence $g_n \in \mathscr{L}_1 \subset \mathscr{L}_2$, $\varphi g_n \in \mathscr{L}_1$, and $I_2(g_n) = I_1(\varphi g_n) \leq I_1(\varphi f)$. By the monotone convergence theorem we conclude that $g \in \mathscr{L}_2$. But then $f \in \mathscr{L}_2$ also, because $\mu_2(E) = 0$. This completes the proof of Theorem 8–6 II.

Theorem 8–6 II is not exactly analogous to the Radon-Nikodym theorem. The assumption that $I_2 \leq I_1$ evidently implies that $\mu_2 \in AC[\mu_1]$ if we restrict $\mu_2$ to $\mathbf{S}_1$. This is because of Theorem 8–6 I (f). But the Radon-Nikodym theorem itself contains nothing like the $I_2 \leq I_1$ situation.

As a first step in the discussion of absolute continuity from the present point of view, we have the following lemma.

LEMMA 8–6 III. *Let $\mathscr{F}$ contain a sequence $\{f_n\}$ such that $\sum_n |f_n(x)| = +\infty$ for each $x$. Suppose that $I_1, I_2, I$ are elementary integrals on $\mathscr{F}$ such that $I_1 \leq I, I_2 \leq I$, and such that $1 \in \mathscr{M}$. Let $\varphi_1$ be a function related to $I_1$ and $I$ as the $\varphi$ of Theorem 8–6 IV is related to $I_2$ and $I_1$ in that theorem, and let $\varphi_2$ be a function of corresponding kind in relation to $I_2$ and $I$. Let $E_i = \{x : \varphi_i(x) = 0\}$, $i = 1, 2$. Then every set of $\mu_1$-measure zero is a set of $\mu_2$-measure zero if and only if the set*

$$F = E_1 \cap (X - E_2) \tag{10}$$

*is a set of $\mu$-measure zero.*

*Proof.* We assume that $\mu(F) = 0$. Suppose $E \in S_1$ and $\mu_1(E) = 0$. Then $0 = I_1(\chi_E) = I(\varphi_1 \chi_E)$, so the set on which $\varphi_1\chi_E$ has nonzero values is a set of $\mu$-measure zero, and hence also a set of $\mu_2$-measure zero. This set is $E \cap (X - E_1)$. We wish to show that $\mu_2(E \cap E_1) = 0$, for then we shall have $\mu_2(E) = 0$. Now,

$$E \cap E_1 = (E \cap E_1 \cap E_2) \cup [E \cap E_1 \cap (X - E_2)].$$

We know from (e) in Theorem 8–6 II that $\mu_2(E_2) = 0$. Hence, $\mu_2(E \cap E_1 \cap E_2) = 0$. Now, $\mu(F) = 0$ implies $\mu_2(F) = 0$, and hence $\mu_2[E \cap E_1 \cap (X - E_2)] = 0$. This finishes one part of the proof.

Now assume that $\mu(F) > 0$. Then, since $\mu$ is $\sigma$-finite, $F$ contains a set $E$ such that $0 < \mu(E) < +\infty$. We observe that $\mu_1(F) \leq \mu_1(E_1) = 0$, and hence $\mu_1(E) = 0$. We shall show that $E$ is not a set of $\mu_2$-measure zero, thus completing the proof of the theorem.

There exists a function $f_0 \in \mathscr{L}_2$ such that $0 < f_0(x) \leq 1$ for every $x$. The set on which the values of $\varphi_2\chi_E f_0$ are positive is precisely $E$ (observe that $E \subset X - E_2$). Hence, $I_2(\chi_E f_0) = I(\varphi_2\chi_E f_0) > 0$. But $\chi_E f_0 \leq \chi_E$, so $N_2(\chi_E) = I_2(\chi_E) > 0$. This means that $E$ has positive outer measure in the sense of the outer measure determined by $I_2$ (see Section 6–7). In view of Theorem 6–7 V, $E$ cannot have $\mu_2$-measure zero.

Now we come to a theorem which corresponds to the Radon-Nikodym theorem.

THEOREM 8–6 IV. *Suppose $I_1$ and $I_2$ are elementary integrals on $\mathscr{F}$ such that every set of $\mu_1$-measure zero is a set of $\mu_2$-measure zero. Suppose that $\mathscr{F}$ contains a sequence $\{f_n\}$ such that $\sum_n |f_n(x)| = +\infty$ for each x, and suppose that $1 \wedge f \in \mathscr{F}$ for each $f \in \mathscr{F}$. Then there exists a function $\psi : X \to R$ such that:* (a) $\psi \geq 0$, $\psi \in \mathscr{M}_1$; (b) $f \in \mathscr{L}_2$ *if and only if* $\psi f \in \mathscr{L}_1$; (c) $I_2(f) = I_1(\psi f)$ *if* $f \in \mathscr{L}_2$.

*Proof.* Let $I = I_1 + I_2$. Then $I$ is an elementary integral, and $I_i \leq I\,(i = 1, 2)$. We know that $1 \in \mathscr{M}$, because we have imposed Stone's axiom (see Section 6–7). It would suffice to assume directly that $1 \in \mathscr{M}$. Using the notations $\varphi_1$, $\varphi_2$, $E_1$, $E_2$, $F$ as in Lemma 8–6 III, we know that $\varphi_i \in \mathscr{M} \subset \mathscr{M}_1 \cap \mathscr{M}_2$ and that $\mu(F) = 0$, whence $\mu(E_1) = 0$. Let us define

$$\psi(x) = \begin{cases} \varphi_2(x)/\varphi_1(x) & \text{if } \varphi_1(x) > 0 \\ 0 & \text{if } \varphi_1(x) = 0. \end{cases}$$

Then $\psi \geq 0$. We observe that, if $c > 0$,

$$\{x : \psi(x) > c\} = \{x : \varphi_1(x) > 0\} \cap \{x : \varphi_2(x) > c\varphi_1(x)\},$$

from which it follows that $\psi \in \mathscr{M}$. From Theorem 8–6 II we know that $f \in \mathscr{L}_2$ is equivalent to $\varphi_2 f \in \mathscr{L}$. Since $\varphi_2(x) = \varphi_1(x)\psi(x)$ except on $E_1$ and $\mu(E_1) = 0$, $\varphi_2 f \in \mathscr{L}$ is equivalent to $\varphi_1\psi f \in \mathscr{L}$. This in turn is equivalent to $\psi f \in \mathscr{L}_1$. Moreover, when $f \in \mathscr{L}_2$, $I_2(f) = I(\varphi_1\psi f) = I_1(\psi f)$. This ends the proof.

## 8–7 The decomposition of linear functionals

In certain situations there is a decomposition of linear functionals, analogous to the Jordan decomposition of a signed measure (see Section 8–1). By decomposing linear functionals into the difference of two positive linear functionals we are able to obtain a precise representation theorem for continuous linear functionals on $C_\infty(R^k)$, and we are able to give an alternative treatment of the representation of continuous linear functionals on $L^p$ spaces.

### ORDER-BOUNDED LINEAR FUNCTIONALS

Let $\mathscr{F}$ be a vector lattice of functions $f : X \to R$ as in Section 6–1. Suppose $\Phi : \mathscr{F} \to R$ is a linear functional. If $f \in \mathscr{F}$ and $f \geq 0$, let $P(f) = \{g : g \in \mathscr{F}, 0 \leq g \leq f\}$. We define

(1) $$\Phi^+(f) = \sup\{\Phi(g) : g \in P(f)\}.$$

Since $0 \in P(f)$ and $\Phi(0) = 0$, we see that $\Phi^+(f) \geq 0$. Also, $f \in P(f)$ and therefore

(2) $$\Phi(f) \leq \Phi^+(f).$$

At this stage we have no assurance that $\Phi^+(f)$ is finite; it may be $+\infty$. We shall say that $\Phi$ is *order-bounded* if $\Phi^+(f) < +\infty$ for each $f$ in $\mathscr{F}$ such that $f \geq 0$.

If $\Phi(f) \geq 0$ whenever $f \geq 0$ (that is, if $\Phi$ is a *positive* linear functional) then $\Phi$ is order-bounded, and $\Phi^+(f) = \Phi(f)$ when $f \geq 0$.

On the assumption that $\Phi$ is order-bounded, we shall see that the definition of $\Phi^+$ can be extended so that $\Phi^+$ becomes a positive linear functional on $\mathscr{F}$. First we shall prove that

(3) $$\Phi^+(f_1 + f_2) = \Phi^+(f_1) + \Phi^+(f_2)$$

when $f_1 \geq 0$ and $f_2 \geq 0$. With $f_1, f_2$ given, suppose $g_i \in P(f_i)$. Then $g_1 + g_2 \in P(f_1 + f_2)$, and

$$\Phi(g_1) + \Phi(g_2) = \Phi(g_1 + g_2) \leq \Phi^+(f_1 + f_2).$$

From this, allowing $g_1$ and $g_2$ to vary, we see that $\Phi^+(f_1) + \Phi^+(f_2) \leq \Phi^+(f_1 + f_2)$. On the other hand, if $g \in P(f_1 + f_2)$, let $g_1 = g \wedge f_1$, $g_2 = 0 \vee (g - f_1)$. By considering separately the cases $g(x) < f_1(x)$, $g(x) \geq f_1(x)$, we see that $g = g_1 + g_2$ and $0 \leq g_2 \leq f_2$. Thus $g_i \in P(f_i)$, and hence

$$\Phi(g) = \Phi(g_1 + g_2) = \Phi(g_1) + \Phi(g_2) \leq \Phi^+(f_1) + \Phi^+(f_2).$$

From this we infer $\Phi^+(f_1 + f_2) \leq \Phi^+(f_1) + \Phi^+(f_2)$. The two inequalities we have established yield (3).

From $f \geq 0$ and $c > 0$ we see that

$$\Phi^+(cf) = \sup \{\Phi(g) : 0 \leq g \leq cf\}$$
$$= \sup \left\{c\Phi\left(\frac{g}{c}\right) : 0 \leq \frac{g}{c} \leq f\right\},$$

whence, since obviously $\Phi^+(0) = 0$, we have

(4) $$\Phi^+(cf) = c\Phi^+(f), \quad c \geq 0.$$

Now, every $f$ in $\mathscr{F}$ can be written in the form $f = f_1 - f_2$, where $f_1 \geq 0, f_2 \geq 0$, and $f_1$ and $f_2$ are in $\mathscr{F}$. One such way is $f = f^+ - f^-$. It can be seen that if $f = f_3 - f_4$ is another such representation of $f$, then $\Phi^+(f_1) - \Phi^+(f_2) = \Phi^+(f_3) - \Phi^+(f_4)$; this comes out easily from the fact that $f_1 + f_4 = f_2 + f_3 \geq 0$. Hence, if we write

(5) $$\Phi^+(f) = \Phi^+(f_1) - \Phi^+(f_2),$$

this defines $\Phi^+$ unambiguously on all of $\mathscr{F}$. It is an easy matter, with the aid of (3) and (4), to verify that $\Phi^+$ is a linear functional on $\mathscr{F}$.

Next, we define

(6) $$\Phi^-(f) = \Phi^+(f) - \Phi(f).$$

The functional $\Phi^-$ is linear; it is also positive, for if $f \geq 0$ we see from (2) that $\Phi^-(f) \geq 0$.

We summarize our findings in a theorem.

THEOREM 8–7 I. *If $\Phi : \mathscr{F} \to R$ is an order-bounded linear functional, there exist positive linear functionals $\Phi^+$, $\Phi^-$ on $\mathscr{F}$ such that*

(7) $$\Phi = \Phi^+ - \Phi^-.$$

We refer to (7) as the Jordan decomposition of $\Phi$.

## RELATIVELY BOUNDED LINEAR FUNCTIONALS ON $C_\infty(R^k)$

One important example of a vector lattice $\mathscr{F}$ is the space $C_\infty(R^k)$ (see Section 6–8). It is a normed linear space with the norm

$$\|f\| = \sup \{|f(x)| : x \in R^k\}.$$

A linear functional $\Phi$ on $C_\infty(R^k)$ is called *relatively bounded* if to each compact set $T$ of $R^k$ corresponds a constant $M$ such that

$$|\Phi(f)| \leq M\|f\| \tag{8}$$

if $f \in C_\infty(R^k)$ and $\{x : f(x) \neq 0\} \subset T$. We know (Theorem 6–9 I) that a positive linear functional on $C_\infty(R^k)$ is relatively bounded, and, moreover, that it is an elementary integral on $C_\infty(R^k)$.

THEOREM 8–7 II. *If $\Phi$ is a relatively bounded linear functional on $C_\infty(R^k)$, it is expressible in the form $\Phi = \Phi^+ - \Phi^-$, where $\Phi^+$ and $\Phi^-$ are elementary integrals on $C_\infty(R^k)$.*

*Proof.* In view of Theorems 8–7 I and 6–9 I it will suffice to show that $\Phi$ is order-bounded. Suppose $f \in C_\infty(R^k)$, $f \geq 0$. Let $T$ be a compact set which contains $\{x : f(x) \neq 0\}$, and let $M$ be chosen as described in connection with (8). If $g \in C_\infty(R^k)$ and $0 \leq g \leq f$, we see that $\|g\| \leq \|f\|$ and $\{x : g(x) \neq 0\} \subset T$. Therefore $|\Phi(g)| \leq M\|g\| \leq M\|f\|$; this shows that $\Phi$ is order-bounded, so the proof is complete.

## CONTINUOUS LINEAR FUNCTIONALS ON $C_\infty(R^k)$

A continuous linear functional $\Phi$ on $C_\infty(R^k)$ is relatively bounded, because $|\Phi(f)| \leq \|\Phi\|\,\|f\|$ for each $f$. The corresponding positive linear functionals $\Phi^+$, $\Phi^-$ are also continuous. From the definition of $\Phi^+$ we see that $\Phi^+(f) \leq \|\Phi\|\,\|f\|$ if $f \geq 0$. For an arbitrary $f$, $\|f^+\| \leq \|f\|$ and $\|f^-\| \leq \|f\|$, and so, from $\Phi^+(f) = \Phi^+(f^+) - \Phi^+(f^-)$ we see that

$$-\|\Phi\|\,\|f\| \leq -\Phi^+(f^-) \leq \Phi^+(f) \leq \Phi^+(f^+) \leq \|\Phi\|\,\|f\|,$$

whence $\|\Phi^+\| \leq \|\Phi\|$. Since $\Phi^-$ is related to $-\Phi$ as $\Phi^+$ is related to $\Phi$ (see Problem 1), we have $\|\Phi^-\| \leq \|-\Phi\| = \|\Phi\|$.

Further important information is contained in the following theorem. All functions mentioned are presumed to be in $C_\infty(R^k)$. We write $f \leq 1$ as a convenient abbreviation for the statement that $f(x) \leq 1$ for every $x$.

THEOREM 8–7 III. *Let $\Phi$ be a continuous linear functional on $C_\infty(R^k)$. Let $\Psi = \Phi^+ + \Phi^-$. Then the following relations hold*

$$\Psi(f) = \sup\{\Phi(g) : |g| \leq f\} \qquad \text{if } f \geq 0. \tag{9}$$

$$\|\Phi\| = \sup\{\Psi(f) : 0 \leq f \leq 1\}. \tag{10}$$

$$\|\Phi\| = \|\Psi\|. \tag{11}$$

$$\|\Phi\| = \|\Phi^+\| + \|\Phi^-\|. \tag{12}$$

*Proof of* (9). The supremum in question is finite; denote it by $A$. We observe that $|g| \leq f$ implies $g^+ \leq f$, $g^- \leq f$. Hence, in this situation, $\Phi(g) = \Phi(g^+) - \Phi(g^-) \leq \Phi^+(f) + \Phi^-(f) = \Psi(f)$, so that $A \leq \Psi(f)$. (For the inequality $-\Phi(g^-) \leq \Phi^-(f)$ see Problem 1.) On the other hand, if $\epsilon > 0$, we can choose $g_1$ and $g_2$ so that $0 \leq g_i \leq f$ and

$$\Phi(g_1) > \Phi^+(f) - \frac{\epsilon}{2}, \qquad -\Phi(g_2) > \Phi^-(f) - \frac{\epsilon}{2}.$$

Let $g = g_1 - g_2$. Then $|g| \leq f$ and $\Phi(g) > \Psi(f) - \epsilon$, so that $A \geq \Psi(f)$. Thus (9) is proved.

*Proof of* (10). Let $B$ denote the supremum in question. Suppose $0 \leq f \leq 1$ and $|g| \leq f$. Then $\|g\| \leq 1$, so $\Phi(g) \leq \|\Phi\| \, \|g\| \leq \|\Phi\|$, whence $\Psi(f) \leq \|\Phi\|$, because of (9). But then $B \leq \|\Phi\|$. On the other hand, we observe from (9) that $\Phi(g) \leq \Psi(|f|)$ if $|g| \leq |f|$. In particular, $\Phi(f) \leq \Psi(|f|)$. With $-f$ in place of $f$ this becomes $-\Phi(f) \leq \Psi(|f|)$. Therefore we have

$$|\Phi(f)| \leq \Psi(|f|). \tag{13}$$

Suppose now that $\|f\| \leq 1$. Then $|f| \leq 1$, so that $\Psi(|f|) \leq B$. Hence, using (13), we see that

$$\|\Phi\| = \sup \{|\Phi(f)| : \|f\| \leq 1\} \leq B.$$

Thus (10) is proved.

*Proof of* (11). Since $\Psi$ is a positive linear functional, $\Psi^+ = \Psi$ and $\Psi^- = 0$. Thus $\Psi$ itself is related to $\Psi$ as $\Psi$ is related to $\Phi$, and (10) holds with $\Phi$ replaced by $\Psi$ on the left side. This gives (11).

*Proof of* (12). If we apply (10) to a positive linear functional $\Phi$, $\Psi$ is the same as $\Phi$ in this case. Hence, we have

$$\|\Phi^+\| = \sup \{\Phi^+(f) : 0 \leq f \leq 1\}, \tag{14}$$

and likewise for $\Phi^-$. Now suppose that $0 \leq f \leq 1$, $0 \leq g \leq 1$, and let $h = f \vee g$. Then $f \leq h$, $g \leq h$, so that $\Phi^+(f) \leq \Phi^+(h)$ and $\Phi^-(g) \leq \Phi^-(h)$; therefore

$$\Phi^+(f) + \Phi^-(g) \leq \Phi^+(h) + \Phi^-(h) = \Psi(h) \leq \|\Phi\|. \tag{15}$$

At the last step here we observe that $0 \leq h \leq 1$ and use (10). From (15), with (14) and what corresponds to (14) for $\Phi^-$, we see that $\|\Phi^+\| + \|\Phi^-\| \leq \|\Phi\|$. Since the reverse inequality also holds, we have proved (12).

We are now in a position to describe the way in which an arbitrary continuous linear functional $\Phi$ on $C_\infty(R^k)$ is composed from a certain kind of signed measure, and to show the relation of $\|\Phi\|$ to this signed measure. The following theorem is commonly called the Riesz representation theorem, in honor of F. Riesz (1880–1956). The original theorem of Riesz dealt with the case of continuous linear functionals on the space $C[a, b]$ (see Theorem 9–5 III), and the representation was by means of a Stieltjes integral of the Riemann type. The theorem has undergone a tremendous generalization. To follow this generalization is, to a certain extent, to view the whole modern development of the theory of integration, evolving towards ever greater abstraction and generality, while at the same time throwing a revealing light on the original setting of the theorem. The theorem as we give it has a more general validity, with $R^k$ replaced by any locally compact Hausdorff space. For this generalization it would be necessary to develop the theory of regular Borel measures in such spaces, and the relation of such measures to elementary integrals, much as we have done for the case of $R^k$ and $C_\infty(R^k)$ in Sections 6–9, 6–10.

THEOREM 8–7 IV. *Let $\Phi$ be a continuous linear functional on $C_\infty(R^k)$, and let $\Phi = \Phi^+ - \Phi^-$ be its Jordan decomposition. Then there exists a unique finite signed measure $\nu$ on the $\sigma$-ring of all Borel sets in $R^k$, such that $\nu^+$ and $\nu^-$ are finite regular Borel measures,* *with*

(16) $$\Phi^+(f) = \int f\,d\nu^+, \qquad \Phi^-(f) = \int f\,d\nu^-,$$

(17) $$\|\Phi^+\| = \nu^+(R^k),\ \|\Phi^-\| = \nu^-(R^k),$$

*and*

(18) $$\|\Phi\| = V_\nu(R^k),$$

*where $V_\nu$ is the total variation of $\nu$.*

*Proof.* Let $\mu_1$ and $\mu_2$ be the measures induced by the elementary integrals $\Phi^+$, $\Phi^-$, respectively. We know by Theorem 6–9 V that $\mu_1$ and $\mu_2$ are regular extensions of Borel measures (see Section 6–10). We shall see that $\mu_1(R^k)$ and $\mu_2(R^k)$ are finite. Let $A$ be any compact set. Choose $f \in C_\infty(R^k)$ so that $0 \leq f \leq 1$ and $f(x) = 1$ if $x \in A$. Then $\chi_A \leq f$ and $\|f\| \leq 1$. Therefore, (see Theorem 6–7 III)

$$\mu_1(A) = \int \chi_A\,d\mu_1 \leq \int f\,d\mu_1 = \Phi^+(f) \leq \|\Phi^+\|.$$

Hence, (see Theorem 6–9 V (e))

(19) $$\mu_1(R^k) \leq \|\Phi^+\|.$$

The same reasoning applies to $\mu_2$ and $\Phi^-$. Now let $\nu_i(E) = \mu_i(E)$ if $E$ is any Borel set, and let $\nu = \nu_1 - \nu_2$. Then $\nu_i$ is a regular Borel measure, and $\nu$ is a finite signed measure. If $f \in C_\infty(R^k)$, $f$ is summable with respect to $\nu_i$ (see the discussion in Section 6–10), and it is easy to see that

$$\int f\,d\nu_1 = \int f\,d\mu_1 = \Phi^+(f),$$

with corresponding results for $\nu_2$ and $\Phi^-$. It follows from Theorem 6–10 III that $\mu_i$ is the completion of $\nu_i$.

Now $\nu^+$ and $\nu^-$ are regular Borel measures (see Problem 7, Section 8–1). We shall prove that $\nu^+ = \nu_1$ and $\nu^- = \nu_1$, thereby establishing (16). If $A$ and $E$ are Borel sets, with $A \subset E$, we have $\nu(A) = \nu_1(A) - \nu_2(A) \leq \nu_1(A) \leq \nu_1(E)$. Hence, from the definition of $\nu^+$ (see (3) in Section 8–1) we can see that

(20) $$\nu^+(E) \leq \nu_1(E).$$

Now $\nu_1 - \nu_2 = \nu^+ - \nu^-$, so $\nu_1 + \nu^- = \nu_2 + \nu^+$. It follows that

$$\int f\,d\nu_1 + \int f\,d\nu^- = \int f\,d\nu_2 + \int f\,d\nu^+,$$

whence

$$\Phi(f) = \int f\,d\nu^+ - \int f\,d\nu^-.$$

Suppose now that $0 \leq g \leq f$ ($f$ and $g$ in $C_\infty(R^k)$). Then

$$\Phi(g) \leq \int g\,d\nu^+ \leq \int f\,d\nu^+;$$

therefore, by the definition of $\Phi^+$,

$$\int f\,d\nu_1 = \Phi^+(f) \le \int f\,d\nu^+. \tag{21}$$

From (21) we can deduce that

$$\nu_1(E) \le \nu^+(E) \tag{22}$$

for each Borel set; this, with (20), will prove that $\nu_1 = \nu^+$. Since

$$\nu_1(E) = \sup\{\nu_1(A) : A \text{ compact, } A \subset E\},$$

it will suffice to prove (22) for compact sets. If $A$ is compact and if $f$ is any element of $C_\infty(R^k)$ such that $\chi_A \le f$, we see from (21) that

$$\nu_1(A) = \int \chi_A\,d\nu_1 \le \int f\,d\nu_1 \le \int f\,d\nu^+. \tag{23}$$

Now, since $\nu^+$ is a regular Borel measure, the infimum of the integrals on the right in (23) is exactly $\nu^+(A)$ (see Problem 3, Section 6–10). Thus $\nu_1(A) \le \nu^+(A)$. This completes the proof that $\nu_1 = \nu^+$; it follows at once that $\nu_2 = \nu^-$.

The uniqueness aspect of $\nu$ is taken care of by Corollary 6–10 IV. It remains to prove (17) and (18). We prove the first equality in (17). The same reasoning applies in the other cases. Note that $\Psi$ in Theorem 8–7 III is represented by the integral with respect to the total variation $V_\nu$. We can then use (11) to obtain (18); or, alternatively, we can use (12).

Given $f \in C_\infty(R^k)$, let $A$ be a compact set such that $\{x : f(x) \ne 0\} \subset A$. Then

$$|\Phi^+(f)| = \left|\int f\,d\nu^+\right| \le \int |f|\,d\nu^+ \le \|f\|\,\nu^+(A) \le \|f\|\,\nu^+(R^k).$$

Therefore $\|\Phi^+\| \le \nu^+(R^k)$. Since $\nu^+(R^k) = \nu_1(R^k) = \mu_1(R^k)$, we see from (19) that $\nu^+(R^k) = \|\Phi^+\|$. This completes the proof.

## CONTINUOUS LINEAR FUNCTIONALS ON $L^p$

We shall now look at the topic of Section 8–4 from a different point of view, using different methods. Here we shall use results about $\mathscr{L}^p$ from Section 6–11. The space $\mathscr{L}^p$ is formed from $\mathscr{L}^p$ in the same manner that $L$ is formed from $\mathscr{L}$. We wish to use Theorem 6–11 I, so we shall impose the necessary conditions on $\mathscr{F}$.

We start from the vector lattice $\mathscr{F}$ and the elementary integral $I$ as in Section 6–1. This leads to $\mathscr{L}$ and a measure $\mu$. We shall assume that all the functions in $\mathscr{F}$ are bounded and that $\mathscr{F}$ satisfies Stone's axiom. Then we can use all the results in Sections 5–8 and 6–11, $\mathscr{L}^p$ being the same as $\mathscr{L}^p(\mu)$. Suppose now that $\Phi$ is a continuous linear functional on $L^p$. We assume throughout this section that $1 \le p < \infty$. We write

$$p' = \frac{p}{p-1} \quad \text{if } 1 < p, \qquad p' = \infty \quad \text{if } p = 1.$$

If we undertake to make a Jordan decomposition of $\Phi$, we meet an obstacle. Theorem 8–7 I does not apply to our situation, because $L^p$ is not a space of real-valued functions. There are two ways around the difficulty. We may generalize Theorem 8–7 I to more general vector lattices, of which $L^p$ is an example. Alternatively, we may work with $\mathscr{L}^p$, defining a function $F : \mathscr{L}^p \to R$ by $F(f) = \Phi([f])$. Now, $\mathscr{L}^p$ is not a vector lattice of real-valued functions; $\pm\infty$ may occur as function values, and on this account the addition of functions is not associative in general, so that we do not have a true vector lattice. Nevertheless, we may imitate the procedure used in proving Theorems 8–7 I, and everything works out successfully, so that we get a decomposition $F = F^+ - F^-$. If we then define $\Phi^+([f]) = F^+(f)$, $\Phi^-([f]) = F^-(f)$, we obtain $\Phi = \Phi^+ - \Phi^-$. This is the same Jordan decomposition we could have gotten by treating $L^p$ directly as a vector lattice. The fact that $\Phi$ is continuous assures us that $\Phi^+$ and $\Phi^-$ are continuous. We have $\|\Phi^+\| \le \|\Phi\|$, and likewise for $\Phi^-$. We shall leave the details of all this to the reader.

The following theorem shows how $\Phi$ is expressed in terms of integrals derived from the Jordan decomposition.

THEOREM 8–7 V. *Let $\Phi$ be a continuous linear functional on $L^p$, where $1 \le p < \infty$ and the basic vector lattice $\mathscr{F}$ is subjected to the conditions described in a preceding paragraph. Then there exist two elementary integrals $J^+$ and $J^-$ on $\mathscr{F}$ such that each $f$ in $\mathscr{L}^p$ is summable with respect to both $J^+$ and $J^-$, and such that*

$$\Phi([f]) = J^+(f) - J^-(f) \tag{24}$$

*if $f \in \mathscr{L}^p$. Furthermore, each set of measure zero with respect to $I$ is of measure zero with respect to both $J^+$ and $J^-$.*

*Proof.* We define $J^+(f) = F^+(f) = \Phi^+([f])$ if $f \in \mathscr{F}$. Then $J^+$ is a positive linear functional on $\mathscr{F}$. It is an elementary integral, as well. For, if $f_n \in \mathscr{F}$ and $f_n \searrow 0$, it follows that $\|f_n\|_p \to 0$; this implies $J^+(f_n) \to 0$, because $|J^+(f_n)| \le \|\Phi\| \, \|f_n\|_p$. Likewise, we define $J^-$ and see that it is an elementary integral.

We shall now show that when $f \in \mathscr{L}^p$, $f$ is summable with respect to $J^+$, with $J^+(f) = \Phi^+([f])$. In the process we shall show that a set of measure zero with respect to $I$ is also of measure zero with respect to $J^+$. The same reasoning applies to $J^-$. In this way we shall establish (24).

Suppose that $E$ is a set of measure zero with respect to $I$; that is, $\chi_F \in \mathscr{L}$ and $I(\chi_E) = 0$. Suppose $\epsilon > 0$. There exists a function $h \in \mathscr{F}^\circ$ such that $\chi_E \le h$ and $\|\Phi\| \, \{I(h)\}^{1/p} < \epsilon$ (see Section 6–3). Choose $f_n$ in $\mathscr{F}$ so that $f_n \nearrow h$. We can suppose $f_n \ge 0$ (otherwise replace $f_n$ by $0 \vee f_n$). Let $g_n = 1 \wedge f_n$. Then $g_n \in \mathscr{F}$ and $g_n \nearrow 1 \wedge h$. Thus $h_1 = 1 \wedge h \in \mathscr{F}$. Evidently $\chi_E \le h_1$ and $I(h_1) \le I(h)$. Now, $g_n \le 1$, so that $g_n^p \le g_n$, whence

$$\|g_n\|_p \le \{I(g_n)\}^{1/p} \le \{I(h)\}^{1/p}.$$

Then $J^+(g_n) \le \|\Phi\| \, \|g_n\|_p$, and so $J^+(h_1) \le \|\Phi\| \, \{I(h)\}^{1/p} < \epsilon$. We conclude from this that $E$ has measure zero with respect to $J^+$.

Now, suppose that $f \in \mathscr{L}^p$. There exists a sequence $\{f_n\}$ in $\mathscr{F}$ such that $\|f_n - f\|_p \to 0$ (Theorem 6–11 I). By picking a subsequence we may assume that $f_n(x) \to f(x)$ except on a set $E$ of measure zero with respect to $I$. (This follows from Theorem 6–11 II, because of the essential uniqueness of the limit in mean.) Now, $J^+(|f_n - f_m|) \le \|\Phi\| \, \|f_n - f_m\|_p$, and this converges to 0 as $m$ and $n \to \infty$. Hence, by Theorem 6–4 IV, there exists a function $g$, summable with respect to $J^+$, such that $J^+(|f_n - g|) \to 0$, and such that a subsequence $\{f_n(x)\}$ converges to $g(x)$ except on a set $F$ of measure zero with respect to $J^+$. Since $E$ is also of measure zero with respect to $J^+$, and since $f(x) = g(x)$ except on $E \cup F$, it follows that $f$ is summable with respect to $J^+$, with $J^+(f) = J^+(g)$. But $\Phi^+([f_n]) = J^+(f_n) \to J^+(g)$ and $\Phi^+([f_n]) \to \Phi^+([f])$. Hence, $\Phi^+([f]) = J^+(f)$. This completes what we set out to prove.

Theorem 8–7 V gives us another way of dealing with Theorem 8–4 I. We use Theorem 8–6 IV instead of Theorem 8–3 I. For this purpose we must, of course, impose the additional condition on $\mathscr{F}$ expressed in Theorem 8–6 IV, which serves to make the measures arising from the integrals $\sigma$-finite. We apply Theorem 8–6 IV with $I$ in place of $I_1$ and $J^+$ in place of $I_2$. The result is that there is a nonnegative real-valued function $g_1$, measurable with respect to $I$, such that $J^+(f) = I(fg_1)$ when $f \in \mathscr{L}^p$. Doing the same thing with $J^-$ in place of $J^+$, we get a function $g_2$. Let $g = g_1 - g_2$. Then $g$ is $I$-summable and $\Phi([f]) = I(fg)$ for each $f \in \mathscr{L}^p$. We can now argue somewhat as in the proof of Theorem 5–8 III, or use that theorem directly, to conclude that $g \in \mathscr{L}^{p'}$ and $\|g\|_{p'} \leq \|\Phi\|$. From here on the argument is the same as in the original proof of Theorem 8–4 I.

## PROBLEMS

1. In connection with (6), verify that

$$-\Phi^-(f) = \inf\{\Phi(g) : g \in P(f)\}$$

and

$$\Phi^-(f) = \sup\{-\Phi(g) : g \in P(f)\}.$$

[*Hint*. Observe that $g \in P(f)$ implies $f - g \in P(f)$.]

2. Let $\mathscr{F}$ be a vector lattice of functions $f : X \to R$ which is also a normed linear space, and let the space be such that (a) $0 \leq g \leq f$ implies $\|g\| \leq \|f\|$ and (b) $f_n \searrow 0$ implies $\|f_n\| \to 0$. Show that any continuous linear functional on $\mathscr{F}$ is order-bounded.

## SUGGESTED READING FOR CHAPTER 8

AUMANN [1], pp. 394–401.
CARATHEODORY [1], Chapter 9.
DUNFORD and SCHWARTZ [1], pp. 126–144, 174–183.
GOFFMAN [1], Chapter 18.
HAHN and ROSENTHAL [1], pp. 16–22, 168–171.
HALMOS [1], Chapter 6.
LEBESGUE [2], Chapter 8.
LOOMIS [1], pp. 40–43.
MCSHANE and BOTTS [1], Chapter 6.
MUNROE [1], pp. 79–83, 190–199, 283–286.
NAIMARK [1], pp. 139–145.
SAKS [1], pp. 30–36.
TAYLOR [2], pp. 373–401.
DE LA VALLÉE-POUSSIN [1], Chapters 5, 6.
WILLIAMSON [1], Chapter 6.
ZAANEN [1], Chapters 7, 11, and pp. 188–203.

CHAPTER NINE

# Functions of One Real Variable

## 9–0 Introduction

The topics in this chapter stand somewhat apart from the subject matter of Chapters 4 to 8. In Sections 9–1, . . . , 9–6, the notions of measure and Lebesgue integration do not occur except in some of the problems. This material belongs to a rather elementary level of the classical theory of functions, and can be studied early in a course based on this textbook, if such an order is preferred by teacher or student. The material in Sections 9–7, 9–8 is less elementary. The first part of Section 9–7 uses from measure theory only the notion of sets of Lebesgue measure zero. For the rest of Section 9–7 and Section 9–8, however, it is necessary to draw heavily on knowledge of standard parts of the theory of Lebesgue integration.

## 9–1 Monotone functions

In this section we consider functions $f: D \to R$, where $D$ is a connected set in $R$ and $D$ has more than one point. The connectedness of $D$ is characterized by the fact that if $x_1 < x < x_2$ and $x_1$, $x_2$ are in $D$, then $x$ is in $D$. The set $D$ has at most two end-points; the rest of the points of $D$ are interior points. The function $f$ is said to be *nondecreasing* if $f(x_1) \leq f(x_2)$ whenever $x_1 < x_2$, and *nonincreasing* if $f(x_1) \geq f(x_2)$ whenever $x_1 < x_2$; in either case $f$ is called a *monotone* (or monotonic) function. If $f(x_1) < f(x_2)$ whenever $x_1 < x_2$, we say that $f$ is a *strictly increasing* function. There is a corresponding concept of a strictly decreasing function.

If $f: D \to R$ is monotone and $D$ is compact, then $f$ is bounded. For, suppose $D = [a, b]$. Then the range of $f$ is the interval whose endpoints are $f(a)$, $f(b)$, if $f(a) \neq f(b)$. Otherwise, the range is one point.

We see that $f$ is nonincreasing if and only if $-f$ is nondecreasing. On this account, in much of the discussion of monotone functions, we can assume that $f$ is nondecreasing.

## RIGHT AND LEFT LIMITING VALUES

Suppose $f : D \to R$ is monotone and suppose $x \in D$, but that $D$ contains points $t$ such that $x < t$. Then $f(t)$ approaches a definite finite limit as $t$ approaches $x$ from the right; we denote this limit by $f(x+)$, and write

$$f(x+) = \lim_{t \to x+} f(t). \tag{1}$$

This means that to each $\epsilon > 0$ corresponds some $\delta > 0$ such that $|f(t) - f(x)| < \epsilon$ if $t \in D$ and $x < t < x + \delta$. When $f$ is nondecreasing, $f(x+)$ is given by

$$f(x+) = \inf \{f(t) : t \in D, x < t\}. \tag{2}$$

It is clear from (2) that $f(x) \leq f(x+)$.

When $f$ is nonincreasing we have

$$f(x+) = \sup \{f(t) : t \in D, x < t\}; \tag{3}$$

in this case $f(x+) \leq f(x)$.

We define $f(x-)$ in an analogous way and write

$$f(x-) = \lim_{t \to x-} f(t) \tag{4}$$

when $f$ is monotone, $x \in D$ and $D$ contains points $t$ such that $t < x$. There are formulas for $f(x-)$ corresponding to (2) and (3).

We call $f(x+)$ and $f(x-)$ the right and left limits respectively, of $f$ at $x$. It is apparent that, when $x$ is an interior point of $D$, $f$ is continuous at $x$ if and only if $f(x) = f(x+) = f(x-)$. If $x$ is an endpoint of $D$ the condition for continuity of $f$ at $x$ is that $f(x)$ coincide with $f(x+)$ or $f(x-)$, whichever is defined.

THEOREM 9–1 I. *If $f : D \to R$ is a monotone function, the set of points of $D$ at which $f$ is discontinuous is countable.*

*Proof.* We may assume that $f$ is nondecreasing. Let $S$ be the set of interior points of $D$ at which $f$ is discontinuous. It will suffice to prove that $S$ is countable. Suppose $c \in S$. Then $f(c-) < f(c+)$. Denote by $I(c)$ the open interval $(f(c-), f(c+))$. If $c_1$ and $c_2$ are in $S$, with $c_1 < c_2$, it is evident that $I(c_1) \cap I(c_2) = \varnothing$; for, if $c_1 < x < c_2$, we have $f(c_1+) \leq f(x) \leq f(c_2-)$. As $c$ varies over $S$ we get a family of disjoint open intervals $I(c)$. Such a family is countable (the reader should see why) and hence $S$ is countable.

## THE JUMPS OF A MONOTONE FUNCTION

If $f : D \to R$ is monotone and $x$ is an interior point of $D$ the number $|f(x+) - f(x-)|$ is called the *jump* of $f$ at $x$. (The Latin word *saltus* is also used.) If $D$ has a left endpoint $a$, the jump of $f$ at $a$ is defined to be $|f(a+) - f(a)|$. At a right endpoint $b$ the jump is $|f(b) - f(b-)|$.

LEMMA 9–1 II. *If $f : D \to R$ is monotone, with $[a, b] \subset D$ and $a < x_1 < \cdots < x_n < b$, the sum of the jumps of $f$ at the points $x_1, \ldots, x_n$ does not exceed $|f(b-) - f(a+)|$.*

*Proof.* We can assume $f$ is nondecreasing. Then $f(a+) \leq f(x_1-), f(x_n+) \leq f(b-)$, and $f(x_i+) \leq f(x_{i+1}-)$ if $i = 1, 2, \ldots, n-1$. Therefore

$$\sum_{i=1}^{n} [f(x_i+) - f(x_i-)] = \sum_{i=1}^{n-1} [f(x_i+) - f(x_{i+1}-)] + f(x_n+) - f(x_1-)$$
$$\leq 0 + f(b-) - f(a+),$$

as asserted.

The foregoing lemma can easily be used to give a different proof of Theorem 9–1 I. For, it is clear that the number of points in $(a, b)$ at which the jump of $f$ exceeds a given positive number $\epsilon$ must be finite. On the other hand, if $f$ is discontinuous at $x$, the jump at $x$ exceeds $1/k$ if $k$ is a sufficiently large positive integer. From this it follows that the number of points of discontinuity in $(a, b)$ must be countable. To finish the argument we observe that the interior of $D$ can be expressed as a countable union of finite open intervals $(a_n, b_n)$.

## THE JUMP FUNCTION

Suppose that $f: D \to R$ is nondecreasing and bounded below. Let the set of interior points of $D$ at which $f$ is discontinuous be not empty, and let it be given the enumeration $x_1, x_2, \ldots$. Then, if $x$ is an interior point of $D$, let

(5) $$s(x) = f(x) - f(x-) + \sum_{x_i < x} [f(x_i+) - f(x_i-)].$$

The notation here means that we add the jumps of $f$ at all points $x_i$ for which $x_i < x$. If there are no such points the expression with the summation sign in (5) is omitted. Even though the sum appearing in (5) may be an infinite series, it is convergent; we do not need to specify the order of the terms, because they are all nonnegative. To prove the convergence of the series, let $M$ be a number such that $M \leq f(x)$ for each $x$ in the interior of $D$. Consider any finite number of $x_i$'s for which $x_i < x$, and let $c$ be the smallest of these $x_i$'s. Then, as in the proof of Lemma 9–1 II, we see that the finite sum of the jumps at these $x_i$'s does not exceed $f(x-) - f(c+)$, which in turn does not exceed $f(x-) - M$. Hence the sum in (5), if it is an infinite series, must be convergent.

We call $s$ the *jump function* associated with $f$. Observe that $s(x)$ remains constant on any open interval throughout which $f$ is continuous.

THEOREM 9–1 III. (a) *The function $s$ defined in* (5) *is nondecreasing.* (b) *The function $F$ defined for $x$ in the interior of $D$ by $F(x) = f(x) - s(x)$ is nondecreasing and continuous.*

*Proof of* (a). If $x < y$, we see that $s(y) - s(x)$ involves

$$\sum_{x \leq x_i < y} [f(x_i+) - f(x_i-)] = f(x+) - f(x-) + \sum_{x < x_i < y} [f(x_i+) - f(x_i-)].$$

Thus,

(6) $$s(y) - s(x) = f(y) - f(x) + f(x+) - f(y-) + \sum_{x < x_i < y} [f(x_i+) - f(x_i-)],$$

and from this we see that $s(x) \leq s(y)$.

*Proof of* (b). We see by Lemma 9–1 II that the sum of the jumps at points $x_i$ between $x$ and $y$ does not exceed $f(y-) - f(x+)$. Therefore, from (6) we see that

(7) $$s(y) - s(x) \leq f(y) - f(x).$$

This means that $F$ is nondecreasing. If we let $y \to x$ in (7), we obtain the result

(8) $$s(x+) - s(x) \leq f(x+) - f(x).$$

We see from (6) that $f(x+) - f(x) \leq s(y) - s(x)$, from which it follows that $f(x+) - f(x) \leq s(x+) - s(x)$. In view of (8) we then have

(9) $$s(x+) - s(x) = f(x+) - f(x) \quad \text{or} \quad F(x+) = F(x).$$

From (6) we can also see that $f(y) - f(y-) \leq s(y) - s(x)$. On letting $x \to y$ in this result and in (7), we find that

(10) $$s(y) - s(y-) = f(y) - f(y-) \quad \text{or} \quad F(y-) = F(y).$$

We conclude from (9) and (10) that $F$ is continuous, so our proof is complete.

It can be seen from (9) and (10) that

(11) $$s(x+) = \sum_{x_i \leq x} [f(x_i+) - f(x_i-)]$$

and

(12) $$s(x-) = \sum_{x_i < x} [f(x_i+) - f(x_i-)].$$

Suppose in particular that $D$ is a finite closed interval $[a, b]$. Then $f(x) \geq f(a+)$ when $a < x < b$, and so we can see that the sum of the $[f(x_i+) - f(x_i-)]$ terms in (5) does not exceed $f(x-) - f(a+)$. Therefore $0 \leq s(x) \leq f(x) - f(a+)$ in this case. It is not hard to see that

(13) $$s(a+) = 0, \qquad s(b-) = \sum_{x_i < b} [f(x_i+) - f(x_i-)].$$

If we wish $s$ to be nondecreasing and $f - s$ to be continuous on the closed interval $[a, b]$, we must define $s(b)$ by (5) when $x = b$, and we must have

(14) $$s(a) = f(a) - f(a+).$$

## 9–2 Vector-valued functions of bounded variation

In this section we consider functions $f : [a, b] \to R^k$, where $[a, b]$ is a finite closed interval in $R$. The cases $k = 1, 2$ are of particular interest and importance in classical analysis. When $k = 2$ we may, if we please, interpret the values of $f$ as complex numbers.

In the present situation we wish to think of $R^k$ as a normed linear space. If $W \in R^k$, $\|W\|$ is the length of the vector $W$, or the distance between $W$ and the origin. If $W = (w_1, \ldots, w_k)$ is the coordinate representation of $W$, we recall that

$$\|W\| = (w_1^2 + \cdots + w_k^2)^{1/2},$$

so that

(1) $$|w_i| \leq \|W\| \quad \text{and} \quad \|W\| \leq |w_1| + \cdots + |w_k|.$$

The function $f : [a, b] \to R^k$ determines and is determined by the $k$ component functions $f_1, \ldots, f_k$, each with values in $R$, where

(2) $$f(x) = (f_1(x), \ldots, f_k(x)).$$

Many of the things we are going to consider can be applied to functions $f : [a, b] \to Y$, where $Y$ is any Banach space (see Section 3–13). However, we shall not consider such generalizations explicitly.

## THE TOTAL VARIATION

Let $\Delta = (x_0, x_1, \ldots, x_n)$ be a partition of $[a, b]$; that is, we suppose $a = x_0 < x_1 < \cdots < x_n = b$. We introduce the notation

$$T(\Delta; f) = \sum_{i=1}^{n} \|f(x_i) - f(x_{i-1})\|. \tag{3}$$

The *total variation* of $f$ on $[a, b]$ is by definition

$$V(f) = \sup_{\Delta} T(\Delta; f), \tag{4}$$

the supremum being taken as $\Delta$ varies over the class of all partitions of $[a, b]$. If $V(f) < +\infty$, we say that $f$ is *of bounded variation* on $[a, b]$.

If we wish to show the dependence of the total variation on the interval $[a, b]$, we write $V_{ab}(f)$ in place of $V(f)$.

We shall denote by $BV_k[a, b]$ the class of all functions $f : [a, b] \to R^k$ which are of bounded variation on $[a, b]$. When $k = 1$ we may write $BV[a, b]$ in place of $BV_1[a, b]$.

*Example 1.* If $f : [a, b] \to R$ is monotone, then $f \in BV[a, b]$ and $V(f) = |f(b) - f(a)|$. Verification is very simple.

*Example 2.* The function $f : \left[0, \frac{2}{\pi}\right] \to R$ defined by $f(0) = 0$, $f(x) = x \sin \frac{1}{x}$ if $x \neq 0$ is not of bounded variation. See Problem 1.

THEOREM 9–2 I. *If $f$ and $g$ are in $BV_k[a, b]$, so is $f + g$, and*

$$V(f + g) \leq V(f) + V(g). \tag{5}$$

*If $c \in R$, $cf$ is in $BV_k[a, b]$, and*

$$V(cf) = |c|\, V(f). \tag{6}$$

The proof is simple; we leave it to the reader.

If $f \in BV_k[a, b]$, each of the component functions $f_i$ (see (2)) is of bounded variation; conversely, if each $f_i$ is of bounded variation, so is $f$. These facts are clear from (1).

## ADDITIVITY OF THE VARIATION

We now consider subintervals of the basic interval. If $a \leq \alpha < \beta \leq b$, a partition of $[\alpha, \beta]$ can always be extended so as to yield a partition of $[a, b]$. From this we can see at once that $V_{\alpha\beta}(f) \leq V_{ab}(f)$. The following theorem is more precise.

THEOREM 9–2 II. *Suppose $f \in BV_k[a, b]$ and $a < c < b$. Then*

$$V_{ab}(f) = V_{ac}(f) + V_{cb}(f). \tag{7}$$

*Proof.* We now need the more explicit notation $T(\Delta; f; a, b)$ for the expression in (3), to show that the interval being considered is $[a, b]$. Suppose $\Delta$ is any partition of $[a, b]$. If $c$ happens to be a point of $\Delta$, then $\Delta$ determines a partition $\Delta_1$ of $[a, c]$ and a partition $\Delta_2$ of $[c, b]$, and it is clear that

$$T(\Delta; f; a, b) = T(\Delta_1; f; a, c) + T(\Delta_2; f; c, b).$$

Therefore, in this case,

$$T(\Delta; f; a, b) \leq V_{ac}(f) + V_{cb}(f). \tag{8}$$

If $c$ is not a point of $\Delta$, let $\Delta'$ be the refinement of the partition $\Delta$ obtained by adding $c$. If $\Delta = (x_0, x_1, \ldots, x_n)$, we have $x_{i-1} < c < x_i$ for some $i$, and

$$\|f(x_i) - f(x_{i-1})\| \leq \|f(c) - f(x_{i-1})\| + \|f(x_i) - f(c)\|;$$

from this it is clear that

$$T(\Delta; f; a, b) \leq T(\Delta'; f; a, b).$$

But (8) holds with $\Delta'$ in place of $\Delta$, and therefore (8) itself holds in this case. It then follows that

$$V_{ab}(f) \leq V_{ac}(f) + V_{cb}(f). \tag{9}$$

Now, suppose $\epsilon > 0$. There exist partitions $\Delta_1$ of $[a, c]$ and $\Delta_2$ of $[c, b]$ such that $T(\Delta_1; f; a, c) > V_{ac}(f) - \frac{\epsilon}{2}$ and $T(\Delta_2; f; c, b) > V_{cb}(f) - \frac{\epsilon}{2}$. By combining $\Delta_1$ and $\Delta_2$ we get a partition $\Delta$ of $[a, b]$ such that

$$T(\Delta; f; a, b) > V_{ac}(f) + V_{cb}(f) - \epsilon.$$

This proves that $V_{ab}(f) > V_{ac}(f) + V_{cb}(f) - \epsilon$. Since $\epsilon$ is arbitrary we thus have the equality opposite to that in (9), and therefore (7) is proved.

*Remark.* From the argument about $\Delta$ and $\Delta'$ in the foregoing proof we see that if $\Delta'$ is *any* refinement of $\Delta$, we have

$$T(\Delta; f; a, b) \leq T(\Delta'; f; a, b). \tag{10}$$

This is because we can obtain any refinement of $\Delta$ by the successive insertions of a finite number of additional points.

## RIGHT AND LEFT LIMITING VALUES

We recall from Section 9–1 the discussion of right and left limiting values of monotone functions. We use the same notations in the present situation, but we argue in a different way.

THEOREM 9–2 III. *If $f \in BV_k[a, b]$, the limit from the right at $x$, denoted by $f(x+)$, exists if $a \leq x < b$; the limit from the left exists if $a < x \leq b$.*

Before proving these assertions we must reflect a bit on how we can be assured of the existence of $\lim_{t \to x+} f(t)$ without some explicit way of obtaining the limit. We recall that in the case of a monotone function, $f(x+)$ is given as a supremum or an infimum of certain functional values. Here we must depend on a suitable modification of the Cauchy convergence criterion for the completeness of the space $R^k$ in which the functional values lie.

*In order that $f(t)$ shall approach a limit in $R^k$ as $t$ approaches $x$ from the right, the following condition is necessary and sufficient: To each $\epsilon > 0$ there corresponds a $\delta > 0$ such that $\|f(s) - f(t)\| < \epsilon$ if $x < s < t < x + \delta$.* The condition is easily seen to be necessary. As to its sufficiency, when the condition is satisfied, let $\{t_n\}$ be a sequence such that $t_n \to x$ and $t_{n+1} < t_n$. Then $\{f(t_n)\}$ is a Cauchy sequence, and so has a limit in $R^k$. It is easy to prove that $\lim_{n\to\infty} f(t_n)$ satisfies the conditions which enable us to assert that $\lim_{n\to\infty} f(t_n) = \lim_{t\to x+} f(t)$.

*Proof of Theorem* 9–2 III. Suppose now that $f \in BV_k[a, b]$, and suppose $a \leq x < b$. If it were not true that $\lim_{t\to x+} f(t)$ exists, we would have the following situation: For some fixed $\epsilon > 0$ there exist sequences $\{s_n\}$, $\{t_n\}$ on $[a, b]$ such that $x < s_n < t_n < x + \frac{1}{n}$ and $\|f(s_n) - f(t_n)\| \geq \epsilon$. Proceeding from this we shall obtain a contradiction of the fact that $f \in BV_k[a, b]$. Now, given $m$, we can find $n > m$ such that $t_n < s_m$. Let $\{n_i\}$ be a sequence of integers such that $n_1 < n_2 < \cdots$ and $t(n_{i+1}) < s(n_i)$. Here, for convenience in printing, we write $t(n)$ and $s(n)$ in place of $t_n$, $s_n$. Now, let $u_i = s(n_i)$, $v_i = t(n_i)$. For any given $N$ consider the following partition of $[a, b]$:

$$\Delta = (a, u_N, v_N, u_{N-1}, v_{N-1}, \ldots, u_1, v_1, b).$$

Then

$$T(\Delta; f) \geq \sum_{i=1}^{N} \|f(u_i) - f(v_i)\| \geq N\epsilon.$$

Since $N$ can be as large as we please, we obtain the contradiction $V(f) = +\infty$. Hence the limit from the right at $x$ exists. The proof concerning limits from the left is made in the same way.

## POINTS OF DISCONTINUITY

Suppose $f \in BV_k[a, b]$. By the *jump* of $f$ at $x$ we mean the number

$$\|f(x) - f(x-)\| + \|f(x+) - f(x)\|$$

if $a < x < b$, the number $\|f(a+) - f(a)\|$ if $x = a$, and the number $\|f(b) - f(b-)\|$ if $x = b$. Evidently $f$ is continuous at $x$ if and only if the jump of $f$ at $x$ is 0.

THEOREM 9–2 IV. *If $f \in BV_k[a, b]$, the set of points of discontinuity of $f$ is countable. If $f$ is discontinuous at each of the points $x_1, x_2, \ldots$, with jump $A_i$ at $x_i$, then $\sum_i A_i \leq V(f)$.*

*Proof.* We first prove the following auxiliary result: If $y_1, \ldots, y_n$ are distinct points of $[a, b]$ and if $B_i$ is the jump of $f$ at $y_i$, then

$$B_1 + \cdots + B_n \leq V_{ab}(f). \tag{11}$$

We can suppose that $y_1 < y_2 < \cdots < y_n$. Choose any $\epsilon > 0$. If $a < y_1$, we choose points $u_1, v_1$ so that $a < u_1 < y_1 < v_1 < y_2$ in such a way that

$$\|f(y_1) - f(u_1)\| + \|f(v_1) - f(y_1)\| > B_1 - \frac{\epsilon}{n}.$$

If $y_1 = a$ we choose $u_1 = a$ and $v_1$ so that $y_1 < v_1 < y_2$ and $\|f(v_1) - f(y_1)\| > B_1 - \frac{\epsilon}{n}$. We then proceed in a similar fashion to choose points $u_i$, $v_i$ in relation to $y_i$ and $B_i$ for $i = 2, \ldots, n$. We make certain that $v_i < u_{i+1}$ and that $u_i < y_i < v_i$ if $y_i$ is an interior point of $[a, b]$, while $u_n < y_n = v_n$ and $\|f(y_n) - f(u_n)\| > B_n - \frac{\epsilon}{n}$ if $y_n = b$. If we now consider the partition

$$\Delta = (a, u_1, y_1, v_1, u_2, y_2, v_2, \ldots, u_n, y_n, v_n, b),$$

we see that

$$V_{ab}(f) \geq T(\Delta; f) \geq B_1 + \cdots + B_n - \epsilon.$$

Since $\epsilon$ is arbitrary, this proves (11).

Now, let $S_p$ be the set of points in $[a, b]$ at which the jump of $f$ exceeds $1/p$ ($p = 1, 2, \ldots$). The number of points in $S_p$ is finite, for by (11) it cannot exceed $pV_{ab}(f)$. But the union of $S_1, S_2, S_3, \ldots$ is the set of *all* points of discontinuity of $f$; hence this set is countable. The last assertion in the theorem follows from (11).

## THE TOTAL VARIATION AS A FUNCTION

If $f \in BV_k[a, b]$, let us define a function $v : [a, b] \to R$ as follows:

(12) $$v(a) = 0, \qquad v(x) = V_{ax}(f) \quad \text{if} \quad a < x \leq b.$$

THEOREM 9–2 V. *The function $v$ defined in* (12) *is nondecreasing; it is continuous at each point where $f$ is continuous.*

*Proof.* If $a \leq x < y \leq b$, we see from (7) that $v(y) - v(x) = V_{xy}(f) \geq 0$. Hence, $v$ is nondecreasing. Suppose $f$ is continuous at $x$, where $a < x \leq b$. We shall prove that $v(x-) = v(x)$. For this it is sufficient, given $\epsilon > 0$, to find a point $y$ such that $a < y < x$ and $v(x) - v(y) < \epsilon$. Let $\Delta$ be a partition of $[a, x]$ such that $T(\Delta; f; a\ x) > v(x) - \frac{\epsilon}{2}$. Choose a point $y$ such that $a < y < x$, $|f(x) - f(y)| < \epsilon/2$, and such that there is no point of the partition $\Delta$ between $y$ and $x$. Let $\Delta'$ be the partition of $[a, x]$ which results by adding $y$ to the points forming $\Delta$. Then $T(\Delta'; f; a, x) \geq T(\Delta; f; a, x)$. Now let $\Delta''$ be the partition of $[a, y]$ formed by using all the points in $\Delta'$ except $x$. Then

$$v(y) \geq T(\Delta''; f; a, y) = T(\Delta'; f; a, x) - |f(x) - f(y)| > v(x) - \frac{\epsilon}{2} - \frac{\epsilon}{2} = v(x) - \epsilon.$$

This gives us what we need to conclude that $v(x-) = v(x)$. It may be noted that we have made use of the continuity of $f$ only to the extent of using the fact that $f(x-) = f(x)$.

The proof that $f(x+) = f(x)$ implies $v(x+) = v(x)$ when $a \leq x < b$ is similar. We leave details to the reader.

## THE JUMP FUNCTION

Suppose $f \in BV_k[a, b]$. If there are points of discontinuity of $f$ in the interior of $[a, b]$, let them be $x_1, x_2, \ldots$. Then define $s : [a, b] \to R^k$ by the following formulas:

(13) $$\begin{cases} s(a) = f(a) - f(a+) \\ s(x) = f(x) - f(x-) + \sum\limits_{x_i < x} [f(x_i+) - f(x_i-)] \quad \text{if} \quad a < x \leq b. \end{cases}$$

Here it is understood that $s(x) = f(x) - f(x-)$ when $a < x \leq b$ if there are no interior points of discontinuity of $f$. The sum involving the $x_i$ in (13) is unambiguously defined, because if the number of $x_i$'s less than $x$ is infinite, the series

$$\sum_{x_i < x} \|f(x_i+) - f(x_i-)\|$$

is convergent. This may be seen by using Theorem 9–2 IV.

THEOREM 9–2 VI. *The function $s$ defined in (13) is of bounded variation on $[a, b]$. If $F = f - s$, then $F$ is continuous and of bounded variation. Furthermore,*

$$(14) \qquad s(a+) = 0, \qquad s(b-) = \sum_{x_i < b} [f(x_i+) - f(x_i-)]$$

*and*

$$(15) \qquad V_{ab}(s) = J,$$

*where $J$ is the sum of the jumps of $f$ at all its points of discontinuity.*

*Proof.* To begin with, we show that $V_{ab}(s) \leq J$. Let $\Delta = (y_0, y_1, \ldots, y_n)$ be a partition of $[a, b]$. Let us call $\|f(x) - f(x-)\|$ and $\|f(x+) - f(x)\|$ the *left jump* and the *right jump*, respectively, of $f$ at $x$. By a careful examination we see that $\|s(y_j) - s(y_{j-1})\|$ does not exceed the sum of the following jumps: the right jump at $y_{j-1}$, the left jump at $y_j$, and all the jumps at points $x_i$ such that $y_{j-1} < x < y_j$. Therefore, $T(\Delta; s) \leq J$, whence $V_{ab}(s) \leq J$.

Next, we establish (14). Since the points of continuity of $f$ are everywhere dense, it follows that $f(a+)$ is the same as $\lim_{x \to a+} f(x-)$, and likewise $f(b-) = \lim_{x \to b-} f(x-)$. (For the fact that $f(x-)$ has unilateral limiting values see Problem 4.) When $x \to a+$, $f(x) - f(x-) \to 0$, and

$$\lim_{x \to a+} \sum_{x_i < x} [f(x_i+) - f(x_i-)] = 0,$$

as a result of the convergence of the series

$$\sum_i [f(x_i+) - f(x_i-)].$$

This proves that $s(a+) = 0$. The proof relating to $s(b-)$ in (14) is similar.

It follows from (13) and (14) that $F$ is continuous at $a$ and $b$. Let us examine the question of continuity of $F$ at $y$, where $a < y < b$. By arguments like the foregoing it is easy to see that

$$s(y-) = \sum_{x_i < y} [f(x_i+) - f(x_i-)]$$

and

$$s(y+) = \sum_{x_i \leq y} [f(x_i+) - f(x_i-)].$$

We then see that $s(y-) = s(y) - f(y) + f(y-)$, whence

$$F(y-) = f(y-) - s(y-) = f(y) - s(y) = F(y).$$

Likewise, $F(y+) = F(y)$. Thus $F$ is continuous.

Now that we know $F$ is continuous, we see that $s$ has the same jumps as $f$. But then $J \leq V_{ab}(s)$, by Theorem 9–2 IV. Since we already know that $J \geq V_{ab}(s)$, we have the proof of (15).

*Example 3.* Suppose that $f: [a, b] \to R^k$ is a *step-function*, defined as follows. Let $\Delta = (x_0, \ldots, x_n)$ be a partition of $[a, b]$ and let $c_1, \ldots, c_n$ and $f(x_0), f(x_1), \ldots, f(x_n)$ be arbitrary elements of $R^k$. Define $f(x) = c_i$ if $x_{i-1} < x < x_i$. Then $f \in BV_k[a, b]$. The only possible points of discontinuity of $f$ are $x_0, \ldots, x_n$, and

$$V_{ab}(f) = \|c_1 - f(a)\| + \|f(b) - c_n\| + \sum_{i=1}^{n-1} [\|f(x_i) - c_i\| + \|c_{i+1} - f(x_i)\|].$$

We leave it to the reader to verify that $s(x) = f(x) - f(a+)$ in this case.

## PROBLEMS

1. Define $f: \left[0, \frac{2}{\pi}\right] \to R$ by $f(0) = 0$, $f(x) = x \sin \frac{1}{x}$ if $x \neq 0$. Show that $f$ is not of bounded variation, by considering the partitions $\Delta_n$, $n = 1, 2, \ldots$, where $x_i = \dfrac{2}{(2i + 1)\pi}$ and the points in $\Delta_n$ are $0, x_{2n+1}, x_{2n}, \ldots, x_1, x_0$.
2. Suppose $f: [a, b] \to R^k$ is such that $\|f(x) - f(y)\| \leq M|x - y|$ for each $x, y$, where $M$ is a constant depending only on $f$. Show that $f \in BV_k[a, b]$.
3. Suppose $f: [a, b] \to R$ is continuous and such that $f'(x)$ exists as a bounded function when $a < x < b$. Show that $f \in BV[a, b]$.
4. If $f \in BV_k[a, b]$, show that the function $g(x) = f(x-)$, defined when $a < x \leq b$, has limiting values from both sides at points $x$ such that $a < x < b$, and from one side at $x = a$ and $x = b$.
5. Suppose $f \in BV_k[a, b]$. Prove that $f$ is bounded and that $\|f(x)\| \leq \|f(a)\| + V_{ab}(f)$ for each $x$.
6. Prove Theorem 9–2 I.
7. Verify that $s(x) = f(x) - f(a+)$ in Example 3.

## 9–3 Rectifiable curves

There is a close relation between the two concepts: length of a curve and *total variation of a function.*

If $f: [a, b] \to R^k$ is a continuous function, we shall say that it is a *curve in* $R^k$. When $f$ is a homeomorphism, we shall call the curve an *arc in* $R^k$. For certain purposes it may be preferable to define curves and arcs in a different way, so that they are more intrinsically geometric entities. This is perhaps especially true in the case of arcs. For instance, the two functions $f$ and $g$ on $[-1, 1]$ to $R^2$ defined by

$$f(t) = (x_1, x_2), \quad \text{where} \quad x_1 = t, \quad x_2 = t^2,$$

$$g(t) = (x_1, x_2), \quad \text{where} \quad x_1 = t^3, \quad x_2 = t^6,$$

are both arcs. In elementary analytic geometry we regard these arcs as identical, namely as the part of the parabola $x_2 = x_1^2$ corresponding to $-1 \leq x_1 \leq 1$. We observe that in this example there is a homeomorphic mapping $\varphi$ of $[-1, 1]$ onto itself, namely $\varphi(t) = t^3$, such that $g(t) = f(\varphi(t))$. This gives a clue to a general procedure for defining a curve in $R^k$ as a certain equivalence class of continuous mappings $f: [a, b] \to R^k$. We shall not go into this; we retain our original definition of a curve in $R^k$.

We observe that in Section 2–8 we defined an arc as a set which is the homeomorphic image of a compact interval in $R$. That definition illustrates one of the situations where it is convenient to think of an arc directly as a geometric entity.

It should be noted that a curve may have a geometric character far different from what is suggested by the word *curve* in common parlance. For instance, if $f : [0, 4\pi] \to R$ is defined by $f(x) = \sin x$, the image $f(x)$ traces out the line segment $[-1, 1]$ in $R$ four times as $x$ goes from 0 to $4\pi$. If $f : [0, 10\pi] \to R^2$ is defined by $f(t) = (x_1, x_2)$, where $x_1 = \cos t$, $x_2 = \sin t$, the image $f(t)$ traces out the circle $x_1^2 + x_2^2 = 1$ five times as $t$ goes from 0 to $10\pi$. It is clear from these examples that we must distinguish sharply between the curve and the range of the function $f$. An astonishing example is furnished by the "space-filling" curve of Peano, in which we have a curve $f : [0, 1] \to R^2$ with the range of $f$ consisting of all points $(x_1, x_2)$ such that $0 \leq x_1 \leq 1$, $0 \leq x_2 \leq 1$. For reference see Dieudonné [1], p. 80, Hobson [1], Vol. 1, pp. 326–458, Hocking and Young [1], pp. 122–123, Peano [1].

## RECTIFIABILITY

A curve $f : [a, b] \to R^k$ is called rectifiable if $f \in BV_k[a, b]$. The *length* of the curve is then defined to be $V_{ab}(f)$. That this definition is compatible with the definition of length as a limit of lengths of inscribed polygonal lines is made clear by the theorem which follows. We observe that, if $\Delta = (x_0, x_1, \ldots, x_n)$ is a partition of $[a, b]$, the points $f(x_0), f(x_1), \ldots, f(x_n)$ are "in order" along the curve, and $\|f(x_i) - f(x_{i-1})\|$ is the length of the chord joining $f(x_{i-1})$ and $f(x_i)$.

We recall the notation $\|\Delta\| = \max |x_i - x_{i-1}|$ used elsewhere in this book.

THEOREM 9–3 I. *If $f : [a, b] \to R^k$ is a rectifiable curve, then to each $\epsilon > 0$ corresponds a $\delta > 0$ such that*

$$0 \leq V_{ab}(f) - T(\Delta; f) < \epsilon \tag{1}$$

*whenever $\Delta$ is a partition of $[a, b]$ such that $\|\Delta\| < \delta$.*

*Proof.* The essence of the theorem is that, when $f$ is not only of bounded variation, but also continuous, then $T(\Delta; f)$ is near its upper bound whenever $\|\Delta\|$ is sufficiently small.

The first step in the proof makes no use of the continuity of $f$. Suppose $\Delta$ is a fixed partition, and let $\Delta'$ be a refinement of $\Delta$ having $N$ points in addition to those of $\Delta$. Let

$$B = \sup \{\|f(x) - f(y)\| : x, y \in [a, b], |x - y| \leq \|\Delta\|\}.$$

Then, as we shall prove,

$$T(\Delta'; f) \leq T(\Delta; f) + 2NB. \tag{2}$$

To begin with we suppose that $\Delta'$ has just one point $y$ not in the partition $\Delta = (x_0, x_1, \ldots, x_n)$, and we suppose $x_{i-1} < y < x_i$. Then we see that

$$T(\Delta'; f) - T(\Delta; f) = \|f(x_i) - f(y)\| + \|f(y) - f(x_{i-1})\| - \|f(x_i) - f(x_{i-1})\| \leq 2B.$$

The general result (2) now comes by working with the successive partitions $\Delta = \Delta_0$, $\Delta_1, \ldots, \Delta_N = \Delta'$, where $\Delta_j$ is obtained from $\Delta_{j-1}$ by inserting just one new point.

At the second step of our proof we use the continuity. Suppose $\epsilon > 0$. Choose a partition $\Delta_0$ of $[a, b]$ such that $T(\Delta_0; f) > V_{ab}(f) - \dfrac{\epsilon}{2}$. Since $T(\Delta_0; f)$ is not diminished if we replace $\Delta_0$ by a refinement of itself, we may assume that $\Delta_0 = (x_0, x_1, \ldots, x_{N+1})$, where $N > 0$.

Now, $f$ is uniformly continuous, so there exists a $\delta > 0$ such that $\|f(x) - f(y)\| < \frac{\epsilon}{4N}$ if $|x - y| \leq \delta$ and $x, y \in [a, b]$. Suppose that $\Delta$ is any partition for which $\|\Delta\| < \delta$, and let $\Delta'$ be the refinement of $\Delta_0$ and $\Delta$ obtained by using all the distinct points of both $\Delta_0$ and $\Delta$. We see that $\Delta'$ contains at most $N$ points in addition to those of $\Delta$. By (2) we have $T(\Delta';f) - T(\Delta;f) \leq 2N\frac{\epsilon}{4N} = \frac{\epsilon}{2}$ in this case. On adding the inequalities

$$V_{ab}(f) - T(\Delta_0;f) < \frac{\epsilon}{2}$$

$$T(\Delta_0;f) - T(\Delta';f) \leq 0$$

$$T(\Delta';f) - T(\Delta;f) \leq \frac{\epsilon}{2},$$

we obtain the required inequality (1). This ends the proof.

In elementary calculus we are accustomed to calculating the lengths of arcs by integrals. For the case of an arc $f : [a, b] \to R^2$, where the component functions $f_1, f_2$ have continuous derivatives, the elementary calculus formula for the arc-length $L$ is

$$L = \int_a^b [(f_1'(x))^2 + (f_2'(x))^2]^{1/2}\, dx. \tag{3}$$

This formula is derived from a definition which can be written in the form

$$L = \lim_{\|\Delta\| \to 0} T(\Delta;f).$$

Therefore, in view of Theorem 9–3 I, the $L$ of (3) is equal to $V_{ab}(f)$ in this special case. These results are also applicable to arcs in $R^k$, with $k \geq 3$, if the component functions $f_1, \ldots, f_k$ have continuous derivatives.

It remains for later to see how $V_{ab}(f)$ can be expressed by a Lebesgue integral under certain circumstances. See Theorems 9–8 VII, VIII.

## 9–4 Real-valued functions of bounded variation

The structure of a function $f \in BV[a, b]$ is of particular interest. We shall see that $f$ is the difference of two nondecreasing functions. The converse of this is more elementary: If $f_1$ and $f_2$ are nondecreasing functions on $[a, b]$ to $R$, and $f = f_1 - f_2$, then Theorem 9–2 I shows that $f \in BV[a, b]$ and $V_{ab}(f) \leq f_1(b) - f_1(a) + f_2(b) - f_2(a)$ (see also Example 1 in Section 9–2).

### THE POSITIVE AND NEGATIVE VARIATIONS

To analyze $f$ when $f \in BV[a, b]$, we introduce the concepts of positive and negative variation. If $\Delta = (x_0, x_1, \ldots, x_n)$ is a partition of $[a, b]$, let

$$P(\Delta;f) = \sum_i{}^{+} \{f(x_i) - f(x_{i-1})\}, \tag{1}$$

where $\sum_i^{+}$ indicates that only those $i$'s are considered for which $\{f(x_i) - f(x_{i-1})\} \geq 0$.

Likewise, let

(2) $$N(\Delta;f) = -\sum_i^- \{f(x_i) - f(x_{i-1})\},$$

where $\sum_i^-$ indicates that only those $i$'s are considered for which $\{f(x_i) - f(x_{i-1})\} \leq 0$. Note, however, that the definition makes $N(\Delta;f) \geq 0$. The following relations are evident:

(3) $$T(\Delta;f) = P(\Delta;f) + N(\Delta;f),$$

(4) $$P(\Delta;f) - N(\Delta;f) = f(b) - f(a).$$

From (3) and (4) we get

(5) $$2P(\Delta;f) = T(\Delta;f) + f(b) - f(a),$$

(6) $$2N(\Delta;f) = T(\Delta;f) - f(b) + f(a).$$

We also have

$$0 \leq P(\Delta;f) \leq T(\Delta;f), \qquad 0 \leq N(\Delta;f) \leq T(\Delta;f).$$

Taking suprema over all partitions, we define

$$P_{ab}(f) = \sup_\Delta P(\Delta;f),$$

$$N_{ab}(f) = \sup_\Delta N(\Delta;f).$$

These are called the *positive* and *negative* variations, respectively, of $f$ on $[a, b]$. From (5) and (6) we see that

(7) $$2P_{ab}(f) = V_{ab}(f) + f(b) - f(a),$$

(8) $$2N_{ab}(f) = V_{ab}(f) - f(b) + f(a).$$

From (7) and (8) we then have

(9) $$P_{ab}(f) + N_{ab}(f) = V_{ab}(f),$$

(10) $$P_{ab}(f) - N_{ab}(f) = f(b) - f(a).$$

Since $f \in BV[a, b]$ implies $f \in BV[a, x]$ when $a < x \leq b$, we can consider the variations $P_{ax}(f)$, $N_{ax}(f)$, $V_{ax}(f)$. For completeness we define

(11) $$P_{aa}(f) = N_{aa}(f) = V_{aa}(f) = 0.$$

We have relations like (7)–(10) with $x$ in place of $b$. We already know (Theorem 9–2 V) that $V_{ax}(f)$ is a nondecreasing function of $x$.

THEOREM 9–4 I. *The functions $P_{ax}(f)$ and $N_{ax}(f)$ are nondecreasing functions of $x$.*

*Proof.* Let $g(x) = V_{ax}(f) - f(x)$, $h(x) = V_{ax}(f) + f(x)$. We shall prove that $g$ is nondecreasing. The proof that $h$ is nondecreasing is similar. If $a \leq x < y \leq b$, we have

(12) $$f(y) - f(x) \leq |f(y) - f(x)| \leq V_{xy}(f).$$

Also, with the help of (12) and Theorem 9–2 II, we see that

$$\begin{aligned} g(y) - g(x) &= V_{ay}(f) - f(y) - V_{ax}(f) + f(x) \\ &= V_{xy}(f) - [f(y) - f(x)] \geq 0. \end{aligned}$$

Hence, $g$ is nondecreasing; likewise for $h$. Since (see (7) and (8))

$$P_{ax}(f) = \tfrac{1}{2}[h(x) - f(a)]$$

and

$$N_{ax}(f) = \tfrac{1}{2}[g(x) + f(a)],$$

the theorem is proved.

We can now discuss the structure of $f$.

THEOREM 9–4 II. *If $f \in BV[a, b]$, there exist nonnegative nondecreasing functions $f_1, f_2$ defined on $[a, b]$ such that $f = f_1 - f_2$. If $f$ is continuous at a certain point $x$, so are $V_{ax}(f)$, $P_{ax}(f)$, and $N_{ax}(f)$. The functions $f_1$ and $f_2$ can be chosen so that, if $f$ is continuous at $x$, so are $f_1$ and $f_2$.*

*Proof.* Let

(13) $$f_1(x) = P_{ax}(f) + \tfrac{1}{2}\{f(a) + |f(a)|\}$$

(14) $$f_2(x) = N_{ax}(f) + \tfrac{1}{2}\{|f(a)| - f(a)\}.$$

Then $f_1$ and $f_2$ are nondecreasing, by Theorem 9–4 I; they are evidently nonnegative. We see that

$$f_1(x) - f_2(x) = P_{ax}(f) - N_{ax}(f) + f(a) = f(x).$$

Here, we have used (10) with $x$ in place of $b$.

Now, suppose $f$ is continuous at $x_0$. Then $V_{ax}(f)$ is continuous at $x_0$, by Theorem 9–2 V. Hence, $P_{ax}(f)$ and $N_{ax}(f)$ are continuous at $x_0$, by (7) and (8) with $x$ in place of $b$. It follows that $f_1$ and $f_2$ are continuous at $x_0$, and the proof is complete.

We remark that the representation of $f$ as the difference of two nondecreasing functions is not unique. The functions $f_1$ and $f_2$ in (13) and (14) have unique qualities, however. If $\varphi_1$ and $\varphi_2$ are any nondecreasing functions such that $f = \varphi_1 - \varphi_2$, it is easy to see that $f(y) - f(x) \le \varphi_1(y) - \varphi_1(x)$ whenever $a \le x < y \le b$. The function $f_1$ in (13) has the property that $f_1(a) = f(a) \vee 0$. Now, let $\Phi$ be the class of all nondecreasing functions $\varphi : [a, b] \to R$ such that $\varphi(a) \ge f(a) \vee 0$ and such that $f(y) - f(x) \le \varphi(y) - \varphi(x)$ whenever $a \le x < y \le b$. By appealing to the definition of $P_{ax}(f)$ it is not difficult to see that $f_1 \le \varphi$ for each such $\varphi$. Since $f_1 \in \Phi$, it follows that

$$f_1(x) = \inf \{\varphi(x) : \varphi \in \Phi\}.$$

A similar characterization can be given for $f_2$.

## 9–5 Stieltjes integrals

A Stieltjes integral is a generalization of a Riemann integral. It was originally conceived by Stieltjes as an analytical tool in connection with the investigation of continued fractions (see Stieltjes [1]). The Stieltjes integral involves two functions: the "integrand" $f$ and the "integrator" $\varphi$. The integral, denoted by

$$\int_a^b f(x)\, d\varphi(x),$$

is defined as the limit (if it exists)

(1) $$\int_a^b f(x)\, d\varphi(x) = \lim_{\|\Delta\| \to 0} \sum_{i=1}^{n} f(t_i)[\varphi(x_i) - \varphi(x_{i-1})],$$

where $\Delta = (x_0, x_1, \ldots, x_n)$ is an arbitrary partition of $[a, b]$ and $t_i$ is an arbitrarily chosen point in $[x_{i-1}, x_i]$. This limit does exist if, for instance, $f : [a, b] \to R$ is continuous and $\varphi \in BV[a, b]$. If $\varphi(x) = x$, we obtain the Riemann integral of $f$ as a special case.

Without changing the form of the definition of the integral we may enlarge the field of choice of the functions $f$, $\varphi$. We consider three possibilities.

I: $f$ and $\varphi$ are complex-valued functions defined on $[a, b]$ (the values may of course be real, as a special case).

II: $f$ has values in $R$ and $\varphi$ has values in $R^k$.

III: $f$ has values in $R^k$ and $\varphi$ has values in $R$.

In cases II and III the terms in the sum on the right in (1) are vectors in $R^k$. In case III $f(t_i)$ is a vector and $\varphi(x_i) - \varphi(x_{i-1})$ is a scalar; we understand that a scalar factor written after a vector means the same as if the factor were written on the left of the vector. In all cases we say that $f$ is $S$-integrable with respect to $\varphi$ if the limit in (1) exists. This means that for each $\epsilon > 0$ there is some $\delta > 0$ such that

$$\left\| \int_a^b f(x)\, d\varphi(x) - \sum_{i=1}^n f(t_i)[\varphi(x_i) - \varphi(x_{i-1})] \right\| < \epsilon$$

provided merely that $\|\Delta\| < \delta$, for all admissible choices of the points $t_1, \ldots, t_n$.

These three cases do not exhaust the possibilities of using (1) as a definition of an integral, but we shall confine our considerations to these cases. There are useful generalizations in which the values of $f$ or $\varphi$ are in a Banach space. One may also consider the case in which the multiplication of $f(t_i)$ and $[\varphi(x_i) - \varphi(x_{i-1})]$ is taken to mean the action of a linear operator on a vector. Thus, for instance, we might have $\varphi \in BV_k[a, b]$ and $f$ a continuous function whose values are linear transformations in $R^k$.

The case I, when $f$ and $\varphi$ are both complex-valued, with $f$ continuous and $\varphi$ of bounded variation, is precisely the case which occurs in the classical theory of complex functions when we define the contour integral

$$\int_C g(z)\, dz, \tag{2}$$

where $C$ is a rectifiable arc in the plane and $g$ is a continuous complex-valued function defined on $C$. Suppose $C$ has the parametric representation $z = \varphi(t)$, $a \le t \le b$, where $\varphi$ is of bounded variation, as well as being a homeomorphism. Let $f(t) = g(\varphi(t))$. Then $f$ is continuous, and the usual definition of the contour integral shows that

$$\int_C g(z)\, dz = \int_a^b f(t)\, d\varphi(t).$$

In our discussion of the Stieltjes integral (1) we shall use notation appropriate to case I ($f$ and $\varphi$ complex-valued). By using norms instead of absolute values in appropriate places, the arguments in Theorems 9–5 I, II apply to cases II and III as well.

We shall not make a full investigation of necessary and sufficient conditions for $f$ to be $S$-integrable with respect to $\varphi$. The case of main interest is when $f$ is continuous and $\varphi$ is of bounded variation, or vice versa.

For a valuable survey article dealing with Stieltjes integrals see Hildebrandt [3]. See also Bray [1].

Our first theorem exhibits the "integration by parts" formula connecting the integral of $f$ with respect to $\varphi$ and the integral of $\varphi$ with respect to $f$.

THEOREM 9–5 I. *If $f$ is S-integrable with respect to $\varphi$, then $\varphi$ is S-integrable with respect to $f$, and*

(3) $$\int_a^b f(x)\,d\varphi(x) + \int_a^b \varphi(x)\,df(x) = f(b)\varphi(b) - f(a)\varphi(a).$$

*Proof.* Let $\Delta = (x_0, x_1, \ldots, x_n)$ be a partition of $[a, b]$ and let points $t_1, \ldots, t_n$ be chosen in any way so that $x_{i-1} \leq t_i \leq x_i$. Let $t_0 = a$, $t_{n+1} = b$. Then the points $t_0, t_1, \ldots, t_{n+1}$ determine a partition of $[a, b]$, although these points are not necessarily all distinct. It can happen that $t_i = t_{i+1}$, but certainly $t_i < t_{i+2}$, because $t_i \leq x_i < x_{i+1} \leq t_{i+2}$. Let us denote by $\Delta_\tau$ the partition determined by the aggregate $\tau = (t_0, \ldots, t_{n+1})$. It is evident that $\|\Delta_\tau\| \leq 2\,\|\Delta\|$.

Let us now write

$$T = \sum_{i=1}^{n} \varphi(t_i)[f(x_i) - f(x_{i-1})],$$

$$U = \sum_{i=0}^{n} f(x_i)[\varphi(t_{i+1}) - \varphi(t_i)].$$

Since $t_i \leq x_i \leq t_{i+1}$, we see that $U$ is a sum of the type which approximates the $S$-integral of $f$ with respect to $\varphi$; it is based on the partition $\Delta_\tau$. An easy calculation shows that

(4) $$T + U = f(b)\varphi(b) - f(a)\varphi(a).$$

We see that $\|\Delta\| \to 0$ implies $\|\Delta_\tau\| \to 0$, and therefore also

$$U \to \int_a^b f(x)\,d\varphi(x),$$

by our hypothesis about $f$ and $\varphi$. But then (4) shows that $T$ approaches a limit as $\|\Delta\| \to 0$. This means that $\varphi$ is $S$-integrable with respect to $f$; relation (3) is obtained from (4) as we pass to the limit.

The next theorem is our main integrability theorem.

THEOREM 9–5 II. *If $f$ is continuous on $[a, b]$ and $\varphi$ is of bounded variation on $[a, b]$ then $f$ is S-integrable with respect to $\varphi$.*

*Proof.* The first step in the argument involves an examination of what happens to the sum in (1) when we pass to a new partition which is a refinement of $\Delta$. For notational convenience let us write

$$\sigma(\Delta; \tau) = \sum_{i=1}^{n} f(t_i)[\varphi(x_i) - \varphi(x_{i-1})].$$

Here, $\Delta$ denotes the partition $(x_0, x_1, \ldots, x_n)$ and $\tau$ denotes the aggregate of $t$-values. Now let

(5) $$M = \sup\{|f(x) - f(y)| : x, y \in [a, b],\ |x - y| \leq \|\Delta\|\}.$$

Let $\Delta'$ be any refinement of $\Delta$ and let $\tau'$ denote the aggregate of $t$-values used in forming the sum corresponding to $\Delta'$; here $\tau'$ is quite independent of $\tau$. Under these conditions we shall establish that

(6) $$|\sigma(\Delta; \tau) - \sigma(\Delta'; \tau')| \leq M V_{ab}(\varphi).$$

This part of the argument uses only the boundedness of $f$, not the continuity.

For $\Delta'$ suppose the new points (if any) between $x_{i+1}$ and $x_i$ are $y_1, \ldots, y_p$, and let the $p + 1$ corresponding points of $\tau'$ be $u_1, \ldots, u_{p+1}$. Thus we have

$$x_{i-1} \leq u_1 \leq y_1 \leq u_2 \leq y_2 \leq \cdots \leq y_p \leq u_{p+1} \leq x_i.$$

Now, so far as $[x_{i-1}, x_i]$ is concerned, the contribution to $\sigma(\Delta'; \tau')$ is

$$\sum_{j=1}^{p+1} f(u_j)[\varphi(y_j) - \varphi(y_{j-1})], \tag{7}$$

where we write $y_0 = x_{i-1}$, $y_{p+1} = x_i$. The corresponding contribution to $\sigma(\Delta; \tau)$, which is $f(t_i)[\varphi(x_i) - \varphi(x_{i-1})]$, can be written in the form

$$\sum_{j=1}^{p+1} f(t_i)[\varphi(y_j) - \varphi(y_{j-1})]. \tag{8}$$

The magnitude of the difference of the sums in (7) and (8) does not exceed

$$M \sum_{j=1}^{p+1} |\varphi(y_j) - \varphi(y_{j-1})|.$$

Therefore, considering $i = 1, \ldots, n$, we see that

$$|\sigma(\Delta; \tau) - \sigma(\Delta'; \tau')| \leq MT(\Delta'; \varphi) \leq MV_{ab}(\varphi).$$

This is precisely (6).

We now go to the second step of the proof. Let $\Delta_n$ be the partition which divides $[a, b]$ into $2^n$ equal subintervals. Let $M_n$ be the $M$ of (5) when $\Delta = \Delta_n$. Let $\tau_n$ be the set of $t_i$'s given by $t_i = x_{i-1}$. Since $\|\Delta_n\| = (b - a)2^{-n}$, the fact that $f$ is uniformly continuous implies that $M_n \to 0$. If $m < n$, $\Delta_n$ is a refinement of $\Delta_m$. Therefore, by (6),

$$|\sigma(\Delta_n; \tau_n) - \sigma(\Delta_m; \tau_m)| \leq M_m V_{ab}(\varphi),$$

and it follows from this that $\{\sigma(\Delta_n; \tau_n)\}$ is a Cauchy sequence. Denote the limit of this sequence by $A$.

Now let $\Delta$ be any partition. Let $\Delta_n'$ be the partition obtained by taking the points of $\Delta$ together with those of $\Delta_n$. Then $\Delta_n'$ is a refinement of $\Delta$ as well as of $\Delta_n$. We use the notations $\tau$, $M$ as in the first step of the proof, and we let $\tau_n'$ be a set of points for evaluating $f$ in connection with $\Delta_n'$. Then

$$|\sigma(\Delta; \tau) - A| \leq |\sigma(\Delta; \tau) - \sigma(\Delta_n'; \tau_n')| \\ + |\sigma(\Delta_n'; \tau_n') - \sigma(\Delta_n; \tau_n)| + |\sigma(\Delta_n; \tau_n) - A|,$$

whence

$$|\sigma(\Delta; \tau) - A| \leq MV_{ab}(\varphi) + M_n V_{ab}(\varphi) + |\sigma(\Delta_n; \tau_n) - A|.$$

Now, $\sigma(\Delta_n; \tau_n) \to A$, $M_n \to 0$, and $M \to 0$ as $\|\Delta\| \to 0$; it is therefore clear that $\sigma(\Delta; \tau) \to A$ as $\|\Delta\| \to 0$. This shows that $f$ is $S$-integrable with respect to $\varphi$, the integral being equal to $A$.

The integral $\int_a^b f(x)\, d\varphi(x)$ is linear in $f$; that is, if $f_1$ and $f_2$ are $S$-integrable with respect to $\varphi$, so is $f_1 + f_2$, and the integral of $f_1 + f_2$ is the sum of the integrals of $f_1 + f_2$. Also, $cf_1$ is $S$-integrable with respect to $\varphi$, and the integral of $cf_1$ is $c$ times the integral of $f_1$ ($c$ a real constant). There are corresponding assertions which can be briefly summed up by saying that the integral of $f$ with respect to $\varphi$ is linear in $\varphi$. The proofs come directly from the definition of the integral.

Another useful property of the integral has to do with subdividing the interval. Suppose $a < c < b$. If $f$ is $S$ integrable with respect to $\varphi$ on $[a, b]$, the same is true on $[a, c]$ and $[c, b]$, and

$$\int_a^b f(x)\, d\varphi(x) = \int_a^c f(x)\, d\varphi(x) + \int_c^b f(x)\, d\varphi(x). \tag{9}$$

See Problem 6.

### THE INTEGRAL WHEN $\varphi$ IS A STEP-FUNCTION

Let us calculate $\int_a^b f(x)\, d\varphi(x)$ on the assumption that $f$ is $S$-integrable with respect to $\varphi$ and that $\varphi$ is a step-function. Let $(a_0, a_1, \ldots, a_n)$ be an arbitrary partition of $[a, b]$. Let $c_1, \ldots, c_n$ be arbitrary values, with $\varphi(x) = c_i$ if $a_{i-1} < x < a_i$, $i = 1, \ldots, n$. Because of the assumed integrability, we can compute the integral as a limit of sums formed with respect to partitions $\Delta_1, \Delta_2, \ldots$, where $\Delta_p$ is a refinement of $(a_0, a_1, \ldots, a_n)$ formed by dividing each interval $[a_{i-1}, a_i]$ into $p + 1$ equal parts. Let the points of subdivision of $[a_{i-1}, a_i]$ in $\Delta_p$ be $y_0, y_1, \ldots, y_{p+1}$, where $a_{i-1} = y_0 < y_1 < \cdots < y_{p+1} = a_i$. In forming the corresponding terms in the approximating sum, let $f$ be evaluated at $y_0, y_2, \ldots, y_p$ (note the irregularity in the case of the first subinterval, where we use the left endpoint, whereas the right endpoint is used in all other cases). Since $\varphi(y_j) - \varphi(y_{j-1}) = 0$ if $j = 2, \ldots, p$, from this part of $\Delta_p$ we get the sum

$$f(a_{i-1})\,[c_i - \varphi(a_{i-1})] + f(a_i)[\varphi(a_i) - c_i].$$

When we sum on $i$ from 1 to $n$, there is a certain amount of cancellation; the complete approximating sum corresponding to $\Delta_p$ turns out to be

$$f(a_0)[c_1 - \varphi(a_0)] + \sum_{i=1}^{n-1} f(a_i)[c_{i+1} - c_i] + f(a_n)[\varphi(a_n) - c_n].$$

This is independent of $p$, and so it is actually the value of the integral. The result can be written in the form

$$\int_a^b f(x)\, d\varphi(x) = \sum_{i=0}^{n} f(a_i)\Big[\varphi(a_i+) - \varphi(a_i-)\Big] \tag{10}$$

if we make the convention that

$$\varphi(a_0-) = \varphi(a) \quad\text{and}\quad \varphi(a_n+) = \varphi(b).$$

Later on we shall be able to generalize formula (10) to the case in which $\varphi$ is the jump function derived from an arbitrary function of bounded variation. (See (7) in Section 9–6.)

### CONTINUOUS LINEAR FUNCTIONALS ON $C[a, b]$

The Banach space $C[a, b]$ of all continuous functions $f : [a, b] \to R$ is naturally of great interest in analysis (see Section 3–15). There is a very close relationship between $C[a, b]$ and $BV[a, b]$. The following theorem is due to F. Riesz (the original source is Riesz [1].)

THEOREM 9–5 III. *If $\Phi$ is a continuous linear functional on $C[a, b]$, there is a $\varphi \in BV[a, b]$ such that*

(11) $$\Phi(f) = \int_a^b f(x)\, d\varphi(x)$$

*for each $f \in C[a, b]$. Moreover*

(12) $$\|\Phi\| = V_{ab}(\varphi).$$

We shall not go into the details of the proof of this theorem. The proof is not very difficult; there is an initial step of extending the definition of the functional $\Phi$ so that it can be applied to certain rather simple discontinuous functions. Riesz did this directly. It may also be done by applying a general extension theorem known as the Hahn-Banach theorem. After this initial step the argument is quite straight-forward. The reader may refer to Taylor [2], 195–200 for a full account.

We have pointed out in connection with Theorem 8–7 IV how this theorem of Riesz (Theorem 9–5 III) has been transformed and generalized in the course of the evolution of the theory of integration. In its original form, the theorem is quite independent of the ideas which are central in Lebesgue's theory of measure and integration.

The correspondence between $\Phi$ and $\varphi$ in Theorem 9–5 III is not one-to-one; $\varphi$ may be changed by adding an arbitrary constant, and its values at the points of discontinuity of $\varphi$ in the interior of $[a, b]$ may be changed at will without affecting formula (11), though such changes may affect formula (12). These matters are discussed in Taylor [2].

It is clear that if $\varphi$ is any given element of $BV[a, b]$, formula (11) may be used to define a continuous linear functional on $C[a, b]$. For, the integral is linear in $f$, and

(13) $$\left|\int_a^b f(x)\, d\varphi(x)\right| \leq \|f\|\, V_{ab}(\varphi),$$

where $\|f\| = \sup\{f(x) : a \leq x \leq b\}$. Thus the $\Phi$ defined by (11) always satisfies the relation $\|\Phi\| \leq V_{ab}(\varphi)$. It is only under certain special conditions on $\varphi$ that (12) holds.

## PROBLEMS

1. Suppose $f(x) = 1$ if $0 \leq x \leq 1$ and $f(x) = 0$ if $1 < x \leq 2$. Suppose $\varphi(x) = 1$ if $0 \leq x < 1$ and $\varphi(x) = 2$ if $1 \leq x \leq 2$. Show that $f$ is $S$-integrable with respect to $\varphi$ on $[0, 1]$ and $[1, 2]$, but not on $[0, 2]$. Calculate $\int_0^1 f(x)\, d\varphi(x)$ and $\int_1^2 f(x)\, d\varphi(x)$.

2. If $f : [a, b] \to R$ is integrable in the Riemann sense and $\varphi : [a, b] \to R$ has a continuous derivative $\varphi'$ defined on $[a, b]$, then $f$ is $S$-integrable with respect to $\varphi$, and the integral is equal to the Riemann integral $\int_a^b f(x)\varphi'(x)\, dx$.

3. If $f : [a, b] \to R$ is bounded and $S$-integrable with respect to $\varphi$ and $\varphi : [a, b] \to R$ has a continuous derivative $\varphi'$ on $[a, b]$, then $f\varphi'$ is Riemann-integrable, and $\int_a f(x)\, d\varphi(x) = \int_a^d f(x)\varphi'(x)\, dx$.

4. Suppose $f \in C[a, b]$ and $\varphi \in BV[a, b]$. Define $F$ by $F(a) = 0$, $F(x) = \int_a^x f(t)\, d\varphi(t)$ if $a < x \leq b$.

Let $v(x) = V_{ax}(\varphi)$. Show that $F \in BV[a, b]$ and $V_{ax}(F) \le \int_a^x |f(t)|\, dv(x)$. Show also that $F(x+) - F(x) = f(x)[\varphi(x+) - \varphi(x)]$ if $a \le x < b$. What is the value of $F(x) - F(x-)$?

5. Suppose $f$ and $g$ are in $C[a, b]$ and $\varphi \in BV[a, b]$. Let $\psi(x) = \int_a^x g(t)\, d\varphi(t)$ if $a < x \le b$, and $\psi(a) = 0$. Show that $\psi \in BV[a, b]$ and $\int_a^b f(x)\, d\psi(x) = \int_a^b f(x)g(x)\, d\varphi(x)$.

6. Prove the assertion made in connection with (9). Observe that (9) is easily proved once it is known that all three integrals exist. To show that the integrals on the right in (9) exist if the one on the left exists, observe the following suggestions. Use $\Delta^1$, $\Delta^2$ to denote partitions of $[a, c]$ and $[c, b]$, respectively, and let $\Delta = (\Delta^1, \Delta^2)$ be the resulting partition of $[a, b]$. Use notations $\tau^1$, $\tau^2$ and $\tau = (\tau^1, \tau^2)$ in a similar way for aggregates of points at which to evaluate $f$, so that $\sigma(\Delta; \tau) = \sigma(\Delta^1; \tau^2) + \sigma(\Delta^2; \tau^2)$. Let $I = \int_a^b f(x)\, d\varphi(x)$. Choose a sequence $\{\Delta_n^1\}$ such that $\|\Delta_n^1\| \to 0$, and choose some corresponding sequence $\{\tau_n^1\}$. Show that $\{\sigma(\Delta_n^1; \tau_n^1)\}$ is a Cauchy sequence, with some limit $A$. Suitable choice of $\Delta^2$, dependent on an $\epsilon$, but independent of $n$, is indicated. A similar procedure will lead to a limit $B$ associated with $[c, b]$, and it can then be seen that $I = A + B$. It remains to show that $\sigma(\Delta^2; \tau^2) \to B$ as $\|\Delta^2\| \to 0$, and that $\sigma(\Delta^1; \tau^1) \to A$ as $\|\Delta^1\| \to 0$.

7. (a) Suppose $g : [a, b] \to R^*$ is $L$-integrable over $[a, b]$. Define $\varphi : [a, b] \to R$ by $\varphi(x) = \int_a^x g(t)\, dt$, where the integral is a Lebesgue integral over $[a, x]$. Show that $\varphi \in BV[a, b]$, with $V_{ab}(\varphi) \le \int_a^b |g(t)| dt$.

(b) Now assume that $f \in C[a, b]$. With $g$, $\varphi$ as in (a) show that

$$\int_a^b f(x)\, d\varphi(x) = \int_a^b f(t)g(t)\, dt,$$

where the integral on the right is a Lebesgue integral.

8. Suppose that $v : R \to R$ is nondecreasing and right-continuous. Let $\mu$ be the measure induced by $v$ by Method I, Section 4–10. Assuming that $f \in C[a, b]$, show that

$$\int_a^b f(x)\, dv(x) = \int_E f\, d\mu,$$

where $E = \{x : a < x \le b\}$.

## 9–6 Convergence theorems for functions of bounded variation

The following theorem, often called the Helly selection theorem, is of considerable importance as a technical tool in working with functions of bounded variation. The theorem is named after E. Helly (1884–1943).

THEOREM 9–6 I. *Let $\{f_n\}$ be a sequence in $BV[a, b]$. Suppose there is a constant $M$ such that*

(1) $$|f_n(x)| \le M \quad \textit{for} \quad x \in [a, b] \quad \textit{and} \quad n = 1, 2, \ldots$$

*and*

(2) $$V_{ab}(f_n) \le M \quad \textit{for each } n.$$

*Then there is a subsequence of $\{f_n\}$ which converges pointwise on $[a, b]$ to a limit function $f$ which is in $BV[a, b]$.*

*Proof*. We know that $V_{ax}(f_n)$ is nondecreasing as $x$ increases. We also know (see the proof of Theorem 9–4 I) that $V_{ax}(f_n) - f_n(x)$ is nondecreasing as $x$ increases. Observe that $0 \leq V_{ax}(f_n) \leq M$ and $|V_{ax}(f_n) - f_n(x)| \leq 2M$. Let us write

$$\varphi_n(x) = V_{ax}(f_n), \qquad \psi_n(x) = \varphi_n(x) - f_n(x),$$

so that $f_n = \varphi_n - \psi_n$. We shall prove that there is a subsequence of $\{\varphi_n\}$, say $\varphi_{n_1}, \varphi_{n_2}, \ldots$ such that $\varphi_{n_i}(x)$ converges to a real limit $\varphi(x)$ as $i \to \infty$ (for each $x$) and such that $\varphi$ is nondecreasing. An application of the same reasoning will show that the sequence $\psi_{n_1}, \psi_{n_2}, \ldots$ has a subsequence which converges pointwise to a function $\psi$ which is nondecreasing. It will then be clear that $f = \varphi - \psi$ is of bounded variation and that a subsequence of $\{f_n\}$ converges pointwise to $f$.

We arrange the rest of the proof in steps.

*Step 1.* Let $E$ be a countable set dense on $[a, b]$ and such that $a \in E$. Let $x_1, x_2, \ldots$ be an enumeration of $E$. Since $|\varphi_n(x_1)| \leq M$ for all $n$, $\{\varphi_n(x_1)\}$ contains a convergent subsequence, which we denote by $\{\varphi_{n1}(x_1)\}$. Since $|\varphi_{n1}(x_2)| \leq M$, $\{\varphi_{n1}(x_2)\}$ contains a convergent subsequence $\{\varphi_{n2}(x_2)\}$. Continuing in this way, we use the familiar "diagonal procedure", and the sequence $\{\varphi_{nn}(x)\}$ is convergent to a finite limit for each $x$ in $E$.

*Step 2.* We now define

$$\varphi(x) = \begin{cases} \lim\limits_{n\to\infty} \varphi_{nn}(x) & \text{if } x \in E, \\ \sup\{\varphi(x_i) : x_i < x\} & \text{if } x \in [a, b] - E. \end{cases}$$

Since $\varphi_{nn}$ is a nondecreasing function, it is clear that $\varphi(x_i) \leq \varphi(x_j)$ if $x_i < x_j$. We leave it for the reader to check that $\varphi$ is a nondecreasing function on $[a, b]$.

*Step 3.* Next, we prove that $\varphi_{nn}(x) \to \varphi(x)$ if $\varphi$ is continuous at $x$. We can assume that $a < x$, because $a \in E$ and $\varphi_{nn}(x) \to \varphi(x)$ if $x \in E$. We deal with the case in which $a < x < b$. The principle is essentially the same if $x = b$. Supposing $\epsilon > 0$, choose points $x_i$, $x_j$ in $E$ so that $x_i < x < x_j$ and $\varphi(x_j) - \varphi(x_i) < \epsilon$. Then $\varphi(x) - \epsilon < \varphi(x_i)$ and $\varphi(x_j) < \varphi(x) + \epsilon$. Now, $\varphi_{nn}(x_i) \to \varphi(x_i)$ and $\varphi_{nn}(x_j) \to \varphi(x_j)$ as $n \to \infty$. Hence, for all sufficiently large values of $n$ we shall have

$$\varphi(x) - \epsilon < \varphi_{nn}(x_i) \leq \varphi_{nn}(x) \leq \varphi_{nn}(x_j) < \varphi(x) + \epsilon;$$

therefore $\varphi_{nn}(x) \to \varphi(x)$.

*Step 4.* It remains to consider the points of $[a, b] - E$ at which $\varphi$ is discontinuous. The set $F$ of such points is countable. Hence, by the argument of Step 1, applied to $\{\varphi_{nn}\}$, we get a subsequence of $\{\varphi_{nn}\}$ which converges to a limit at each point of $F$. This subsequence is convergent to $\varphi(x)$ at the points of $[a, b] - F$. Hence, if we redefine $\varphi(x)$ suitably at the points of $F$, the subsequence converges to $\varphi(x)$ for every $x$. The modified $\varphi$ is still nondecreasing, because it is the limit of a sequence of nondecreasing functions. This finishes the proof.

We have no immediate need of Theorem 9–6 I, but the reader may find it interesting to know of a significant application of this theorem. For that reason we mention that Theorem 9–6 I plays a part in the consideration of *the moment problem of Hausdorff*. This problem is to determine conditions on a sequence of numbers $c_0, c_1, c_2, \ldots$ which will give assurance that there is some function $\varphi \in BV[0, 1]$ such that

$$\int_0^1 x^n \, d\varphi(x) = c_n, \qquad n = 0, 1, 2, \ldots$$

For a discussion of this problem see Chapter 3 in Widder [1]; the application of Theorem 9–6 I comes on p. 104 of Widder's book. Under suitable conditions the function $\varphi$ is obtained as a limit of a sequence of step functions. Theorem 9–6 II, which we consider next, also has an application in the moment problem.

These Theorems 9–6 I, II belong to a general class of theorems which in functional analysis are known as theorems on *the weak convergence of linear functionals.* The connection with linear functionals is through Theorem 9–5 III, of course. Theorem 9–6 I is related to the concept of *weak compactness* for functionals. See Section 4.41 and Section 4.61 in Taylor [2].

The next main result is a convergence theorem for integrals. Before stating the theorem we take note of something which will be useful to us. Suppose $\{f_n\}$ is a sequence of functions, with $f_n \in BV_k[a, b]$ for each $n$. Suppose also that $f_n(x) \to f(x)$ (limit in $R^k$) for each $x$. Then

$$V_{ab}(f) \leq \liminf_{n\to\infty} V_{ab}(f_n). \tag{3}$$

Hence, if the sequence $\{V_{ab}(f_n)\}$ is bounded, we can conclude that $f \in BV_k[a, b]$. The proof of (3) is easy; we leave it to the reader.

THEOREM 9–6 II. *Suppose $f \in C[a, b]$, that $\{\varphi_n\}$ is a sequence in $BV[a, b]$ such that $\{V_{ab}(\varphi_n)\}$ is bounded, and that $\lim_{n\to\infty} \varphi_n(x) = \varphi(x)$ exists (finite) for each $x$. Then*

$$\int_a^b f(x)\, d\varphi_n(x) \to \int_a^b f(x)\, d\varphi(x). \tag{4}$$

*Proof.* It follows from (3) that $\varphi \in BV[a, b]$. The proof of (4) now depends on obtaining a controlled estimate of the difference

$$\int_a^b f(x)\, d\varphi_n(x) - \sum_{i=1}^{p} f(x_i)[\varphi_n(x_i) - \varphi_n(x_{i-1})], \tag{5}$$

where $\Delta = (x_0, \ldots, x_p)$ is a partition of $[a, b]$. We shall show that for a given $\epsilon > 0$ we can choose $\Delta$ in such a way that for all $n$ the magnitude of the difference in (5) does not exceed $\epsilon/3$, and also so that this same estimate holds when $\varphi_n$ is replaced by $\varphi$. In fact, let $M = \sup_n V_{ab}(\varphi_n)$. Then $V_{ab}(\varphi) \leq M$, by (3). Now, let $\Delta$ be chosen with $\|\Delta\|$ so small that $|f(x) - f(y)| < \epsilon/3M$ if $|x - y| \leq \|\Delta\|$. Then

$$\left|\int_{x_{i-1}}^{x_i} f(x)\, d\varphi_n(x) - f(x_i)[\varphi_n(x_i) - \varphi_n(x_{i-1})]\right|$$
$$= \left|\int_{x_{i-1}}^{x_i} [f(x) - f(x_i)]\, d\varphi_n(x)\right| \leq \frac{\epsilon}{3M} V_{in},$$

where $V_{in}$ is the total variation of $\varphi_n$ on $[x_{i-1}, x_i]$. Since

$$\int_a^b f(x)\, d\varphi_n(x) = \sum_{i=1}^{p} \int_{x_{i-1}}^{x_i} f(x)\, d\varphi_n(x),$$

we see that

$$\left|\int_a^b f(x)\, d\varphi_n(x) - \sum_{i=1}^{p} f(x_i)[\varphi_n(x_i) - \varphi_n(x_{i-1})]\right| \leq \frac{\epsilon}{3M} \sum_{i=1}^{p} V_{in} = \frac{\epsilon}{3M} V_{ab}(\varphi_n) \leq \frac{\epsilon}{3}.$$

The same result clearly holds with $\varphi$ in place of $\varphi_n$.

It is now evident, from the triangular inequality, that

$$\left|\int_a^b f(x)\,d\varphi_n(x) - \int_a^b f(x)\,d\varphi(x)\right|$$
$$\leq \frac{2\epsilon}{3} + \left|\sum_{i=1}^{p} f(x_i)[\varphi_n(x_i) - \varphi_n(x_{i-1})] - \sum_{i=1}^{p} f(x_i)[\varphi(x_i) - \varphi(x_{i-1})]\right|.$$

The absolute difference on the right approaches 0 as $n \to \infty$, because $\varphi_n(x) \to \varphi(x)$ for each $x$. The conclusion of the theorem now follows.

With the aid of Theorem 9–6 II it is possible to calculate $\int_a^b f(x)\,ds(x)$, where $s$ is the jump function corresponding to an arbitrary function of bounded variation $\varphi$ (see (13) in Section 9–2). For present purposes it is convenient to observe that we can rewrite the definition of $s$ as follows:

$$(6)\qquad \begin{cases} s(a) = \varphi(a) - \varphi(a+), \\ s(x) = \sum\limits_{x_i < x} [\varphi(x_i+) - \varphi(x_i)] + \sum\limits_{x_i \leq x} [\varphi(x_i) - \varphi(x_i-)] \quad \text{if} \quad a < x < b, \\ s(b) = \sum\limits_{x_i < b} [\varphi(x_i+) - \varphi(x_i)] + \sum\limits_{x_i < b} [\varphi(x_i) - \varphi(x_i-)] + \varphi(b) - \varphi(b-). \end{cases}$$

Let us now define $s_n$ by these same formulas, except that in the summation expressions we consider only those $x_i$'s for which $i \leq n$. It is then evident that $s_n(x) \to s(x)$ for each $x$. Also, $s_n(x) = s_n(y)$ if $a < x < y < b$ and if none of the points $x_1, \ldots, x_n$ falls in the interval $[x, y]$. Thus $s_n$ is a step-function whose only points of discontinuity in the open interval $(a, b)$ are at $x_1, \ldots, x_n$. It follows by (10) in Section 9–5 that

$$\int_a^b f(x)\,ds_n(x) = f(a)[s_n(a+) - s_n(a)]$$
$$+ \sum_{i=1}^{n} f(x_i)[s_n(x_i+) - s_n(x_i-)] + f(b)[s_n(b) - s_n(b-)].$$

But, as is not hard to calculate, $s_n(a+) - s_n(a) = \varphi(a+) - \varphi(a)$, $s_n(b) - s_n(b-) = \varphi(b) - \varphi(b-)$, and $s_n(x_i+) - s_n(x_i-) = \varphi(x_i+) - \varphi(x_i-)$ if $i \leq n$. Therefore

$$\int_a^b f(x)\,ds_n(x) = f(a)[\varphi(a+) - \varphi(a)]$$
$$+ \sum_{i=1}^{n} f(x_i)[\varphi(x_i+) - \varphi(x_i-)] + f(b)[\varphi(b) - \varphi(b-)].$$

We can apply Theorem 9–6 II, with $s_n$ and $s$ in place of $\varphi_n$ and $\varphi$. If we then make the convention that

$$\varphi(a-) = \varphi(a) \quad \text{and} \quad \varphi(b+) = \varphi(b),$$

we obtain the formula

$$(7)\qquad \int_a^b f(x)\,ds(x) = \sum_x f(x)[\varphi(x+) - \varphi(x-)],$$

where the sum is extended over all the points of discontinuity of $\varphi$ in $[a, b]$. For clarity we repeat that we assume $f \in C[a, b]$, $\varphi \in BV[a, b]$. The jump function $s$ is defined by (6).

## 9–7 Differentiation of monotone functions

One of the main topics in Section 9–8 is to be the relation between differentiation and Lebesgue integration, as applied to real-valued functions of a real variable. Functions of bounded variation play an important part in these considerations. Because of Theorem 9–4 II, the theory of differentiation of functions of bounded variation can be based on the theory of differentiation of monotone functions. The fundamental result is that a monotone function is differentiable almost everywhere. In order to reach this result (Theorem 9–7 V), we need quite a bit of preparatory work.

### LIMITS SUPERIOR AND INFERIOR

We shall give some definitions in a very general context. Let $X$ be a topological space, and suppose we are given $g : D \to R^*$, where $D \subset X$. We then define a function on $\bar{D}$ to $R^*$, called *the limit superior* of $g$, and denoted by $\bar{L}g$. The value of $\bar{L}g$ at $x$ is written either as $(\bar{L}g)(x)$ or $\limsup_{t\to x} g(t)$. To define $(\bar{L}g)(x)$ let $\mathcal{N}$ be the class of all sets $N = D \cap U$, where $U$ can be any neighborhood of $x$. We assume $x \in \bar{D}$; therefore $N \neq \varnothing$. Then, by definition

$$(1) \qquad (\bar{L}g)(x) = \inf_{N\in\mathcal{N}} \sup\{f(t) : t \in N\}, \qquad x \in \bar{D}.$$

Likewise, we define *the limit inferior* of $g$ at $x$, denoted by $(\underline{L}g)(x)$ or $\liminf_{t\to x} g(t)$. The definition is

$$(2) \qquad (\underline{L}g)(x) = \sup_{N\in\mathcal{N}} \inf\{f(t) : t \in N\}, \qquad x \in \bar{D}.$$

It is easy to see that

$$(3) \qquad (\underline{L}g)(x) \leq (\bar{L}g)(x) \quad \text{if} \quad x \in \bar{D}$$

and

$$(4) \qquad (\underline{L}g)(x) \leq g(x) \leq (\bar{L}g)(x) \quad \text{if} \quad x \in D.$$

If $x \in D$, $g$ is continuous at $x$ if and only if both equality signs hold in (4) (see Problem 1).

### SEMICONTINUITY

This concept was introduced in Section 6–9. We now need it again. The definitions in Section 6–9 are equivalent to the following definitions:

The function $g : D \to R^*$ is *upper semicontinuous* at the point $x \in D$ if $(\bar{L}g)(x) = g(x)$, and *lower semicontinuous* at $x$ if $(\underline{L}g)(x) = g(x)$.

It is not hard to prove (see Problem 2) that $\bar{L}g$ is upper semicontinuous at each point of $\bar{D}$ and $\underline{L}g$ is lower semicontinuous at each point of $\bar{D}$.

We also observe that

$$(5) \qquad \underline{L}(-g) = -\bar{L}g;$$

this is a direct result of the definitions.

## THE FOUR DERIVATES OF A FUNCTION

In studying the derivative of a function we have need of the more general consideration of the four derivates of a function at a point. As a preliminary explanation of notation, suppose that $g$ is a real-valued function defined on some open interval $(0, \delta)$, where $\delta > 0$. Then $\bar{L}g$ is defined on the closed interval $[0, \delta]$; we denote $(\bar{L}g)(0)$ by $\limsup_{h\to 0+} g(h)$. Likewise, we write $(\underline{L}g)(0) = \liminf_{h\to 0+} g(h)$. In what follows $g$ will be a difference quotient formed from another function.

Suppose $f : (a, b) \to R$ is given, where $a < b$. If $a < x < b$, the *upper right derivate of $f$ at $x$ is*, by definition,

$$D^+f(x) = \limsup_{h\to 0+} \frac{f(x + h) - f(x)}{h}, \tag{6}$$

and the *lower right derivate of $f$ at $x$* is

$$D_+f(x) = \liminf_{h\to 0+} \frac{f(x + h) - f(x)}{h}.$$

The upper and lower *left* derivates of $f$ at $x$, $D^-f(x)$ and $D_-f(x)$, are defined as the limit superior and the limit inferior, respectively, of the ratio

$$\frac{f(x - h) - f(x)}{-h}$$

as $h \to 0+$. The values of the derivates are in $R^*$.

The function $f$ is *differentiable* at $x$ if and only if all four derivates have the same finite value; this common value is then the derivative $f'(x)$.

*Example 1.* Suppose $f$ is defined by $f(0) = 0, f(x) = x \sin (1/x)$ if $x \neq 0$. Then $D^+f(0) = D^-f(0) = 1$ and $D_+f(0) = D_-f(0) = -1$.

*Example 2.* Suppose $f$ is defined by $f(0) = 0$, $f(x) = x\{1 + \sin (\log x)\}$ if $x > 0$, and $f(x) = x + \sqrt{-x} \sin^2 (\log x)$ if $x < 0$. Then $D^+f(0) = 2$, $D_+f(0) = 0$, $D^-f(0) = 1$, $D_-f(0) = -\infty$.

It is always true (see (3)) that $D_-f(x) \leq D^-f(x)$ and $D_+f(x) \leq D^+f(x)$. Hence, at a point $x$ where $D^+f(x) \leq D_-f(x)$ and $D^-f(x) \leq D_+f(x)$, we have

$$D^+f(x) \leq D_-f(x) \leq D^-f(x) \leq D_+f(x) \leq D^+f(x), \tag{7}$$

and it follows that all four derivates have the same value; if this value is finite, $f$ must be differentiable at $x$. This argument will be used in our discussion of the differentiability of monotone functions (see the proof of Theorem 9–7 V).

## F. RIESZ'S PROOF OF THE FUNDAMENTAL THEOREM

It was established by Lebesgue that a continuous monotone function is differentiable almost everywhere. Subsequently, in 1911, W. H. Young gave a proof without the assumption of continuity (see Hobson [1], Vol. 1, p. 400). We are going to give a proof which is due to F. Riesz (in 1932). As references we cite Kestelman [1], pp. 199–202, Riesz and Nagy [1], pp. 6–9, and Boas [1], pp. 134–138.

In the following lemma we use the symbol $\exists$. It means "there exists."

LEMMA 9–7 I. *Given $g : (a, b) \to R$, let $G = \overline{L}g$. Let subsets $E$ and $F$ of $(a, b)$ be defined as follows:*

$$E = \{x : \exists t \in (x, b) \text{ with } G(x) < g(t)\},$$
$$F = \{x : \exists t \in (a, x) \text{ with } G(x) < g(t)\}.$$

*Then $E$ and $F$ are open sets. If $E \neq \varnothing$, and if $E = \bigcup_n I_n$, where $I_1, I_2, \ldots$ are disjoint open intervals, with $I_n = (a_n, b_n)$, then $g(x) \leq G(b_n)$ when $x \in I_n$. If $F \neq \varnothing$ and $F = \bigcup_n J_n$, where $J_1, J_2, \ldots$ are disjoint open intervals with $J_n = (c_n, d_n)$, then $g(x) \leq G(c_n)$ when $x \in J_n$.*

*Proof.* It is enough to deal with $E$. Once the assertion about $E$ has been proved, we can prove the assertion about $F$ as an application, by using the following device: Let $g_1(x) = g(-x)$, $-b < x < -a$, and let $G_1 = \overline{L}g_1$. Then what has already been proved about $E$, when applied to $g_1$ with $(-b, -a)$ in place of $(a, b)$, leads to what is asserted about $F$ in relation to $g$.

The fact that $E$ is open comes from the fact that $G$ is upper semicontinuous (see Problem 2). If $x_0 \in E$, there is some $t_0 \in (x_0, b)$ such that $G(x_0) < g(t_0)$. Then the set $\{x : G(x) < g(t_0)\}$ is open, because $G$ is upper semicontinuous (see Section 6–9). This set contains $x_0$, and therefore contains an open interval $(x_0 - \delta, x_0 + \delta)$, where $\delta$ may be chosen so small that $x_0 + \delta < t_0$ and $a < x_0 - \delta$. Then this open interval lies in $E$.

Now suppose that $E \neq \varnothing$, and write $E = \bigcup_n I_n$, $I_n = (a_n, b_n)$, in the notation explained in the theorem. Select and fix any $x \in I_n$. Let $C = \{t : x \leq t \leq b_n, g(x) \leq G(t)\}$. Then $x \in C$, because $g(x) \leq G(x)$ (see (4)). Let $M = \sup C$. Then $x \leq M$. It must be true that $G(M) \geq g(x)$; for, by the upper semicontinuity of $G$, $G(M) < g(x)$ would imply $G(t) < g(x)$ for all $t$ in $[a, b]$ sufficiently near $M$, and so in particular for some $t \in C$, which would involve a contradiction. Now, perhaps $M = b_n$. In this case we are finished. Otherwise, $M < b_n$. Then $M \in I_n$, and hence there exists some $t$ such that $M < t < b$ and $G(M) < g(t)$. Then $g(x) \leq g(M) < g(t) \leq G(t)$. But $t \notin C$, because $M < t$. Therefore, $b_n < t$. If it were true that $G(b_n) < g(t)$, the definition of $E$ would show that $b_n \in E$. Since $b_n \notin E$, we must have $g(t) \leq G(b_n)$. This implies $g(x) < G(b_n)$, and the proof is finished.

We are now going to apply Lemma 9–7 I to the function $g(x) = f(x) - cx$, where $f : (a, b) \to R$ is a bounded and nondecreasing function and $c$ is a positive constant.

LEMMA 9–7 II. *Suppose $f : (a, b) \to R$ is bounded and nondecreasing. Suppose $c > 0$, and define $g(x) = f(x) - cx$. Then define $G$, $E$, and $F$ as in Lemma 9–7 I. For the cases in which $E$ or $F$ is not empty, with the meanings of $a_n, b_n, c_n, d_n$ in Lemma 9–7 I we have*

(8) $$c \sum_n (b_n - a_n) \leq f(b-) - f(a+),$$

(9) $$f(d_n-) - f(c_n+) \leq c(d_n - c_n).$$

*Proof.* Here, $G(x) = \limsup_{t \to x} [f(t) - ct]$. To compute $G(a)$ we suppose $a < t < b$. Then $f(t) - ct < f(t) - ca$, so $G(a) \leq f(a+) - ca$. Likewise, to compute $G(b)$ we assume $a < t < b$ and observe that $f(t) - ct \leq f(b-) - ct$, so that $G(b) \leq f(b-) - cb$. When $a < x < b$ we have $f(t) - ct < f(t) - cx$ if $x < t < b$ and $f(t) - ct \leq f(x+) - ct$ if $a < t \leq x$; from these inequalities we see that $G(x) \leq f(x+) - cx$. Since $f$ is bounded, $f(a+)$ and $f(b-)$ are finite.

Now suppose $E = \bigcup_n I_n$, in the notation of Lemma 9–7 I. We are assured by that lemma that $f(x) - cx \leq G(b_n)$ if $a_n < x < b_n$. Hence $f(a_n+) - ca_n \leq G(b_n)$. From the preceding paragraph we then see that

(10) $$c(b_n - a_n) \leq f(b_n+) - f(a_n+) \quad \text{if} \quad b_n < b,$$

(11) $$c(b_n - a_n) \leq f(b_n-) - f(a_n+) \quad \text{if} \quad b_n = b.$$

It is easy to deduce (8) from (10) and (11), in view of the fact that the open intervals $I_1, I_2, \ldots$ are nonoverlapping and $f$ is nondecreasing.

To deal with (9) we suppose that $F = \bigcup_n J_n$, $J_n = (c_n, d_n)$. Then $f(x) - cx \leq G(c_n)$ if $c_n < x < d_n$, whence $f(d_n-) - cd_n \leq G(c_n)$. We know that $G(c_n) \leq f(c_n+) - cc_n$ from the first paragraph of the present proof; (9) is an immediate consequence.

We come now to some lemmas on derivates.

LEMMA 9–7 III. *Suppose that* $f : (a, b) \to R$ *is a bounded nondecreasing function. Then the set* $\{x : D^+f(x) = +\infty\}$ *has Lebesgue measure zero.*

*Proof.* Let $S$ be the set of points in $(a, b)$ at which $f$ is discontinuous; we know that $S$ is countable, and hence of measure zero. For each $c > 0$ let $B(c) = \{x : D^+f(x) > c\}$. We shall use $g$, $G$, $E$ with the meanings given in Lemmas 9–7 I, II. If $x \in B(c)$, there exist positive values of $h$ as small as we please such that

(12) $$\frac{f(x + h) - f(x)}{h} > c, \quad \text{or} \quad f(x + h) - c(x + h) > f(x) - cx.$$

If $x \in B(c) - S$, we know that $g(x) = G(x)$ (by continuity) so that (12) can be written $g(x + h) > G(x)$; this implies that $x \in E$. That is, $B(c) - S \subset E$. Now, $D^+f(x) = +\infty$ implies $x \in B(c)$. Hence

$$\{x : D^+f(x) = +\infty\} \subset S \cup E,$$

and so the measure of the set $\{x : D^+f(x) = +\infty\}$ does not exceed $\mu(S) + \mu(E) = \mu(E)$. If $E = \varnothing$, our proof is finished. If $E \neq \varnothing$, we know by the preceding lemmas that

$$\mu(E) = \sum_n (b_n - a_n) \leq \frac{f(b-) - f(a+)}{c}.$$

Since $c$ can be chosen as large as we like, this shows that the measure of $\{x : D^+f(x) = +\infty\}$ is zero.

LEMMA 9–7 IV. *Suppose that* $f : (a, b) \to R$ *is a bounded nondecreasing function. Suppose* $0 < \alpha < \beta$, *and let* $A(\alpha) = \{x : D_-f(x) < \alpha\}$, $B(\beta) = \{x : D^+f(x) > \beta\}$. *Then* $\mu\{A(\alpha) \cap B(\beta)\} = 0$.

*Proof.* As in the proof of Lemma 9–7 III, let $S$ be the countable set of points of discontinuity of $f$ in $(a, b)$. It will be sufficient to show that $A(\alpha) \cap B(\beta) - S$ has measure zero.

In what follows we are going to need to apply Lemma 9–7 II with $\alpha$ or $\beta$ in place of $c$; we shall also need to apply the lemma with $(a, b)$ replaced by a subinterval of $(a, b)$. For clarity we must therefore introduce some further notation. We define $g_\alpha(x) = f(x) - \alpha x$ and $G_\alpha = \bar{L}g_\alpha$; here $\alpha$ can be any positive real number. Regarding $a$, $b$ as variables, with $a < b$, we define

$$E(a, b; \alpha) = \{x : a < x < b, \exists t \in (x, b) \ \text{with}\ G_\alpha(x) < g_\alpha(t)\},$$

$$F(a, b; \alpha) = \{x : a < x < b, \exists t \in (a, x) \ \text{with}\ G_\alpha(x) < g_\alpha(t)\}.$$

As in the proof of Lemma 9–7 III we observe that $B(\beta) - S \subset E(a, b; \beta)$. Likewise, $x \in A(\alpha)$ implies the existence of positive numbers $h$ as small as we please such that

$$\frac{f(x-h) - f(x)}{-h} < \alpha \quad \text{or} \quad f(x) - \alpha x < f(x-h) - \alpha(x-h),$$

from which it can be seen that $A(\alpha) - S \subset F(a, b; \alpha)$. Now let us write $T = A(\alpha) \cap B(\beta) - S$. We are trying to prove that $\mu(T) = 0$, so we consider the case in which $T \neq \varnothing$. Then $E(a, b; \beta) \neq \varnothing$, so $E(a, b; \beta)$ is a countable union of disjoint open intervals $I_n = (a_n, b_n)$. Then

$$[A(\alpha) - S] \cap I_n \subset F(a_n, b_n; \alpha),$$

and

$$T \subset \bigcup_n \{[A(\alpha) - S] \cap I_n\} \subset \bigcup_n F(a_n, b_n; \alpha).$$

We consider only those $F(a_n, b_n; \alpha)$ which are nonempty, and write $F(a_n, b_n; \alpha) = \bigcup_i J_{ni}$, $J_{ni} = (c_{ni}, d_{ni})$, where $J_{n1}, J_{n2}, \ldots$ are disjoint. Now, $[B(\beta) - S] \cap J_{ni} \subset E(c_{ni}, d_{ni}; \beta)$, and therefore

$$T = T \cap [B(\beta) - S] \subset \bigcup_n \bigcup_i E(c_{ni}, d_{ni}; \beta).$$

Let us write $V_1 = \bigcup_n \bigcup_i E(c_{ni}, d_{ni}; \beta)$. By a proper application of Lemma 9–7 II we see that

$$\mu\{E(c_{ni}, d_{ni}; \beta)\} \leq \frac{f(d_{ni}-) - f(c_{ni}+)}{\beta} \leq \frac{\alpha}{\beta}(d_{ni} - c_{ni}),$$

and therefore that

$$\mu(V_1) \leq \sum_{n,i} \frac{\alpha}{\beta}(d_{ni} - c_{ni}) \leq \frac{\alpha}{\beta}(b - a). \tag{13}$$

The foregoing reasoning can be applied to investigate the part of $T$ contained in any open subinterval of $(a, b)$. We can state the result as follows: If I is an open subinterval of $(a, b)$, there exists an open subset $V$ of $I$ such that $I \cap T \subset V$ and $\mu(V) \leq (\alpha/\beta)\, \mu(I)$. We now construct a sequence $\{V_n\}$ of open subsets of $(a, b)$ such that

$$T \subset V_n \quad \text{and} \quad \mu(V_n) \leq \left(\frac{\alpha}{\beta}\right)^n (b - a).$$

From this, since $0 < \alpha < \beta$, we can conclude that $\mu(T) = 0$, thus finishing the proof of the lemma. We already have what is required for the case $n = 1$. Assuming (14) for $n \leq m$, we express $V_m$ as a disjoint union of open intervals $I_{m1}, I_{m2}, \ldots$. There exists an open subset $V_{mi}$ of $I_{mi}$ such that $T \cap I_{mi} \subset V_{mi}$ and $\mu(V_{mi}) \leq (\alpha/\beta)\, \mu(I_{mi})$. Let $V_{m+1} = \bigcup_i V_{mi}$. Then

$$T = T \cap V_m = \bigcup_i (T \cap I_{mi}) \subset \bigcup_i V_{mi} = V_{m+1}$$

and

$$\mu(V_{m+1}) = \sum_i \mu(V_{mi}) \leq \frac{\alpha}{\beta} \sum_i \mu(I_{mi}) = \frac{\alpha}{\beta} \mu(V_m) \leq \left(\frac{\alpha}{\beta}\right)^{m+1} (b - a).$$

This completes the construction by induction.

We come now to the main result of this section.

THEOREM 9–7 V. *Let $f: (a, b) \to R$ be a nondecreasing function. Then $f$ is differentiable almost everywhere.*

*Proof.* It will suffice to give the proof under the additional assumption that $f$ is bounded, for $(a, b)$ is a countable union of open subintervals on each of which $f$ is bounded.

Since $f$ is nondecreasing, each of the derivates of $f$ is nonnegative at each point of $(a, b)$. We assert that

$$\mu(\{x : D^+f(x) > D_-f(x)\}) = 0. \tag{15}$$

For, let $\{(\alpha_n, \beta_n)\}$ be an enumeration of the pairs of rational numbers $\alpha$, $\beta$ such that $0 < \alpha < \beta$. We see that

$$\{x : D^+f(x) > D_-f(x)\} = \bigcup_n \{A(\alpha_n) \cap B(\beta_n)\};$$

the truth of (15) therefore follows by Lemma 9–7 IV.

Next, we prove that

$$\mu(\{x : D_+f(x) < D^-f(x)\}) = 0. \tag{16}$$

This is done by a simple device. Let $t = a + b - x$, so that $t$ decreases from $b$ to $a$ as $x$ increases from $a$ to $b$. Let $F(t) = -f(x)$. Then $F$ is nondecreasing on $(a, b)$, and we see by easy calculations that

$$D^+F(t) = D^-f(x), \qquad D_-F(t) = D_+f(x). \tag{17}$$

Since the mapping $t = a + b - x$ is measure-preserving (see Theorem 4–8 VII) and since $D_+f(x) < D^-f(x)$ is equivalent to $D_-F(t) < D^+F(t)$, we see by applying (15) to $F$ that (16) is true.

If we now use (15), (16) and Lemma 9–7 III, and refer to the discussion accompanying (7), we see that $f$ is differentiable almost everywhere.

*Further comment on Theorem* 9–7 V. The theorem may be proved in a quite different way, using what is known as *the Vitali covering theorem.* See, for instance, Natanson [1], Vol. 1, pp. 208–212, Williamson [1], pp. 83–86. There is a valid counterpart of Theorem 9–7 V in the theory of additive set functions and the differentiation of such functions; see Saks [1], pp. 114–116. The Vitali covering theorem (for sets in $R^k$) is needed in this theory of differentiation of additive set functions. We do not consider these things in this book, however.

## THE INTEGRAL OF THE DERIVATIVE

The following theorem is interesting and important.

THEOREM 9–7 VI. *Suppose $f : [a, b] \to R$ is a nondecreasing function. Let $E$ be the set of points in $(a, b)$ at which $f$ is differentiable. Then the derivative $f' : E \to R$ is summable in the Lebesgue sense, and*

$$\int_E f' \, d\mu \leq f(b-) - f(a+). \tag{18}$$

*Proof.* The function $f$ itself is easily seen to be measurable, as a direct consequence of the fact that it is nondecreasing. (Actually, $f$ is integrable over $[a, b]$ in the Riemann sense. This may be seen in various ways, by Theorem 5–3 V, for example.) Let us extend the definition of $f$ by setting $f(x) = f(b)$ if $b < x$. Then we define $\varphi_n : [a, b] \to R$ by

$$\varphi_n(x) = \frac{f\left(x + \dfrac{1}{n}\right) - f(x)}{1/n}.$$

It is clear that $\varphi_n(x) \to f'(x)$ if $x \in E$. Also, $\varphi_n$ is measurable. Hence $f'$ is measurable, by Theorem 5–1 VII. Since $[a, b] - E$ is a set of measure zero, we have

$$\int_E \varphi_n \, d\mu = \int_a^b \varphi_n(x)\, dx = n\left\{\int_a^b f\left(x + \frac{1}{n}\right) dx - \int_a^b f(x)\, dx\right.$$

$$= n\left\{\int_{a+(1/n)}^{b+(1/n)} f(x)\, dx - \int_a^b f(x)\, dx\right.$$

$$= f(b) - n\int_a^{a+(1/n)} f(x)\, dx.$$

The integrals after the first one may be thought of as Riemann integrals. We now see that

$$\int_E \varphi_n \, d\mu \le f(b) - f(a). \tag{19}$$

By Fatou's lemma it follows that $f'$ is summable over $E$, and

$$\int_E f' \, d\mu \le f(b) - f(a). \tag{20}$$

Suppose $a < \alpha < \beta < b$, and let $F$ be the part of $E$ in $(\alpha, \beta)$. Applying (20), we have

$$\int_F f' d\mu \le f(\beta) - f(\alpha) \le f(b-) - f(a+).$$

On letting $\alpha \to a$ and $\beta \to b$ we obtain (18) (we can use Theorem 5–5 IV).

## A CURIOUS EXAMPLE

We shall exhibit a continuous nondecreasing function $f : [0, 1] \to R$ such that $f(0) = 0$, $f(1) = 1$, and $f'(x) = 0$ a.e. This will demonstrate that the equality need not hold in (20). We use the Cantor set and the notations established in our discussion of this set in Section 2–10. To begin with we define

$$f(x) = \frac{2i - 1}{2^n} \quad \text{if} \quad x \in E_{ni}, \qquad i = 1, \ldots, 2^{n-1}.$$

This defines $f$ on $\bigcup_n E_n$, and the definition is such that $f(x) \le f(y)$ if $x < y$. This monotone character of $f$ becomes apparent if one visualizes the way in which the intervals $E_{n1}, E_{n2}, \ldots$ fall into the spaces not occupied by the intervals forming $E_1, E_2, \ldots, E_{n-1}$, if one at the same time examines the values assigned to $f$. An indication of this is given in the accompanying display. We omit a formal proof.

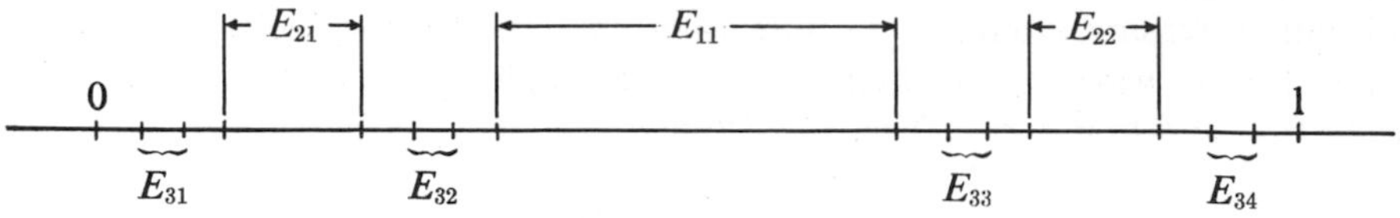


FIGURE 39

$E_{11}$

$\frac{1}{2}$

$E_{21}$ $\quad$ $E_{22}$

$\frac{1}{4}$ $\quad$ $\frac{3}{4}$

$E_{31}$ $\quad$ $E_{32}$ $\quad$ $E_{33}$ $\quad$ $E_{34}$

$\frac{1}{8}$ $\quad$ $\frac{3}{8}$ $\quad$ $\frac{5}{8}$ $\quad$ $\frac{7}{8}$

$E_{41}$ $\quad$ $E_{42}$ $\quad$ $E_{43}$ $\quad$ $E_{44}$ $\quad$ $E_{45}$ $\quad$ $E_{46}$ $\quad$ $E_{47}$ $\quad$ $E_{48}$

$\frac{1}{16}$ $\quad$ $\frac{3}{16}$ $\quad$ $\frac{5}{16}$ $\quad$ $\frac{7}{16}$ $\quad$ $\frac{9}{16}$ $\quad$ $\frac{11}{16}$ $\quad$ $\frac{13}{16}$ $\quad$ $\frac{15}{16}$

Display of values of $f$ on sets $E_{ni}$

Next, we define $f(0) = 0, f(1) = 1$. If $0 < x < 1$ and $f(x)$ has not yet been defined, there is an increasing sequence $\{x_n\}$ such that $f(x_n)$ has been defined and $x_n \to x$. The limit of $\{f(x_n)\}$ exists, and it is easy to see that it is independent of the choice of $\{x_n\}$. Hence, we can without ambiguity define $f(x) = \lim f(x_n)$. It is then readily evident that $f$ is a nondecreasing function defined on all of $[0, 1]$. Since the range of $f$ is dense on $[0, 1]$, $f$ must be continuous. Finally, we observe that $f'(x) = 0$ if $x \in \bigcup_n E_n$, so that $f'(x) = 0$ a.e.

## FUNCTIONS OF BOUNDED VARIATION

Our results on monotone functions enable us to assert the following theorem.

THEOREM 9–7 VII. *Suppose $f \in BV[a, b]$. Then $f$ is differentiable a.e. For convenience let us write $v(x) = V_{ax}(f)$. If $E$ is the subset of $(a, b)$ on which $f$ is differentiable, the function $f' : E \to R$ is summable in the Lebesgue sense, and*

$$\int_E |f'|\, d\mu \leq v(b-) - v(a+). \tag{21}$$

*Proof.* We know (Theorem 9–4 II) that $f$ is expressible as $f = f_1 - f_2$, where $f_1$ and $f_2$ are nondecreasing (and therefore bounded) on $[a, b]$. Hence, by Theorem 9–7 V, $f$ is differentiable a.e. on $(a, b)$, with $f'(x) = f_1'(x) - f_2'(x)$ when $f_1$ and $f_2$ are both differentiable. It follows from Theorem 9–7 VI that $f'$ is summable over $E$.

From Section 9–4 we see that

$$f'(x) = \frac{d}{dx} P_{ax}(f) - \frac{d}{dx} N_{ax}(f) \qquad \text{a.e.}$$

and

$$\frac{d}{dx} V_{ax}(f) = \frac{d}{dx} P_{ax}(f) + \frac{d}{dx} N_{ax}(f) \qquad \text{a.e.}$$

Therefore, since the derivatives of $P_{ax}(f)$ and $N_{ax}(f)$ are nonnegative, we have

$$|f'(x)| \leq \frac{d}{dx} V_{ax}(f) = v'(x) \qquad \text{a.e.} \tag{22}$$

If $F$ is the set of points $x$ on $(a, b)$ where $f'(x)$ and $v'(x)$ both exist, we see from (22) and Theorem 9–7 VI that

$$\int_E |f'|\, d\mu = \int_F |f'|\, d\mu \leq \int_F v'\, d\mu \leq v(b-) - v(a+).$$

Thus (21) is proved.

We remark that if $f$ is also assumed to be continuous, then $v$ is continuous, and (21) can be written in the form

$$\int_E |f'|\, d\mu \leq V_{ab}(f).$$

In Section 9–8 we shall discuss when the equality holds in (21).

## PROBLEMS

1. (a) In connection with (4), show that $g : D \to R^*$ is continuous at $x \in D$ if and only if $(\overline{L}g)(x) = (\underline{L}g)(x)$. (b) Verify (5).

2. Prove that $\overline{L}g$ is upper semicontinuous at each point of $\bar{D}$. [*Suggestion.* If this were false, then for some $x \in \bar{D}$ and some $c \in R^*$ we would have $(\overline{L}g)(x) < c$ but $\sup \{(\overline{L}g)(t) : t \in V \cap \bar{D}\} \geq c$ for every neighborhood $V$ of $x$. Choose $c_1$ so that $(\overline{L}g)(x) < c_1 < c$. This has implications about $g(t)$ for $t \in D \cap U$, where $U$ is a certain neighborhood of $x$, and this in turn leads to a contradictory implication about $\overline{L}g$ on $U \cap \bar{D}$.]

3. For each $n$ let $u_n : [a, b] \to R$ be a nondecreasing function. Let the series $\sum_{n=1}^{\infty} u_n(x)$ be convergent for each $x$, with sum $f(x)$. Prove that $f'(x) = \sum_{n=1}^{\infty} u'_n(x)$ a.e. [*Suggestions.* First prove that $\sum_{n=1}^{\infty} u'_n(x)$ is convergent a.e. Let $r_n(x) = \sum_{i=n+1}^{\infty} u_i(x)$. Since $f'(x) = \sum_{i=1}^{n} u'_i(x) + r'_n(x)$, it will then be enough to show that there is a subsequence $\{n_i\}$ of the integers such that $r'_{n_i}(x) \to 0$ a.e. as $i \to \infty$. Show that such a subsequence can be obtained by choosing $\{n_i\}$ so that $|r_{n_i}(x)| \leq 2^{-i}$ if $x \in [a, b]$, $i = 1, 2, \ldots$.]

## 9–8 Absolutely continuous functions

In this section we define a concept of absolute continuity for functions $f: D \to R$, where $D$ is a connected subset of $R$. This concept plays a key role in the elucidation of the relation between differentiation and integration in the Lebesgue sense for real-valued functions defined on $R$.

Two finite intervals on $R$ are said to be *nonoverlapping* if they have no interior points in common. By a *spread* we shall mean a finite family of compact intervals, no two of which overlap. If all the intervals belong to a set $D$, we say the spread is on $D$. By the *measure of the spread* we mean the sum of the lengths of the intervals which compose it. If $S = (I_1, \ldots, I_n)$ is a spread, with $|I_i| = \mu(I_i)$ the length of $I_i$, we write $\mu(S) = \sum_i |I_i|$ for the measure of the spread. This $\mu(S)$ is equal to the measure of the union of the intervals $I_1, \ldots, I_n$. There is a distinction, however, between $S$ and this point-set union; $S$ is not a point set in $R$, but a certain finite family of intervals. Our introduction of the concept and the terminology of a spread is entirely for convenience in exposition.

Now, suppose we are given $f : D \to R$, where $D$ is a connected subset of $R$. We say that $f$ is *absolutely continuous* on $D$ if to each $\epsilon > 0$ corresponds a $\delta > 0$ such that, for an arbitrary spread $S = (I_1, \ldots, I_n)$ on $D$, with $I_i = [a_i, b_i]$,

(1) $$\mu(S) < \delta \quad \text{implies} \quad \sum_i |f(b_i) - f(a_i)| < \epsilon.$$

*Example 1.* Suppose $g : [a, b] \to R^*$ is summable in the Lebesgue sense. When $a \leq \alpha < \beta \leq b$, the integral of $g$ over the interval $[\alpha, \beta]$ will be denoted by $\int_\alpha^\beta g \, d\mu$. We add the convention that $\int_\alpha^\alpha g \, d\mu = 0$. Since the integral over $[\alpha, \beta]$ is equal in value to the integral over $(\alpha, \beta]$ or $[\alpha, \beta)$, it is clear that $\alpha < \beta < \gamma$ implies

$$\int_\alpha^\gamma g \, d\mu = \int_\alpha^\beta g \, d\mu + \int_\beta^\gamma g \, d\mu.$$

Now, let us define $f : [a, b] \to R$ by the formula

(2) $$f(x) = \int_a^x g \, d\mu.$$

Then $f$ is absolutely continuous on $[a, b]$. To prove this we use Theorem 5–5 III. Given $\epsilon > 0$, there is a $\delta > 0$ such that

$$\int_E |g| \, d\mu < \epsilon \qquad \text{if} \quad \mu(E) < \delta,$$

where $E$ is a measurable subset of $[a, b]$. Now suppose that $S = (I_1, \ldots, I_n)$ is a spread on $[a, b]$, with $I_i = [a_i, b_i]$ and $E = \bigcup_i I_i$. Then

$$\sum_i |f(b_i) - f(a_i)| \leq \sum_i \int_{a_i}^{b_i} |g| \, d\mu = \int_E |g| \, d\mu < \epsilon$$

if $\mu(S) < \delta$, because $\mu(S) = \mu(E)$; therefore $f$ is absolutely continuous.

*Example 2.* Suppose $g : R \to R^*$ is summable. We denote by $(-\infty, a]$ the set $\{x : -\infty < x \leq a\}$, and we denote the integral of $g$ over this set by $\int_{-\infty}^a g \, d\mu$. We denote the integral of $g$ over all of $R$ by $\int_{-\infty}^\infty g \, d\mu$. Now, let $f : R \to R$ be defined by

(3) $$f(x) = \int_{-\infty}^x g \, d\mu.$$

Just as in Example 1 we see that $f$ is absolutely continuous.

We observe that $f$ is bounded. In fact,

$$|f(x)| \leq \int_{-\infty}^x |g| \, d\mu \leq \int_{-\infty}^\infty |g| \, d\mu.$$

Finally, we observe that $|f(x)| \to 0$ as $x \to -\infty$. For, suppose that $E_n = (-n - 1, -n]$, $n = 1, 2, \ldots$. Evidently,

$$|f(x)| \leq \int_{-\infty}^{-n} |g| \, d\mu = \sum_{k=n}^\infty \int_{E_k} |g| \, d\mu$$

if $x \leq -n$ (see Theorem 5–5 II). Since the series of integrals converges, it is clear that $|f(x)| \to 0$ as $x \to -\infty$.

If a function $f$ is absolutely continuous on $D$, it is continuous at each point of $D$; in fact it is uniformly continuous on $D$. But the reverse is not true as a general proposition. See the comment later on following the proof of Theorem 9–8 I.

It can happen that a function $f : R \to R$ is absolutely continuous on each finite interval, but is not absolutely continuous on $R$. This is the situation if $f(x) = x^2$, for instance. It can also happen that $f$ is absolutely continuous on each closed subinterval of $(0, 1)$, but not absolutely continuous on $(0, 1)$. This is the case with $f(x) = x^{-1}$.

There are various simple sufficient conditions for a function to be absolutely continuous. The simplest, perhaps, is to have the function satisfy a Lipschitz condition. This means that there is some constant $M$ such that $|f(x) - f(y)| \leq M|x - y|$ for each pair $x, y$ in $D$. It is obvious that this makes $f$ absolutely continuous. In particular, $f$ satisfies a Lipschitz condition, and is therefore absolutely continuous, on any interval throughout which $f'(x)$ exists and is bounded. This can be seen with the aid of the law of the mean of differential calculus.

It is easy to see that if $f$ and $g$ are defined and absolutely continuous on $D$, the sum $f + g$ and any constant multiple of $f$ are absolutely continuous on $D$. If $f$ and $g$ are also bounded on $D$, the product $fg$ is absolutely continuous on $D$. If $f$ is absolutely continuous on $D$ and $|f(x)| \geq c > 0$ ($c$ a constant) on $D$, then the reciprocal of $f$ is absolutely continuous on $D$. We leave details to the reader.

THEOREM 9–8 I. *If $f : [a, b] \to R$ is absolutely continuous, it is of bounded variation.*

*Proof.* Suppose $\epsilon = 1$, and choose $\delta$ to satisfy (1) in the expression of the fact that $f$ is absolutely continuous. Consider a fixed partition $\Delta = (x_0, x_1, \ldots, x_N)$ of $[a, b]$ such that $x_i - x_{i-1} < \delta$ for $i = 1, \ldots, N$. The condition of absolute continuity then shows that the total variation of $f$ on $[x_{i-1}, x_i]$ does not exceed 1. Hence, by Theorem 9–2 II, the total variation of $f$ on $[a, b]$ does not exceed $N$.

*Comment.* Since there exist functions $f : [a, b] \to R$ which are continuous, but not of bounded variation, it follows that there exist uniformly continuous functions which are not absolutely continuous. See Example 2, Section 9–2.

We shall see a bit later on (after Corollary 9–8 IV) that there exist continuous functions of bounded variation (even continuous monotonic functions!) which are not absolutely continuous.

THEOREM 9–8 II. *Let $f : [a, b] \to R$ be absolutely continuous and let $v(x) = V_{ax}(f)$ (notation as in Section 9–2). Then $v$ is absolutely continuous on $[a, b]$. As a consequence, $f$ can be expressed as the difference of two nondecreasing absolutely continuous functions.*

*Proof.* By Theorem 9–2 II we see that $v(\beta) - v(\alpha) = V_{\alpha\beta}(f)$ if $a \leq \alpha < \beta \leq b$. Suppose $\epsilon > 0$ and let $\delta$ be matched to $\epsilon$ as in condition (1) for the absolute continuity of $f$. Let $S_0 = (I_1, \ldots, I_n)$ be any spread on $[a, b]$ such that $\mu(S_0) < \delta$. Let $I_i = [a_i, b_i]$. We shall show that

$$\sum_i [v(b_i) - v(a_i)] < \epsilon, \tag{4}$$

and this will prove that $v$ is absolutely continuous. If $\Delta_i$ is any partition of $[a_i, b_i]$, all the subintervals in $\Delta_1, \ldots, \Delta_n$, taken together, form a spread $S$ with $\mu(S) = \mu(S_0) < \delta$. Hence, since $f$ is absolutely continuous, we see that

$$\sum_i T(\Delta_i; f; a_i, b_i) < \epsilon. \tag{5}$$

Here, we use notation explained in the proof of Theorem 9–2 II. Since the partitions $\Delta_i$ are arbitrary, and since $v(b_i) - v(a_i)$ is the total variation of $f$ on $[a_i, b_i]$, (4) follows from (5).

Since the sum and difference of absolutely continuous functions are absolutely continuous, it is easy to see that $P_{ax}(f)$ and $N_{ax}(f)$ are absolutely continuous functions of $x$ (see (7) and (8) in Section 9–4, with $x$ in place of $b$). Hence also the $f_1$ and $f_2$ in Theorem 9–4 II are absolutely continuous. This completes the proof.

## DIFFERENTIATION AND INTEGRATION

If $f$ is absolutely continuous on $[a, b]$, it is of bounded variation; hence, by Theorem 9–7 VII, $f$ is differentiable a.e. and the derivative $f'$ is summable. We shall now investigate the value of the integral of $f'$.

THEOREM 9–8 III. *Suppose that $f : [a, b] \to R$ is absolutely continuous. Let $E$ be the set of points $x$ on $(a, b)$ such that $f$ is differentiable at $x$. Then*

$$\int_E f' \, d\mu = f(b) - f(a). \tag{6}$$

*Proof.* We write $f = f_1 - f_2$, where $f_1$ and $f_2$ are nondecreasing and absolutely continuous. From this we can see that it suffices to prove (6) under the additional assumption that $f$ is nondecreasing. Hence, we make this assumption.

Let us extend the definition of $f$ by setting $f(x) = f(b)$ if $b < x$. Define $\varphi_n : [a, b] \to R$ by

$$\varphi_n(x) = \frac{f\left(x + \dfrac{1}{n}\right) - f(x)}{1/n}.$$

Evidently $\varphi_n$ is continuous, and $\varphi_n(x) \to f'(x)$ if $x \in E$. By a calculation given in the proof of Theorem 9–7 VI we see that

$$\int_E \varphi_n \, d\mu = \int_a^b \varphi_n(x) \, dx = f(b) - n \int_a^{a+(1/n)} f(x) \, dx,$$

where the integral on the right is a Riemann integral. Since $f$ is continuous, we see that

$$\int_E \varphi_n \, d\mu \to f(b) - f(a).$$

We already know that $f'$ is summable over $E$. If we can prove that

$$\int_E \varphi_n \, d\mu \to \int_E f' \, d\mu, \tag{7}$$

we shall have the proof of (6). Suppose $\epsilon > 0$ is given. The way in which we extended the definition of $f$ leaves it absolutely continuous on the interval $[a, b + 1]$. Hence there is a $\delta_1 > 0$ such that for any spread $S = (I_1, \ldots, I_n)$ on $[a, b + 1]$ with $I_i = [\alpha_i, \beta_i]$ and $\mu(S) < \delta_1$, we have

$$\sum_i [f(\beta_i) - f(\alpha_i)] < \frac{\epsilon}{3}.$$

Moreover, there is a $\delta_2 > 0$ such that $\int_F f'\,d\mu < \epsilon/3$ if $F$ is any measurable subset of $E$ such that $\mu(F) < \delta_2$. It is allowable to choose $\delta_2 < \delta_1$, and we do this. Now, by Egoroff's theorem (Theorem 5–3 I), there is a measurable subset $F$ of $E$ with $\mu(F) < \delta_2$ such that $\varphi_n(x) \to f'(x)$ uniformly on $E - F$. With $F$ thus fixed, there is then some $N$ such that

$$\int_{E-F} |\varphi_n - f'|\,d\mu < \frac{\epsilon}{3}$$

if $n \geq N$. We then have

$$\int_E \varphi_n\,d\mu - \int_E f'\,d\mu = \int_{E-F} (\varphi_n - f')\,d\mu + \int_F (\varphi_n - f')\,d\mu,$$

$$\left|\int_E \varphi_n\,d\mu - \int_E f'\,d\mu\right| < \frac{\epsilon}{3} + \frac{\epsilon}{3} + \int_F \varphi_n\,d\mu.$$

To prove (7) it remains to show that for each $n$ we have

(8)
$$\int_F \varphi_n\,d\mu \leq \frac{\epsilon}{3}.$$

Since $\mu(F) < \delta_2 < \delta_1$, there exists an open subset $V$ of $(a, b)$ such that $F \subset V$ and $\mu(V) < \delta_1$. We can express $V$ as a countable union of disjoint open intervals $(a_1, b_1)$, $(a_2, b_2)$, .... For any $x$ such that $0 \leq x \leq 1$, and for any positive integer $m$, the intervals $[a_1 + x, b_1 + x], \ldots, [a_m + x, b_m + x]$ form a spread on $[a, b + 1]$ of measure less than $\delta_1$, and hence

(9)
$$\sum_{i=1}^{m} [f(b_i + x) - f(a_i + x)] < \frac{\epsilon}{3}.$$

Now,

$$\begin{aligned}\int_{a_i}^{b_i} \varphi_n(x)\,dx &= n\left\{\int_{a_i}^{b_i} f\left(x + \frac{1}{n}\right)dx - \int_{a_i}^{b_i} f(x)\,dx\right\}\\ &= n\left\{\int_{b_i}^{(b_i+1/n)} f(x)\,dx - \int_{a_i}^{(a_i+1/n)} f(x)\,dx\right\}\\ &= n\int_0^{1/n} [f(b_i + x) - f(a_i + x)]\,dx.\end{aligned}$$

Therefore,

$$\sum_{i=1}^{m} \int_{a_i}^{b_i} \varphi_n(x)\,dx = n\int_0^{1/n}\left\{\sum_{i=1}^{m} [f(b_i + x) - f(a_i + x)]\right\}dx \leq \frac{\epsilon}{3},$$

as a consequence of (9). It follows that

$$\int_F \varphi_n\,d\mu \leq \int_V \varphi_n\,d\mu = \sum_i \int_{a_i}^{b_i} \varphi_n(x)\,dx \leq \frac{\epsilon}{3}.$$

Thus (8) is proved, and the proof of Theorem 9–8 III is complete.

Theorem 9–8 III shows that every absolutely continuous function $f: [a, b] \to R$ can be expressed in the form

$$f(x) = \int_a^x g\,d\mu + C,$$

where $C$ is a constant and $g : [a, b] \to R$ is summable. We have merely to define $g(x) = f'(x)$ at the points in $(a, b)$ where $f$ is differentiable and assign $g(x)$ arbitrary values at the other points of $[a, b]$. If we then apply (6) to $[a, x]$ instead of $[a, b]$, we have

$$f(x) = f(a) + \int_a^x g\, d\mu. \tag{10}$$

From this we obtain the following result:

COROLLARY 9–8 IV. *If $f : [a, b] \to R$ is absolutely continuous and $f'(x) = 0$ a.e., then $f$ is a constant function.*

*Proof.* Under the given condition $g(x) = 0$ a.e. in (10), and $f(x) = f(a)$ for each $x$.

*Comment.* From this corollary we see that the continuous nondecreasing function which was described after the proof of Theorem 9–7 VI is not absolutely continuous, because $f'(x) = 0$ a.e. on $(0, 1)$, but $f(1) - f(0) = 1$.

For the proof of our next main theorem we need the following lemma.

LEMMA 9–8 V. *Suppose $g : [a, b] \to R^*$ is summable and that $\int_a^x g\, d\mu = 0$ for each $x$ on $[a, b]$. Then $g(x) = 0$ a.e.*

*Proof.* The hypothesis implies that $\int_I g\, d\mu = 0$ for each subinterval $I$ of $[a, b]$. We shall prove that $\int_E g\, d\mu = 0$ for each measurable subset $E$ of $[a, b]$. The result will then follow from Theorem 5–4 VII, by considering the sets $\{x : g(x) > 0\}$, $\{x : g(x) < 0\}$.

Suppose, to the contrary, that $\int_E g\, d\mu \neq 0$ for some $E$. Let $\epsilon = \left|\int_E g\, d\mu\right|$, and choose $\delta > 0$ so that $\left|\int_F g\, d\mu\right| < \epsilon$ whenever $F$ is a measurable subset of $[a, b]$ such that $\mu(F) < \delta$. Now, choose an open set $U$ so that $E \subset U$ and $\mu(U) < \mu(E) + \delta$. Express $U$ as a countable disjoint union of open intervals $I_1, I_2, \ldots$. Let $V_n = I_n \cap [a, b]$, $V = \bigcup_n V_n$. Then (Theorem 5–5 II)

$$\int_V g\, d\mu = \sum_n \int_{V_n} g\, d\mu = 0,$$

as a result of the hypothesis. But $E \subset V \subset U$, so $\mu(V - E) < \delta$, and therefore $\left|\int_{V-E} g\, d\mu\right| < \epsilon$. Now,

$$0 = \int_V g\, d\mu = \int_E g\, d\mu + \int_{V-E} g\, d\mu,$$

and so

$$\left|\int_{V-E} g\, d\mu\right| = \left|-\int_E g\, d\mu\right| = \epsilon.$$

This contradiction yields the proof that $\int_E g\, d\mu = 0$ for every $E$.

The next theorem and Theorem 9–8 III present the two principal propositions about the relation between differentiation and integration, so far as Lebesgue integration and functions of one real variable are concerned.

THEOREM 9–8 VI. *If $g : [a, b] \to R^*$ is summable and if $f : [a, b] \to R$ is defined by*

$$f(x) = \int_a^x g\, d\mu,$$

*then $f'(x) = g(x)$ a.e. in $(a, b)$.*

*Proof.* We know that $f$ is absolutely continuous (see Example 1). Let $h : [a, b] \to R$ be defined by $h(x) = f'(x)$ if $x \in (a, b)$ and $f$ is differentiable at $x$; let $h(x)$ be defined arbitrarily for other values of $x$. Then

$$\int_a^x h\, d\mu = f(x) - f(a) = f(x)$$

as a consequence of Theorem 9–8 III. Hence

$$\int_a^x (h - g)\, d\mu = 0$$

for each $x$. Lemma 9–8 V then shows that $h(x) = g(x)$ a.e., whence $f'(x) = g(x)$ a.e.

It is possible to push much further with investigation of the situation presented in Theorem 9–8 VI. It is known that $f'(x) = g(x)$ at each point $x$ such that

$$\lim_{\epsilon \to 0} \frac{1}{\epsilon} \int_x^{x+\epsilon} G\, d\mu = 0,$$

where $G$ is defined by $G(t) = |g(t) - g(x)|$. Such a point $x$ is called a *Lebesgue point* of $g$. The set of non-Lebesgue points on $(a, b)$ has measure zero. Every point of continuity of $g$ is a Lebesgue point. See Titchmarsh [1], pp. 362–364 and Natanson [1], Vol. 1, p. 256.

## MORE ABOUT TOTAL VARIATION

Our next result complements Theorem 9–7 VII. If $g$ is any function defined almost everywhere on $[a, b]$ and summable over its domain of definition $D$, let us for convenience understand that $\int_\alpha^\beta g\, d\mu$ denotes the integral of $g$ over $D \cap [\alpha, \beta]$.

THEOREM 9–8 VII. *If $f \in BV[a, b]$, $f$ is absolutely continuous if and only if*

(11) $$\int_a^b |f'|\, d\mu = V_{ab}(f).$$

*Proof.* Suppose that $f$ is absolutely continuous. Let $g(x) = f'(x)$ at the points of $(a, b)$ where $f$ is differentiable, and let $g(x) = 0$ elsewhere on $[a, b]$. We can write

$$g = g^+ - g^-, \qquad |g| = g^+ + g^-.$$

Let

$$h_1(x) = \int_a^x g^+\, d\mu, \qquad h_2(x) = \int_a^x g^-\, d\mu.$$

Then $h_1'(x) = g^+(x)$ a.e. and $h_2'(x) = g^-(x)$ a.e., by Theorem 9–8 VI. Evidently, $h_1$ and $h_2$ are absolutely continuous and nondecreasing. Since $f'(x) = h_1'(x) - h_2'(x)$ a.e., the application of Theorem 9–8 III shows that $f(x) - f(a) = h_1(x) - h_2(x)$ for each $x$. It is then easy to see that

$$V_{ab}(f) \le V_{ab}(h_1) + V_{ab}(h_2) = h_1(b) + h_2(b) = \int_a^b |g|\, d\mu,$$

whence

$$V_{ab}(f) \leq \int_a^b |f'| \, d\mu.$$

We already know the reverse of this inequality, by Theorem 9–7 VII. Therefore (11) holds.

Now suppose, conversely, that (11) holds. Let $v(x) = V_{ax}(f)$. We shall show that

$$v(x) = \int_a^x v' \, d\mu, \tag{12}$$

so that $v$ is absolutely continuous. But, if $x < y$, we know that

$$|f(y) - f(x)| \leq V_{xy}(f) = v(y) - v(x).$$

The absolute continuity of $v$ then implies that of $f$. Hence, the proof of the theorem will be complete as soon as we prove (12).

In the proof of Theorem 9–7 VII we saw that $|f'(x)| \leq v(x)$ a.e. By Theorem 9–7 VI we know that

$$\int_\alpha^\beta v' \, d\mu \leq v(\beta-) - v(\alpha+). \tag{13}$$

From (11) we see that

$$v(b) = \int_a^b |f'| \, d\mu \leq \int_a^b v' \, d\mu \leq v(b-) - v(a+),$$

whence $0 \leq v(b) - v(b-) \leq -v(a+) \leq 0$. It follows that $v(b) = v(b-)$ and $v(a+) = 0$. Also, if $a < x < b$,

$$v(b) = \int_a^b v' \, d\mu = \int_a^x v' \, d\mu + \int_x^b v' \, d\mu. \tag{14}$$

Applying (13), we find

$$v(b) \leq v(x-) + v(b) - v(x+),$$

whence $0 \leq v(x+) - v(x-) \leq 0$. It follows that $v(x+) = v(x-) = v(x)$. From (13) we now know that

$$\int_a^x v' \, d\mu \leq v(x). \tag{15}$$

If the equality does not hold in (15), we see by (14) that

$$v(b) < v(x) + v(b) - v(x) = v(b).$$

Hence, (12) must hold, and the argument is complete.

## MORE ABOUT RECTIFIABLE CURVES

We return now to the subject of the length of a rectifiable curve, as considered in Section 9–3. Suppose $f: [a, b] \to R^k$ is a rectifiable curve, so that $f$ is continuous and of bounded variation. If we consider just that part of the curve which corresponds to the interval $[a, x]$, where $a < x \leq b$, the length $L(x)$ of this part of the curve is $L(x) = V_{ax}(f)$. We define $L(a) = 0$. We know (Theorem 9–2 V) that $L$ is a continuous nondecreasing function. Hence, $L$ is differentiable a.e. on $(a, b)$. Let $f_1, \ldots, f_k$ be the real-valued component functions of $f$, so that $f(x) = (f_1(x), \ldots, f_k(x)) \in R^k$. Since

$$\|f(x) - f(y)\|^2 = \sum_{i=1}^k |f_i(x) - f_i(y)|^2,$$

it is clear that each $f_i$ is of bounded variation, and hence differentiable almost everywhere.

THEOREM 9–8 VIII. *With the notation just explained in connection with the curve* $f: [a, b] \to R^k$, *we have*

(16) $$\left\{\sum_{i=1}^{k} |f_i'(x)|^2\right\}^{1/2} \le L'(x) \quad a.e.$$

*and*

(17) $$\int_a^b \left\{\sum_{i=1}^{k} |f_i'|^2\right\}^{1/2} d\mu \le L(b).$$

*The equality holds in* (17) *if and only if each* $f_i$ *is absolutely continuous.*

*Proof.* Suppose $x$ and $x + h$ are in $(a, b)$, with $h > 0$. Then

$$L(x + h) - L(x) = V_{x,x+h}(f) \ge \|f(x + h) - f(x)\|,$$

and hence

$$\frac{L(x + h) - L(x)}{h} \ge \left\{\sum_{i=1}^{k} \left|\frac{f_i(x + h) - f_i(x)}{h}\right|^2\right\}^{1/2}.$$

From this we obtain (16). The inequality (17) follows when we integrate and use Theorem 9–7 VI on $L$.

If the equality holds in (17), we have

$$\int_a^b L' \, d\mu = L(b),$$

and this implies that $L$ is absolutely continuous, by Theorem 9–8 VII. Now, if $x < y$,

$$|f_i(y) - f_i(x)| \le \|f(y) - f(x)\| \le L(y) - L(x).$$

From this and the absolute continuity of $L$, we see that $f_i$ is absolutely continuous.

Now, suppose that each $f_i$ is absolutely continuous. We wish to show that the equality holds in (17). For this it is enough to show that

(18) $$L(b) \le \int_a^b \left\{\sum_{i=1}^{k} |f_i'|^2\right\}^{1/2} d\mu.$$

To begin with we shall show that

(19) $$\|f(\beta) - f(\alpha)\| \le \int_\alpha^\beta \left\{\sum_{i=1}^{k} |f_i'|^2\right\}^{1/2} d\mu$$

if $a \le \alpha < \beta \le b$. Since $f_i$ is absolutely continuous, we have

$$f_i(\beta) - f_i(\alpha) = \int_\alpha^\beta f_i' \, d\mu,$$

and hence

(20) $$\|f(\beta) - f(\alpha)\| = \left\{\sum_{i=1}^{k} \left|\int_\alpha^\beta f_i' \, d\mu\right|^2\right\}^{1/2}.$$

Let us write $A = \|f(\beta) - f(\alpha)\|$. In proving (19) we may assume that $A > 0$, for (19) is certainly true if $A = 0$. We introduce numbers $c_1, \ldots, c_k$ defined by

$$c_i A = \int_\alpha^\beta f_i' \, d\mu.$$

By (20) we see that $\sum_{i=1}^{k} c_i^2 = 1$. It is then easy to verify that

(21) $$\int_\alpha^\beta \left(\sum_{i=1}^{k} c_i f_i'\right) d\mu = A.$$

But

$$\left|\sum_{i=1}^{k} c_i f_i'\right| \le \left(\sum_i c_i^2\right)^{1/2}\left(\sum_i |f_i'|^2\right)^{1/2} = \left\{\sum_i |f_i'|^2\right\}^{1/2},$$

and hence from (21) we obtain (19).

Now, let $\Delta = (x_0, x_1, \ldots, x_n)$ be a partition of $[a, b]$. From (19) we see that

$$T(\Delta; f) = \sum_{j=1}^{n} \|f(x_j) - f(x_{j-1})\| \le \sum_{j=1}^{n} \int_{x_{j-1}}^{x_j} \left\{\sum_{i=1}^{k} |f_i'|^2\right\}^{1/2} d\mu,$$

or

$$T(\Delta; f) \le \int_a^b \left\{\sum_{i=1}^{k} |f_i'|^2\right\}^{1/2} d\mu.$$

Since $L(b) = V_{ab}(f) = \sup_{\Delta} T(\Delta; f)$, this proves (18). The proof of Theorem 9–8 VIII is now complete.

## INTEGRATION BY PARTS

As an important application of Theorems 9–8 III, VI we have the following result:

THEOREM 9–8 IX. *Suppose that $F : [a, b] \to R$ is absolutely continuous and that $g : [a, b] \to R^*$ is summable. Define $f : [a, b] \to R$ so that $f(x) = F'(x)$ a.e., and let $G(x) = \int_a^x g\, d\mu + C$, where $C$ is an arbitrary constant. Then $Fg$ and $fG$ are summable, and*

$$\int_a^b Fg\, d\mu + \int_a^b fG\, d\mu = F(b)G(b) - F(a)G(a). \tag{22}$$

*Proof.* As mentioned prior to Theorem 9–8 I, it is easy to prove that $FG$ is absolutely continuous, because $F$ and $G$ are bounded and absolutely continuous. Hence, $(FG)'$ is summable, and

$$\int_a^b (FG)'\, d\mu = F(b)G(b) - F(a)G(a). \tag{23}$$

We know from Theorem 9–7 VII that a function $f$ of the required sort exists, and that it is summable. Hence

$$(FG)'(x) = F(x)g(x) + f(x)G(x) \qquad \text{a.e.} \tag{24}$$

The function $Fg$ is measurable, and $F$ is bounded. Suppose $|F| \le M$. Then $|Fg| \le Mg$, and from this it follows that $Fg$ is summable. A similar argument applies to $fG$. We now get (22) by integrating (24) and using (23).

## PROBLEMS

1. Suppose that $f$ and $g$ are absolutely continuous on $D$. Prove that any linear combination of $f$ and $g$ is absolutely continuous on $D$. Prove that $fg$ is absolutely continuous on $D$ if $f$ and $g$ are bounded on $D$. Assume further that $\inf_{x \in D} |f(x)| > 0$; then prove that the reciprocal of $f$ is absolutely continuous on $D$.

2. Suppose $f \in BV[a, b]$. Prove that there exists a pair of functions $g, h$ on $[a, b]$ to $R$ such that $g$ is absolutely continuous on $[a, b]$, $h \in BV[a, b]$, $h'(x) = 0$ a.e. and $f = g + h$. Moreover, $g$ and $h$ are uniquely determined by $f$, apart from an additive constant.

3. Suppose that each of the functions $f : [a, b] \to R$ and $v : [\alpha, \beta] \to R$ is absolutely continuous on the interval where it is defined. Suppose further that $v$ is a nondecreasing function whose range lies in $[a, b]$. Define $F : [\alpha, \beta] \to R$ by $F(x) = f(v(x))$. Prove that $F$ is absolutely continuous on $[\alpha, \beta]$.

4. Define $f : [0, 1] \to R$ by $f(0) = 0$, $f(x) = x^p \sin(x^{-q})$, where $p > 0, q > 0$. Show that $f$ is absolutely continuous if $0 < q < p$, and not of bounded variation if $0 < p \leq q$.

5. Let $f : D \to R$ be absolutely continuous. Show that $f(E)$ is $L$-measurable whenever $E$ is an $L$-measurable subset of $D$. The proof may be made conveniently in the following stages: (a) Use the fact that $f(E)$ is compact when $E$ is compact to show that $f(E)$ is an $F_\sigma$-set if $E$ is an $F_\sigma$ set. (b) Show that the general problem can be reduced to the problem of showing that $f(E)$ is of $L$-measure zero if $E$ is of $L$-measure zero. Then show the truth of this last proposition.

6. Let $v : [\alpha, \beta] \to R$ be absolutely continuous and strictly increasing.

(a) Show that

$$\mu(v(E)) = \int_E v' \, d\mu$$

for each measurable subset $E$ of $[\alpha, \beta]$. The fact that $v(E)$ is measurable follows from Problem 5. (b) Let $G$ be a set of measure zero contained in $[v(\alpha), v(\beta)]$. Show that the set $\{t : v(t) \in G$ and $v'(t) \neq 0\}$ has measure zero.

7. Let $v$ be as in Problem 6, and suppose that $f : [a, b] \to R$ is continuous, where $a = v(\alpha)$, $b = v(\beta)$. Show that

$$\int_a^b f(x)\, dx = \int_\alpha^\beta f(v(t))v'(t)\, dt,$$

where both integrals are $L$-integrals. [*Suggestion.* The integral on the left can be calculated as a Riemann integral. Show that the integral on the right lies between the upper and lower approximating sums for the Riemann integral, using an arbitrary partition.]

8. Prove that the equality of the integrals in Problem 7 is maintained when $f$ is any $L$-summable function defined on $[a, b]$. [*Suggestion.* For such an $f$ there exists a sequence $\{f_n\}$ of continuous functions on $[a, b]$ such that $f_n(x) \to f(x)$ a.e. and $\int_a^b |f_n(x) - f(x)|\, dx \to 0$. Use Problem 6 to show that $f_n(v(t))v'(t) \to f(v(t))v'(t)$ a.e. Then, using convergence in mean, deduce what is needed for the desired conclusion.]

9. Let $f : [0, 2\pi] \to R^*$ be $L$-summable, and such that all its Fourier coefficients are zero:

$$\int_0^{2\pi} f(x) \sin nx\, dx = \int_0^{2\pi} f(x) \cos nx\, dx = 0, \qquad n = 0, 1, 2, \ldots.$$

Show that $f(x) = 0$ a.e. [*Suggestion.* Consider the Fourier coefficients of $g(x) = \int_0^x f(t)\, dt$, and see Problem 7, Section 3–14.]

10. Let $f$ and $g$ be summable over $R$ and such that

$$\int_{-\infty}^{\infty} [f(x)h(x) + g(x)h'(x)]\, dx = 0$$

for all functions $h : R \to R$ such that $h$ and $h'$ are continuous and $h(x) = 0$ if $x$ is outside some finite interval. Deduce that $g(x) = \int_{-\infty}^{x} f(t)\, dt$ a.e. [*Suggestion.* First prove the following lemma. If $F$ is summable over $R$ and if $\int_{-\infty}^{\infty} F(x)G(x)\, dx = 0$ whenever $G$ is a continuous function such that $G(x) = 0$ when $x$ is outside some finite interval, then $F(x) = 0$ a.e.]

11. Assume that $\nu$ is a measure on the $\sigma$-ring of all Borel sets in $R$. Let $\mu$ be Lebesgue measure, restricted to this same $\sigma$-ring. Let $v : R \to R$ be a function related to $\nu$ in such a way that $\nu(E) = v(b) - v(a)$ if $a < b$ and $E = (a, b]$. Show that $v$ is a right-continuous nondecreasing function such that $v(x) - v(x-) = \nu(\{x\})$. Now assume that $\nu \in AC[\mu]$ (notation as in Section 8–2). Show that $v$ is absolutely continuous on every finite interval. Show also that $\nu(E) = \int_E v' \, d\mu$ for each $E$ such that $\nu(E)$ is finite.

12. Let $v : R \to R$ be nondecreasing and absolutely continuous on each finite interval. Let $\nu^*$ be the outer measure, and $\nu$ the measure, generated by $v$ as in Section 4–10. Show that $\nu^*(E) = 0$ for every set $E$ of $L$-measure zero, and deduce from this that every $L$-measurable set is $\nu^*$-measurable. Observe also that, if $\nu$ is considered as a measure restricted to the $L$-measurable sets, then $\nu \in AC[\mu]$, where $\mu$ is Lebesgue measure.

## SUGGESTED READING FOR CHAPTER 9

AUMANN [1], Chapter 7.
BURKILL [1], Chapter 4 and pp. 58–61 in Chapter 5.
CARATHEODORY [1], Parts of Chapter 10, especially pp. 542–590.
GOFFMAN [1], Chapter 19.
GRAVES [1], Sections 5, 6, 7 in Chapter 10, Sections 3, 4 in Chapter 11, and Chapter 12.
HOBSON [1], Vol. 1, pp. 325–330, 337–341, and 585–606.
KESTELMAN [1], Chapter 7.
LEBESGUE [2], Chapters 4, 8, 9, 11.
MCSHANE [1], Chapter 5.
NATANSON [1], Chapters 8, 9 in Vol. 1, Appendices 1, 4, 6 in Vol. 2.
RIESZ and NAGY [1], pp. 5–17, 47–57.
SAKS [1], pp. 96–104.
THIELMAN [1], Chapter 10.
TITCHMARSH [1], Chapter 11 and pp. 375–380 in Chapter 12.
WILLIAMSON [1], Chapter 5.
ZAANEN [1], Section 34 in Chapter 9, and Chapter 10.

# Bibliography


G. Aumann

[1] *Reele Funktionen*, Springer, Berlin-Göttingen-Heidelberg, 1954.

R. Baire

[1] "Sur les fonctions de variables réeles," *Annali di Matematica Pura e Applicata* (3), Vol. 3 (1899), pp. 1–123.

S. Banach

[1] *Opérations linéaires*, Monografje Matematyczne, Warsaw, 1932.

E. F. Beckenbach and Richard Bellman

[1] *Inequalities*, Ergebnisse der Mathematik und Ihrer Grenzgebiete, Springer, Berlin-Göttingen-Heidelberg, 1961.

S. K. Berberian

[1] *Introduction to Hilbert Space*. Oxford University Press, New York, 1961.

G. Birkhoff

[1] *Lattice Theory* rev. ed. American Mathematical Society Colloquium Publications, Vol. 25. New York, 1948.

G. Birkhoff and S. MacLane

[1] *A Survey of Modern Algebra* rev. ed. Macmillan, New York, 1953.

G. A. Bliss

[1] "Integrals of Lebesgue," *Bulletin of the American Mathematical Society*, Vol. 24 (1917), pp. 1–47.

R. P. Boas, Jr.

[1] *A Primer of Real Functions*, Carus Mathematical Monograph No. 13, Mathematical Association of America 1960.

E. Borel

[1] *Leçons sur la théorie des fonctions*, Gauthier-Villars, Paris, 1898. (Also, 3d ed. of same, 1928.)

N. Bourbaki

Each of the following is in the series, *Eléments de mathématique*, Actualités Scientifiques et Industrielles, Hermann, Paris. Each title is identified by a serial number.

[1] *Théorie des ensembles*,

(a) *Fascicule des résultats*, No. 846 (1939).

(b) Chapters 1, 2, No. 1212 (1954).

(c) Chapter 3, No. 1243 (1956).

[2] *Topologie générale*,

(a) Chapters 1, 2, No. 858 (1940).

(b) Chapter 9, No. 1045 (1948).
(c) Chapter 10, No. 1084 (1949).
[3] *Intégration*,
(a) Chapters 1–4, No. 1175 (1952).
(b) Chapter 5, No. 1244 (1956).
(c) Chapter 6, No. 1281 (1959).

H. E. BRAY
[1] "Elementary properties of the Stieltjes integral," *Annals of Mathematics* (2), Vol. 20 (1919), pp. 177–186.

J. C. BURKILL
[1] *The Lebesgue Integral* (Cambridge Tracts in Mathematics and Mathematical Physics, No. 40) Cambridge University Press, Cambridge, 1951.

C. CARATHEODORY
[1] *Vorlesungen über reele Funktionen* (2d ed.), Chelsea, New York, 1948.

P. J. DANIELL
[1] "A general form of integral," *Annals of Mathematics* (2), Vol. 19 (1917–18), pp. 279–294.
[2] "Further properties of the general integral," *Annals of Mathematics* (2), Vol. 22 (1919–20), pp. 203–220.

M. M. DAY
[1] *Normed Linear Spaces*, Ergebnisse der Mathematik und Ihrer Grenzgebiete, Springer, Berlin-Göttingen-Heidelberg, 1958.

J. DIEUDONNÉ
[1] *Foundations of Modern Analysis*, Academic Press, New York, 1960.

N. DUNFORD and J. T. SCHWARTZ
[1] *Linear Operators Part I: General Theory*, Interscience, New York, 1958.

D. EGOROFF
[1] "Sur les suites de fonctions measurables," *Comptes Rendus des Séances de l'Académie des Sciences, Paris*, Vol. 152 (1911), pp. 244–246.

P. FATOU
[1] "Séries trigonométriques et séries de Taylor," *Acta Mathematica*, Vol. 30 (1906), pp. 335–400.

M. FRÉCHET
[1] *Les espaces abstraits*, Gauthier-Villars, Paris, 1928.

G. FUBINI
[1] "Sugli integrali multipli," *Accademia dei Lincei, Rendiconti, Classe di scienze fisiche, matematiche e naturali*, Rome, Ser. 5, Vol. 16, Part 1 (1907), pp. 608–614.

C. GOFFMAN
[1] *Real Functions*, Rinehart, New York, 1953.

L. M. GRAVES
[1] *The Theory of Functions of Real Variables* (2d ed.), McGraw-Hill, New York, 1956.

H. HAHN
[1] *Reele Funktionen*, Chelsea, New York, 1948.

H. HAHN and A. ROSENTHAL
[1] *Set Functions*, University of New Mexico Press, Albuquerque, N.M., 1948.

D. W. HALL and G. L. SPENCER
[1] *Elementary Topology*, John Wiley, New York, 1955.

P. R. HALMOS
[1] *Measure Theory*, D. Van Nostrand, Princeton, 1950.
[2] *Finite Dimensional Vector Spaces* (2d ed.) D. Van Nostrand, Princeton, 1958.
[3] *Naive Set Theory*, D. Van Nostrand, Princeton, 1960.

G. HAMEL
[1] "Eine Basis aller Zahlen und die unstetige Lösungen der Funktionalgleichung $f(x + y) = f(x) + f(y)$," *Mathematische Annalen*, Vol. 60 (1905), pp. 459–462.

G. H. HARDY, J. E. LITTLEWOOD, and G. PÓLYA
[1] *Inequalities*, Cambridge University Press, Cambridge, 1934.
F. HAUSDORFF
[1] *Set Theory*, Chelsea, New York, 1962. (A translation of *Mengenlehre*, 3d ed., de Gruyter, Berlin, 1935.)
E. HEWITT
[1] "On two problems of Urysohn," *Annals of Mathematics* (2), Vol. 47 (1946), pp. 503–509.
D. HILBERT and S. COHN-VOSSEN
[1] *Anschauliche Geometrie*, Dover, New York, 1944. (Also available in English translation, as *Geometry and the Imagination*, Chelsea, New York, 1952.)
T. H. HILDEBRANDT
[1] "On integrals related to and extensions of the Lebesgue integral," *Bulletin of the American Mathematical Society*, Vol. 24 (1917), pp. 113–144 and pp. 177–202.
[2] "The Borel theorem and its generalizations," *Bulletin of the American Mathematical Society*, Vol. 32 (1926), pp. 423–474.
[3] "Stieltjes integrals of the Riemann type," *American Mathematical Monthly*, Vol. 45 (1938), pp. 265–267.
E. W. HOBSON
[1] *The Theory of Functions of a Real Variable and the Theory of Fourier Series*, Vol. 1 (3d ed.) and Vol. 2 (2d ed.) reprinted by Dover, New York, 1957.
J. G. HOCKING and G. S. YOUNG
[1] *Topology*, Addison-Wesley, Reading, Mass., 1961.
E. KAMKE
[1] *Das Lebesgue-Stieltjesintegral*, Teubner, Leipzig, 1956.
J. L. KELLEY
[1] *General Topology*, D. Van Nostrand, Princeton, 1955.
H. KESTELMAN
[1] *Modern Theories of Integration*, Oxford University Press, Oxford, 1937.
K. KNOPP
[1] *Theory and Application of Infinite Series*, Blackie and Son, London, 1928.
A. N. KOLMOGOROFF and S. V. FOMIN
[1] *Measure, Lebesgue Integrals, and Hilbert Space*, Academic Press, New York, 1961.
C. KURATOWSKI
[1] *Topologie I*, Monografje Matematyczne, Warsaw, 1933.
E. LANDAU
[1] *Grundlagen der Analysis* (3d ed.), Chelsea, New York, 1960.
[2] *Foundations of Analysis* (English language edition of "*Grundlagen*"), Chelsea, New York, 1951.
H. LEBESGUE
[1] "Intégrale, longeur, aire," *Annali di Matematica Pura e Applicata* (3), Vol. 7 (1902), pp. 231–359. (This is based on Lebesgue's dissertation.)
[2] *Leçons sur l'intégration et la récherche des fonctions primitives* (2d ed.), Gauthier-Villars, Paris, 1928.
L. H. LOOMIS
[1] *An Introduction to Abstract Harmonic Analysis*, D. Van Nostrand, Princeton, 1953.
E. J. MCSHANE
[1] *Integration*, Princeton University Press, Princeton, 1947.
[2] *Order-Preserving Maps and Integration Processes*, Annals of Mathematics Studies No. 31, Princeton University Press, Princeton, 1953.
[3] "A theory of limits," pp. 7–29 in *Studies in Mathematics*, Vol. 1, *Studies in Analysis*, Mathematical Association of America and Prentice-Hall, New York, 1962.
E. J. MCSHANE and T. A. BOTTS
[1] *Real Analysis*, D. Van Nostrand, Princeton, 1959.

M. E. MUNROE
[1] *Introduction to Measure and Integration*, Addison-Wesley, Cambridge, Mass., 1953.
M. A. NAIMARK
[1] *Normed Rings*, P. Noordhoff, Groningen, 1960.
I. P. NATANSON
[1] *Theory of Functions of a Real Variable*, 2 vols., Ungar, New York; Vol. 1, 1955, and Vol. 2, 1960.
M. H. A. NEWMAN
[1] *Elements of the Topology of Plane Sets of Points* (2d ed.), Cambridge University Press, Cambridge, 1951.
O. NIKODYM
[1] "Sur une généralisation des intégrales de M. Radon," *Fundamenta Mathematica*, Vol. 15 (1930), pp. 131–179.
W. F. OSGOOD
[1] "Nonuniform convergence and the integration of series term by term," *American Journal of Mathematics*, Vol. 19 (1897), pp. 155–190.
[2] *Lehrbuch der Funktionentheorie*, Vol. 1 (5th ed.), Teubner, Leipzig, 1928.
L. J. PAIGE and J. D. SWIFT
[1] *Elements of Linear Algebra*, Ginn, Boston, 1961.
G. PEANO
[1] "Sur une courbe, qui remplit toute une aire plane," *Mathematische Annalen*, Vol. 36 (1890), pp. 157–160.
J. RADON
[1] "Theorie und Anwendungen der absolutadditiven Mengenfunktionen," *Sitzungsberichte der kaiserlichen Akademie der Wissenschaften zu Wien*, Vol. 122 (1913), IIa, pp. 1295–1438.
F. RIESZ
[1] "Sur les opérations fonctionelles linéaires," *Comptes Rendus des Séances de l'Académie des Sciences, Paris*, Vol. 149 (1909), pp. 974–977.
[2] "Sur l'intégrale de Lebesgue," *Acta Mathematica*, Vol. 42 (1920), pp. 191–205.
F. RIESZ and BÉLA SZ.-NAGY
[1] *Leçons d'analyse fonctionelle* (3d ed.), Gauthier-Villars, Paris, 1955.
W. W. ROGOSINSKI
[1] *Volume and Integral*, Oliver and Boyd, Edinburgh, 1952.
W. RUDIN
[1] *Principles of Mathematical Analysis*, McGraw-Hill, New York, 1953.
S. SAKS
[1] *Theory of the Integral* (2d ed.), Monografje Matematyczne, Warsaw, 1937.
H. SEIFERT and W. THRELFALL
[1] *Lehrbuch der Topologie*, Chelsea, New York, 1947.
W. SIERPINSKI
[1] *Leçons sur les nombres transfinis*, Gauthier-Villars, Paris, 1950.
T. J. STIELTJES
[1] "Récherches sur les fractions continues," *Annales de la Faculté des Sciences de Toulouse*, Vol. 8 (1894), pp. 1–122.
M. H. STONE
[1] "The generalized Weierstrass approximation theorem," *Mathematics Magazine*, Vol. 21 (1948), pp. 167–254.
[2] "Notes on integration" (in four parts), *Proceedings of the National Academy of Sciences, U.S.A.*, Vol. 34 (1948), pp. 336–342, 447–455, 483–490, and Vol. 35 (1949), pp. 50–58.
[3] "A generalized Weierstrass approximation theorem," pp. 30–87 in *Studies in Mathematics*, Vol. 1, *Studies in Analysis*, Mathematical Association of America and Prentice-Hall, New York, 1962.

A. E. TAYLOR
[1] *Advanced Calculus*, Ginn, Boston, 1955.
[2] *Introduction to Functional Analysis*, John Wiley, New York, 1958.
H. P. THIELMAN
[1] *Theory of Functions of Real Variables*, Prentice-Hall, New York, 1953.
E. C. TITCHMARSH
[1] *The Theory of Functions* (2d ed.), Oxford University Press, Oxford, 1939.
C. DE LA VALLÉE-POUSSIN
[1] *Intégrales de Lebesgue, fonctions d'ensemble, classes de Baire* (2d ed.), Gauthier-Villars, Paris, 1934.
B. L. VAN DER WAERDEN
[1] *Modern Algebra*, Vol. 1, Ungar, New York, 1949 (English language edition of *Moderne Algebra* I, Springer, 1930).
D. V. WIDDER
[1] *The Laplace Transform*, Princeton University Press, Princeton, 1946.
R. L. WILDER
[1] *Introduction to the Foundations of Mathematics*, John Wiley, New York, 1952.
J. H. WILLIAMSON
[1] *Lebesgue Integration*, Holt, Rinehart, and Winston, New York, 1962.
W. H. YOUNG
[1] "A new method in the theory of integration," *Proceedings of the London Mathematical Society* (2), Vol. 9 (1911), pp. 15–50.
A. C. ZAANEN
[1] *An Introduction to the Theory of Integration*, North-Holland Pub. Co., Amsterdam, 1958.
E. ZERMELO
[1] "Untersuchung über die Grundlagen der Mengenlehre I," *Mathematische Annalen*, Vol. 65 (1908), pp. 261–281.
M. ZORN
[1] "A remark on method in transfinite algebra," *Bulletin of the American Mathematical Society*, Vol. 41 (1935), p. 667–670.

# List of Special Symbols

| | |
|---|---|
| $\in$ | Is an element of, 7 |
| $\notin$ | Is not an element of, 7 |
| $\subset$ | Is a subset of (set inclusion relation), 7 |
| $\{x : \cdots\}$ | Set description by exhibit of conditions, 7 |
| $\varnothing$ | The empty set, 8 |
| $\cup$ | Union, 8 |
| $\cap$ | Intersection, 8 |
| $A^{\sim}$ | Complement of $A$, 9 |
| $A - B$ | Difference of sets, 9 |
| $A \Delta B$ | Symmetric difference, 10 |
| $R^*$ | The extended real number system, 29 |
| $\langle x, y\rangle$ | Inner product, 41, 153 |
| $\|x\|$ | Norm, 42, 144 |
| $S'$ | Derived set, 51 |
| $\bar{S}$ | Closure of $S$, 52 |
| $\beta(S)$ | Boundary of $S$, 52 |
| $S^o$ | Interior of $S$, 52 |
| $F_\sigma$ | A kind of set, 55 |
| $G_\delta$ | A kind of set, 55 |
| $S_C[0, 1]$ | Cantor set, 87 |
| $C[a, b]$ | A space of continuous functions, 115 |
| $l^p$ | A space of sequences, 120, 142 |
| $B(x_0; r)$ | Closed ball, 128 |
| $\Pi_{\alpha\in A} X_\alpha$ | Cartesian product, 136 |
| $(f, \mathcal{N}) \to z$ | Convergence of a directed function, 139 |
| $B(T)$ | Space of bounded functions, 142, 164 |
| $C(T)$ | Space of bounded continuous functions, 142, 164 |
| $C(T; X)$ | Space of bounded continuous functions on $T$ to $X$, 167 |
| $x \vee y$ | Lattice lub of $\{x, y\}$, 171 |
| $x \wedge y$ | Lattice glb of $\{x, y\}$, 171 |

# Index

ABCDEFGHIJ 0698765

# ABOUT THE AUTHOR

Angus E. Taylor has been a member of the faculty at University of California, Los Angeles since 1938, specializing in the field of mathematical analysis (from calculus to functional analysis). He did his undergraduate work at Harvard and his graduate work at California Institute of Technology. In 1937–38, Dr. Taylor was a National Research Fellow at Princeton, and in 1955 he was chosen to be a Fulbright Fellow at the Johannes Gutenberg University in Mainz, Germany. He was appointed Professor of Mathematics at UCLA in 1947 and Chairman of the Mathematics Department from 1958 to 1964. Professor Taylor is the author of many research papers and several well-known books: *Advanced Calculus* (Blaisdell), *Calculus with Analytic Geometry*, and *Introduction to Functional Analysis*.

THIS BOOK WAS SET IN

TIMES ROMAN AND PERPETUA TYPES

BY THE UNIVERSITIES PRESS

IT WAS DESIGNED BY THE STAFF OF

BLAISDELL PUBLISHING COMPANY